A HISTORY OF LAND MAMMALS IN THE WESTERN HEMISPHERE

HENRY FAIRFIELD OSBORN   WILLIAM BERRYMAN SCOTT
FRANCIS SPEIR, JR.

"The Triumvirate," Expedition of 1878

(*Cf. Preface to First Edition, paragraph 1*)

A
HISTORY OF LAND MAMMALS

IN THE

WESTERN HEMISPHERE

BY

WILLIAM BERRYMAN SCOTT

PH.D. (Heidelberg), HON.D.SC. (Harvard, Oxford and Princeton),
LL.D. (Univ. of Pennsylvania)

BLAIR PROFESSOR EMERITUS OF GEOLOGY IN PRINCETON UNIVERSITY

ILLUSTRATED BY

R. BRUCE HORSFALL and CHARLES R. KNIGHT

Revised Edition

HAFNER PUBLISHING COMPANY

NEW YORK

1962

Reprinted by Arrangement

Reprinted and Published by
HAFNER PUBLISHING CO., INC.
31 East 10th Street
New York 3, N. Y.

Library of Congress Catalog Card Number: 62-15585

Printed in the U.S.A.

NOBLE OFFSET PRINTERS, INC.
NEW YORK 3, N. Y.

DEDICATED

TO THE DEAR MEMORY OF

MY CLASSMATES

HENRY FAIRFIELD OSBORN AND FRANCIS SPEIR, JR.

RECALLING A NOTABLE SUMMER AFTERNOON

IN 1876 AND IN REMEMBRANCE OF SIXTY

YEARS' UNCLOUDED FRIENDSHIP

Speak to the earth and it shall teach thee.

— JOB, xii, 8.

Can these bones live?

— EZEKIEL, xxxvii, 3.

FROM THE PREFACE TO THE FIRST EDITION

One afternoon in June, 1876, three Princeton undergraduates were lying under the trees on the canal bank, making a languid pretence of preparing for an examination. Suddenly, one of the trio remarked: "I have been reading an old magazine article which describes a fossil-collecting expedition in the West; why can't we get up something of the kind?" The others replied, as with one voice, "We can; let's do it." This seemingly idle talk was, for Osborn and myself, a momentous one, for it completely changed the careers which, as we then believed, had been mapped out for us. The random suggestion led directly to the first of the Princeton palæontological expeditions, that of 1877, which took us to the "Bad Lands" of the Bridger region in southwestern Wyoming. The fascination of discovering and exhuming with our own hands the remains of the curious creatures which once inhabited North America, but became extinct ages ago, has proved an enduring delight. It was the wish to extend something of this fascinating interest to a wider circle, that occasioned the preparation of this book.

The western portion of North America has preserved a marvellous series of records of the successive assemblages of animals which once dwelt in this continent, and in southernmost South America an almost equally complete record was made of the strange animals of that region. For the last half-century, or more, many workers have coöperated to bring this long-vanished world to light and to decipher and interpret the wonderful story of mammalian development in the Western Hemisphere. The task of making this history intelligible, not to say interesting, to the layman, has been one of formidable difficulty, for it is recorded in the successive modifications of the bones and teeth.

No one who has not examined it, can form any conception of the enormous mass and variety of material, illustrating the history of American mammals, which has already been gathered into the various museums. A full account of this material would require many volumes, and one of the chief problems in the preparation of this book has been that of making a proper selection of the most instructive and illuminating portions of the long and complicated story. Indeed,

vii

so rapid is the uninterrupted course of discovery, that parts of the text became antiquated while in the press and had to be rewritten. As first prepared, the work proved to be far too long and it was necessary to excise several chapters, for it seemed better to cover less ground than to make the entire history hurried and superficial.

The facts which are here brought together have been ascertained by many workers, and I have borrowed with the greatest freedom from my fellow labourers in the field of palæontology. As every compiler of a manual finds, it is not feasible to attribute the proper credit to each discoverer. Huxley has so well explained the situation in the preface to his *Anatomy of Vertebrated Animals*, that I may be permitted to borrow his words: "I have intentionally refrained from burdening the text with references; and, therefore, the reader, while he is justly entitled to hold me responsible for any errors he may detect, will do well to give me no credit for what may seem original, unless his knowledge is sufficient to render him a competent judge on that head."

A book of this character is obviously not the proper place for polemical discussions of disputed questions. Whenever, therefore, the views expressed differ widely from those maintained by other palæontologists, I have attempted no more than to state, as fairly as I could, the alternative interpretations and my own choice between them. Any other course was forbidden by the limitations of space.

For thirteen years past I have been engaged in the study of the great collections of fossil mammals, gathered in Patagonia by the lamented Mr. Hatcher and his colleague, Mr. Peterson, now of the Carnegie Museum. This work made it necessary for me to visit the museums of the Argentine Republic, which I did in 1901, and was there received with the greatest courtesy and kindness by Dr. F. Moreno, Director, and Dr. Santiago Roth, of the La Plata Museum, and Dr. F. Ameghino, subsequently Director of the National Museum at Buenos Aires. To all of these gentlemen the chapters on the ancient life of South America are much indebted, especially to Dr. Ameghino, whose untimely death was a great loss to science.

W. B. S.

PRINCETON, N. J.
June 1, 1913

PREFACE TO THE SECOND EDITION

Almost twenty-four years have passed since the appearance of the first edition of this book, and during all that time the work of exploring and collecting has gone on unremittingly. The expeditions of the Field Museum to South America and of the American Museum to South America and Mongolia have resulted in the gathering of an immense mass of new material illustrative of mammalian evolution. Equally important and productive has been the work of the many museums of the United States and Canada in the fossil fields of North America. It was quite impossible to incorporate all this new material in the old work, and complete rewriting has been found necessary. Only the chapter on the skeleton and teeth has been taken over, practically unchanged, from the former edition. A great many new illustrations have been included, though it has been thought desirable to retain a considerable number of the old ones. The figures now published for the first time are either from photographs, or from drawings by Mr. R. Bruce Horsfall.

Plan and purpose of the work remain as before, and these are sufficiently explained in the extracts from the old preface, herewith reproduced. In the former edition the history of the successive faunas and the various mammalian groups was told in the reverse order of time. This method has its inconveniences and would not have been employed, had I been writing a text-book or a scientific treatise for professional readers. To the amateur it has the advantage of beginning with the familiar life of to-day and working gradually back to the less and less known. To commence with the Paleocene would have landed the reader in a world where every mammal was altogether strange and unlike anything he had ever seen. So far as I can discover, this inverted narrative has been approved and objected to in almost equal measure and I trust that I shall not be regarded as unduly obstinate in adhering to it in favour of the non-professional reader. Perhaps it was unjustifiable optimism to assume the existence of a body of readers of this subject, but I hope, nevertheless, that they are to be found.

A formidable obstacle to the general appreciation of the pleasures and wonders of palæontology lies in the technical nomenclature which it is necessary to employ. "Oh! those dreadful names!" is an ever recurring complaint and, it must be acknowledged, not an unreasonable one. I had a forcible illustration of this in a visit which I once paid to a retired whaling captain on the island of Martha's Vineyard. To my surprise, he produced a copy of the *Land Mammals* and asked me if I had ever seen it before. With a shake of his head, he added: "It's mighty tough readin'," to which I replied: "I know it is and I don't see how to make it any easier." The palæontologist who is attempting to popularize his subject would gladly welcome vernacular names for the strange beasts he is describing; but *there are no vernacular names* and it would not help matters to invent them, for such names would be no more intelligible than the technical terms. Furthermore, vernacular names would lack the precision and the international intelligibility which technical nomenclature possesses. Only the slow process of scientific education can remove this difficulty. Technical terms have been avoided in this book as far as possible, but they cannot be dispensed with altogether.

W. B. S.

PRINCETON, N. J.
September 1, 1937

ACKNOWLEDGMENTS

In the spring of 1934 the American Philosophical Society made me a "grant in aid" for the purpose of preparing and publishing a monograph on *The White River Mammalian Fauna* and, accordingly, Mr. Horsfall and I visited some eleven museums, from Cambridge, Massachusetts, to Denver, and from Washington to Rapid City, South Dakota. At all of these museums we were received with the utmost kindness and liberality, and their treasures were put freely at our disposal. From this generous reception both undertakings, the monograph and the second edition of this book, received great benefit, for in this manner a wonderful series of the most beautifully preserved fossils was made available and these could not have been obtained in any other way. We are greatly indebted to Dr. Thomas Barbour, Director of the Museum of Comparative Zoölogy, Harvard University, and Mr. George Nelson of the same museum; Dr. Lull and Dr. Thorpe of the Peabody Museum, Yale University; Professor F. B. Loomis of Amherst College; Director Avinoff and Messrs. Burke and Kay of the Carnegie Museum, Pittsburgh; Director Simms, and Messrs. E. S. Riggs and Bryan Patterson, of the Field Museum of Natural History and Mr. Paul Miller of the Walker Museum of the University of Chicago; Professor E. H. Barbour of the University of Nebraska; Director J. D. Figgins and Messrs. Rogers and Miller, of the Denver Museum; the late President C. C. O'Harra, Mr. J. D. Bump and Dr. George Hernon, of the State School of Mines, Rapid City, South Dakota; Messrs. C. W. Gilmore and C. L. Gazin, of the National Museum, Washington; and to nearly every member of the Department of Vertebrate Palæontology in the American Museum of Natural History, Drs. Gregory, Simpson, Granger, Colbert, Schlaikjer, Mr. Childs Frick, the Misses Lucas and Percy and Mrs. John Nichols.

While I am exceedingly grateful to all this company of friends and well-wishers for their indispensable help in a long and arduous undertaking, there are certain names which I must especially emphasize for the very great benefits which I owe to unremitting kindness. My beloved and life-long friend, Professor Henry Fairfield Osborn, placed at my disposal the advance sheets of his magnificent

xii   ACKNOWLEDGMENTS

monograph on the Proboscidea: Childs Frick, Esq., supplied me with
the unpublished drawings of his great work on the antelopes and deer
of the later Tertiary: Dr. G. G. Simpson has read much of the manuscript, especially the chapters dealing with South American mammals, and has given me most helpful counsel. To Mr. Riggs, of the
Field Museum, I am indebted for the highly prized opportunity to
describe and figure the unique fossils which he collected in South
America. My colleagues, Professors E. G. Conklin, who read many
chapters in manuscript, and G. L. Jepsen, who prepared the sections
on the stratigraphy and faunas of the Paleocene, have placed me
under great obligations by their coöperation. To my faithful friend
and long-time associate, the late Professor W. J. Sinclair, I owe much
valued assistance in the early stages of this undertaking, until his
lamentably early death deprived me of his help.

I have, happily, once more the opportunity to express my hearty
thanks to Mr. R. Bruce Horsfall for his fine work in illustrating the
new edition. What I said of the first edition is equally true of the
second, that a great part of its value is due to his skill.

Finally, and most of all, am I indebted to the American Philosophical Society, "held at Philadelphia for promoting Useful Knowledge," the great generosity of which has made possible the publication
of this new edition. I can only hope that the Society may have no
reason to regret its most liberal encouragement of my work.

                                                    W. B. S.

PRINCETON, N. J.
September 1, 1937

CONTENTS

CONTENTS

† Extinct.

A HISTORY OF LAND MAMMALS IN THE WESTERN HEMISPHERE

A HISTORY OF LAND MAMMALS IN THE WESTERN HEMISPHERE

CHAPTER I

DEFINITION AND CLASSIFICATION OF MAMMALS

The term *Mammal* is artificial and has no exact equivalent in the true vernacular of any language. The late Dr. Theodore Gill, of the Smithsonian Institution, investigated the history of the word and his results may be briefly summarized. The older English names, such as "beast" and "quadruped," are not quite the same as "mammal," for they do not include men, bats, or whales and their allies, which are unmistakable mammals. "It was one of the happiest inspirations of Linnæus to segregate all the mammiferous animals, — the hairy quadrupeds, the sirenians, and the cetaceans — in a single class. No one before had appreciated the closeness of the relations of the several types and there was no name for the new class, as there was for all the others, fishes, reptiles and birds. The name *'Mammalia'* was taken from the Latin *mamma* [i.e. teat] and made in analogy with *animalia"* (Gill).

While the artificial Latin word Mammalia was used in all formal classifications of animals in English works on natural history, the vernacular *mammal*, now so frequent, was not current and appears to have been introduced by Dr. John Mason Good about 1813. In *Pantologia* (Vol. VIII), he speaks of Linnæus' having made the word *Mammalia* and adds, "we have thought ourselves justified in vernacularizing the Latin term and translating 'mammalia' 'mammals.'"

The other European languages have adopted or coined artificial terms of similar meaning, such as the French *mammifères*, Spanish *mammíferos*, Italian *mammiferi*. The German *Säugethiere* (i.e. sucking animals) is a vernacular form of the same idea, as are also the Dutch and Scandinavian terms.

The definition of the term *Mammal* might be so expressed as to include all the structural features of the head, body and limbs, but, for our present purposes the definition may be greatly shortened by

1

omitting all but a few conspicuous and characteristic features. *Mammals are air-breathing vertebrates, which are warm-blooded and have a four-chambered heart; the body-cavity is divided by a diaphragm into two chambers, one of which contains the heart and lungs and the other the digestive organs. Except in the lowest division* (the Monotremata) *the young are born alive and are always suckled, the milk-glands being universal in the class. In the great majority of mammals the body is covered with hair, though in a few, the skin is naked and, in still fewer, there is a covering of scales.*

Among the mammals there is a wonderful diversity in size, form, appearance and manner of life. This diversification has been aptly compared to a musical theme, which a musician develops into endless variations, preserving an unmistakable unity through all the changes. So, in the mammals, the plan of structure is obviously the same in every member of the class, whether we examine a tiny Shrew (*Sorex*) no bigger than one's finger, or a great Greenland Whale (*Balæna mysticetus*) which may reach a length of ninety feet, a bat, or an elephant, a lion or a mouse, the uniformity of structure is always clear. Not only in size and weight, but also in habits and in adaptation to different modes of life, mammals are remarkably diversified. Most mammals are *terrestrial,* and live not only on the land, but on the ground. The word "terrestrial" is, however, often used in a different sense, to include all land mammals in contradistinction from aquatic and marine forms. Much the greater number of mammals are more or less exclusively herbivorous, that is, feeding chiefly on plants, but there are many of radically different habits. Another mode of existence is the burrowing, or *fossorial,* which in varying degree has been acquired by several, not very many, mammals, in which the fore-feet have been adapted to efficient digging. Some burrowers, like the fancifully named Prairie Dog (*Cynomys*) and the badgers (*Taxidea*), pass much of their time at the surface, others live almost entirely underground, such as the moles, while some rodents, like *Spalax,* of southern Russia, and *Bathyergus,* of South Africa, which are blind and the latter with naked skin, are altogether subterranean in habit. Monkeys, squirrels, sloths and opossums, are examples of *arboreal* mammals, which are so modified as to enable them to live in the trees and, in the sloths, structural modification is carried so far that the creatures are extremely slow when on the ground. Except bats, sloths are the only mammals, which hang *suspended* from the branches of trees, and this has brought about unique skeletal changes. — Flying, no doubt, arose from the arboreal habit and, among mammals, only the bats have powers of true flight, but there are several *gliders*, in which a fold of skin forms an air-plane, connecting all four legs. The flying squirrels of West Africa (*Anomalurus*), of Europe (*Pteromys*) and of North America (*Sciuropterus*), and the so-called Flying Lemur (*Cheiromys*) of Madagascar and the Flying Phalanger, an Australian marsupial (*Petaurus*) make prodigious leaps through the air (80 yards, or more) by gliding and such animals are exclusively arboreal.

Many mammals are *aquatic*, such as otters (*Lutra*), beavers (*Castor*), muskrats (*Fiber*); these pass their lives chiefly in fresh water, but are able to walk and run freely on the land. *Marine* mammals, such as seals, walruses, whales and porpoises, are more or less completely adapted to life in the sea.

It will be observed that in each of these groups there is a series of more and more complete adaptations to the environment, as is particularly noticeable among marine mammals. Sea-otters (*Latax*) come ashore frequently, as do the more completely marine sea-lions (*Otaria*, etc.), hair-seals (*Phoca*) and walruses (*Odobænus*). The fur-seals of the north Pacific, spend their lives at sea, except in the breeding season, when they land on islands. All of these are primarily swimmers and have a slow and awkward gait on land. The Cetacea (whales, dolphins, porpoises, etc.) and the Sirenia (dugongs and sea-cows) are so exclusively marine in habits, that stranding is fatal to them. Arboreal, flying and fossorial mammals, display similar degrees in the completeness of their adaptation.

It would be manifestly impossible to classify mammals according to their mode of living, assigning all arboreal forms to one group, all burrowers to a second, all swimmers to a third and so on. This would result in utter confusion, for mammals of similar habits may or may not be related to one another, and the members of the most widely different natural groups, or *orders*, have frequently acquired similar habits. Monkeys and squirrels, for example, though both arboreal, are almost as widely apart as two orders of the higher, or *placental*, mammals can be. The Sirenia and the Cetacea, are both completely marine, but are in no way related. Conversely, within the limits of the same order, we find terrestrial, arboreal, burrowing and aquatic animals. The same kind of adaptation has occurred independently in many most diverse animal groups.

This rapid and superficial survey will suffice to show the wonderful plasticity of the mammalian structural plan and its adaptability to the most diverse conditions. Were an engineer required to design a steamship, a submarine, a locomotive, a steam-shovel, a tunnelling machine and an air-plane by varying a single fundamental plan, he could, at best, produce but a series of unsatisfactory makeshifts. Yet that is just what evolution has accomplished in a singularly perfect manner, by gradual steps of modification. One of the principal objects of this book is to make plain, so far as present knowledge permits, the steps of modification in the various genetic series of the land mammals, confining attention to the denizens of the Americas.

THE CLASSIFICATION OF THE MAMMALIA

The terms used in the various sciences unfortunately form a barrier which often prevents the layman from following the discoveries in which he is interested. Complaints of the "scientific jargon" are a commonplace and an observer might be tempted to think that the jargon had been devised to keep intruders out of the temple of science and served no legitimate purpose. However deplorable its effects in certain ways, scientific terminology is a necessity, for ordinary speech has neither the precision nor the abundance of terms which are indispensable. Who could find or make vernacular names for four hundred thousand species of beetles? to mention only one group. The common names of animals and plants are very loose and inexact, especially in the New World, where the European settlers gave the names with which they had been familiar at home to the creatures which they found in the Western Hemisphere. Some of the names, such as deer, fox, wolf, rabbit, etc., are accurate enough for ordinary purposes, while others are altogether wrong. The bird that we call the "Robin" is a thrush and very different from the "Red Breast" of England, whose name it bears. The so-called Elk is really a great stag and is better named by the Indian "Wapiti," while the Moose is nearly or quite identical with the European Elk. The Bison, of which immense herds once blackened the Great Plains, was improperly termed "Buffalo," a name which belongs to very different members of the ox-tribe found in Asia and Africa. A terminology which shall be exact, voluminous and capable of indefinite expansion, is a necessity in zoölogy, botany and palæontology.

In dealing with fossils, the difficulties of nomenclature become formidable indeed. The larger and more conspicuous mammals of the modern world are more or less familiar to all educated people and such names as elephant, rhinoceros, hippopotamus, kangaroo, will call up a definite and fairly accurate image of the animal in question. For the strange creatures that vanished from the earth ages before the appearance of Man, *there are no vernacular names*, and coining such names is not very helpful. To the layman, such names as †*Uintatherium*, or †*Smilodon* convey no idea whatever, and all that can be done is to attempt to give these terms a meaning by illustration and description, using the name merely as a peg upon which to hang the description.

The system of classification which is still in use, was, in essentials, devised by the great Swedish naturalist, Linnæus, about the middle of the XVIII Century. More especially, it is the Linnæan plan of nomenclature which is still employed, for, it should be noted, nomenclature and classification are not the same thing. The Linnæan scheme is an organized arrangement of groups in an ascending order of comprehensiveness. As the unit of the plan may be taken the *species*, a concept which has been the object of many fierce controversies and even yet there is much difference of opinion and practice concerning species. Originally a term in logic, it first received a definite meaning in zoölogy and botany from John Ray (1628–1705) who used it to indicate a group of animals, or plants, with marked common characteristics and freely interbreeding.

While some of Linnæus' expressions of opinion sound very much as though he were an evolutionist, the belief of naturalists in general at that time and long afterwards was that "there are as many species now as God created in the beginning." This is the doctrine of *Special Creation*, according to which species are fixed entities, concrete things, which it is the particular business of the naturalist to identify and name.

This belief in the objective reality and essential unchangeability of species was almost unanimously held among naturalists until 1859, when the publication of Darwin's *Origin of Species* effected a most remarkable revolution of opinion and led to the well-nigh universal acceptance of the evolutionary conception. One result of this great change was the conclusion that species are subjective and artificial and that the only objective reality among living things is the individual animal or plant. Almost certainly, however, this reaction against the older belief goes too far in the opposite direction; the chemistry of the blood gives strong evidence that the species concept corresponds to a natural reality, though this reality is vague and difficult to grasp. Leaving aside these theoretical questions, the following definition may be adopted as sufficient for all practical purposes. Species signifies a "grade or rank assigned by systematists to an assemblage of organic forms which they judge to be more closely interrelated by common descent than they are related to forms judged to be outside the species" (P. Chalmers Mitchell). The species concept is often inapplicable to fossil mammals and discussions concerning such fossils are usually in terms of genera. This is partly because external characters, such as hair, colour, markings and the like, which are so much relied upon in discriminating modern mammals, are but very rarely preserved in the fossils and then only in the latest deposits. Another reason why it is so often all but impossible to recognize the species of extinct mammals is because of their frequent great variability. In some cases no two individuals of a genus appear to belong to the same species. As it is manifestly impossible to make a separate species for every individual, specific distinction becomes an arbitrary and more or less meaningless procedure.

The technical name of a species, which is normally in Latin, or a latinized form, consists of two words, one the name of the genus (see below) and the other the name of a species of that genus. For instance, the domestic Horse is called *Equus caballus*, the wild Asiatic Horse is *E. przewalskii;* the African Wild Ass, *E. asinus*, is the parent of the domesticated animal, which has the same name. In Asia are several species of wild asses, of which the Mongolian *E. hemionus* is an example. This is the *binomial nomenclature*, perhaps the most useful part of the Linnæan system. Standing by itself, a species name is not identifiable.

A refinement of the binomial system is the *trinomial*, now in very extensive use, the third term denoting the subspecies or variety, and marking a definite and constant difference, which is yet not of sufficient importance to require reference to another species. It is but very rarely the case that subspecies can be distinguished among fossil mammals.

Among systematic zoölogists, there are great differences in application of the generally accepted definition of species, some making their groups much more comprehensive than others, according as they are, in slang phrase, "lumpers" or "splitters." The difficulty arises from the lack of definite criteria by which a given series of individuals can certainly be distinguished as a variety, subspecies, species or genus. It is a matter for the judgment and experience of the systematist himself. No two individuals of a species agree in every particular, but the majority depart but little from the average, or *norm*, of the species. Taking a character so easily determinable as size or weight and measuring or weighing several thousand individuals of a species, we note that the great majority are of average size, while very large or very small individuals are rare in proportion to the amount by which they exceed, or fall short of the norm.

A group of the second rank is a *Genus*, which may contain few or many species, or even a single one. In the latter case, the species is so isolated in character, that it cannot be properly referred to the same genus with any other species. A genus which includes many species, often falls naturally into *subgenera*, each comprising several species which are more nearly alike than those of any other group.

In ascending order the next main group is the *Family*, which ordinarily consists of a greater or less number of allied genera, united by the possession of certain characters. A family may consist of a single isolated genus, but this is exceptional; families of several genera are often conveniently divided into *subfamilies*. The family name, which is taken from the first described, or best known genus, always has the termination *-idæ*, while the name of a subfamily ends in *-inæ*. For instance, the family Felidæ (derived from the genus *Felis*) which includes all the cats and cat-like mammals, living and extinct, has two subfamilies, the Felinæ, or true cats and the extinct †Machairodontinæ, or "†sabre-tooth tigers," so-called. Vernacular names in the plural, as used in technical books, such as dogs, cats, bears, horses, etc., are nearly always to be taken as family names, and equivalent to Canidæ, Felidæ, Ursidæ, Equidæ, etc.

It is becoming a wide-spread practice in classifying mammals to employ the *superfamily* as a very significant group intermediate between family and order, or suborder. To the superfamily is given the uniform termination of *-oidea*.

The *Order* is the fourth of the principal grades and it usually includes many families, united by some fundamental characteristics of structure. Rarely, however, an order may include but a single family, a single genus, or even a single species, because, in essential characteristics, that genus or species is so unlike any other as not to be assignable to the same order. Such isolation implies that the genus or species in question is the sole survivor of a once extensive series. It is often necessary to recognize natural groups within the limits of an order, and such groups are called *suborders;* these are particularly necessary in the case of very large orders comprising many families.

In the scheme of Linnæus the group of next higher rank is the *Class*, which includes all mammals whatsoever, but the advance of knowledge has made it necessary to interpolate several grades intermediate between order and class, which, in the descending scale, are *subclass, infraclass, cohort, superorder*, etc. Above the class is the subkingdom of the Vertebrata, which includes mammals, birds, reptiles, amphibians and fishes, using the latter term in the widest possible sense.

The conventions of printing technical names should be understood: The names of species in American practice are in small letters, but in Europe specific names which are proper nouns or adjectives are usually with capital initials. Names of genera, families and all groups of higher rank begin with capitals, unless used in vernacular form, e.g. Artiodactyla and artiodactyls; genus and species names are always in italics, and groups of higher rank in roman. It is usual to give capitals to the vernacular names of species, such as Grizzly Bear, Moose, Caribou, etc.

Such a scheme of classification as is shown in the subjoined table has a very artificial air, yet it not only serves a very useful purpose, but it also expresses the facts of relationship, so far as those facts are known. The scheme is graphically displayed by a genealogical or family tree, and though this deals with individuals, the analogy is a real one, for the blood-relationship is the principle in all modes of classification in which the theory of Evolution is postulated.

The system of Linnæus, as modified by the advance of knowledge, is still well adapted to the study of the living world. Its application to the fossils is much less satisfactory, for they introduce, so to speak, a third dimension, that of time, for which the system was not designed. The element of time involves the successive modifications in a genetically connected series. The cumulative effect of such modifications is so great, that the definitions of the changing groups must be vague. In attempting to apply the system of Linnæus to the successive faunas which have inhabited the earth, palæontologists have employed several different methods. One plan is to classify the fauna of each minor division of geological time without reference to those which precede and follow it, but this has the great drawback of ignoring the genetic relationships, to express which is the object of classification. A more logical method is to treat families and orders as *genetic series* and include in each series the main line of descent and such side-branches as do not depart too widely from the type. For example, the horses (family Equidæ), which have a very long history, would, under the first arrangement, be divided into several families, while, under the second they would all be included in a single one, which contains one main line of descent and several divergent side-branches. Branches which ramify extensively and depart widely from the principal stem may require separation as distinct families.

An instructive instance is furnished by the rhinoceroses, a very ancient and widely ramified group, which includes three distinctly marked genetic series. The first is that of the true rhinoceroses, several genera of which still survive in Africa and Asia. The second, extinct, is that of the cursorial †hyracodonts, lightly built, long-necked and long-legged, but still unmistakable rhinoceroses. The third, also extinct, is that of the presumably aquatic †amynodonts, massive and hippopotamus-like animals. The problem of classifying this assemblage is solved differently by different writers; some make each series a family and group the three in a superfamily, the Rhinoceroidea. Others make one family for all the rhinoceroses and three subfamilies for the three distinct series. Others again, group the three lines in two families.

In many families, the history of which has been made out with some degree of completeness, there are two or more separate series which independently passed through parallel courses of development, each series keeping remarkably even pace with the others in progressive modification. It is customary to call such a genetic series within the family a *phylum*, but as this term is also used in a different sense, the Latin equivalent, *tribe*, of the Greek phylum, will be used here.

Genera and species are relatively short-lived and therefore do not offer the same problem in classification as do the larger groups. Among fossil mammals, as mentioned above, discrimination of species is so difficult that they are frequently disregarded and the arrangement of genetic series is made almost entirely according to genera.

Unfortunately, no method has been devised of satisfactorily applying the Linnæan classification to fossil vertebrates and it is only the gaps in the palæontological record which make it possible to use the scheme at all. If we could obtain approximately complete series of all the mammals which have lived upon the earth, it would be necessary to devise some new scheme of classification.

In the present state of knowledge, classification can be made only in a tentative way, and there is great difference in the amount of information which has been obtained concerning the different mammalian orders. Of the history of some orders very little is known, while of others a surprisingly full account may be given. The mutual relationships of the great groups, or orders, is still very largely obscure, because their beginnings were in a time of which we have hardly any information. The table of classification given below and followed in this book, is taken, with a few changes, from that prepared by Dr. G. G. Simpson of the American Museum of Natural History, and represents the latest stage of a revision that has been in progress since the publication of Linnæus' plan in 1758, in the tenth edition of his *Systema Naturæ*, in which binomial nomenclature was first systematically employed. Throughout the later XVIII and earlier XIX Centuries, various great naturalists added to and modified the Linnæan plan, and in 1834 the French zoölogist, de Blainville proposed an important innovation. He divided the Mammalia into three subclasses, which he called the Ornithodelphia, the Didelphia and the Monodelphia, and though his terms have been largely superseded, the underlying idea is still retained in modified form. In 1872 Dr. Theodore Gill improved de Blainville's plan by making the primary division into two, instead of three subclasses, I Prototheria (= Ornithodelphia), and II Eutheria (= Didelphia and Monodelphia). Gill's terms have been much misunderstood and their application changed, especially by European writers and, in justice to the memory of a great naturalist, these terms are here employed in Gill's original sense and, for the same reason, two of de Blainville's terms are retained. Gill's classification was devised primarily for existing mammals and palæontological discovery has necessitated some additions, which, however, do not change its essential nature.

The subclass Prototheria is represented in the modern world only by the strange order Monotremata, which is confined to Australia, Tasmania and New Guinea. The Duck-billed Mole (*Ornithorhynchus*) and Spiny Anteater (*Tachyglossus*, generally, but improperly, called *Echidna*) are the only existing Prototheria and they are much the most primitive of living mammals. They do not bring forth living young, but reproduce by means of eggs and they retain many reptilian characteristics, which other mammals have lost. Upon this structure, fundamentally so primitive, are superposed remarkable specializations which render difficult any fruitful comparison between the living Monotremata and the even more primitive mammals of the Triassic and Jurassic periods. The latter are still very incompletely known, but they tell us much that is of the highest interest and significance, indispensable to any understanding of the origin and early history of the Mammalia. For some of these Mesozoic genera there has been formed a third subclass, the †Allotheria, of which more complete knowledge may lead to inclusion in the Prototheria as a very distinct infraclass.

The second subclass, that of the Eutheria, comprises all other mammals, which bring forth living young. As at present constituted, the subclass includes one extinct infraclass, the †Pantotheria and two existing ones, the Didelphia and the Monodelphia. Inclusion of the †Pantotheria within the Eutheria is probable, but by no means certain.

The two existing infraclasses are of very unequal size, the Didelphia including but a single order, the Marsupialia, or pouched mammals. In this group, the young, though alive at birth, are in an extremely immature and helpless state and are carried in the pouch for varying periods. With the exception of one genus (*Perameles*) the fœtus is not attached to the womb of the mother by means of a placenta. The marsupials which were once spread all over the world, are now almost entirely confined to Australia and its islands, the exceptions being the opossums of North and South America and one small and rare genus (*Cænolestes*) in the latter continent. The second infraclass, the Monodelphia, is incomparably larger and more diversified than the marsupials. These mammals are especially characterized by the *placenta*, a special growth, partly of fœtal, partly of maternal origin, by means of which the unborn young are attached to the mother and nourished during the fœtal period; hence the Monodelphia are often called the Placentalia, or placental mammals. The young are born in a relatively mature state, resembling their parents in nearly all respects. The vast assemblage of the placental mammals is divisible into numerous orders, most of which appear to be natural groups of truly related forms, while some are but doubtfully so. As noted above, the mutual relationships of the orders, as expressed in the groups of higher than ordinal rank, offer a much more difficult problem, because the early history of almost all the orders is very imperfectly, or not at all known. The evolutionary history of many genera and families may be determined in a very convincing manner, but the origin of the larger groups can rarely be made out. Nevertheless, there is very general agreement among the students of mammals as to the number and limits of the orders themselves.

In the following table only the major groups are included and those which are extinct are marked here and throughout the book by a dagger (†). The arrangement of Dr. Simpson is followed, with a few exceptions, which, for the most part, have to do with terms rather than with concepts, older terms being retained so far as possible. Of the Rodentia, which are by far the most numerous of mammalian orders, the classification is still disputed and is therefore here omitted. For the sake of completeness, all of the mammalian orders are included in the table and those which are not dealt with in the succeeding chapters, either because they are marine, or because they have not been found in the Western Hemisphere, or for lack of space, are enclosed in brackets.

CLASS MAMMALIA

I. [Subclass PROTOTHERIA. Egg-laying Mammals.
    Order **MONOTREMATA,** e.g. the Duck-billed Mole and Spiny
        Anteaters.]

II. Subclass †ALLOTHERIA.
    Order †**MULTITUBERCULATA.**
    Suborder †**Tritylodontoidea.**
    Suborder †**Plagiaulacoidea.**
    INCERTÆ SEDIS.
    Order †**TRICONODONTA.**

III. Subclass EUTHERIA. Viviparous Mammals.
    A. Infraclass †PANTOTHERIA.
      1. Order †**TRITUBERCULATA.**
      2. Order †**SYMMETRODONTA.**
    B. Infraclass DIDELPHIA. Non-placental Mammals.
      Order **MARSUPIÁLIA.** Opossums, Kangaroos, etc.
    C. Infraclass MONODELPHIA. Placental Mammals.
    AA. Cohort UNGUICULATA. Clawed Mammals.
      1. Order [**INSECTIVORA**]. Moles, Shrews, Hedgehogs,
        etc.
      2. Order [†**TILLODONTIA**].
      3. Order [**DERMOPTERA**]. The "Flying Lemur."
      4. Order [**CHIROPTERA**]. Bats.
      5. Order [†**TÆNIODONTA**].
      6. Order **EDENTATA.**
        Suborder †**Palæanodonta.**
        Suborder **Xenarthra.**
          Infraorder *Pilosa.* Hairy Edentates.
          Infraorder *Loricata.* Armoured Edentates.
      7. Order [**PHOLIDOTA**]. Scaly Ant-eaters.
      8. Order [**RODENTIA**]. Gnawing Mammals.
      9. Order [**LAGOMORPHA**]. Hares and Rabbits.

10. ORDER **CARNIVORA**. Beasts of Prey.
    SUBORDER †**Creodonta**. Primitive Carnivores.
    SUBORDER **Fissipedia**. Land Carnivores.
    SUBORDER [**Pinnipedia**]. Marine Carnivores.
11. ORDER [**PRIMATES**].
BB. COHORT [MUTILATA].
    12. ORDER [**CETACEA**]. Whales, Dolphins, etc.
        SUBORDER [†**Archæoceti**]. Primitive Cetaceans.
        SUBORDER [**Odontoceti**]. Toothed Cetaceans.
        SUBORDER [**Mystacoceti**]. Whalebone Whales.
CC. COHORT UNGULATA. Hoofed Mammals.
    13. ORDER †**CONDYLARTHRA**. Primitive Ungulates.
    14. ORDER [**TUBULIDENTATA**]. The Aard Vark.
    15. ORDER †**AMBLYPODA**.
        SUBORDER †**Pantodonta**.
        SUBORDER †**Dinocerata**.
    16. ORDER †**NOTOUNGULATA**.
        SUBORDER †**Toxodonta**.
        SUBORDER †**Typotheria**.
        SUBORDER †**Entelonychia**.
    17. ORDER †**ASTRAPOTHERIA**.
    18. ORDER †**PYROTHERIA**.
    19. ORDER †**LITOPTERNA**.
    20. ORDER **PROBOSCIDEA**. Elephants.
    21. ORDER [†**BARYTHERIA**].
    22. ORDER [†**EMBRITHOPODA**].
    23. ORDER [**HYRACOIDEA**]. Klip Dasses.
    24. ORDER [**SIRENIA**]. Sea-Cows and Dugongs.
    25. ORDER **PERISSODACTYLA**. Horses, Tapirs, Rhinoceroses.
        SUBORDER **Chelopoda**. Hoofed Perissodactyls.
        SUBORDER †**Ancylopoda**. Perissodactyls with claws.
    26. ORDER **ARTIODACTYLA**.
        SUBORDER †**Palæodonta**. Most ancient Artiodactyls.
        SUBORDER **Hyodonta**. Hippopotamus, Swine, etc.
        SUBORDER †**Ancodonta**. Primitive Artiodactyls.
        SUBORDER **Tylopoda**. Camels, Llamas.
        SUBORDER **Pecora**. Ruminants.

CHAPTER II

THE SKELETON AND TEETH OF MAMMALS

With very rare exceptions and those almost all of very late geological date, the fossil remains of mammals consist exclusively of bones and teeth. Even when these are petrified, they generally retain the minutest microscopic structure of their original state. The steps of evolution are recorded in the successive modifications of bones and teeth and it is, therefore, necessary to understand something of the mammalian dentition and skeleton, and, though the non-professional reader cannot be expected to take a course in osteology or odontology, he may use this chapter for explanations when the need is felt. While it is not possible to avoid the use of technical terms altogether, they are minimized so far as is practicable. Most of the bones have vernacular, as well as Latin names, those of the skull excepted, for common speech deals with the skull as an indivisible unit.

I. The Skeleton

The skeleton comprises all the bones of the organism, and, leaving aside for the present the external armour of bony scutes, the skeleton proper is plainly divisible into *axial* and *appendicular* portions. The axial skeleton is that of the middle line, comprising the skull, backbone, or vertebral column, the ribs and breast-bone, or sternum, and, except the ribs and most of the elements of the skull, its bones are not paired. The appendicular skeleton includes the limb-girdles, limbs and feet, all the bones of which are in pairs, left and right.

1. AXIAL SKELETON

In describing the axial skeleton, the quadrupedal position is assumed; the erect attitude requires a change of terms, anterior becoming *superior* and posterior changing to *inferior*. For back and front, or upper and lower aspects, of the body, the more exact terms *dorsal* and *ventral* are employed, as these are equally applicable to the quadrupedal and the bipedal attitudes.

The *Skull* is made up of many elements, all of which, except the lower jaw and the *hyoid arch*, which supports the tongue, are im-

14

movably fixed together and, after maturity, their lines of junction, or *sutures*, are obliterated by co-ossification. The uses of the skull are manifold; in the first place, it lodges and protects the brain and higher sense-organs; in the second place, it carries the teeth and uses them for taking and masticating food; and, thirdly, most mammals use their teeth as weapons and the jaws must employ these weapons to the best advantage.

The part of the skull which lodges the brain and organs of sight and hearing is called the *cranium*, and the part in front of this, the

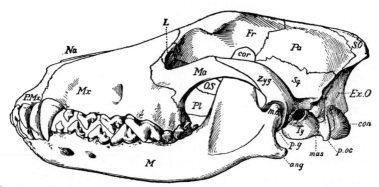

Fig. 1. — Skull of Wolf, *Canis occidentalis*, left side. *P.Mx*, premaxillary. *Mx*, maxillary. *Na*, nasal. *L*, lachrymal. *Ma*, malar or jugal. *Fr*, frontal. *Pa*, parietal. *Sq*, squamosal. *Zyg*, zygomatic process of squamosal. *O.S*, orbitosphenoid. *Pl*, palatine. *M*, inferior maxillary or mandible. *cor*, coronoid process of mandible. *m.c*, condyle of mandible. *ang*, angular process of mandible. *P.g*, post-glenoid process of squamosal. *Ty*, tympanic (auditory bulla). *mas*, mastoid. *p.oc*, paroccipital process. *con*, occipital condyle. *Ex.O*, exoccipital. *S.O*, supraoccipital.

face. The boundary between the two regions is an oblique line along the front margin of the eye-socket (or *orbit*) and passing downward and backward behind the last upper tooth. Differing proportions of cranium and face have much to do with producing the endless variety of the mammalian skull. In Man the cranium is enormously developed into a great dome-like brain-case, while the face is shortened as far as is possible without being "pugged." On the other hand, the skull of the Horse goes to the opposite extreme of a very long face and short cranium.

The construction of the skull is somewhat like that of a decked boat; the keel is represented by a line of unpaired bones along the base of the skull, while the sides and top are, for the most part, made by symmetrical pairs. The posterior surface of the cranium, the *occiput*, is made up of four bones, which, in most adult mammals, fuse into a single bone, the *occipital*. A large, round opening at the base of the occiput, the *foramen magnum*, gives entry to the spinal cord for its junction with the brain, and, on each side of the foramen is a smooth oval prominence, the *occipital condyles*, which serve for articulation of the skull with the first vertebra of the neck, or *atlas*. The *paroccipital processes* are bony styles, of very different length and thickness in different mammals, and these arise, one on each side, external to the condyles. The roof and much of the sides of the cranium are made up of two pairs of large bones, the *parietals*, which border on the occipital, and the *frontals*. Along the median line, the junction of the two parietals is, in many mammals, a prominent ridge, the *sagittal crest*, which serves to increase the surface of attachment of powerful masticatory muscles. When the cranium is so enlarged that its walls give sufficient surface of attachment for the temporal muscles, the sagittal crest disappears.

The cranial walls are partly made up of the *sphenoid* bones, two in the middle line at the base of the skull and two on each side. In Man all six of these elements are fused together, but in most mammals they remain separate till after maturity, and each one has its name. The side wall of the cranium is completed on each side by the *squamosal*, a large bone which articulates with the parietals and frontals above, the occipital behind, and the sphenoids below; it also carries the lower jaw; the groove, or pit, with which condyle of the lower jaw articulates, is the *glenoid cavity*. Behind this cavity is a prominence, or ridge, which prevents backward dislocation of the jaw and is called the *post-glenoid process*. From the squamosal is given off a long, forwardly directed arm, the *zygomatic process*, which with the cheek-bone (*jugal*, or *malar*) forms the *zygomatic arch*, extending forward to the eye-socket.

Behind the postglenoid process is the groove for the opening into the ear, the *meatus auditorius externus*. All the bones connected with the middle and internal ear are of great importance in questions of relationship. The labyrinth of the internal ear is, as its name implies a membranous structure of extreme complexity, which is enclosed in the *petrosal*, the bone embracing the membranous organ, but with a lymph-filled space between. The labyrinth consists of the three semi-circular canals and, connected with these, the *cochlea*, the real organ of hearing, in which the fibrils of the auditory nerve terminate. In the Eutheria the cochlea is a spiral coil of one and a half to five turns, but in the Monotremata it is a semi-circular curve and in those Mesozoic mammals in which it is known, it is straight, as it is also in the reptiles.

The petrosal, so called from its stony hardness, is, in Man, united with the squamosal and the compound bone is the *temporal* of human anatomy. The part of the petrosal called the *mastoid* (*pars mastoidea*) often appears on the surface of the cranium between

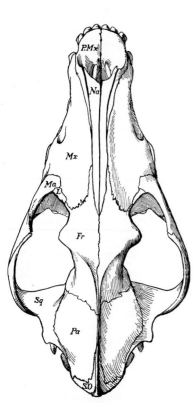

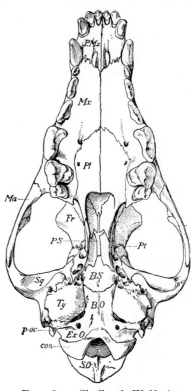

FIG. 2. — Skull of Wolf, top view. *P.Mx*, premaxillary. *Na*, nasal. *Ma*, malar or jugal. *L*, lachrymal. *Fr*, frontal. *Sq*, squamosal. *Pa*, parietal. *S.O*, supraoccipital. *Mx*, maxillary.

FIG. 3. — Skull of Wolf, base view. *P.Mx*, premaxillary. *Mx*, palatine process of maxillary. *Pl*, palatine. *Fr*, frontal. *Pt*, parietal. *Ma*, malar or jugal. *Sq*, glenoid cavity of squamosal. *B.S*, basisphenoid. *B.O*, basioccipital. *Ty*, tympanic (auditory bulla). *P.S*, presphenoid. Other letters as in Figs. 1 and 2.

squamosal and occipital, but may be covered by the junction of these two bones. When exposed, it bears a more or less prominent projection, the *mastoid process;* it may be inflated and contain the large membrane-lined cavity, or *sinus*, as in Man; in certain rodents it is relatively enormous.

The mechanism of the middle ear is lodged in the *auditory bulla*, which is usually inflated and hollow, when it forms a resonator for intensifying the sound waves. The bulla is made up in different ways in the various mammalian groups. In primitive and in very young animals the *tympanic bone* is a more or less incomplete ring, which supports the ear-drum. In most of the higher mammals the tympanic enlarges greatly and is inflated to form the auditory bulla, which, in that case, is a *tympanic bulla*. In the cat-like Carnivora, there is another element, the *entotympanic*, behind and internal to the first, which is inflated into an additional chamber and may remain separate or fuse with the tympanic proper. Still a third method of forming the bulla is exemplified by the Marsupialia in which one of the sphenoid bones is inflated for this purpose.

The structure of the cranial bones, especially of the parietals and frontals, differs in the various mammalian groups. In most of these groups they are of moderate thickness and have smooth dense layers, or "tables" forming the outer and inner surfaces, and, between these, a layer of spongy bone, the *diploë*. In many large mammals, especially those which have massive horns or tusks, such as rhinoceroses and elephants, the bones are enormously thickened and the diploë is expanded into a mass of communicating cells, lined with membrane, the partitions between the cells acting as braces and making the skull very strong in proportion to its weight. *Frontal sinuses* are very generally present, even in animals of moderate size, such as wolves, and the mastoid sinus occurs in many mammals. The frontals form the eye-sockets, or orbits and there is very often a projection from each frontal, the *postorbital process*, which marks the boundary of the orbit behind.

The facial region is mostly made of the jaw-bones, of which there are three on each side, the *maxillaries*, *premaxillaries* and *inferior maxillaries; maxilla* is often used instead of maxillary. The maxillaries are the largest of the three pairs, making up nearly all of the sides and roof of the face, they carry all the upper teeth except the incisors and enclose the nasal passage between them. The *anterior nares* make the forward opening of this passage, the floor of which is the bony palate. In front of the maxillaries are the very much smaller premaxillaries, between which the anterior nares open and which lodge the upper incisor teeth.

The roof of the facial region is completed in the middle line by the *nasals*, which are usually narrow and splint-like bones, but which may become very broad and thick, as they do in the rhinoceroses. In most mammals the nasals are rather long and have a considerable articulation with the premaxillaries, but in those which, like the elephants and tapirs, have a proboscis, or a much inflated muzzle such as may be seen in the Moose (*Alce machlis*) or the Saiga Antelope (*Saiga tatarica*), the nasals are much shortened, widely removed from the premaxillaries and more or less modified in shape.

The zygomatic arch is completed by the *jugal*, or *malar* (cheek-bone) which articulates behind with the zygomatic process of the squamosal, which rests upon it, and sometimes it extends almost to the glenoid cavity. The jugal articulates anteriorly with a process of the maxillary and forms the lower and more or less of the front border of the orbit. The jugal often has a postorbital process, which extends toward the corresponding process of the frontal and, when the two meet, the orbit is completely encircled with a bony ring. The thickness of the zygomatic arches and the extent of their outward curvature from the skull are subject to great variation and, as a rule, thickness and curvature are greatest in the Carnivora, while in some Insectivora the arch is interrupted by the failure of the jugal to ossify. The upper front border of the orbit is formed by the *lachrymal*, a small bone, but sometimes important in determining relationships.

The hard, or bony, *palate* is composed of three pairs of bones, the *palatine processes* of the maxillaries usually forming most of the palate; the corresponding processes of the premaxillæ are much smaller. Behind, a varying proportion of the palate is made by the *palatines*, which also help to enclose the *posterior nares*, the hinder opening of the nasal canal, which makes breathing possible through the nose, when the mouth is shut.

The lower jaw-bone (*inferior maxillary*, or *mandible*), the only freely movable element of the skull, consists of two halves, which meet at the chin, in a contact of varying length, called the *symphysis*. In nearly all young animals and most adult forms, the two halves of the mandible are separate and held together only by an interlocking joint and transverse ligaments. In other mammals, such as horses and elephants, the symphysis is so firmly co-ossified that the lower jaw-bone is a single piece. Each half of the jaw is composed of a *horizontal ramus*, in which the lower teeth are lodged and an *ascending ramus*, or vertical portion, a broad and rather thin plate, which divides above into two projections. Of these, the posterior one, a rounded, hemispherical, or semi-cylindrical *condyle*, fits into the glenoid cavity of the squamosal to form the joint on which the mandible moves. The anterior portion is the *coronoid process*, which usually rises high above the condyle and passes inside of the zygomatic arch, giving attachment to the temporal muscle. This muscle, as stated above, covers the side of the cranium and its contraction closes the jaw. A second biting muscle is the *masseter*, which arises along the lower edge of the zygomatic arch and is inserted in the depression, called the *masseteric fossa*, on the lower part of the ascending ramus. On the inner side of the mandible, the *external* and *internal pterygoid* muscles also close the jaw and tend to draw it forward, greatly assisting in mastication.

At the postero-inferior point of the jaw is the *angle*, or *angular process*, the shape of which is characteristically different in the different groups of mammals and the complete absence of which is a noteworthy feature of the Monotremata and of the Mesozoic †Multituberculata.

The *hyoid arch* is a U-shaped series of slender, rod-like bones, with an unpaired element closing the arch below, and each vertical arm is attached to the tympanic of its own side. The whole arch forms a flexible support for the tongue and is an important point of attachment for the muscles of swallowing and depressing the lower jaw, but it has no freely movable joint.

This brief sketch of the skull is necessarily incomplete, for no mention has been made of several bones, such as the turbinals, ethmoid and vomer, which are concealed within the nasal canal and can rarely be observed in fossil skulls.

In its primitive form the mammalian skull may be regarded as a tube divided into two parts, the hinder one of which is the brain-cavity and the forward one the nasal passage. With the enlargement of the brain and cranium the tubular shape is lost and the various modifications of the teeth, jaws and facial region and the development of horns, or tusks, bring about the many changes which the mammalian skull has undergone. Throughout all these changes, the unity of plan persists and the skull of a large whale, an elephant, a man, or a mouse, retains this fundamental identity. The number of bones is not increased, but may be diminished by co-ossification, and the unending adaptations to new purposes are accomplished through modifications of the shape and size of those elements which remain. This principle applies generally to the teeth and all parts of the skeleton.

The *vertebral column*, or backbone, is made up of many separate *vertebræ*, which are so articulated as to give the requisite degree of flexibility and strength. The function of the backbone is twofold: (1) to give a firm support to the body and afford strong points of attachment for the limbs, and (2) to lodge and protect the spinal cord, which is the great central axis of the nervous system and innervates the limbs, body and tail. Protection of the cord against injury, or compression in the flexible tube of the backbone is a vital necessity. The vertebræ are all constructed on the same plan, though differing much in appearance. In a vertebra the principal mass of bone is the body, or *centrum*, a more or less modified cylinder. The two ends are the *faces*, by means of which the successive vertebræ are joined together. In the young animal the faces are separate bony disks, the *epiphyses*, and growth takes place by the deposition of bone between the centrum and the epiphyses. When the latter unite with the body, growth ceases. Epiphyses of the vertebræ and the long bones are an exclusively mammalian feature. In life, the successive vertebræ are separated by disks of cartilage, which are attached to the bone and increase the flexibility of the column. From the dorsal surface of the centrum arises the *neural arch*, which, with the centrum, forms the *neural canal*, and lodges the spinal cord.

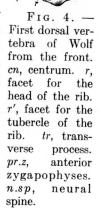

Contact of the centra with one another would not give sufficient strength to the backbone; additional means of articulation are therefore provided and these vary in size and shape in nice adjustment to the different degrees of strength and mobility needed in different parts of the column. Of these *zygapophyses*, each vertebra has two pairs, anterior and posterior, placed upon or on each side of the neural arch. From the summit of the neural arch is given off the *neural spine*, a usually straight rod, or narrow plate of bone, which may be enormously long, or very short, slender or massive, according to the muscular attachments. Finally, should be mentioned the *transverse processes*, which are rod-like, or plate-like projections from the centrum or neural arch, and are directed laterally outward, and these likewise differ greatly in the various regions of the column. Anatomists distinguish several other processes of the vertebræ, but these it is not necessary to consider here.

FIG. 4. — First dorsal vertebra of Wolf from the front. *cn*, centrum. *r*, facet for the head of the rib. *r'*, facet for the tubercle of the rib. *tr*, transverse process. *pr.z*, anterior zygapophyses. *n.sp*, neural spine.

There are five regions of the backbone, in each of which the vertebræ have characteristic forms. (1) The *cervical region*, or neck, has the greatest need for flexibility, yet, with one or two exceptions, it has the constant number of seven vertebræ, a characteristic of mammals; the Giraffe has no more than seven cervicals and the almost neckless whales have no less. Elongation of the neck is accomplished by lengthening the vertebræ, not by increasing their number. (2) The vertebræ to which ribs are attached are called *thoracic*, or *dorsal*, and may be recognized by the pits on the centra for the heads of the ribs. (3) Next follow the *lumbar* vertebræ, or those of the loins, which are without ribs. The dorso-lumbars collectively are the *trunk-vertebræ* and are generally constant in number for a given group of mammals, though often differently divided between the two regions. In the order Artiodactyla for example, the number of trunk-vertebræ is very constantly nineteen; the Hippopotamus has fifteen dorsals and four lumbars, the Reindeer (*Rangifer*) fourteen dorsals, five lumbars, the Ox (*Bos taurus*) thirteen dorsals, six lumbars, and the Camel (*Camelus dromedarius*) 12 D. and 7 L. (4) Following the lumbar is the *sacral* region; the *sacrum* is a single bone formed by the coalescence of several vertebræ (2 to 13) which serves for the attachment of the *pelvis*, or hip-bones. The usual number is three to five. (5) Finally, there are the caudal vertebræ, which differ greatly in number and form according to the length and thickness of the tail.

Fig. 5. — Atlas of Wolf, anterior end and left side. *cot*, anterior cotyles. *n.c*, neural canal. *tr*, transverse process. *n.a*, neural arch. *v.a*, posterior opening of the canal for the vertebral artery.

The first two cervical vertebræ, called the *atlas* and *axis* respectively, are especially modified to make the connection between head and neck and give to the skull the necessary freedom of motion. The *atlas* is hardly more than a ring of bone, with a pair of deep, oval, cupshaped depressions, the *anterior cotyles*, into which are fitted the occipital condyles of the skull; the nodding, or up and down, movement of the head is accomplished by the movement of the condyles in the anterior cotyles, but this joint does not permit movement from side to side. The turning movement is done by the partial rotation of skull and atlas together upon the axis. On the hinder side of the atlas are the *posterior cotyles*, shaped like the anterior pair, but slightly concave, or flat, and these are in contact with corresponding, slightly convex surfaces on the axis. The neural arch of the atlas is broad and low and the canal is, in life, divided by a transverse liga-

Fig. 6. — Axis of Wolf, left side. *od.p*, odontoid process. *cot*, anterior cotyles. *n.a*, neural arch. *n.sp*, neural spine. *pt.z*, posterior zygapophyses. *tr*, transverse process. *v.a'*, anterior opening of canal for the vertebral artery. *v.a''*, posterior opening of the same.

ment into two parts, the upper and larger one for the spinal cord, the lower one for a projection from the axis. The atlas usually has no neural spine and never a prominent one; the transverse processes are broad, wing-like plates, each of which is perforated by a canal for the vertebral artery.

The second vertebra, or *axis*, has a distinct and usually elongate centrum, on which are the cotyles for articulation with the atlas. Between the cotyles is a prominent projection, the *odontoid process*, which fits into the ring of the atlas and has a special articular facet for the lower bar of that ring. The partial rotation of the atlas, carrying the skull with it, is around the fixed point of the odontoid process. In most mammals, the odontoid is a blunt, conical peg, differing only in length and thickness, but in the long-necked forms, it takes on a spout-like shape, convex below and concave above, where it embraces the spinal cord. The neural spine of the axis is a large, hatchet-shaped plate and the transverse processes are slender rods, perforated for the vertebral arteries.

The five succeeding cervical vertebræ are much alike, but each one is distinctive of its place in the series. The centra have convex anterior and concave posterior faces, which in long-necked animals, such as the horses, are very perfect examples of the "ball and socket" joint. The zygapophyses are very characteristic of the region, being carried on projections which extend before and behind the neural arch. The transverse processes are large and plate-like and, except in a few forms (e.g. the camel family) are perforated by the vertebral artery. Neural spines are short and slender, never very prominent. The seventh cervical is distinguished by stout, rod-like transverse processes, which are not perforated, and by having on the posterior face cup-shaped depressions for the heads of the first pair of ribs, which articulate equally with the last cervical and the first dorsal.

FIG. 7. — Fifth cervical vertebra of Wolf, left side. *tr*, transverse process. *va"*, posterior opening of canal for vertebral artery. *pr.z* and *pt.z*, anterior and posterior zygapophyses. *n.sp*, neural spine.

The *dorsal*, or *thoracic*, *vertebræ* have more or less cylindrical centra, with flattened faces, which are indented by the circular depressions for the rib-heads; posteriorly, these rib-facets may shift toward the middle of the centrum. The zygapophyses are entirely different from those of the cervical region; the anterior pair, borne on the top of the neural arch, present upward, and the posterior pair, on the under side of the arch, face downward, but, in the hinder part of the region, one or more vertebræ take on zygapophyses of the lumbar type. The neural spines are very much longer than those of the neck, and the spines of the anterior dorsals, especially in large hoofed animals, are often enormously long but they diminish in length and thickness posteriorly.

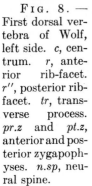

FIG. 8. — First dorsal vertebra of Wolf, left side. *c*, centrum. *r*, anterior rib-facet. *r''*, posterior rib-facet. *tr*, transverse process. *pr.z* and *pt.z*, anterior and posterior zygapophyses. *n.sp*, neural spine.

The *lumbar vertebræ*, those of the loins, are larger and heavier than the dorsals; they have no ribs and their spines and transverse processes are broad and plate-like, the latter far longer than in the dorsal region. As an especial degree of strength and flexibility are frequently required in the loins, the zygapophyses are more complicated and firmly interlocking than in the dorsal region. In the xenarthrous sec-

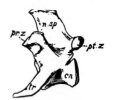

FIG. 9. — Third lumbar vertebra of Wolf, front end and left side. *tr*, transverse process. *cn*, centrum. *pr.z* and *pt.z*, anterior and posterior zygapophyses. *n.sp*, neural spine.

tion of the Edentata, additional articulations make the connections more elaborately complex than in any other mammals. In the series

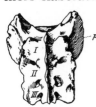

FIG. 10. — Sacrum of Wolf, upper side. *I*, *II*, *III*, first, second, third sacral vertebræ. *pl*, surface for attachment to hip-bone.

of trunk vertebræ the neural spines are, in most mammals, inclined backward from the front of the dorsal region to near its hinder end and there, or in the anterior lumbars, there is a vertebra with erect spine and behind that point the spines incline forward. In the elephants, however, all the neural spines of the body have a backward inclination.

The *sacral vertebræ* are co-ossified into one solid mass, the neural canal forming a continuous tube and the coalesced spines a ridge. Usually, only the two anterior vertebræ support the hip-bones, the remainder of the sacrum projecting freely to the root of the tail. When the sacrum is very long it may form a connection with the hinder end of the hip-bone.

The *caudal vertebræ* vary greatly in number and size; when the tail is long and thick several of the anterior caudals have the parts of a typical vertebra, centrum, neural arch and spine, zygapophyses and transverse processes. Posteriorly, the arch and processes gradually diminish, though in a long, heavy tail, such as that of the Leopard, the centra grow longer and thicker to the middle of its length, growing shorter and more slender behind that point. The processes are reduced to knobs and ridges and the neural arch dies away. In some mammals *chevron-bones* are attached to the un-

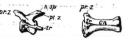

Fig. 11. — Caudal vertebræ of Wolf, left side, from anterior and middle parts of tail. Letters as in Fig. 9.

der side of the caudal centra, in the anterior and middle parts of the tail; these are Y-shaped bones, which form a canal for the larger blood-vessels.

The *ribs*, together with the dorsal vertebræ and the breast-bone, form the *thorax*, or chest; they are movably attached to the vertebræ

by means of the convex *head*, which is, as it were, wedged in between two vertebræ and has a facet for each, though, in some groups, the posterior ribs articulate with but one vertebra each. More or less removed from the head is the *tubercle*, a projection which articulates with the transverse process of the vertebra, but in a number of the hindmost ribs the tubercle disappears. In general, the ribs are complexly curved, bony rods, which, in small animals and the clawed orders, are slender and rounded, while in most large hoofed mammals they are broad and plate-like, especially in the anterior part of the thorax.

Fig. 12. — Ribs of Wolf from anterior and middle parts of thorax. *cp*, head. *t*, tubercle.

The number of pairs of ribs is most commonly 13, but varies from 9 in certain whales to 24 in the Two-toed Sloth (*Cholœpus didactylus*). The double curvature of the ribs, outward and backward, is important in respiration; when, by muscular action, they are drawn forward (in Man upward) the capacity of the chest is increased and air rushes into the lungs (inspiration) to be again expelled, when the ribs are allowed to drop back into the position of rest (expiration).

Ventrally, more or fewer of the ribs are connected with the breast-bone by cartilages, which, in some instances, are ossified and are then called *sternal ribs*, but, in such cases, there is always a movable joint between the sternal and the true rib. In certain of the Edentata the sternal ribs have very complex articulations with the breast-bone by means of heads and tubercles. A varying number of the hindmost ribs have no connection with the sternum and these are said to be *floating*.

The breast-bone, or *sternum*, is composed of a number of seg-ments, which are usually broad and flat, but often cylindrical, as

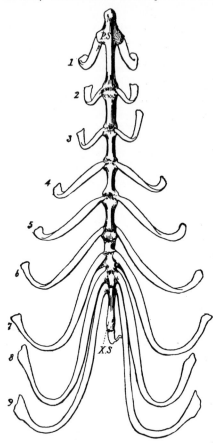

in the Wolf (Fig. 13). The first segment, the *pre-sternum*, or *manubrium*, has a different shape from the others and is consider-ably longer; the last segment, the *ensiform cartilage* of human anat-omy, is called the *xiphisternum*, from its fancied resemblance to a sword.

2. APPENDICULAR SKELETON

The appendicular skeleton comprises the bones of the limb-girdles, limbs and feet. The limb-girdles are connected more or less fixedly with the vertebral column and afford attachment to the limbs, which, in all land mam-mals are freely movable on the girdles. The anterior, *shoulder*, or *pectoral girdle* has no bony connection with the vertebræ, but is held in place by muscles and ligaments, and has two ele-ments, the *shoulder-blade* and *collar-bone*, though the latter is frequently lost. The shoulder-blade, or *scapula*, is a broad,

FIG. 13. — Sternum and rib-carti-lages of Wolf, lower side. *P.S*, manu-brium. *X.S*, xiphisternum.

thin, bony plate, of very varying form, which contracts downward to a narrow *neck* and ends in a concave articular surface, the *glenoid cavity*, which receives the head of the upper-arm bone, thus making the shoulder-joint. On the outer face of the blade is the *spine*, a prominent ridge, which usually ends downward in a conspicuous projection, the *acromion*, but may die away on the neck, as it does in the Horse (Fig. 15). An additional process given off backward from the spine, is the *metacromion*, of which there may be more than one.

A hook-like process, the *coracoid*, rises from the antero-internal side of the glenoid cavity and varies greatly in size in the different mammalian orders, though in most groups it seems to be merely a projection from the scapula, with which it is co-ossified. It is, on

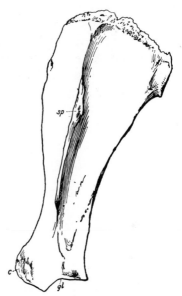

FIG. 14. — Left scapula of Wolf. *gl*, glenoid cavity. *c*, coracoid. *ac*, acromion. *sp*, spine.

FIG. 15. — Left scapula of Horse drawn on much smaller scale than Fig. 14. Letters as in Fig. 14.

the contrary, a distinct element of the shoulder girdle, and an inheritance from reptilian ancestors. The exact equivalent of this element in the reptilian shoulder girdle is not yet clear and the interpretation of the embryological development of these structures in mammals is full of difficulties and has occasioned much discussion.

This is not the place for taking part in the debate; for our purposes, the important fact is the clear derivation of the mammalian pectoral girdle from that of certain reptiles. In the Monotremata, most primitive of existing

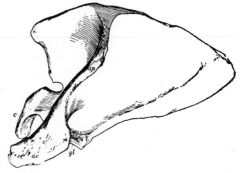

FIG. 16. — Left scapula of Man in position of creeping on all fours. Letters as in Fig. 14.

mammals, the girdle is more reptilian than Eutherian in character. A large element, which is usually called the coracoid, forms part of the glenoid cavity and extends to an articulation with the sternum just as it does in reptiles and birds. This persistent reptilian character was formerly believed to separate the Monotremata from all the viviparous mammals, or Eutheria, until Dr. R. Broom made the very interesting discovery that in the Marsupialia, the embryonic development of the girdle passes through a stage essentially like that of the monotremes. Combining the testimony of embryology and palæontology, we find a complete transition from the reptilian shoulder girdle through that of the monotremes and marsupials to that of the higher mammals.

The collar-bone, or *clavicle*, is an irregularly curved bar which, when fully developed, extends from the sternum to the acromion

FIG. 17. — Left clavicle of Man, front side.

of the scapula, thus bracing the shoulder-joint. The monotremes retain another reptilian feature in having a T-shaped interclavicle which is applied to the front of the sternum, the clavicles resting on the arms of the T. In many mammals, including all existing hoofed animals, except the primitive Hyracoidea, the clavicles have been lost. Generally speaking, the development of these bones is in proportion to the freedom of motion of the fore limb at the shoulder and to the power of rotating the hand, as in monkeys, apes and Man. Many burrowing mammals, such as the moles, have relatively massive clavicles.

The posterior, or *pelvic girdle*, or *pelvis*, is composed, on each side, of a large, irregularly shaped bone, the hip-bone, which is firmly attached to the sacrum, affording a strong support to the hind leg. Each hip-bone consists of three elements; the anterior one is the *ilium*, the posterior dorsal one the *ischium* and the posterior ventral the *pubis*. All three unite

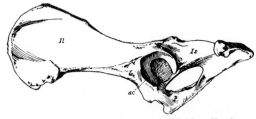

FIG. 18. — Left hip-bone of Wolf. *Il*, ilium. *Is*, ischium. *P*, pubis. *ac*, acetabulum.

to form the *acetabulum*, a deep, hemispherical pit, which receives the head of the thigh-bone and thus forms the hip-joint, a perfect example of the "ball and socket." The smooth, articular surface of the acetabulum is deeply emarginated by the pit for the round ligament, which is also inserted in the head of the thigh-bone. In the inferior median line, the two pubes meet in a *symphysis*, which may close by co-ossification, or remain permanently open. Pelvis and sacrum together form a short wide tube, the diameter of which is normally greater in the female than in the male, for the young must pass through it at birth.

Each limb is divisible into three segments, which are, in the fore limb, the arm, fore-arm and hand and, in the hind limb, the thigh, leg and foot. Because of the vagueness so often attending the use of "hand" and "foot" it is preferable to call them *manus* and *pes* respectively. The bones of the limbs are the "long bones" and, except in a few very massive animals, the long bones are tubular cylinders, a form which gives the greatest strength per unit of weight. The tube is filled with marrow and hence is called the *medullary cavity*. In the young animal each long

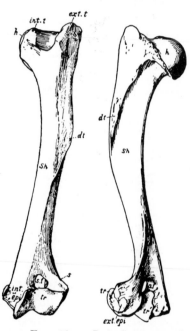

bone consists of three portions; there is (1) the *shaft*, which makes by far the greater part of the length, and (2) the *epiphyses*, bony caps, one at each end. As in the vertebræ, growth takes place by the deposition of bone between shaft and epiphyses and, when the three coalesce, growth is at an end.

The upper segment of the fore limb has a single bone, the *humerus*, the rounded, convex head of which fits into the glenoid cavity of the scapula. In front of the head are two prominent, rough and sometimes very large projections for muscular attachment, called the *internal* and *external tuberosities*, and separated by a groove, in which play the two tendons of the *biceps* muscle and therefore called the *bicipital groove*. In a few mammals, such as camels, horses and giraffes, the bicipital groove is double, divided by the *bicipital tubercle*. From the external tuberosity, a roughened and sometimes very prominent ridge, the *deltoid crest*, passes down the shaft

Fig. 19. — Left humerus of Wolf from front and outer side, the latter somewhat oblique. *h*, head. *int.t*, internal tuberosity. *ext.t*, external tuberosity. *b.c*, bicipital groove. *dt*, deltoid ridge. *sh*, shaft. *s*, supinator ridge. *int.epi*, internal epicondyle. *s.f*, anconeal foramen. *tr*, trochlea. *tr'*, trochlea, posterior side. *ext.epi*, external epicondyle. *a.f*, anconeal fossa.

FIG. 20. —
Left humerus of
Horse, front
side. *i.t*, internal
tuberosity. *ex.t*,
external tuber-
osity. *b.c*, outer
part of bicipital
groove. *dt*, del-
toid ridge.   *s*,
supinator ridge.
tr, trochlea.

and gives attachment to the great deltoid muscle;
the crest is especially developed in burrowers.

At the lower end of the humerus is the *trochlea*
(Latin for pulley), an irregular half-cylinder for articulation with the two bones of the fore-arm, and varying in shape according to the form and relative sizes
of those bones. On each side of the trochlea is frequently a rugose projection, the *epicondyles*, and
above the internal one is the *entepicondylar foramen*,
a perforation for the transmission of the ulnar nerve.
This foramen is characteristic of the more primitive
mammals, most of the higher groups
have lost it. Extending up the shaft
from the outer epicondyle is the
supinator ridge, to which is attached
the muscle of that name, one of the
muscles that rotate the hand on the
arm. Like the deltoid crest, the
supinator ridge is especially developed in burrowers. On the posterior
face, above the trochlea, is a deep
pit, the *anconeal fossa*, into which
fits the beak of the ulna.

The two bones of the fore-arm, the *radius* and
ulna, are, in most mammals, separate from each
other, but in many of the more specialized hoofed
animals, such as horses and ruminants, the two are
co-ossified. Primitively, ulna and radius were of
nearly equal size, but in the hoofed animals, as a
rule, there is a tendency for the radius to enlarge at
the expense of the ulna. Except where the two
bones are co-ossified, they are crossed, the radius
having its upper end external and its lower internal
to the ulna. The radius varies much in form, in
adjustment to the uses to which the manus is put;
when this is capable of rotation, the head, or upper
end of the radius is cylindrical, and covers but
little of the humeral trochlea, but, when the head
is widened to cover and interlock with the trochlea,
then all power of rotation is lost and the elbow joint
becomes hinge-like, moving only in one plane. Gen-

FIG.   21. —
Left humerus of
Man. Letters as
in Fig. 19.

erally speaking, the radius broadens downward and covers two-thirds, or more, of the width of the wrist-bones.

The ulna makes the principal part of the elbow-joint by means of a concave semi-circular articular surface which embraces the hu-

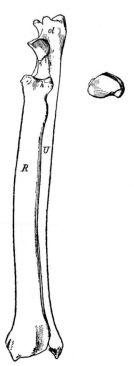

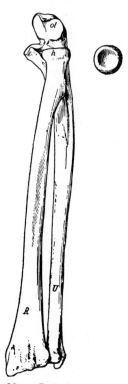

FIG. 22. — Left fore-arm bones of Wolf, front side. *R*, radius. *U*, ulna. *ol*, olecranon. *h*, head of radius.

FIG. 23. — Left fore-arm bones of Man, front side. Letters as in Fig. 22. The small object at the right of each figure is the head of the radius, seen from above.

meral trochlea and the projecting antero-superior angle, or beak, of this surface fits into the anconeal fossa of the humerus. The ulna is considerably longer than the radius, the upper end being extended as a stout and usually elongate process, the *olecranon*, or *anconeal process*, into which is inserted the tendon of the powerful *triceps* muscle, the principal extensor of the fore leg, straightening the leg, as the biceps bends it. The ulna tapers downward and its lower end covers but one of the wrist-bones. In the specialized hoofed animals, such as horses, ruminants and camels, the ulna has become extremely slender and more or less of the shaft has been lost, while

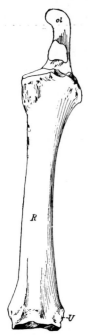

FIG. 24. —
Co-ossified bones
of left fore-arm
of Horse, front
side. For most
of its length, the
ulna is concealed
by the radius.
Letters as in Fig.
22.

the two ends are co-ossified with the radius, which
supports the whole weight. The olecranon is always
retained because of the important leverage which it
gives to the triceps muscle. In the
young even of these highly differentiated hoofed animals, the two
bones are separate. In the elephant
tribe the normal modification of the
fore-arm bones is reversed, the ulna
becoming extremely massive and the
radius, except at its lower end,
relatively very slender.

The fore foot, hand, or *manus*,
is in three parts, corresponding in
Man to the wrist, back and palm of
hand, and fingers. The bones of the
wrist form the *carpus*, the long
bones of the hand the *metacarpus*
and the finger-bones are the *phalanges*.

The carpus is a mosaic of small,
closely fitted bones, with very little
motion between them. Primitively
there were nine carpals, including
the *pisiform*, which is not a true
carpal. The carpals are of irregularly polygonal shape, somewhat
rounded and arranged in two transverse rows; the
upper consists of three true carpals, the *scaphoid*,
lunar and *pyramidal* (or *cuneiform*) enumerating
from the inner, or radial side. The scaphoid and
lunar support the radius and the pyramidal the
ulna. The *pisiform*, though constantly present,
is an ossification in the tendon of one of the flexor
muscles and is one of the numerous group of small
bones formed in the tendons at the joints of the
feet and called *sesamoids*. The function of the
sesamoids is to hold the tendons in place.

The second row of the carpus comprises four
bones, which, from within outward are the *trapezium*, *trapezoid*,
magnum and *unciform*. The relations of the two rows vary very much

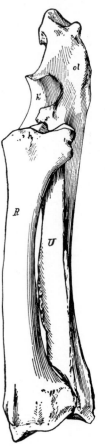

FIG. 25. —
Left fore-arm
bones of the Tapir,
*Tapirus terres-
tris*. R, radius.
U, ulna. h, head
of radius. h', sig-
moid notch of
ulna. ol, olecra-
non. N.B. This
figure is on a much
larger scale than
Fig. 24.

in different mammals, in accordance with the number of digits present and the manner in which they are used. The eighth carpal, the *central*, which is, as it were wedged in between the two rows, an interesting relic of reptilian ancestry, is a primitive element which has been suppressed, or lost, in most adult mammals, though indicated in embryos.

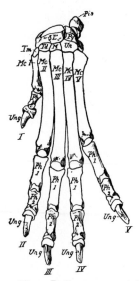

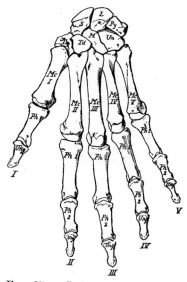

Fig. 26. — Left manus of Wolf, front side. *SL*, scapho-lunar. *Py*, pyramidal. *Pis*, pisiform. *Tm*, trapezium. *Td*, trapezoid. *M*, magnum. *Un*, unciform. *Mc I–V*, first to fifth metacarpals. *Ph 1*, first phalanx. *Ph 2*, second phalanx. *Ung*, ungual phalanx. *I*, first digit or pollex. *II–V*, second to fifth digits.

Fig. 27. — Left manus of Man. *S*, scaphoid. *L*, lunar. *Py*, pyramidal (pisiform not shown). *Tm*, trapezium. *Td*, trapezoid. *M*, magnum. *Un*, unciform. Other letters as in Fig. 26.

It persists as a distinct bone in most rodents, insectivores and in the extinct carnivorous group of the †Creodonta, in the lemurs, most monkeys and the Hyracoidea, very primitive hoofed animals. In most other mammals, the central has united with the magnum, or the scaphoid, and appears to be absent from the adult carpus. Other coalescences of carpals occur in different groups; such as the compound *scapho-lunar* of all existing Carnivora and many Rodentia.

The carpals of the second row are connected with the metacarpals and in those mammals which retain five digits, the trapezium, trapezoid and magnum support one digit each and the unciform has two. As digits are lost, the various connections are readjusted.

The *metacarpus* consists typically of five members, never more, but there may be four, three, two, or even one, through successive losses of digits. As the metacarpals are reduced, functionless vestiges of them may long persist as splints, or nodules. The metacarpals are numbered from I to V, beginning with the internal digit, the thumb, or *pollex*. In the great majority of mammals the power of rotating the manus has been lost, and the fore foot is permanently fixed in the *prone* position, palm downward. This brings the lower end of the radius and the pollex to the inner side of the manus, the

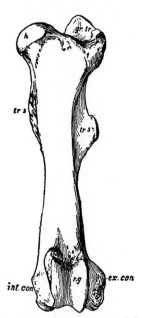

Fig. 28. — Left femur of Wolf, front side. *h*, head. *gt.tr*, great trochanter. *tr 2*, second trochanter. *int.con*, internal condyle. *r.g*, rotular groove. *ext.con*, external condyle.

Fig. 29. — Left femur of Horse. *tr 3*, third trochanter. Other letters as in Fig. 28, than which this drawing is very much more reduced.

ulna and little finger, or digit V, to the outer side. The *supine* position, with palm upward, is possible only to those forms which can rotate the manus.

Except in massive animals, such as rhinoceroses, hippopotamuses, elephants and several extinct groups, the metacarpals are elongate, more or less cylindrical. When employed for grasping, as in many arboreal mammals and, pre-eminently, in Man, the pollex has much freedom of motion and may be opposed to the other digits. The human hand has long been justly admired as an implement of superlative delicacy and efficiency, qualities which are dependent on the opposability of the thumb.

Co-ossification of the metacarpals takes place in certain hoofed animals. Thus, in the camels and true ruminants the median pair (III and IV) coalesce to form a *cannon-bone*, which, externally, seems to be a single piece, but its elements are separate in the young, and in the adult the marrow cavities of the two metacarpals are distinct.

The *phalanges*, in land mammals, never exceed three in each digit and two in the pollex. These numbers are characteristic of mammals, for in the reptiles, except some mammal-like groups, the number is much greater. In a lizard, for instance, the formula is 2, 3, 4, 5, 4, in digits I to V respectively. Except in the very heavy animals, the phalanges are relatively slender and diminish in length from the first to the third row. In some instances the phalanges are much modified for special purposes; thus, in the cats, those of the second row are asymmetrical and so shaped as to permit the retraction of the claws into the feet. The terminal joint of each digit is the ungual phalanx, which supports the claw, nail or hoof, its shape varying accordingly.

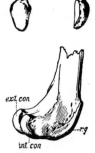

Fig. 30. — Left femur of Wolf, inside of lower end. *ext. con*, external condyle. *int.con*, internal condyle. *r.g*, rotular groove. Above, are two views of the left patella, anterior and internal sides.

Though constituted very much like the fore leg, the hind leg displays conspicuous differences. The thigh-bone, or *femur*, is usually the longest and stoutest of the limb-bones, though there are many exceptions to this rule. At the upper end is the *head*, which is set upon a constricted *neck* and projects upward and inward, fitting into the acetabulum of the hip-bone, and in nearly all mammals there is on the head a pit for the round ligament (*ligamentum teres*) the other end of which is attached to the bottom of the acetabulum.

On the outer side of the femur's upper end is a large, rough prominence, which often rises higher than the head, and is called the *great trochanter*. The importance of this process is shown by the fact that of the twenty-three muscles which are attached to the femur, no less than eight have their origin or insertion in the great trochanter. The *second*, or *lesser trochanter* is a small, more or less conical prominence on the inner side of the shaft, below the head. These two processes are well-nigh universal among land mammals;

much less common is the *third trochanter*, which arises on the outer side of the shaft, usually at, or above the middle of its length. Though rather rare in the modern world, the third trochanter is a significant feature, and the early members of most, if not all the mammalian orders possessed it. The shaft of the femur is elongate and, except

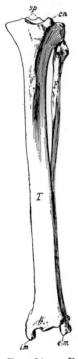
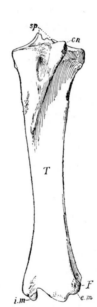

FIG. 31. — Bones of left lower leg of Wolf, front side. *T*, tibia. *F*, fibula. *sp*, spine of tibia. *cn*, cnemial crest. *i.m*, internal malleolus. *e.m.*, external malleolus.

FIG. 32. — Bones of left lower leg of Horse (much more reduced). *cn*, cnemial crest. *F*, lower end of fibula, co-ossified with tibia. Other letters as in Fig. 31.

FIG. 33. — Bones of lower leg, left side, of Tapir. *T*, tibia. *F*, fibula. *sp*, spine of tibia. *cn*, cnemial crest. *i.m*, internal malleolus. *e.m*, external malleolus. N.B. This figure is on a much larger scale than Fig. 32.

in very heavy animals, is of cylindrical shape. The lower end is thick and relatively massive and bears, on the posterior side, two prominent knobs, the *condyles* of the femur, which articulate with the tibia in the knee-joint. On the anterior side is the *rotular trochlea*, a broad, shallow groove in which glides the knee-cap, or *patella*.

The *patella* is a large ossification in the tendon common to the four great extensor muscles of the thigh, called collectively the *quadriceps femoris*, which straightens the leg, if bent.

The lower leg has two parallel bones, the shin-bone, or *tibia*, on the inside, and the splint, or *fibula*, on the outside. The tibia is always the larger of the two, and, in the Eutheria, forms the knee-joint with the femur. In those highly specialized hoofed animals in which the radius is so enlarged as to carry all the weight borne on the fore leg, and the ulna so greatly reduced, the tibia is similarly enlarged and the fibula diminished almost to the vanishing point. The upper end of the tibia is broad and extends over that of the fibula; for articulation with the condyles of the femur; it bears two slightly concave surfaces, the approximate edges of which are raised into a bifid *spine*. The upper part of the shaft is triangular, with one edge directed forward, and the superior end of this edge is thickened and roughened to form the *cnemial crest*, in which is inserted the patellar ligament and which thus receives the pull of the great extensor muscles.

The middle portion of the shaft of the tibia is cylindrical and the lower end is broadened. Connection with the ankle-bone (*astragalus*) is usually by means of two grooves, separated by a ridge, all forming a continuous articular surface. Primitively, the surface is nearly flat and without the dividing ridge. From the inner side of the lower end is always a strong downward projection, the *internal malleolus*, which prevents inward dislocation of the ankle.

The *fibula* is relatively stoutest in the less specialized mammals and is usually straight and slender, with enlarged ends, the lower one being the *external malleolus*, which prevents outward dislocation of the ankle. In many mammals the tibia and fibula are co-ossified at both ends, less frequently at one end only. In the horses there seems to be no fibula, as the shaft has disappeared and the two ends are fused with the tibia, and in the ruminants and camels the fibula is equally reduced, but the lower end remains separate and is wedged in between the tibia and the heel-bone or *calcaneum;* this remnant of the fibula is called the *malleolar bone*.

Like the manus, the hind foot, or *pes*, is obviously divisible into three parts, the bones of which are the *tarsus, metatarsus* and *phalanges*. The *tarsus* consists typically of seven bones, the upper two of which are especially modified to form the ankle-joint. The ankle-bone, or *astragalus*, is the inner one of this superior pair; it has a more or less grooved trochlea for articulation with the tibia and a longer or shorter *neck*, ending in a flat or convex *head*, which articulates with the *navicular* and, as a secondary modification, with the *cuboid*. The external element of the upper pair of tarsals is the heel-

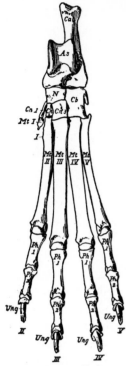

FIG. 34. — Left pes of Wolf, front side. *Cal*, calcaneum. *As*, astragalus. *N*, navicular. *Cb*, cuboid. *Cn 1*, *Cn 2*, *Cn 3*, internal, middle and external cuneiforms, *Mt I*, rudimentary first metatarsal. *Mt II–V*, second to fifth metatarsals. *Ph 1*, first phalanx. *Ph 2*, second phalanx. *Ung*, ungual phalanx. *I*, rudimentary hallux. *II–V*, second to fifth digits.

bone, *calcaneum*, which extends beneath and supports the astragalus; it has a heavy, rather elongate free portion, the *tuber calcis*, into which is inserted the *Achilles tendon*, the largest and strongest tendon of the whole organism, and which is common to the two largest muscles of the back of the leg. "Hamstringing" a horse, or "houghing" a cow means cutting the Achilles tendon and results in irremediable helplessness. The calcaneum has no contact with the tibia, save very exceptionally, and in most mammals it does not support the fibula, but there are several groups (e.g. the Artiodactyla) in which it has a prominent facet for the fibula.

The *navicular*, corresponds in position to the central of the carpus, but unlike the central, it is a very important element and is never lost in any land mammal, though it may co-ossify with the cuboid. Its upper surface fits the head of the astragalus and below it rests upon the three *cuneiforms*, the *internal, middle* and *external*. Finally, the *cuboid*, the external bone of the second row, is a large element which supports the calcaneum and often part of the astragalus.

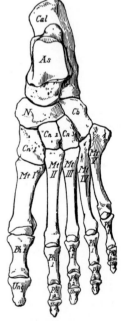

FIG. 35. — Left pes of Man. Note the large size of *Mt I*, the metatarsal of the first digit, or hallux. Letters as in Fig. 34.

The long bones of the *pes* are the *metatarsals*, which never exceed five, but may be present in any less number, four, three, two or one. In form and size the metatarsals are much like the metacarpals, but, if either manus or pes is greatly modified in adaptation to some particular kind of work, there may be great difference between metacarpals and metatarsals. For example, in the moles the fore foot is a burrowing shovel and all its bones are much modified, while the hind foot retains a primitive structure. Still greater is the difference between the wing and foot of a bat. When there is a difference in number, it is the general rule that the reduction and loss of digits take place first in the pes, as is shown by the tapirs, which have four toes in the fore foot, three in the hind.

Those animals which have a cannon-bone in the manus likewise have one in the pes, but there are several genera which have it only in the latter, as in the peccaries, or American wild swine (*Tagassu*) and the jumping rodents called Jerboa (*Gerbillus*). The jerboas are very exceptional in having the compound bone made up of three metatarsals, the II, III and IV, as in the foot of a bird.

It is often necessary to speak of the metacarpals and metatarsals together and, for this purpose, the general term *metapodial* is very convenient.

The first, or inner, metatarsal is that of the great toe, or *hallux*, and is sometimes opposable to the other digits, making the pes a grasping organ. In lemurs, monkeys and apes, the hind foot is so like a hand, that Cuvier made an order, Quadrumana, for their reception, in distinction from the two-handed

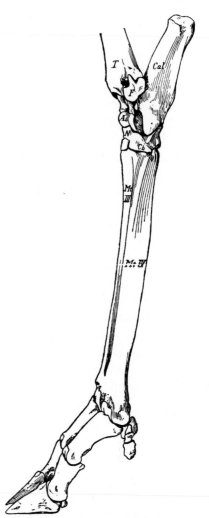

Fig. 36. — Left pes of Patagonian Deer, *Hippocamelus bisulcus*, showing the unguligrade gait. *T*, tibia. *F*, lower end of fibula (malleolar bone). *Cal*, calcaneum. *As*, astragalus. *N*, *Cb*, co-ossified cuboid and navicular. *cn*, ectocuneiform, *Mt III*, *Mt IV* cannon-bone, formed by the co-ossification of the third and fourth metatarsals.

Bimana, containing only Man. Several marsupials, including the opossums, have the opposable hallux, but all these quadrumanous creatures are arboreal in habits. The human foot is made unique by the great enlargement of the hallux, which is parallel to the other toes, thus making possible the erect gait, which is characteristic of Man.

The phalanges of the pes are so like those of the manus as to require no particular description; it is only when one or the other pair of extremities is highly specialized and the other pair is not, that there is any notable difference in their phalanges.

The gait and method of locomotion are important in endeavouring to explain the structure of mammalian limbs and feet. When, in the standing position, the entire sole of the foot is in contact with the ground and weight comes upon the heel, the gait is *plantigrade,* and is exemplified in Man, raccoons, bears and many other mammals; it is the most primitive manner of using the feet. In the *digitigrade* gait, the feet are nearly erect, with wrist and heel raised well above the ground; the weight is borne upon ball-like pads, one under the phalanges of each digit, arranged around a larger, central pad, which is under the metapodials. Wolves, cats and most of the other higher

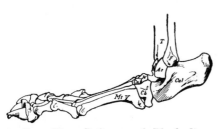

FIG. 37. — Left pes of Black Bear, *Ursus americanus,* showing the plantigrade gait. *T,* tibia. *F,* fibula. *Cal,* calcaneum. *As,* astragalus. *N,* navicular. *Cn 3,* external cuneiform. *Cb,* cuboid. *Mt V,* fifth metatarsal.

Carnivora have the digitigrade gait and, among the hoofed mammals, the camels and llamas have become digitigrade, though having unguligrade ancestors. Transitions between plantigrade and digitigrade are called *semi-plantigrade, semi-digitigrade,* etc. An animal is said to be *unguligrade* when the weight is carried entirely on the hoofs, which is, in fact, walking on tip-toe. Horses, cattle, sheep, antelopes, deer, swine, etc., are unguligrade, a term which is used of hoofed animals only. The so-called "knee" of a horse is his wrist and the "hock-joint" his ankle.

Very large and massive ungulates, such as elephants, rhinoceroses, hippopotamuses and several extinct groups, are secondarily digitigrade and in a peculiar way. The foot is a heavy column, externally hardly demarcated from the leg, though bending at wrist and ankle is still feasible, and the weight is borne on a great pad of elastic tissue, which lies upon the thick integument of the sole. The hoofs, which are hardly more than nails, support but little of the weight. In such feet, the ungual phalanges have lost their original shape and become more or less nodular.

A very peculiar mode of walking is seen in the great Ant Bear (*Myrmecophaga jubata*) in which the fore foot is so curved that its outer border rests on the ground and the palm is turned inward. In the extinct †Ground-sloths, or †Gravigrada, all four feet were thus employed and this must have produced a slow, clumsy and club-footed gait. There is reason to think that in an ancient hoofed animal, †*Homalodotherium*, from the Miocene of Patagonia, the hind feet were placed with the outer border on the ground, while the fore feet had the digitigrade position.

Other gaits, such as the hopping, or *saltatory*, of kangaroos, and of jumping mice and other rodents, and the swimming, or *natatory* as well as gliding and flying, enter at present so little into the known history of land mammals that they call for no special consideration.

II. THE TEETH

Many fossil mammals are known only from teeth and a knowledge of them is essential to the palæontologist, but too much emphasis must not be put upon them, for great errors have been made in depending exclusively on teeth for assigning mammals to their proper position in the scheme of classification.

There is extraordinary variety in the size, shape and composition of mammalian teeth in adaptation to the character of the food and the manner of seizing and disposing of it. In beasts of prey the teeth are admirably fitted for seizing and killing the victims, shearing flesh and crushing bones. Herbivora, or plant-feeders, have teeth which are adapted to cropping grass, leaves, twigs and other vegetable substances and triturating them as in a mill. Insect-eaters, especially those which feed upon ants and termites, may have no teeth at all or else those with numerous sharp points. In the Rodentia, the sharp, chisel-like incisors are wonderfully efficient in gnawing wood, as the beavers demonstrate, when they cut down trees of eighteen inches diameter. Even among mammals which consume the same sort of food, there are often great differences in the elaboration of the masticating mill, and it is possible, in many instances, to follow the steps of evolutionary change by which a high degree of complexity has been attained from simple beginnings. This is pre-eminently true of the genetic series of the elephants and the horses.

Teeth are often used as weapons of offence or defence, quite apart from the problem of killing prey for food. The tusks of elephant and hippopotamus are defensive weapons and the sharp scimitar-like tusks of several small Asiatic deer, which either have very small antlers, or no antlers at all, are very efficient against the attacks of the smaller carnivores, and in the fights between bucks in the breeding season.

Fig. 38. — Dentition of Wolf, left side. $i\,3$, third incisor. c, canine. $p\,1$, first premolar. $p\,4$, fourth premolar. $m\,1$, first molar.

In some mammals, such as the marine porpoises and dolphins, and in the armadillos among terrestrial mammals, the teeth are very numerous, from fifty to a hundred in each jaw, and these are all alike and of the simplest conical shape, but, as will be seen later, such teeth are very exceptional among mammals and are not primitive, but have resulted from degenerative changes. Absence of teeth likewise is never a primitive character, but has always been due to reduction and loss.

In the very great majority of mammals, including the most ancient known genera of the Mesozoic Era, the teeth are of four different kinds: (1) *incisors*, or front teeth, which, in the upper jaw, are implanted in the premaxillary bones; (2) canines, or eye-teeth, of which there are never more than one on each side of each jaw, four in all; (3) the *premolars* (called bicuspids in dentistry) grinding teeth which have predecessors in the milk, or deciduous series; (4) *molars*, grinding teeth which have no predecessors in the first set. All the molars and premolars taken together are the *cheek-teeth*.

It is usual to give a brief expression of the numbers and kinds of teeth in a given species by means of a dental formula. In Man, for instance, the formula is: $i\,\frac{2}{2}$, $c\,\frac{1}{1}$, $p\,\frac{2}{2}$, $m\,\frac{3}{3}$, $\times\,2 = 32$. This means that in Man there are two incisors, one canine, two premolars and three molars on each side of each jaw and as the formula gives only the numbers of one side, to get the total, it is necessary to double it. In practice, however, it is usual to take the doubling for granted, because, normally, the number of teeth is always the same on both sides, but is frequently different in the upper and lower jaws. Thus, in the Sheep, the formula is: $i\,\frac{0}{3}$, $c\,\frac{0}{1}$, $p\,\frac{3}{3}$, $m\,\frac{3}{3}$, $\times\,2 = 32$; put in words this means that in the Sheep there are no incisors or canines in the upper jaw, three incisors and a canine in the lower, and three premolars and three molars in each jaw. The horizontal lines in the formula mark the division of upper and lower teeth and are also employed as symbols in designating single teeth; thus $i\,\underline{3}$ means the third upper incisor, and $p\,_{\overline{4}}$, the fourth lower premolar, while $m\,\frac{2}{2}$ means the second molar, both upper and lower.

The history of dental evolution in the land Monodelphia has very rarely recorded any increase in the number of teeth, but a great many examples of reduction. The typical formula for the Monodelphia, which was reached in the Eocene and has been but seldom exceeded is: $i\,\frac{3}{3}$, $c\,\frac{1}{1}$, $p\,\frac{4}{4}$, $m\,\frac{3}{3}$, $\times 2 = 44$. Relatively few mammals of the modern world have so many teeth as are given in this formula, but their ancestors had.

With few exceptions, mammals have two sets of teeth, or *dentitions*, the first, milk, deciduous or temporary set as it is variously called, and the permanent, or second, set. Concerning the origin and significance of the two dentitions, there have been great controversies, but the combined labours of zoölogists, embryologists and palæontologists have resulted in a very general and satisfactory agreement, though some minor details remain to be cleared up. The reptilian ancestors of mammals had an indefinite number of teeth, which were worn out, shed and replaced throughout life. When the number of dentitions was restricted to two and whether that took place in the earliest mammals, or in their reptilian ancestors, are questions not yet to be answered.

In existing marsupials, only one tooth in each jaw, usually regarded as the third premolar, is replaced, but a full second dentition is indicated by tooth germs, which are not fully developed and are never erupted. This last term is the same as the more familiar "cutting the teeth." Sometimes the milk-teeth are shed at, or even before birth. The toothed whales, including the dolphins and porpoises, have a first dentition which is not changed, but a second set of abortive tooth-germs are formed, though they do not reach maturity. The armadillos, it had been believed, had but one dentition, but the second set has been discovered. It may be said confidently that all mammals now have, or formerly had two dentitions, the incisors, canines and premolars being shed and replaced.

With regard to the shape and construction of the individual teeth, the milk dentition is frequently more conservative than the permanent one, retaining ancestral features in the first set, which have been lost from the second. Important indications as to the steps of phylogenetic descent may often be gained from a study of the milk teeth. A very striking example of this is furnished by the middle Miocene horse *Merychippus*, which had milk teeth like those of the

Fig. 39. — First upper molar, right side of Deer, *Odocoileus.* On the left, the masticating surface; heavy black line, enamel. On the right, external side showing crown and roots. *Brachyodont.*

earlier, preceding genera and permanent teeth like those of the later and succeeding genera of the equine family.

The structure of mammalian teeth is very varied and ranges from the simplest conical form to an enormous and highly complicated grinding apparatus. In all primitive mammals and many of the higher groups also (including Man) a tooth consists of the *crown,* or portion which is exposed when in use, and the *roots,* one or more in number, by which the tooth is implanted in the jaw, and these are at least partly formed when the crown is ready for wear. Such a tooth is said to be low-, or short-crowned, or *brachyodont.* In many plant-feeders, such as horses and oxen, elephants and beavers, the teeth continue to grow in height (or length) long after they have been erupted and do not form roots until late in life, or, perhaps, not at all. Such teeth are called high-, or long-crowned, or *hypsodont* and, in many families, the transition from a brachyodont to a hypsodont dentition may be traced step by step. The persistently growing, hypsodont teeth are a great advantage, for they prolong the life of the animal by compensating, through growth, for the abrasion of the teeth. Serious trouble has often been caused for captive elephants by feeding them with material so soft, that the growth of the grinding teeth is not properly balanced by wear.

Rootless teeth are those which continue to grow so long as the possessor lives and do not form roots at all, the pulp-cavity remaining open and uncontracted throughout life. Such teeth are always simple and conical, or cylindrical in form, almost never complex. Examples of the rootless type are to be seen in the toothed

Fig. 40. — First upper molar, left side, of a fossil horse, *Equus sp.* On the right, external side. On the left, the grinding surface, showing two stages of wear. Heavy black line, enamel; white, dentine; shaded, cement. *Hypsodont,* roots not yet formed.

whales, including porpoises and dolphins, the armadillos and tree-sloths; the tusks of elephants and the chisel-like, gnawing incisors of the Rodentia belong in the same category.

The typical mammalian tooth is made up of three kinds of material, all differing in microscopic structure and in degrees of hardness; these are (1) dentine, (2) enamel, (3) cement. (1) The bulk of the tooth, both crown and roots, is composed of *dentine*, or ivory, which is the indispensable material; the other substances may be absent, but never the dentine. Chemically, it is like bone, an organic substance, with its interstices filled with calcium compounds, chiefly the phosphate, but the microscope shows a structure very different from that

FIG. 41. — Dentition of Beaver, *Castor canadensis. m 3*, last molar. *p 4*, last premolar. *i*, scalpriform incisors; enamel face black, dentine in vertical lines.

of bone. Dentine is composed of an immense number of fine tubules, which radiate from the pulp-cavity, or central chamber, which contains the nerves and blood-vessels essential to a living tooth. The roots, when present, are tubular and open at the end, allowing the passage of blood-vessel and nerve to and from the pulp-cavity. The dentinal tubules lodge excessively fine fibrillæ of the nerve, which make the tooth sensitive.

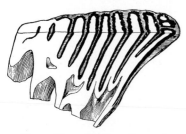

FIG. 42. — Section through a lower molar of the Indian Elephant, *Elephas maximus*. Enamel, heavy black; dentine, white; cement, horizontal lines.

(2) The hardest of all animal tissues and the only one containing fluorine, is *enamel*, which has a polished and lustrous appearance. Enamel is composed of a mosaic of prisms of microscopic size and closely packed together, and these prisms are solid in most mammals, tubular in the marsupials. Normally, the enamel covers the entire crown of the tooth, but does not extend upon the roots. As a secondary specialization, the enamel does not cover the entire crown, but is confined to vertical bands, which may cover one side, or be arranged at intervals around the periphery. The gnawing, *scalpriform* incisors of rodents have the enamel band only on the front face of the tooth; the softer dentine behind wears away more rapidly, thus keeping the cutting end bevelled, like the edge of a chisel, the enamel

forming the sharp edge. The enamel may be absent altogether and then the teeth are made of dentine, as in the tusks of modern elephants and the teeth of the existing Edentata.

(3) *Cement* differs but slightly from true bone in microscopic structure; it is not quite so hard as dentine, but is more resistant to decay. In the brachyodont tooth, such as a human molar, or the molar of a dog or a bear, the cement merely forms a sheath for the roots, but in many hypsodont teeth, such as the grinders of a horse, or an elephant, the cement extends over the crown and completely encases the entire tooth in a thick layer, filling the depressions and irregularities of the enamel surface and making the unworn tooth look like a shapeless lump. When the cement and enamel covering have been partially worn through, the masticating surface is made up of all three substances, each having a different degree of hardness and thus, through unequal wear, keeping the surface rough and efficient in grinding.

CHAPTER III

FOSSILIZATION OF MAMMALS — TECHNIQUE OF PALÆONTOLOGY

Fossil mammals have been found most abundantly, but by no means exclusively, in the arid and semi-arid regions of the world. The Great Plains and Rocky Mountain regions of North America, Patagonia, and the Gobi Desert of Mongolia, Egypt and the central desert of Australia, are the sources of most of the great collections, though France, Italy and northern India have yielded very important material. The reasons for this association of dry climates with rich deposits of fossil vertebrates are many, but it is not feasible to consider them in this book, though something must be said concerning the various ways in which mammals have been buried and preserved as fossils throughout the long ages of the Mesozoic and Cenozoic Eras of the earth's history.

As indicated in Chapter VI, the deposits of the various stages and substages of the Tertiary are found in different areas, and it is comparatively rare to find several of these geological divisions in direct superposition. Fortunately, however, a sufficient number of such superpositions have been observed to make certain the order of succession of the various fossiliferous divisions and subdivisions. On that head there is hardly any difference of opinion among palæontologists, though there is not quite complete agreement as to where the boundary lines between successive epochs should be drawn.

Remains of land mammals are seldom preserved in marine deposits and, when found, are almost exclusively teeth, for the bones are destroyed by the action of sea-water. The discovery of such fossils in the Atlantic coast border, from Florida to Massachusetts, is of importance as showing how uniformly Tertiary mammals were spread over the continent and also in the correlation of marine and continental deposits, but the remains are far too incomplete to be of much use for any other purpose. We may therefore confine attention to the problems of preservation of fossil mammals in deposits which were accumulated on land, or in bodies of water which formed no part of the sea.

The degree of preservation of mammals differs according to the circumstances of death and burial and also according to geological antiquity. As one extreme may be taken the complete preservation of frozen carcasses of the †Mammoth and the †Woolly Rhinoceros in Siberia, in which the hide and soft parts are preserved indefinitely and so perfectly that wolves greedily devour the flesh of these long-buried creatures, when they are washed out by a swollen river. Dried skeletons, still retaining the ligaments and portions of the skin, have been found in caverns in New Mexico and Patagonia. All of these

Fig. 43. — Skeleton of †ground-sloth, †*Scelidotherium*, exposed in cutting through Pampean Loess, Argentina, as mounted in the Field Museum of Natural History.

instances of the preservation of soft parts are of very late geological date, Pleistocene or post-Pleistocene.

The state of preservation in which Pleistocene mammals are usually found is determined by the material in which they are embedded, as well as by the climate of the region in which they died. In dry caverns, in or beneath peat bogs, in arid regions and in deposits of asphalt the bones are remarkably sound and fresh, almost like those of animals recently killed. In moist climates, percolating waters have frequently removed more or less of the animal matter, leaving the bones very friable and difficult of removal.

The bones of Tertiary mammals are very generally *petrified*, that is to say, the original material of the bone or tooth has been more or less completely removed and some mineral substance, commonly silica, has been substituted for it. The substitution has been effected molecule by molecule and so perfectly that the most minute microscopic structure is exactly reproduced. While there is no mathematical ratio, it is generally true that the greater the geological antiquity of a bone, the more completely petrified it is and the greater its fluorine content. Skeletons from the Paleocene and Eocene are usually heavy and dark coloured from the infiltration of iron compounds, while Miocene and Pliocene fossil bones are usually light coloured. There are many exceptions to this rule; Valentine fossils (upper Miocene, or lower Pliocene) are often black, and John Day fossils are generally dark brown, while those of the preceding White River are buff, or white. The soft parts of Tertiary mammals

FIG. 44. — Tail of †*Propalæotherium hassiacum*, middle Eocene of Messel, near Darmstadt, Germany. (From Abel after Haupt.)

are very rarely preserved, but in the Brown Coals of Germany some very interesting examples of carbonized hairs have been found. Recognizable impressions of birds' feathers have been found several times in Mesozoic and Cenozoic shales.

In endeavouring to account for the manner in which the fossils became entombed, it must be remembered, in the first place, that fossils are found only in the bedded, or *stratified* rocks, which were deposited under water, or by the wind, and that each bed, or stratum, in its turn, formed the surface of the earth, however deeply it may now be buried. Each bed was accumulated, either beneath some body of water, or on dry land, and the nature of the fossils is largely dependent upon the manner in which the sediment was deposited.

When the Tertiary fossil beds of the Great Plains and Rocky Mountain regions were first examined geologically, it was assumed that these beds had been laid down in large permanent lakes, but more careful study showed that this explanation was not satisfactory. Large lakes are unfavourable to the preservation of land animals for the same reason that the sea is unfavourable. The Green River Shales (Eocene) of southern Wyoming, northern Utah and Colorado are lake-deposits and are famous for the great number of beautifully preserved fossils which they contain; plants, insects and fishes are there in countless multitudes, even a few birds have been obtained, but no mammals, other than occasional obscure footprints, have ever been found.

Small lakes and ponds preserve land animals much more frequently than do permanent large lakes, while temporary lakes, or *playas*, are among the most important places of fossilization. In western North America, for instance, the richest and most extensive sources of fossil mammals are the deposits made by rivers. Over much of the northwestern Great Plains, in Nebraska, South Dakota and adjoining states, the region was featureless and flat, with a great network of streams meandering over it, a condition which persisted throughout most of the Oligocene, Miocene and Pliocene epochs. The divides between the streams were very low and, in time of flood, vast areas were covered by the shallow playas, in which fine clays and other sediments were deposited, thus burying the carcasses, skeletons and scattered bones that were lying about on the surface. The fine deposits are transected by many ancient channels, which were choked with cross-bedded sands (now hardened to sandstone) or gravels of varying coarseness, abandoned, and subsequently buried under renewed flood-plain deposits. In the badlands many of these ancient channels are exposed in cross-section, at many different levels in the finer strata.

A great many of the bones show evidence of having been exposed to the air after the death and decay of the animals. An especially convincing proof of this is given by the frequent tooth-marks, showing where rodents have gnawed the bones, something that could not well have happened beneath a body of water.

It is interesting to note that the fossils found in the channel sandstones are, as a rule, quite different from those which occur in the clays, though a certain number of similar fossils is found in both. In all probability, this difference is to be interpreted as being due to a difference in habitat. The channel sandstones and conglomerates contain chiefly the bones of semi-aquatic, amphibious animals and of forest-dwellers, while the fossils found in the clays are, for the most part, those of plains and open-country animals. Another proof that a great many of these Tertiary mammals died on dry ground and that their carcasses, or skeletons, were subsequently buried under flood-deposits, is the frequency with which the fossil skeletons are found in the "death pose," the head bent back over the neck by muscular contraction, and the limbs stretched out from the body. The group of skeletons of the little †gazelle-like camels †*Stenomylus*, found together in the Miocene of Nebraska and now mounted in the

American Museum of Natural History, display these death poses very distinctly, though often it is lost, the carcass having been pulled about and dismembered by carrion-feeding carnivores.

Observations of modern events, which show mass-destruction of mammals have frequently been recorded. In an oft-quoted passage Darwin gives a vivid description of the effects of the long drought in Argentina in 1827–1832. "During this time so little rain fell, that the vegetation, even to the thistles, failed; the brooks were dried up and the whole country assumed the appearance of a dusty high road." "I was informed by an eyewitness that the cattle in herds of thousands rushed into the Parana and being exhausted by hunger they were unable to crawl up the muddy banks, and thus were drowned." "Without doubt, several hundred thousand animals thus perished in the river; their bodies when putrid were seen floating down the stream and many in all probability, were deposited in the estuary of the Plata." "Azara describes the fury of the wild horses on a similar occasion rushing into the marshes, those which arrived first being overwhelmed and crushed by those which followed. He adds that more than once he has seen the carcasses of upward of a thousand horses thus destroyed." "Subsequently to the drought of 1827–1832, a very rainy season followed, which caused great floods. Hence it is almost certain that some thousands of the skeletons were buried by the deposits of the very next year."

In the arid interior of Australia is a series of great dry lakes, which only occasionally contain water and are usually "clay pans," mud-bottomed or encrusted with salt. One of these, Lake Callabonna, is of great interest because of the number of Pleistocene mammals and birds which have been entombed there. Dr. E. C. Stirling, who studied the region, reports that the bed of the "lake" is "a veritable necropolis of gigantic extinct Marsupials and Birds, which have apparently died where they lie, literally in hundreds. The facts that the bones of individuals are often unbroken, close together and frequently in their proper relative positions, the attitude of many of the bodies, and the character of the matrix in which they are embedded, negative any theory that they have been carried thither by floods. The probability is rather that they met their death by being entombed in the effort to reach food or water, just as even now happens in dry seasons to hundreds of cattle which, exhausted by want of food, are unable to extricate themselves from the boggy places that they have entered." "The accumulation of so many bodies in one locality points to the fact of their assemblage around one of the last remaining oases in the region of desiccation which succeeded an antecedent condition of plenteous rains and abundant waters."

"The heads were pointed in all directions, and the remains of different animals frequently much mixed. Where, however, the bones of an individual were lying in juxtaposition, they preserved fairly constant relations to one another. . . . The bones and the head, which was often much flattened laterally, as if by pressure, were usually lying either in their proper position with the dorsal surfaces uppermost, or were turned over on their sides. The pelvis was usually horizontal; of the ribs, some were *in situ*, others either widely separated from their fellows, or several firmly welded together. The limbs, almost invariably at a greater depth than the rest of the skeleton, had their various segments greatly flexed. The feet were deepest of all. . . . A very similar attitude was assumed by the camels on the occasions when they got bogged in crossing from the sand islets to the main land."

Quicksands, it would seem, have been frequent places of burial and fossilization of many mammals, sometimes singly, sometimes in multitudes. At least, the quicksand hypothesis best explains the facts. When a quicksand has hardened into rock, it forms a fine-grained sandstone, not distinguishable from sandstones of a different mode of origin. The famous bone-bed of Agate, Nebraska, is an extraordinary accumulation of thousands of bones, mostly belonging to the small †two-horned rhinoceros (†*Diceratherium cooki*) the bones mingled in the wildest confusion, hardly any two in their natural connections. This confusion was caused partly by the struggles of newly trapped animals and partly by the internal movements of the sands.

The entombment of individual animals is exemplified by two remarkable specimens in the American Museum of Natural History, skeletons which were found in the standing position. One of these, a primitive rhinoceros from the Bridger Eocene of Wyoming, was found in the vertical face of a bluff by the late Professor Cope, who told the author that it reminded him of the winged bulls of ancient Assyria. The other is the remnant of a skeleton of the colossal rhinoceros (†*Baluchitherium*), from the Oligocene of the Gobi Desert of Mongolia. All four feet are standing and in their natural position to one another, while the remainder of the skeleton and the rock enclosing it have been carried away by erosion.

Wind-made accumulations of sand and dust often enclose great quantities of fossil bones, which are not uniformly distributed through

FIG. 45. — Bone-bed in lower Miocene of Agate, Neb. Bones mostly of small †pair-horned rhinoceros, †*Diceratherium cooki*. (Amer. Mus. Nat. Hist.)

the mass, but are concentrated in "pockets." In dry climates the wind-made accumulations pile up rapidly, burying and preserving the skeletons and scattered bones that lay on the ground and sometimes burying animals alive. It was the special places of bone-accumulation, such as those mentioned above, that gave rise to the "pockets," in which the bones are so thickly crowded. Isolated skele-

Fig. 46. — Four feet of †*Baluchitherium,* †colossal rhinoceros, found in standing position at Loh, Mongolia. Remainder of skeleton and enclosing matrix removed by erosion. (Amer. Mus. Nat. Hist.)

tons do occur, as well as scattered bones, but in most fossiliferous deposits the distribution of bones is very uneven.

Conspicuous examples of wind-made deposits are the Sheridan beds that cover so much of the Great Plains, like a mantle, and the Pampean loess of Argentina. In the Sheridan of northwestern Kansas Professor Williston found nine skeletons of the large peccary (†*Platygonus leptorhinus*) lying huddled together, with the heads all pointing in the same direction. The unfortunate creatures had evidently perished in a storm, turning their tails to the wind, but whether the storm was a blizzard of snow, or a desert sand-storm, it is not possible to decide. However that may be, the bodies were eventually buried under an accumulation of wind-driven sand.

In the uppermost Miocene of South Dakota the late Mr. J. W. Gidley discovered the skeletons of six †three-toed horses (†*Neohipparion whitneyi*) crowded together. These animals were also probably killed and buried in a sand-storm, as there is small likelihood of blizzards in the genial Miocene climates.

The Pampas of Argentina are everywhere covered with a thick mantle of compacted, wind-accumulated dust, which is known as the Pampean formation and is one of the richest sources of fossil mammals that has been found anywhere. So hard and stony has this compacted dust become, that it is difficult to believe that it is of so late a geological date as the Pleistocene, as most, if not all, of it undoubtedly is. Many museums, in various parts of the world, beside the remarkable Argentine collections in Buenos Aires and La Plata, have obtained wonderfully preserved Pampean fossils, which had attracted the attention of geologists before the end of the XVIII Century.

A mode of preservation of the bones of mammals, which is unfortunately rare, is exemplified by the asphalt pits of southern California, especially those in the vicinity of Los Angeles at Rancho La Brea. In this area, the oil-bearing marine Pliocene, which is folded and truncated to a level surface, is covered by a land-made deposit, built up by wind and streams, through which the oil rose from below, forced upward by gas pressure. Even at the present time, small pools of oil and "tar volcanoes" continue to be formed at the surface and the oil is gradually converted into asphalt by oxidation and by the evaporation of the volatile constituents, and in this conversion one stage is an exceedingly viscous and adhesive tar, in which small mammals and birds are caught and, unable to extricate themselves, slowly perish. At the time of the author's visit to Rancho La Brea, in 1915, rabbits and birds trapped and killed in this manner were not an uncommon sight. "Around the borders of the pools the tar slowly hardens by the evaporation of the lighter constituents until it becomes as solid as an asphalt pavement. Between the hard and soft portions of the mass there is a very indefinite boundary, the location of which can often be determined only by experiment, and large mammals in many cases run into very tenacious material in this intermediate zone from which they are unable to extricate themselves " (J. C. Merriam).

In the Pleistocene the oil rose more copiously from below and formed much larger pools on the surface than is the case to-day. In these death-traps great numbers of mammals and birds were held to their destruction, and in their desperate struggles to escape they attracted carnivorous mammals and birds of prey, which in their turn were caught and inextricably held in the viscid tar. At Rancho La Brea, an astonishing quantity of mammalian and bird bones have been excavated from the irregularly cylindrical pits, the bottom of which is twenty to forty feet below the surface of the ground. When

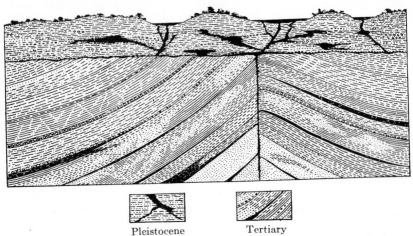

Pleistocene   Tertiary

FIG. 47. — Section showing relations of Tertiary and Pleistocene beds near Los Angeles, Cal. (From Stock after Arnold.)

cleaned, the bones are remarkably sound and fresh, but connected skeletons are rare, the bones are mostly dissociated and scattered. When the carcasses had putrified, the struggles and tramplings of newly trapped victims would tend to scatter the bones, but even more effective were the internal movements within the tar itself, which carried remains as far down as thirty to forty feet from the surface, which was, at the same time, building up by wind- and water-laid deposits upon and around the tar-pools.

A very interesting illustration of the manner in which the plain at Rancho La Brea was built up in the Pleistocene epoch was brought to light in one of the bone-pits, in the shape of an upright coniferous tree, which, at a depth of twelve feet, was rooted in a stiff clay soil, and some eight feet below the surface gave off a large branch. The tree was buried in a mass of clay, sand and asphalt and around the trunk and branch were masses of skulls and bones belonging to many of the mammals and birds characteristic of the fauna.

No soft parts, not even ligaments, hide or hair, have been discovered in the asphalt deposits of California, but in the oil fields of Roumania, a rhinoceros carcass was found, in which much of the soft anatomy was preserved. No doubt, the Roumanian oil is more effectively antiseptic than the Californian.

Caves and caverns and fissures in the rocks (all of which are very generally in limestone) have yielded a considerable quantity of Pleistocene mammals. The Port Kennedy cavern, on the Schuylkill above Philadelphia, the Franktown fissure in central Pennsylvania, the Cumberland fissure in Maryland and the Conard fissure in Arkansas, have all supplied valuable, though fragmentary, Pleistocene material. These remains are of animals which fell, or were washed into the fissures, and a few skeletons have also been obtained in true caves of Virginia, Tennessee, California, New Mexico and Texas. The Brazilian caverns were the prolific sources of the great collections made in the XIX Century by Dr. P. W. Lund and now in the Lund Museum of Copenhagen. But in North America caves have furnished comparatively little information as to Pleistocene life.

In Europe caves have been of the utmost importance. In part this fact has been due to the fierce carnivores, the Cave Lion, the Cave Hyena and the Cave Bear, which lived in caverns and dragged their prey into their dens. We know of no such cave-dwelling beasts of prey in the North American Pleistocene. Another factor was the cave-dwelling habit of Palæolithic Man in the Old World, who, in addition to the bones of slaughtered animals, left on the walls and ceilings most spirited and accurate paintings of the animals which he hunted.

Volcanic dust and so-called ash are produced in nearly all eruptions of volcanoes and sometimes in incredible quantities. In many instances, the ejectamenta have covered thousands of square miles to a depth of many feet, the thickness diminishing with greater distance from the vent. The finer particles are carried for long distances by prevailing winds and deposited, in some cases, in beds of pure ash, in others mingled in all proportions with ordinary sediments. In South Dakota, Kansas and Nebraska are beds twenty-five to thirty feet thick of pure ash, which must have been carried by the wind for at least four hundred miles from the nearest volcanoes. Such showers of volcanic débris, whether falling on a dry land surface, or into some body of shallow water, will cover up and bury whatever carcasses, skeletons or separate bones may be exposed, and when the fall of ash is copious, living animals are often buried and preserved as so many complete skeletons.

The first historic eruption of Vesuvius, which took place in 79 A.D., was remarkable for the absence of molten lava and for the vast quantity of fragmental material, coarse and fine, which was discharged, burying Herculaneum, Pompeii, Stabiæ and other cities and villages. The great eruption was witnessed by Pliny the Younger from Misenum, which was more than twenty miles to the west of Vesuvius, and described by him in two famous letters to Tacitus. Even at that distance the day was completely darkened, "not," says Pliny, "like a starless night, but like a tightly closed room." He adds that the fall of ash was so copious that people sitting out of doors had frequently to rise and shake off the dust for fear of being overwhelmed by it. At Pompeii, it is estimated that 20,000 people lost their lives and unnumbered domestic animals, chiefly dogs and horses, likewise perished. The excavation of Pompeii has brought these skeletons to light.

The continental Tertiary deposits of both North and South America are largely made up of volcanic material, stratified by the sorting action of wind or water, and the proportion of volcanic particles and grains to those of sand, clay and other ordinary sediments, varies much in the different formations, but concerning some of these the necessary microscopic studies have not yet been made. The deposits of the Wasatch, or lower Eocene, so far as known, are built up of ordinary sediments, sand, clay and mud, but the material of the middle Eocene, or Bridger stage, is chiefly volcanic and the frequent remains of fish and crocodiles show deposition in water, probably temporary playas. The White River beds, which are very regularly stratified, and were, as previously shown, principally laid down in the flood-plains of rivers, contain some volcanic materials disseminated through the clays and some beds of pure ash, which are easily recognizable by their snowy whiteness. The John Day is a very thick mass (2000 feet) almost entirely volcanic in origin, but for the Miocene and Pliocene stages of the Great Plains and Great Basin areas, the determination of the volcanic content has not yet been made.

In South America, the Eocene and Oligocene deposits (Rio Chico, Casa Mayor, Musters) occur in central Patagonia and are very largely composed of fine volcanic débris. The Miocene (Deseado, Colhué-Huapi and Santa Cruz) is more southern in distribution, the Santa Cruz extending to the Straits of Magellan. These formations, especially the last-named, are very largely volcanic in origin, which probably explains the large number of complete skeletons found in the Santa Cruz, for, no doubt, many of the animals were smothered and buried alive in the heavy falls of ash. The volcanic ash and dust have been compacted into a firm rock which is usually quite soft, but is sometimes made very hard by the infiltration of calcite.

The fossils of a given area and geological date can never give more than a very inadequate conception of the mammals of that time and place. Fossilization is a lucky accident which many kinds of animals escape and the proportion of species preserved to those which are lost is generally indeterminable. Volcanic accumulations which were showered indiscriminately over hill and valley, mountain and plain, forests and grasslands are likely to have preserved a larger proportion of an entire fauna than are the ordinary processes of sedimentation. But even in the ash beds there is a certain selection, except in the case of animals buried alive, and, speaking generally, it is mammals of large and medium size, whose bones best resist destruction that have the best chance of preservation. Of course, the more numerous the individuals of a species are, the better is the chance of that species being represented among the fossils, other things being equal. It is not surprising, therefore, that in all the continental Tertiary formations, the gregarious hoofed animals are by far the most abundant fossils, while those of solitary habit are very much less common. From the lower Eocene to the close of the Pleistocene horses are on the whole much the most numerous fossils, though after the middle Eocene the camel-llama tribe rivals them in numbers. Each stage, however, has its own peculiar families, which, for the time being, outnumber all others. Thus, in the Bridger stage, the †brontotheres are by far the commonest fossils, as are the †oreodonts in the White River, but the horses and camels hold their own throughout and were most numerous in the Pleistocene. Tapirs, on the other hand, are rare as fossils as far back as we can trace them, and this rarity is very probably due to the solitary habits which characterize them to-day and presumably always have been characteristic of them. Small mammals are usually fragmentary as fossils and complete skeletons of them are much more rare than those of the larger species. This fact is partly due to the delicate and frail character of the bones and partly to the complete way in which they are devoured by their enemies. A wolf will pick the bones of an antelope, but will leave very little of a rabbit or a prairie dog, and this is why the rodents are seldom so abundant in the fossil state as would be expected from their numbers. In any region, carnivorous animals are always much less abundant than the Herbivora upon which they prey. In central Africa, for example, the lions, leopards, hyenas and wolves are far outnumbered by the antelopes and zebras which furnish their food. In the Tertiary formations the same general numerical proportion between carnivores and herbivores may be observed, but in the Pleistocene of Rancho La Brea the Carnivora are overwhelmingly preponderant, more than 90% of the Los Angeles Museum collection representing three species, the †Sabre-tooth Tiger (†*Smilodon californicus*), the †American Lion (*Felis* †*atrox*)

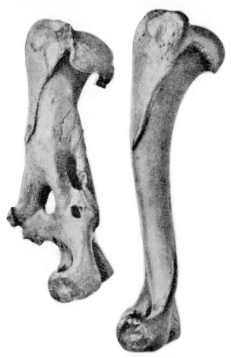

FIG. 48. — Left humeri of *Canis* †*dirus*, the †Dire Wolf, on the same scale. On the left, bone showing healed fracture, with abnormal deposit of bone. On the right, uninjured humerus. Pleistocene of Rancho La Brea. (From Stock.)

and the †Dire Wolf (†*Ænocyon* or *Canis* †*dirus*), the bears, smaller cats and mustelines being much less common.

Such an astonishingly disproportionate number of beasts of prey could not possibly obtain in a community of living animals and is explained by the peculiar circumstances of fossilization in the Pleistocene tar-pools of southern California, as is admirably set forth by Dr. J. C. Merriam. "In the natural accumulation of remains at the tar pools through accidental entangling of animals of all kinds, it is to be presumed that a relatively large percentage of the individuals entombed would consist of young animals with insufficient experience to keep them away from the most dangerous places, or with insufficient strength to extricate themselves. There would also be a relatively large percentage of old, diseased, or maimed individuals that lacked strength to escape when once entangled." Of the immense number of †sabre-tooths which have been taken out of the asphalt, the majority are nearly or quite mature, but there is a very unusual proportion of old, diseased and crippled animals. In many instances bones were broken, doubtless in fighting, and the wounds so inflicted became infected and inflamed, resulting in the deposition of bone upon and around the fractured elements. Often a broken bone would knit in such a manner as to shorten the limb and cause permanent lameness. The †sabre-tooth cats were also subject to a disease very like that known in Man as *spondylitis deformans*, which causes the lumbar vertebræ to co-ossify into a single mass and thus make the loins perfectly rigid. Frequently, the great sabre-like tusks were broken and the worn condition of the broken ends shows that the fracture occurred a considerable time before the death of the animal.

The altogether exceptional proportion of Carnivora and raptorial birds in the asphalt pits is to be explained by the fact that the struggling victims already caught attracted the beasts of prey to their own destruction. A single bird or small mammal might lead to the ensnaring of a dozen carnivores, which owing to the greater weight, were helplessly mired before they could even reach the lure. The high proportion of old, crippled and broken-toothed carnivores is, no doubt, due to their inability to catch their prey on hard ground and, hence, they were driven by hunger to take desperate chances. Dr. Merriam states that "in the first excavations carried on by the University of California a bed of bones was encountered in which the number of saber-tooth and wolf skulls together averaged twenty per cubic yard."

The foregoing account of the various ways in which mammals have been fossilized is by no means exhaustive, but it includes the most important of these methods, and will suffice for the purposes of this book. Tertiary mammals of North and South America owe their preservation almost entirely to burial in volcanic ash, to the deposits of flooded rivers, or the covering of skeletons and carcasses by dust or sand driven before the wind.

The Technique of Mammalian Palæontology

The collecting of fossil vertebrates began in an entirely unsystematic way. Dr. Leidy's material was picked up from the surface of the ground, where the bones had weathered out of the enclosing rock, or matrix, by men who could collect only incidentally, as other work permitted. Professors Cope and Marsh, who had large funds at their disposal, trained a corps of collectors who speedily raised the status of collecting to an art requiring great skill. The late Dr. J. L. Wortman for Professor Cope, and the late Mr. J. B. Hatcher for Professor Marsh, and the assistants and successors whom they taught, so revolutionized and refined the field and laboratory methods, that incomparably better and more complete fossils were brought in, prepared and mounted for exhibition in the museums. To say nothing of the fine university museums, there are the public institutions such as the American Museum in New York, the United States National Museum in Washington, the Carnegie Museum in Pittsburgh, the Field Museum of Chicago, the Colorado Museum of Denver, which have brought together a truly marvellous series of the ancient mammals of North and South America, and the American and Field Museums, especially the former, have extended their activity to all parts of the world, Asia, Africa, South America as well as Canada, the United States and Mexico. The field workers have learned how to find and bring in, not only huge and ponderous brutes, but also the finest and most delicate of minute creatures, and the preparators, with wonderful skill, free the bones from the enclosing matrix, repair the shattered ones, harden those that have been softened by the weather and make them fit for study and exhibition. This is no place to enlarge upon the arts of the laboratory, but the reader should understand how dependent the science of palæontology is upon the patience of preparator and collector.

Judging from many inquiries, the author is inclined to believe that the public regards the collector's work as a random digging in fossiliferous country, but such haphazard procedure would be a mere waste of time. One must look for "sign," either fragments of bone lying on the surface, or a small exposure of bone in the rock. The fragments are traced upward to their source, if that can be found, and there excavation begins, cutting with fine, sharp hand-picks, or chisels, until the extent and character of the fossil is ascertained and then it is taken up in blocks of matrix and packed for shipment. Often the bones are so fragile that they must be protected by strips of muslin soaked in flour paste and the blocks of matrix wrapped in burlap bands saturated with wet plaster of Paris, like the surgeon's plaster bandages. The task of the preparator is to free the bones from the matrix, often a work of the utmost delicacy, cement all fragments in their proper places and harden the bones, when necessary, with shellac or other alcoholic solution and, in short, render them fit for handling and study. The mounting of skeletons for exhibition is done in several different ways, according to the completeness and condition of the bones. The most satisfactory, though also the most difficult and expensive method is to erect the skeleton as if it were that of a modern animal, without embedding in plaster.

It is highly desirable that all the bones should be those of a single individual, but composite mounts, in which the elements are taken from two or more individuals, are often adequate for all purposes, if care is taken to make use only of such bones as are of the proper size, and provided that the identification of the species to which each bone belongs can be made with certainty.

It has been emphasized that, save in a very few instances, only the hard parts of an animal, bones and teeth, are preserved, yet very important information may often be obtained concerning the size, shape and external characteristics of the brain from what are somewhat loosely called "brain casts." More accurately, these are casts of the brain cavity, the walls of which more or less closely fit the surface of the brain, and may be natural or artificial. When an animal dies and is buried in sediment, or in volcanic ash, the brain, like all the other soft parts, decays and disappears, leaving the cranial cavity empty. The plastic mud, or volcanic dust is forced by the pressure of the overlying mass into all the vacant parts of the skull, the brain cavity, the sinuses and the canals for nerves and blood-vessels, and eventually hardens into a rock-like consistency. When the skull is weathered, the removal of the cranial roof exposes the "brain cast" and very frequently the cast remains intact when the skull has been more or less completely destroyed. The accuracy with which the external form of the brain is reproduced depends upon the closeness of the fit of the cranial walls and, in this respect, there is very great difference between mammals.

Artificial casts are made by sawing the skull lengthwise into two equal halves and then carefully removing the matrix which fills the brain cavity. When the cavity has been thoroughly cleaned out, liquid plaster of Paris, or better, gelatine, is poured into each half-cavity and, when hardened, the two halves are put together. The bisecting of the skull, if competently done, does not injure the specimen and gives valuable information as to the internal structure of the skull, which may be supplemented by cross-sections.

The geological history of mammals was recorded by the preservation of bones and, more particularly, of teeth, which, to the uninitiated must seem meaningless, but it is the practicable task of palæontology to make these dry bones live. It is a widespread delusion, however, that the palæontologist can reconstruct from a single bone, or tooth, an otherwise unknown animal. This hydra-headed absurdity has been slain innumerable times, but continues to flourish nevertheless. No illustration is more dear to the heart of the non-scientific writer than this imaginary power of the palæontologist, and it meets one at every turn. So far from being able to restore any creature from a few scattered bones, palæontologists have gone completely

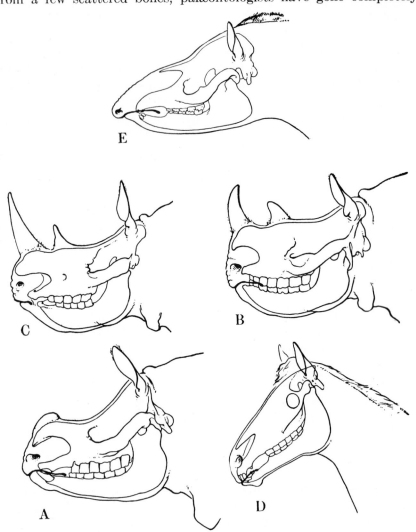

Fig. 49. — Relation of skull form to head. A, Indian Rhinoceros. B, Black Rhinoceros. C, Broadlipped African Rhinoceros. D, Horse. E, American Tapir. (From Gregory.)

astray in associating the bones of one and the same species, when found separately. More than once has it happened that the dissociated skull and feet of the same animal have been assigned to different *orders;* no less than six such instances might be enumerated. Such blunders have been due to the fact that, in advance of experience, no one could have imagined that an animal with such a skull and teeth could possibly have had such feet. The error could not be corrected till skeletons were found with all the essential parts in their natural connection.

Even though an unlimited number of fossilized skeletons were available, what would be their scientific value? In the first place, they have preserved in chronological order the successive steps in the evolutionary development of many groups, not only of mammals, but of birds, reptiles, amphibians and fishes, as well. In the second place, the skeleton permits the making of close approximations to the anatomy of the soft parts which have vanished through decay. The skeleton is not merely the mechanical frame-work and support of the organism; it is that, of course, but much more beside. The bones are the living and growing expression of the whole animal and they are modified, not only by age, but also by accidents and by the condition of the environment. The bones of the same individual, human or animal, differ greatly in youth, maturity and old age, and the individual age of a fossil bone, or tooth, is immediately obvious. So long as the animal lives its bones are undergoing constant slow changes and responding quickly to changed needs. Dislocated bones frequently develop entirely new joints, and the internal structure is changed to meet the requirements of new stresses. Fractured bones are reknit, either with or without dislocation of the broken ends.

The form and proportions of an animal are chiefly determined by its muscular system and this may be accurately deduced from the skeleton, for the muscles which are important for the work of restoration are attached to the bones and leave their unmistakable marks upon them. The intimate relation between bone and muscle is made clear in every treatise on anatomy, and it is shown how each attachment of muscle, tendon and ligament is plainly indicated by rough lines, ridges, projections or depressions. With the skeleton before him, any competent anatomist can reconstruct the muscles in sufficient detail. Significant additional information is given by the teeth, especially as to the food-habits, for the bulk of the viscera, an important factor in the animal's appearance, is chiefly determined by the diet, and animals which have similar ways of feeding, have a certain similarity of appearance, even though they should be very distantly related. "Having a good skeleton as a model, one versed in the use of pencil or brush can readily invest bare bones with flesh, sinew, and hide. No flight of the imagination is necessary, and it is quite possible to faithfully portray extinct creatures much as they must have appeared in life" (E. Barbour).

Beasts of prey, which belong to widely separated groups, look more or less alike. The so-called "Tasmanian Wolf" (*Thylacynus cynocephalus*), is deceptively like the true wolves in form and proportions and yet is a marsupial, related to the opossums, while wolves belong to the Carnivora, which are almost as far removed from the marsupials as any mammals can be. The resemblance is as close in the skeletons as in the living animals, though the fundamental differences of structure which distinguish marsupials from placentals, are unmistakable in the bony frame-work.

Large plant-feeders, though referable to very different orders, bear a decided resemblance to one another, the differences chiefly affecting the head. Because of this likeness, Cuvier proposed his order of "Pachydermata," a heterogeneous assemblage, which included elephants, rhinoceroses, hippopotamuses, etc., which are now distributed in three different orders.

External features, such as ears, snout and hair, have a very large share in determining the general appearance of a mammal and these, save in such rare instances as to be negligible, are not preserved in the fossil state. Two mammals which have skeletons very much alike, may yet be markedly different in appearance because of differences in the character of the skin, such as, for example, are displayed in the Bornean and Indian rhinoceroses. Yet even in regard to external features there is often more to go upon than mere conjecture. The position of the ears is given by the skull, and ears of unusual size or form often leave some indication of these facts on the bones, and the presence or absence of a proboscis can nearly always be determined by the character and marking of the bones to which it was attached. The length of the tail and the thickness of its muscles may be deduced directly from the caudal vertebræ, but whether it was short haired, as in the Leopard, or bushy, as in the Fox, or tufted at the end, as in the Lion, or naked, as in rats, or scaly, flat and trowel-like, as in the Beaver, cannot be determined from bones. Sometimes, though very rarely, carbonized hairs, or impressions of hairs are preserved. Figure 44 shows the caudal vertebræ, hairs and terminal tuft of the tail of a small perissodactyl (†*Propalæotherium*) from the Brown Coal of Messel, near Darmstadt, Germany.

Accumulations of subcutaneous fat sometimes influence very strongly the outward appearance of an animal, with no indication left on the bones. A familiar instance of this condition is the hump of the Camel, and in the head of the Sperm Whale the immense mass of blubber produces an appearance altogether unlike the form which would be inferred from the skull only. No doubt, among the extinct mammals were many in which a more or less grotesque appearance was produced by masses of subcutaneous fat, but rarely can any evidence of this be discovered. However, a probable instance is given by the paintings of the †Mammoth (†*Mammuthus*

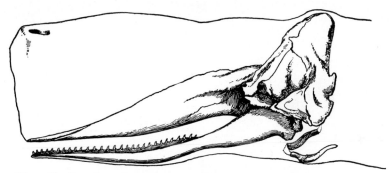

FIG. 50. — Skull and outline of head of Sperm Whale, *Physeter macrocephalus.*
(From Lydekker.)

primigenius) made by the Palæolithic artists on the roofs and walls of caverns in the Pyrenees and the south of France. Most (but not all) of these admirable and unmistakable representations of the "†hairy elephant" show a large dome on the top of the head and another over the shoulders, with a deep notch between. (Fig. 167, p. 275.) Very probably these swellings were accumulations of fat and varied with the seasons; the frozen carcasses of Siberia do not show these humps.

Of all the characters which determine the outward appearance of a mammal, none are more effective than the hair and the pattern of colouration, and of these the skeleton affords no hint. The living Horse and Zebra differ much more decidedly in appearance than their skeletons would suggest, and the same is true of the great cats, the Lion, the Tiger and the Leopard. Oldfield Thomas once remarked that the altogether exceptional colour-pattern of the Okapi made it look more like a beast out of a fairy book than an actual living creature, and the skeleton of this giraffe-like animal, discovered comparatively lately in the Congo forests, gives no hint of the remarkable colouration.

In making restorations of extinct mammals the colour-scheme must be left to the imagination and yet there is more guidance than random guess-work. Certain definite principles of animal colouration have been learned, but, in applying these principles to particular cases, we meet with great difficulty, chiefly because our knowledge of the creature's habits is usually so vague.

The naked, hairless skin is never primitive in a mammal, but always a late acquisition, is comparatively rare and, in many mam-

FIG. 51. — Life-size clay model of White River horse, †*Mesohippus bairdi*, by F. Blashke; used in making group shown in Fig. 52. (Field Mus. Nat. Hist.)

malian orders, never occurs. Aside from a few domestic animals, this type of skin is found only in marine mammals, such as whales, porpoises, walruses, etc., in very large herbivorous animals living in warm climates, such as elephants, rhinoceroses, hippopotamuses, and in a few blind burrowers which shun the daylight. How many of the large extinct quadrupeds which lived in past ages were hairless, there is no way of determining, but, in view of the generally warm climate that prevailed through most of the Tertiary period, it may be assumed that the large ponderous herbivores were hairless.

Useful suggestions as to the colour-pattern of extinct mammals may be gained from a study of series of modern animals, such as

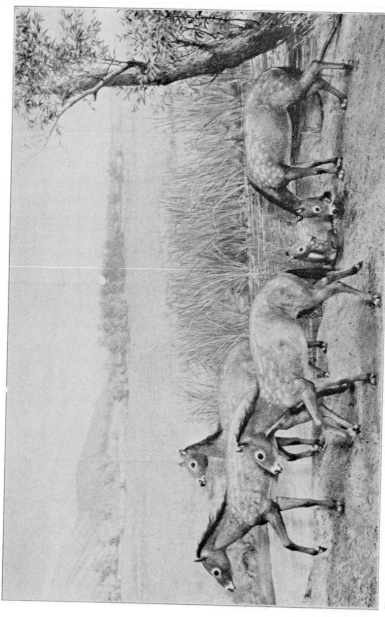

Fig. 52. — Restorations of †three-toed White River horse, †*Mesohippus bairdi*, modelled by F. Blashke. (Field Mus. Nat. Hist.)

lizards and butterflies, in which the development of a pattern may be followed step by step. Young mammals frequently retain traces of an ancestral colouration which disappears in the adult. In many mammals in which the adult colouration is uniform, except for a lighter, or white, belly, the young are striped or spotted, indicating that their ancestral forms were striped or spotted. Thus, the full-grown Wild Boar (*Sus scrofa*) is uniformly coloured, the young are longitudinally striped. Many deer are spotted throughout life, such as the Fallow Deer (*Dama*) and the Axis Deer of India (*Axis*) but most of the species, including all of the American ones, are of a uniform dun colour in the adult, while the fawns are always spotted. The American Tapir (*Tapirus terrestris*), when grown, is of a mouse-grey, or brown but the young are much darker and have broken longitudinal stripes of white. Lion cubs are spotted, adults are uniformly tawny, and there are many other examples of the sort.

The study of colouration among modern animals has led to the conclusion that, in mammals, the most primitive type of colour-pattern is that of longitudinal stripes, such as is seen in chipmunks (*Tamias*) and ground squirrels (*Spermophilus*). In the second stage the stripes break up into spots, which retain the longitudinal arrangement and are either light on a dark ground, or dark on a light ground. In the third stage the spots coalesce into transverse stripes, or they may disappear entirely. The changes of pattern have not gone on at a uniform rate in the different mammalian orders, or even in the same order, for a determining factor is the habitat and mode of life of a particular species. As a rule, the colour-scheme is such as to render its possessor inconspicuous, and many an animal that is most strikingly coloured in a museum-case, is all but invisible in its habitual surroundings. The winter colouring of Arctic mammals and birds is white, desert animals of all sorts are isabelline, so as to be hardly visible against a sandy background. Forest-dwellers are frequently spotted, while those that haunt cane-brakes have transverse stripes. Species that live on open plains are largely of uniform colouring, though the zebras that seem to be so conspicuous, when near at hand, are very much less so at a distance. These principles are by no means without exceptions, but they generally hold good and may be applied when a careful study of the skeleton and teeth of some extinct mammal has led to probable inferences as to its normal habitat and mode of life.

We must avoid, however, the mistake of claiming too great a degree of accuracy for these attempts to reconstruct the life of a

long-vanished world. The general form, size and proportions of the
head, neck, body, tail, limbs and feet may be confidently inferred
from a close study of the skeleton, and the teeth give trustworthy
information as to the diet and habits of feeding, whether omnivorous,
herbivorous, carnivorous, or insectivorous. The external characteristics, such as fat-accumulations, growth of hair and colour-pattern,

Fig. 53. — Cohoes †Mastodon, †*M. americanus.* (Life-size model in the N. Y.
State Mus., courtesy of Dr. R. Ruedemann.)

can only be conjectured, yet there is something in the way of general
principles to guide the imagination and keep it in due bounds. No
doubt many of the extinct animals, owing to local accumulations of
fat, or growth of hair, were much more grotesque in appearance
than we can venture to represent them. The instances of the Horse,
Camel and Sperm Whale, already cited, and many others that might
be added, show how easy it is to go astray in the matter of external
appearances. The fundamentals of structure are accurately given
by the bones and teeth.

The work of restoration of extinct animals is, obviously enough,
beset with difficulties, but that is no sufficient reason for the uncritical scepticism which rejects the results as entirely fanciful, or
for the equally uncritical faith which accepts them as unquestionably

accurate. Probably a main source of error lies in making the restoration follow too closely the outward aspect of some existing animal which is taken as a model.

Though restorations are interesting and not without importance, the really significant subjects of palæontological study are the teeth and the skeleton, for in them is recorded the marvellous story of evolutionary development.

CHAPTER IV

GEOLOGICAL CHRONOLOGY

The history of any group of animals or plants requires as a necessary precondition some system by which its events may be arranged in order of time, for a history without chronology is meaningless. Geological history is recorded in the rocks, especially in the *bedded*, or *stratified* rocks, which were deposited by wind or water and were subsequently consolidated. The consolidation of loose materials, gravel, sand, clay, silt, into hard rock, is generally speaking, most complete in the older rocks, least so in the newest. Of the stratified rocks there are two kinds which it is essential to distinguish: (1) *marine rocks*, such as were deposited on the bed of the sea, and (2) *continental rocks*, those laid down on the land or in bodies of water which formed no part of the sea, such as lakes and rivers. Fossils of land animals and plants are obtained almost entirely from continental deposits and though occasionally found in marine rocks, they are then rare and fragmentary.

Limitations of space forbid any account of the methods by which geologists have ascertained the sequence in time of the rocks which make up the accessible crust of the earth; these methods are explained in every text-book of Geology. Here only those results which are required in making plain the history of mammals can be displayed. It should be emphasized, however, that there is substantial unanimity among geologists as to the divisions of geological time and the order of their chronological succession; such differences of opinion as there are, have to do with names rather than with facts.

Geological time, which embraces two billion years, or more, is divided into sections of decreasing comprehensiveness, until units of only a few feet of strata are reached. The major time-divisions, eras, periods, epochs, are of world-wide applicability and are employed in all civilized lands of all continents, but the minor subdivisions are local and are given local names.

Much the longer portion of geological time is represented by unfossiliferous rocks which are called Pre-Cambrian because that non-committal term implies merely that the rocks in question are

73

older than the first Palæozoic period, the Cambrian. The following
tables are to be read from below upward, thus graphically expressing
the order of superposition, the oldest strata being at the bottom,
the latest at the top. The divisions and the names given them differ
somewhat among geologists; the table gives the names most widely
employed.

MAJOR DIVISIONS OF GEOLOGICAL TIME

Cenozoic Era	Quaternary period Tertiary period
Mesozoic Era	Cretaceous period Jurassic period Triassic period
Palæozoic Era	Permian period Carboniferous period Devonian period Silurian period Ordovician period Cambrian period

Pre-Cambrian Time = Archæan, etc.

For the purposes of mammalian palæontology it is necessary to
carry the division and subdivision of the Cenozoic Era much farther
than this, for it was in that era that the extraordinary development
and diversification of the mammals took place. No trace of mammals
has been found in Palæozoic rocks and though they did exist in the
Mesozoic, mammals of that era are so extremely rare, that it is unnecessary to give any detailed account of Mesozoic geology. The
Cenozoic, on the contrary, must be examined much more minutely,
in order that every step in the evolution of the various orders and
families may be detected. How far this subdivision of Cenozoic beds
has been carried, is made plain by the fact that no less than 130 names
have been proposed for subdivisions of the Tertiary period in the
United States alone. Happily, it will not be necessary to mention
more than a fraction of these names, and, at this point, we need give
only such subdivisions as are valid for the world in general and
North and South America in particular.

The term *formation*, it should be explained, is here used in a vague,
indeterminate sense for any succession of strata which form a natural
group, whether thick or thin.

The local subdivisions, or such of them as are needful for our
purpose, are enumerated in Chapter VI.

CENOZOIC FORMATIONS

Quaternary Period { Recent epoch, or series
Pleistocene epoch

Tertiary Period { Pliocene epoch
Miocene epoch
Oligocene epoch
Eocene epoch
Paleocene epoch

The spread of species of mammals from their place of origin is called by the unfortunate term *migration*. To understand this so-called migration of mammals, it is necessary to learn something of the geographical and climatic changes through which the continents have passed. Regions which are now land, but were formerly submerged by the sea, can be determined from the marine rocks which cover them and the geological date of the sea's invasion is given by the fossils. The marine deposits of the Isthmus of Panama, for instance, show that in the Miocene epoch the isthmus was submerged by a sea which separated the two continents. Former land areas, on the contrary, which are now covered by the sea, give no direct evidence of their terrestrial state, which must be determined indirectly. Bering Sea and Strait between Alaska and Kamchatka, were land for ages and connected Asia and North America, as a result of which connection the Eocene and Oligocene mammals of western America and eastern Asia were largely the same. The land-bridge first made its effects evident in the Mesozoic Era, during which the connection was repeatedly made and broken, but persisted through nearly, if not quite, all the Tertiary period and was finally submerged late in the Pleistocene.

The spread of mammals is also very largely dependent upon climate, and in order to comprehend the back and forth wanderings of the creatures from Asia to America, from North to South America, it is necessary to know something of the climatic vicissitudes, which led from the mild and genial climates of the Tertiary to the vast ice-fields of the Quaternary periods. These extraordinary and in-explicable climatic revolutions had a profound effect upon animal life and occasioned, or at least accompanied, the great extinctions which, at the end of the Pleistocene, decimated the mammals over three-fifths of the earth's land-surface. The climatic changes are unmistakably recorded in the rocks, though no satisfactory explanation of them has yet been devised.

The geology of the Mesozoic Era may be very briefly treated. During the Triassic and Jurassic periods all the marine rocks of North America north of Mexico were laid down along the Pacific Coast region, as far east as Nevada and Idaho. The same is true of South America where the Triassic and Jurassic strata of marine origin are upturned in the Andes for nearly their whole length, but are not found on the Atlantic slope. From the geological point of view, Mexico and Central America may be regarded as belonging to the Pacific province of the two continents.

A belt of continental rocks, representing the upper Triassic, runs, with some interruptions, from Prince Edward Island to North Carolina, but there is no marine Jurassic of any sort on the Atlantic slope north of Texas. Highly important is a continental uppermost Jurassic formation, known as the *Morrison*, a narrow belt of dark sandstone, which runs parallel to the Front Range of the Rocky Mountains through Colorado into Wyoming, with separate areas in Montana, Oklahoma and Texas. The Morrison, which seems to be the exact equivalent of the English Purbeck, is the only formation of the North American Jurassic which has yielded mammals, while in England, the Purbeck, and the Stonesfield of the middle upper Jurassic, have been the sources of supply of Jurassic mammals. Almost all the Jurassic mammals so far discovered have been obtained from the Stonesfield, the Purbeck and the Morrison. The last-named beds have long been famous for the wonderful fossils they have yielded, not only of mammals, but also of gigantic †Dinosaurs.

The lower Cretaceous covers great areas in Mexico and Texas with marine deposits, the sea advancing in the successive stages until it covered southern Kansas and extended into Wyoming. Marine deposits of this date also form a band among the Pacific Coast from southern California into British Columbia. Continental deposits of the lower Cretaceous form large areas in the northern interior, from South Dakota into Alberta, and in the East a narrow belt of continental lower Cretaceous, the *Potomac* formation, extends from Virginia across New Jersey. The upper Cretaceous was a time of a great advance of the sea over the land, submerging broad areas along all the coasts and cutting the continent into two unequal parts by a broad sound which extended from the Gulf of Mexico to the Arctic Sea, covering all the Great Plains area of the United States and Canada. In the northern interior, Colorado and Wyoming,

Montana and Alberta, continental formations, some of them mammal-bearing, under various names, are intercalated between marine series and toward the close of the period, when the sea withdrew, large areas of continental deposits were laid down, including coal measures, second in importance only to those of the Carboniferous period of the Palæozoic Era. The uppermost Cretaceous in Wyoming, the *Lance*, which seems to pass up uninterruptedly into the Tertiary, has yielded great numbers of mammals, most of them isolated teeth. Many magnificent †dinosaurs have also been found in the Lance, the last of these monsters of which any record has been found in North America.

The Cretaceous period and, with it, the Mesozoic Era, was brought to an end in both continents by a great mountain-making revolution, which raised the Rocky Mountains from Alaska to New Mexico, and the Andes throughout the entire length of South America; the mountain ranges of Mexico and Central America belong to a different system and were elevated at different times. All of these ranges were greatly modified by subsequent movements, the latest of which were in the late Tertiary (Pliocene) and even in the Quaternary (Pleistocene), and the changes have been so great that it is hard to imagine what these immense ranges were like in their pristine state.

Mesozoic climates were uniformly mild and climatic zones were obscurely indicated. If, as the astronomers assure us, the inclination of the earth's axis is constant, there must always have been differences of temperature between the equatorial and the polar regions, but throughout Mesozoic time the difference must have been far less than at present. Even in Antarctica, most deserted of lands, the Jurassic vegetation was closely similar to that of England. Large reptiles can exist in warm climates only, but they occur in Jurassic rocks of the Arctic archipelago, and the Cretaceous of Greenland had forests of such trees as grow in temperate climates now.

A determining factor in the evolution of any group of animals is the nature of the plants upon which they feed directly or indirectly. Animals are absolutely dependent upon plants, for they cannot subsist upon inorganic food. Even carnivorous and insectivorous forms must feed upon prey which is herbivorous; their dependence upon plants is one step removed, but none the less absolute. Hence the astonishing multiplication, diversification and development of mammals, which form the most characteristic feature of Cenozoic life, were impossible before the true flowering plants, or Angiosperms, had spread over all the continents, and that did not take place until the upper Cretaceous, when modern vegetation was fully established. Could the modern mammalian fauna be transferred back into the Jurassic period, it would speedily starve for lack of needful vegetable food. As we shall see later, the spread of grassy plains in the mid-Tertiary time produced a very surprising series of changes among herbivorous mammals. Climate and vegetation are thus factors of supreme importance in making possible the full development of mammalian potentialities. The appearance and dominance of modern vegetation was a condition precedent to the development of modern mammals, and the late coming of the one explains the still later coming of the other.

CHAPTER V

ORIGIN OF THE MAMMALIA — MESOZOIC MAMMALIA

The problem as to the origin of the Mammalia was long a bone of contention among naturalists. Huxley derived them directly from the Amphibia, others maintained that they were descended from reptiles, though admitting that reptiles, in their turn, must have originated from the Amphibia. The progress of palæontological discovery seems to have decided this question in favour of the reptilian ancestry of mammals.

The most significant differences between the two classes in the structure of the skeleton are the characteristics of the jaws. In mammals the lower jaw of each side is a single bone which may, or may not, be co-ossified with that of the other side, as it is in Man, for example, and further, the lower jaw, or mandible, is articulated directly with the skull by the squamosal bone. In reptiles, on the other hand, each lower jaw is composed of six separate bones, though in a few forms, such as the turtles, all the elements fuse into a single lower jaw-bone. The lower jaw is, as it were, suspended from the skull by the *quadrate* bone, which mammals do not possess, or, if they do, it has been transformed into one of the minute ossicles of the internal ear.

Needless to say, a comparison of the soft parts reveals many other and more fundamental differences between reptiles and mammals but these are never preserved in the fossil state, and as to changes in the nervous, respiratory, circulatory and digestive systems, palæontology can afford no evidence, but, in certain important respects, the comparative anatomy of existing animals can supply the lack. A very marked difference is that reptiles are cold-blooded, mammals warm-blooded, a difference which is due to the strict separation of arterial and venous blood in the latter, owing to the four-chambered structure of the heart. On the other hand, crocodiles have the four-chambered heart and it would require but a minimal change in the blood-vessels to convert these reptiles into warm-blooded forms. The reptilian type of the reproductive organs is retained in the lowest known mammals, the Monotremata, as are also many reptilian features in the skeleton, which all other mammals have lost. So far as we at present know, the jaw-structure is diagnostic, though, as will presently be seen, there were transitions, knowledge of which is chiefly owing to the researches of Professor R. Broom in South Africa. Dr. Broom's results may be briefly summarized as follows.

In the American Permian rocks are found the most primitive reptiles which are at all adequately known, members of an order, the †Anapsida, from which probably all of the higher vertebrates were derived. From the †Anapsida there were at least two main lines of descent, one of which gave rise to almost all the reptilian orders of the Mesozoic Era and eventually to the birds. The second led to the mammal-like reptiles and through them to the mammals. The earliest representatives of the mammal-like reptiles were probably lizard-like in appearance, though more heavily built, and there are many orders and suborders of the mammal-like reptiles, which were almost as varied as the mammals themselves, and are found chiefly in the nearly continuous series of strata in South Africa from the middle Permian to the Jurassic, — a wonderful record.

Much the commonest mammal-like reptiles of the Permian and Triassic of South Africa are the †Anomodonta, which cannot have been truly ancestral to the mammals, because of their aberrant specialization, but they have many mammal-like characters. Associated with the †anomodonts in the upper Permian are two suborders, through one or the other of which the line of mammalian descent almost certainly passed. These reptiles had specialized teeth, which may be grouped into incisors, canines, and post-canines; they had relatively long and slender limbs and, though probably covered with scales, they had more the appearance of mammals than of ordinary reptiles. In the Triassic arose a group of carnivorous reptiles, the †Cynodontia, which in many characteristics closely approximated mammals and these were succeeded in the Rhætic or uppermost Trias, by the †Ictidosauria, very small reptiles, which in almost all points of skeletal structure, might be regarded as mammals, except that they retained the quadrate bone, articulating with the lower jaw. If we had the soft parts of the anatomy we might class the †Ictidosauria as mammals, notwithstanding the quadrate. Dr. Broom is of the opinion that "there can be no reasonable doubt that all the mammals have originated from Ictidosaurian ancestors." The question as to whether mammals were derived independently from one, or more †Ictidosaurian lines cannot yet be answered.

It is now generally accepted that the more primitive of the

†Cynodontia represent the Triassic ancestors of the mammals, though the more advanced members of that order are much too specialized to have been such ancestors. In the less specialized †cynodonts the skull has a very mammalian appearance, save for the extremely small size of the brain, and the bony palate is strikingly like that of a mammal, and correspondingly different from that of a typical reptile, though it must be remembered that this "secondary palate" is not entirely confined to mammals and their direct ancestors; it is very perfectly developed in the crocodiles.

In the †cynodont reptiles the quadrate bone is greatly reduced in size, and especially important is the presence of two occipital condyles, which form the joint between the skull and the neck. It is characteristic of birds and of almost all reptiles that the occipital condyle is single and placed in the middle line of the skull. In all mammals, without any known exception, there are two condyles, one on each side of the large opening (the *foramen magnum*) through which the spinal cord passes into the skull. That the condyle should have become double in the †Cynodontia is a very significant feature of their anatomy. The lower jaw was evidently in course of development toward the mammalian type, and successive stages of this approximation may be seen in passing from the more primitive to the more advanced †cynodonts. Seen from the outside, each lower jaw seems to be made up of a single bone, which almost touches the skull, but on the inner side are several elements which remain distinct.

In the Rhætic of South Africa occur the †Ictidosauria, which complete the transition from †cynodont to mammal. Some of these, no larger than rats, had a skull which was much more mammalian than reptilian, and the brain, though relatively larger than in reptiles was still smaller than in mammals. Each lower jaw is composed almost entirely of a single bone, the dentary, though a small articular still articulates with a greatly reduced quadrate to form the joint. If these small †ictidosaurians could be known in the living state, they might very well turn out to be mammals, with four-chambered heart, warm blood and hairy covering. With only the bones before us, the construction of the jaw-hinges requires that these transitional forms should be classified as reptiles.

It is not only in the skull that the mammal-like reptiles display transitional features, leading from reptiles to mammals. In the limb-bones and in the structure of the feet similar gradations may be observed. In the typical reptiles, for example, the number of phalanges, or joints, in the toes of fore and hind feet is greater by one, except in the fifth digit, than the numerical place of the toe in the series, counting from within outward. Thus, the first digit has two phalanges, the second three, the third four, the fourth five, the toes thus increasing in length regularly from the first to the fourth, the fifth has four, but in all land mammals the first digit (thumb, or great toe) has two phalanges and each of the others has three. Among the mammal-like reptiles the gradual reduction of the phalanges to the mammalian formula may be clearly followed.

It has often been made an objection to the theory of Evolution that no transitions between major groups of animals, orders or classes, were to be found among the fossils. The many groups of mammal-like reptiles furnish a complete answer to that objection and, if fossils have any meaning at all, they clearly demonstrate the reptilian origin of the mammals.

Throughout the Mesozoic Era the mammals played a very subordinate part. Except in the later Cretaceous, near the close of the Era, they were of minute size, rat-like and shrew-like in appearance, and remains of them are among the rarest of fossils. As will be shown below, however, there is good reason to think that they were common when in life, and their scarcity is due to conditions of fossilization. Despite their extreme rarity, Mesozoic mammals have been found in every continent, except Australia and Antarctica, and they are so generally of the same types everywhere as to indicate that these faunas were of world-wide distribution.

The history of Mesozoic mammals is broken by long gaps, and there are but three regions of the world where they have been found in any considerable numbers. Not only are these fossils very rare, they are also very fragmentary and the great majority of them are jaws, with more or less complete dentition. The Paleocene has yielded much fuller information concerning some of the persistent Mesozoic types.

All but a very few of the Mesozoic mammals have been obtained in the upper Jurassic (Stonefield Slates) of England, the uppermost Jurassic of England (Purbeck) and of Wyoming (Morrison) and the very late Cretaceous of Wyoming (Lance) and of Mongolia (Djadochta). The only Triassic mammals as yet definitely known are from the Rhætic of Germany and South Africa. There are but two extensive collections of Jurassic mammals, those of the British Museum and of Yale University, and of Cretaceous mammals in the latter and the American Museum of Natural History. Dr. G. G. Simpson of the American Museum has studied and described all known specimens of Mesozoic Mammalia and has brought admirable order out of the chaos in which they were formerly involved. This chapter follows Simpson's results with a few slight changes in nomenclature.

Fossils of six orders of mammals have been found in Mesozoic rocks which may be grouped as follows:

SUBCLASS †ALLOTHERIA

  ORDER 1. †MULTITUBERCULATA
    SUBORDER a. †Tritylodontoidea
    SUBORDER b. †Plagiaulacoidea

INCERTÆ SEDIS
  ORDER 2. TRICONODONTA

SUBCLASS EUTHERIA
  INFRACLASS †PANTOTHERIA
  ORDER 3. †TRITUBERCULATA

INCERTÆ SEDIS
  ORDER 4. †SYMMETRODONTA
  INFRACLASS DIDELPHIA
  ORDER 5. MARSUPIALIA
  INFRACLASS MONODELPHIA
  ORDER 6. INSECTIVORA

The Subclass Prototheria and order Monotremata have not been definitely identified among the Mesozoic mammals, though, as some authorities have maintained, the †Allotheria may prove to be referable to this subclass.

ORDER 1. MULTITUBERCULATA

These are the pre-eminently characteristic mammals of the Mesozoic Era and had a range in time and space unequalled by any other group of mammals. First known from the Rhætic, they flourished throughout the whole of the Jurassic and Cretaceous and persisted through the Paleocene into the lower Eocene. They have been discovered in every continent except Australia, South America and Antarctica in which no Mesozoic mammals of any kind have been obtained, but the group was probably cosmopolitan, the failure to find them being no proof of their absence. Most of our knowledge concerning the structure of these aberrant creatures is derived from Paleocene material, which contains skulls and partial skeletons; from the Mesozoic strata little more than jaws and teeth have been obtained. The South African †*Tritylodon*, however, which is from the Jurassic, or latest Triassic, gives invaluable information concerning the skull. All the known features of this order are peculiar and are not suggestive of relationship to any other group of mammals, except perhaps the Monotremata. The teeth are especially characteristic and were so remarkably specialized, as to give assurance that a long period of development, antecedent to the oldest known genera, must have taken place. The second upper incisor is enlarged, the first and third are much reduced, while in the lower jaw a single incisor remains and this is relatively very large; there are no canines above or below, their function being assumed by the enlarged incisors.

The grinding, or cheek-teeth underwent much change in number, form and size in the course of the long history of the order, but the cuspidate, crushing pattern was always retained in some of these teeth. In the suborder †Tritylodontoidea, the teeth had each three longitudinal rows of four cusps in the upper jaw (the lower dentition is not known) and there are no shearing teeth. No representative of this suborder has yet been found in North America and it did not persist beyond the Purbeck in Europe. Despite its great antiquity, this suborder is regarded as a specialized side-branch of the stock.

The second suborder, the †Plagiaulacoidea, continued to flourish till a much later time, but is not known before the uppermost Jurassic of England and North America (Purbeck and Morrison) but, because of the extreme rarity of these fossils, not much importance can be attached to such a negative statement. Practically nothing is known of lower or middle or early upper Cretaceous mammals, and hence it is impossible to say when the great change between upper Jurassic and upper Cretaceous mammals took place. The suborder, †Plagiaulacoidea, is represented in the upper Cretaceous and throughout the Paleocene of Europe and North America and continued into the American Wasatch, which is its latest known appearance.

In this group there are two molar teeth on each side, above and below, each with two or three rows of cusps. The premolars are very different from the molars and the posterior ones, especially in the lower jaw, form a shearing apparatus which is very characteristic of the suborder, though some of the Paleocene genera have secondarily lost it. The genus †*Ctenacodon*, common to the Morrison and the Purbeck, has four premolars in the lower jaw, three of which are shearing, and two of these, at least, have prominent, oblique enamel ridges on the outer side of the tooth, near the upper cutting border.

There is a single enlarged and somewhat tusk-like incisor on each side of each jaw, which in some of the Paleocene genera becomes a chisel-like, or *scalpriform*, tooth such as the rodents have, and which was used in gnawing.

In the Jurassic genera in which the lower jaw is known, such as †*Ctenacodon* and †*Plagiaulax*, it is unlike that of any Eutherian mammal, whether marsupial or placental. As in the monotremes, it is peculiar in having no angle, or angular process; the condyle, which articulates with the skull, has the position usually taken by the angle, at the extreme hinder end of the jaw and the lower border of the mandible runs in an uninterrupted curve from the condyle to the chin, a very reptilian characteristic.

Between the English Purbeck and the American Morrison, on the one hand, and the uppermost Cretaceous, as exemplified by the Lance of Wyoming, and the somewhat earlier Djadochta of Mongolia, on the other, there was an immense lapse of time, during which the strata then formed have, as yet, yielded no mammals of any kind, except a single †Multituberculate tooth from the Wealden (lowest Cretaceous) of England, and when the story of mammalian development was resumed in the latest Cretaceous, an entirely new and different chapter had been opened. Only the †Multituberculata persisted, in modified form, while the other Jurassic orders, the †Triconodonta, †Symmetrodonta and †Pantotheria, had died out, though it is extremely probable that the †Pantotheria continued to live in their descendants, both marsupial and placental.

Fig. 54. — Lower jaw, right side, of †*Plagiaulax becklesii*, × 2, upper Jurassic.

Of the uppermost Cretaceous †Multituberculata in North America the commonest and most typical genera were †*Meniscoëssus* and †*Cinolomys*. The Paleocene †*Ptilodus* was very similar to the latter, of which it was probably a direct descendant, and its structure is much better known than that of any other genus of the order. Complete skulls, with the lower jaw attached and all the teeth in place, and much of the skeleton, have been described and figured by the late J. W. Gidley, of the U. S. National Museum. These specimens illustrate again the oft-proved absurdity of the popular fallacy, that the palæontologist is able to reconstruct a vanished animal from a single bone or tooth. The lower teeth of †*Ptilodus* were those from which the genus was originally described, while the upper teeth had been referred to an altogether different genus and even a different *family*. Outside of this order no such association of teeth had ever

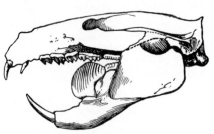

been known and it is not at all surprising that, when found dissociated, they should have deceived the ablest palæontologists.

The skull of †*Ptilodus*, while typically mammalian, is yet extremely primitive and has certain features which seem to point to a relationship with the monotremes, though, in the existing members of that group,

FIG. 55. — Skull, left side, of †*Ptilodus gracilis*, enlarged. Fort Union. (From Gidley.)

the skull is much specialized without losing its primitive character. As in the monotremes, the glenoid cavities, with which the lower jaw articulates, are nearly at the hinder end of the skull, a fact which is also true of the mammal-like reptiles of the order †Cynodontia. Thus †*Ptilodus* and, no doubt, all other multituberculates also, has hardly any post-glenoid region of the cranium, while in the marsupials this region is short and in all the placental mammals it is much elongated.

The skull of †*Ptilodus* is quite rodent-like in appearance, with flattened cranial roof and with the zygomatic arches inserted nearly level with that roof. The resemblance was

FIG. 56. — Head of †*Ptilodus gracilis*, about natural size. Restored from skull shown in Fig. 55.

probably independently acquired and due to a somewhat similar manner of using the teeth. As in marsupials, the auditory bullæ are formed by the inflation of the alisphenoids, not of the tympanics, as in placental mammals, and there are large vacuities in the bony palate.

Another Paleocene family, that of the †Tæniolabididæ, with the type genus, †*Tæniolabis*, represents the almost final stage of multituberculate development. In †*Tæniolabis* the incisors, especi-

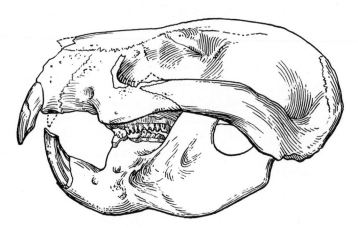

FIG. 57. — Skull of †*Tæniolabis taöensis*, left side, × ½, Puerco. (From Granger and Simpson.)

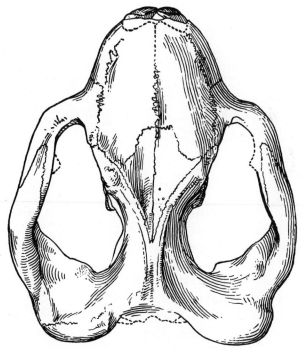

FIG. 58. — Skull of †*Tæniolabis taöensis*, top, × ½, Puerco. (From Granger and Simpson.)

ally the lower pair, are chisel-like, the premolars have lost their shearing function and are reduced in number to a single one on each side of each jaw, and there are two molars above and below, the first one much larger than the second, with many crescentic cusps arranged in rows. The animal was far larger than any of the Cretaceous genera, or the Paleocene †*Ptilodus* and had more powerful jaws and heavier skull; in appearance, it was probably not unlike the modern Australian Wombat. In the genus †*Eucosmodon* the incisors are fully scalpriform, the enamel being restricted to a broad band on the front of each tooth, as in the rodents. This was the last known representative

Fig. 59. — Head of a Paleocene †multituberculate, †*Tæniolabis taöensis*, Puerco. Restored from skull shown in Figs. 57 and 58.

of the order, which persisted into the lower Eocene and then became extinct.

The †Multituberculata thus flourished for a longer period of time than any other mammalian order, from the Rhætic through the Jurassic, Cretaceous and Paleocene, dying out in the lower Eocene, and, so far as can be judged from the fragmentary material, they underwent comparatively little change. Like the existing monotremes, the †multituberculates had a very primitive, archaic type of structure, combined with a remarkable degree of specialization, which, in the fossils, however, is confined to the teeth. It is not conceivable that these peculiar creatures should have been ancestral to any other group of mammals. Their wide separation from other known mammalian orders is shown by the researches of Dr. T. J. Carter on the microscopic structure of the tooth-enamel, which gives a trustworthy indication of relationships. In the Paleocene †multituberculates, at least, the minute structure of the enamel is characteristic and different from that of any other known vertebrates.

INCERTÆ SEDIS

ORDER 2. †TRICONODONTA

According to present information, this order is entirely Jurassic in distribution; in the middle Jurassic of Stonesfield and the upper

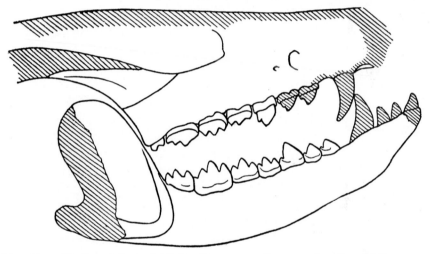

FIG. 60. — Skull and jaw of †*Priacodon*, composite reconstruction, × 3, upper Jurassic of Wyo. (From Simpson.)

Jurassic of the Purbeck, in England, and the Morrison in Wyoming, these fossils are relatively numerous, but they died out leaving no descendants. More is known of their structure than of any other Mesozoic group, save that of the †multituberculates, and it may be assumed that this knowledge is of value in considering the course of mammalian evolution, for, though the ††triconodonts seem not to have given rise to any other group, they show in all respects, save the teeth, what the true ancestors were probably like. That is to say, the ††triconodonts were "structurally ancestral," not directly ancestral to the later and higher groups.

In this order there are three or four small incisors and one canine on each side, above and below. The molars always have three main cusps in a longitudinal row, and in the lower teeth the middle cusp is higher than the one before, or that behind it. The molars of the two jaws form a cutting apparatus, the upper ones shearing down past the outer side of the lower in a manner suggestive of carnivorous habits. Much the best known genera of the order are the English †*Triconodon* and the American †*Priacodon*.

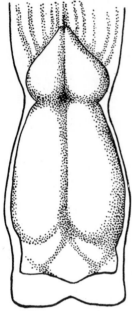

FIG. 61. — Braincast of †*Triconodon mordax*, × 3, English Jurassic. (From Simpson.)

Considerable portions of the skull of †*Triconodon* have been recovered and these yield most important information as to the skull of the Mesozoic mammals in general. So far as at present known, the skull was elongate and tubular, with the nasal cavity almost as wide as the brain-case, resembling that of many Insectivora in general and the modern East Indian *Gymnura*, in particular. The fragments of the skull suffice to reveal the character of the upper side of the brain, which, as would naturally have been expected, is extremely primitive in character, though distinctively mammalian. The olfactory lobes are relatively very large, the cerebral hemispheres long, narrow and flattened on top, without any sign of convolutions. The cerebellum is fully exposed, as the hemispheres did not overlap it at all.

The cochlea of the internal ear is, in all existing Eutheria, spirally coiled, as its name implies, but in †*Triconodon* it is almost straight, as it is in reptiles. This is an entirely unique feature among mammals, and though it probably characterized the other Mesozoic Mammalia, it has, as yet, been found only in †*Triconodon*.

SUBCLASS *EUTHERIA*

This term, proposed by Dr. Theodore Gill in 1872 to include both marsupials and placentals, has been employed by various writers in widely different senses, but there seems to be no good reason why this perversion of Gill's nomenclature should be accepted. Marsupials and placentals differ from one another in fundamental ways, yet they have much in common that places them far above the Prototheria and the †Allotheria, if it be proper to separate these two subclasses. The Eutheria have not yet been found in beds earlier than the Stonesfield Slates, which are in the middle Jurassic of England, or in this country before the Morrison of Wyoming. These Jurassic Eutherians are not referable to either of the existing Infraclasses, Didelphia and Monodelphia, but must be placed in another, and extinct Infraclass, the †Pantotheria, in which, to all appearances, were the common ancestors of the other two.

INFRACLASS I. †*PANTOTHERIA*

It is extremely tantalizing that these extraordinarily interesting animals should be so incompletely known, for only jaws and teeth have been discovered, so far. Nevertheless, these rare and imperfect remains are highly important, and it may well be that the †Pantotheria were actually ancestral to all of the later Eutheria. On the other hand, it is entirely possible that fuller knowledge may disprove this conclusion and show that the †pantotheres formed a collateral, not a directly ancestral line. The apparent restriction of these animals to the middle and upper Jurassic is probably due to accidental circumstances and to our complete ignorance concerning all but the latest of the Cretaceous mammals. It is, however, a significant fact that remains of the †Pantotheria should be entirely lacking in the Lance formation, which has yielded such great numbers of mammalian teeth. Even if they had not then become entirely extinct, they had at least diminished greatly in relative importance.

There is much reason to believe that in the Jurassic period the †pantotheres were of world-wide distribution, though they have actually been found only in North America, England and East Africa. In the Jurassic and Cretaceous, the †dinosaurs, which were land reptiles, extended their range to every continent except, perhaps, Antarctica, and the tiny †pantotheres apparently followed the same paths of migration from one continent to another, across land-bridges that were long ago broken down and foundered in the sea.

ORDER 3. †TRITUBERCULATA

This order comprises small Jurassic mammals, which have unspecialized incisors, canines often two-rooted, premolars usually very different from the molars and never entirely molariform, of piercing and trenchant shape. The triangular upper molars have one principal inner and one principal outer cusp and two or more other cusps of varying size, lower molars with three principal cusps and a heel. The primitive formula for the cheek-teeth is $p\,\frac{4}{4}$, $m\,\frac{8}{8}$ (see p. 42) but some of the genera have a smaller number of teeth. In the lower jaw the coronoid and angular processes are distinctly developed, a notable difference from the †Multituberculata; the angle is not inflected, as it is in the marsupials.

Simpson divides the order into four families: (1) the †Amphitheriidæ, with the single known genus, †*Amphitherium*, of the middle Jurassic; (2) the †Dryolestidæ, containing most of the genera of the uppermost Jurassic (Purbeck and Morrison); (3) the †Paurodontidæ, with rather more primitive molars than the other upper Jurassic forms; and (4) the †Docodontidæ, with a small number of genera that had an extremely aberrant dentition.

The single †pantotherian genus as yet obtained from the middle Jurassic, †*Amphitherium*, was a most fortunate discovery, for it is in all respects extremely primitive, without any specializations, and

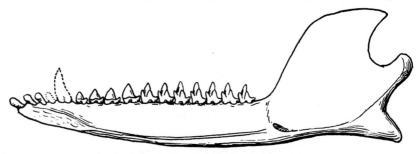

Fig. 62. — Right half of lower jaw, inside, of †*Amphitherium prevostii*, × 4, middle Jurassic of England. (From Simpson.)

it may very well have been directly ancestral to all subsequent mammals, save, of course, the †multituberculates, which long antedated †*Amphitherium* and long outlived it, as such. In its descendants the tiny mid-Jurassic creature may be said to be living yet.

The three Purbeck-Morrison families were each specializing in its own characteristic fashion from an †*Amphitherium*-like ancestry. The †Paurodontidæ seem to be in the direct line of descent of the later mammals; they retained the primitive type of molar seen in *Amphitherium*, while the jaw was shortened and the number of cheek-teeth diminished, the molar formula being $\frac{4}{4}$. This is just what must have taken place in the history of both placentals and marsupials.

The †Dryolestidæ are much the largest of the three families, containing most of the best-known upper Jurassic genera, especially †*Dryolestes* itself. The †dryolestids were developing in their own characteristic fashion and are not to be regarded as even structurally ancestral to any subsequent group.

The same statement applies to the †Docodontidæ, an extraordinarily peculiar family, with highly complicated teeth. This group is an example of rapid and premature specialization and was short-lived.

"To sum up: on the basis of the facts now known and without making a futile attempt to discount the future, it may justly be said that the †pantotheres show no features which would indicate exclusive relationships with either marsupials or placentals, that they exhibit no characters that would exclude them from the ancestry of either group and that, in the known parts, they display, as an order, all the characters which would necessarily occur in the common ancestor of [both] marsupials and placentals. The characters involved are too many and too intricately co-ordinated for this to be mere coincidence and the only conclusion possible at the present time seems to be that the Order †Pantotheria [i.e. †Trituberculata] does represent the ancestry of both marsupials and placentals without itself belonging to either group." (Simpson, G. G., British Museum Catalogue Mesozoic Mammals, p. 182.)

INCERTÆ SEDIS

ORDER 4. †SYMMETRODONTA

These animals have small incisors and distinct canines, with triangular upper molars, which have a high internal cusp and smaller

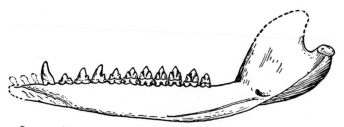

FIG. 63. — Lower jaw, inside, of †*Spalacotherium tricuspidens*, × ⅖, upper Jurassic of England. (From Simpson.)

anterior and posterior cusps and no heel. The lower jaw has no angle.

The †symmetrodonts are relatively rare as fossils and less is known of them than of the other Mesozoic orders. The best known genera are †*Spalacotherium* from the uppermost Jurassic of England and North America, and †*Tinodon* from the latter.

Skeletal Bones of Uncertain Reference

A few limb-bones have been found in the Stonesfield, Purbeck and Morrison deposits, not associated with jaws or teeth and, therefore, not referable to any definite group of mammals, but of great interest, nevertheless, as showing the evolutionary level attained by some groups, at least, of Jurassic mammals. The skeletal elements so far discovered are thigh-bones from the Stonesfield, Purbeck and Morrison horizons, and upper-arm bones from Stonesfield. The femur from Stonesfield is very peculiar and not closely similar to that of any other animal, though its mammalian character is unmistakable. It has no indication of either marsupial or placental affinities, but in many ways it resembles the femur of the monotremes, with which it is in a similar evolutionary stage. In life, the femur must have had an almost horizontal position, producing a sprawling reptile-like gait, such as the †cynodont ancestors of the mammals also had.

The Stonesfield humerus is unlike any other humerus whatever and is more like that of the †cynodont reptiles than is any other known mammalian humerus. The differences from the †cynodonts in the form of this bone are distinct advances toward the primitive Eutherian type, to which it would seem to have been directly ancestral.

Femora have also been found in the Purbeck and Morrison formations and these, if compared with the thigh-bone of such a primitive Eutherian as the Opossum (*Didelphis*) on the one hand and the Stonesfield specimens, on the other, form an ideal transition between the earlier and the later stages, and plainly show how one was derived from the other.

Mammalia of the Cretaceous Period

Following the upper Jurassic there was an immense lapse of time, covering all of the lower and most of the upper Cretaceous, when almost nothing is known of mammals, and when these reappear in the upper Cretaceous (Djadochta) of Mongolia, of Wyoming, Montana and Alberta they have undergone a complete transformation. As in so many other groups of animal and plant life, the upper Cretaceous marks the beginning of the modern order.

Of the Jurassic groups, the †Triconodonta and †Symmetrodonta have entirely disappeared, leaving no descendants and the †Pantotheria, as such, were also extinct, but were represented by Eutherian descendants. The †Multituberculata, alone of the Jurassic orders,

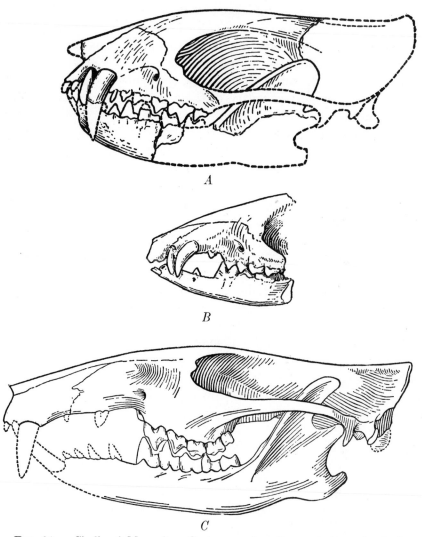

FIG. 64. — Skulls of Mongolian Cretaceous Insectivora, twice natural size. *A, †Deltatheridium pretrituberculare. B, †Hyotheridium dobsoni. C, †Zalambdalestes lechei.* (From Simpson.)

persisted, though with considerable modification, as they were destined to continue throughout the whole Paleocene and into the lower Eocene, maintaining an existence of unparalleled duration.

The first known Eutherians, both marsupials and placentals, date from the upper Cretaceous and there can be no reasonable doubt that both were derived from †Pantotherian ancestors. The earliest marsupial so far discovered is †*Eodelphis* from the Belly

River, of Canada, and the Lance of Wyoming has yielded a large variety of teeth referable, like †*Eodelphis,* to the opossum family, which was spread all over the world, except perhaps Africa, where nothing is yet known of Cretaceous mammals. For reasons that have nothing to do with palæontology, the opossums have been long regarded as the most primitive of the marsupials and it is a matter of interest to see this conclusion supported by the geological record. Some of the Lance genera, such as †*Thlæodon,* show a considerable degree of specialization without, however, exceeding the family limits. Indeed, these late Cretaceous opossums were undergoing a rapid diversification which may have been important for South America and Australia, though its permanent results in the northern hemisphere were of little significance.

The most ancient known placental mammals are the Insectivora of the Lance and, in a much better state of preservation, from the Djadochta of Mongolia. The Insectivora have, on entirely independent grounds, been considered the most primitive of placental mammals and, so long ago as 1880, Huxley selected this group as being ancestral to all the higher mammals. In the Djadochta beds have been found several well-preserved skulls of simple, primitive insectivores, which fit admirably, as the postulated ancestors, into the hypothetical scheme.

CHAPTER VI

CENOZOIC CONTINENTAL FORMATIONS OF NORTH AMERICA

The regions which have yielded well-preserved fossils of terrestrial mammals are all in the West and along the Pacific Coast, especially in Oregon and southern California. The table on page 75 gives the major divisions (periods and epochs) of the Cenozoic Era which are applicable throughout the world, but it is necessary to carry the divisions and subdivisions much further, in order to make clear the successive steps of evolution, by which the Mammalia attained their modern state. These minor subdivisions are local and not recognizable in all parts of the continent, still less in other continents. The more important subdivisions of the continental Tertiary formations of the western U. S. are given in the subjoined table.

TERTIARY PERIOD

Pliocene Epoch
Hagerman Stage (Idaho)
Devil's Gulch Stage (Nebraska)
Blanco Stage (Texas)
Hemphill Stage (Texas)
Clarendon Stage (Texas) Snake C'k (Neb.) Alachua (Fla.)
Upper Santa Fé (N. M.)

Miocene Epoch
Valentine Stage (Loup Fork) Lower Santa Fé (N. M.)
Deep River (Mont.) Mascall (Oregon)
Upper Harrison Stage
Lower Harrison Stage
Gering and Monroe C'k Stages

Oligocene Epoch
John Day Stage
White River Stage — Brulé Substage | Sespé
Chadron Substage | Series
Duchesne River Stage

Eocene Epoch
Uinta Stage
Bridger Stage
Wind River Stage |
Gray Bull Stage | Wasatch Series, Green River

Paleocene Epoch
Clark Fork Stage |
Torrejon Stage | Fort Union Series
Puerco Stage |

97

In studies which enter minutely into the structure and development of the various mammalian families, it is necessary to take into account geographical, as well as geological distinctions. For the purposes of this book it will suffice to mention the chief geographical provinces which the specialist is compelled to recognize. There are (1) the Great Plains, which cover the western part of the Mississippi Valley and extend far into Canada and Mexico; (2) the Rocky Mountains, including the high plateaus which lie to the west of those ranges; (3) the southwestern region, including western Texas, New Mexico, Arizona and southeastern California; (4) the Great Basin, Utah, Nevada and parts of the adjoining states, and finally, (5) the Pacific Coast region, of which Oregon and southern California are, so far as is yet known, the only important parts. A few very fragmentary specimens of Tertiary mammals have been found on the Atlantic Coast, but these are significant only as showing that, along the same parallels of latitude, similar mammals ranged across the continent from ocean to ocean.

In discussions concerning the place of origin of the different families and genera of mammals, it is commonly overlooked that, from this point of view, nothing is known as to an immense area, which comprises more than half of the continent, nearly all of Canada and the northeastern region from Pennsylvania, through New England, Labrador and Greenland. Of the northern half of the continent, only Alaska has yielded fossil mammals of importance and these all belong to the latest of the geological periods, the Quaternary. Many unsolved problems which present themselves in the southern continental area would, no doubt, find solutions, did we know the Tertiary history of the northern area and its faunas.

I. Tertiary Period

1. Paleocene Epoch

(By G. L. Jepsen)

Two marine formations in North America have been assigned to this epoch, the Martinez of California and the Midway of the Gulf Coast, although the latter has affinities with both younger and older rocks in other regions. There has been subsidence (with which deposition may have kept pace, however) in the west Gulf Coast region since Paleocene time, as evidenced by the recovery of the skull of a small mammal (†*Anisonchus*) from an oil well in Louisiana at a depth of 2460 feet, but the north central part of the continent has risen with respect to sea-level because the last interior marine invasion of that area, the Cannonball Sea, had occurred in the just-ended Cretaceous period.

Four stages, or faunal zones, have been distinguished in the thick terrestrial deposits of the Paleocene. In the San Juan Basin of northwestern New Mexico a series of badland clays and sandstones, about 900 feet thick, lies unconformably upon the late Cretaceous Ojo Alamo formation and yields two faunas. The older and lower zone is termed the *Puerco,* and is separated by barren strata from the upper zone, *Torrejon.* To the north, in southwestern Colorado, strata of unknown thickness bear the fauna of the third stage, the *Tiffany,* which follows the Torrejon in time. In middle western Colorado another series of sediments, the *Plateau Valley,* contains a mammalian fauna which appears to be near Tiffany age.

Fort Union is the name applied to a great thickness of sediments (2000–5000 feet) widely distributed in Wyoming, Montana, the Dakotas, Alberta and farther north. Probably the whole of Paleocene time is represented in this formation. It was originally considered to be of Cretaceous age on the evidence afforded by fossil leaves, but a more intensive study of the Fort Union flora and the discovery of large mammalian faunas have led to its reference to the earliest Tertiary. The Fort Union of the Big Horn Basin in Wyoming rests upon the uppermost Cretaceous dinosaur-bearing formation, the *Lance,* and contains all four stages of the Paleocene, each with a distinctive mammalian horizon. From the base to the top of the formation they have been named: (1) *Mantua;* (2) *Rock Bench;* (3) *Silver Coulee;* and (4) *Clark Fork.* The first two represent the approximate time equivalents of the Puerco and the Torrejon, respectively, and the third was about contemporary with the Tiffany. Clark Fork strata form the summit of the Paleocene and are separated from overlying Eocene sediments by an angular unconformity around the margin of their exposure in the Big Horn Basin; but in the middle of this area there appears to be no discordance and the rocks of the two epochs are locally difficult to distinguish except by their fossils.

A small Fort Union fauna has come from a coal mine at Bear Creek, near the middle of the south boundary of Montana. It correlates with the Silver Coulee. North of this, in the vicinity of the Crazy Mountains, the so-called "Lebo member" of the Fort Union contains fossil mammals of Torrejon stage and also of a higher level, like the Silver Coulee. Fossils of Silver Coulee and Clark Fork ages have also been found at several localities in the *Paskapoo* of Alberta.

It is difficult to picture the conditions under which the Fort Union strata were laid down, but it would seem that the entire region had sluggish, sediment-laden streams meandering across it and, in the seasons of high water, immense areas were converted into temporary lakes, in which regularly stratified beds were deposited. There were also marshes and bogs where masses of vegetable matter were accumulated, and these subsequently formed deposits of lignite. So favorable were the conditions that leaf-impressions were abundantly preserved. No less than 500 species of plants have been named, most of which are forest trees of very modern type. Commonest are the poplars, but sycamores, maples, elms, oaks, hickories, birches, etc., are all very frequently found. Palms and herbaceous plants are rare.

Climate of the Paleocene. — This may be confidently inferred from the character of the Fort Union plants. Though genial, with no polar ice-caps and with the climatic zones much less definitely marked than at present, Paleocene climates were, in general, rather cooler than those of the preceding Cretaceous and those of the succeeding Eocene. In England also, the fossil plants indicate a cooler European climate than in the Eocene or the Cretaceous.

2. Eocene Epoch

The marine beds of this series form a narrow coastal belt on the Atlantic side, a broad plain along the Gulf of Mexico, a long narrow band on the Pacific side, but, except in the lower Mississippi Valley, they nowhere extend far into the interior. These marine beds have yielded a few very fragmentary mammalian fossils, which, nevertheless, have a certain geographical importance.

The continental formations of the Eocene in North America are largely confined to the plateau region which lies to the west of the Rocky Mountains in the states of Wyoming, Utah, western Colorado and New Mexico, where immense "badland" areas cover many thousands of square miles. The deposition was done partly in lakes, but much more extensively by rivers and the wind, while, in the middle part of the epoch, volcanic material contributed extensively to the deposits.

a. Gray Bull Stage. — The term "Wasatch," as it was so long and familiarly used, is equivalent to "Gray Bull," but has been employed in so many different senses that it is no longer tenable except as a collective name for the whole lower Eocene. The Gray Bull is typically displayed in the great Big Horn Basin of northern Wyoming and Montana, where the beds have a thickness of 1800 to 2000 feet, principally deposited by river action. Great badland areas have been cut in these rocks by the weather. These beds, which have no precise equivalents elsewhere in North America, are richly fossiliferous, yielding many mammals.

b. *Wind River Stage.* — Upon the Gray Bull, with no apparent unconformity, are the clays and sandstones of the *Wind River*, divided into two substages, the lower, *Lysite*, and the upper, *Lost Cabin*. The type locality of the Wind River and its substages is in the Wind River Basin of central Wyoming, south of the Bridger and Owl Creek Mountains, and east of the Wind River, where the strata rest upon pre-Tertiary rocks of various geological dates. There is also a vast southern area referred to this stage in New Mexico and northward through eastern Utah and western Colorado to the Uinta Mountains, around the eastern end of which it passes, expanding again over southwestern Wyoming. A small isolated area of Wind River beds occurs in southeastern Colorado. Geographically, the Wind River is by far the largest of the Eocene areas.

c. *Green River Stage.* — This is a phase of the lower Eocene, rather than a separate stage, as it is made up of a thick mass of very finely laminated shales ("paper shales"), the laminæ of which are no thicker than sheets of coarse paper. These shales are found in the valley of the Green River, both north and south of the Uinta Mountains, where they rest upon the Wind River beds and are overlain by the Bridger, but at the borders the shales interdigitate with Wind River beds, showing their contemporaneity with the upper part of the latter. The Green River Shales were laid down in two very large, but extremely shallow, connected lakes, one north and the other south of the Uinta Mountains. Exquisitely preserved fishes, insects and leaf-impressions, in countless multitudes, are found in these beds, which, however, have yielded hardly any mammals, other than a few obscurely marked footprints. The Green River flora, on the other hand, gives clear indications of climatic conditions in the lower Eocene, and the even more abundant flora of the Wilcox affords very full information concerning the Gulf Coast climate at approximately the same time.

d. *Bridger Stage.* — This is named from Fort Bridger and its beds are in two basins, about 100 miles apart, though it is not yet practicable to say how much of this interval has been due to erosion. The western, or Bridger Basin proper, is in southwestern Wyoming and Fort Bridger stands nearly in the middle of it; the strata of this basin are somewhat older than those of the eastern, or Washakie Basin. The beds of the latter extend around the eastern end of the Uinta Mountains and expand into a wide area on the south side of that range.

In contradistinction to the beds of the lower Eocene, those of the middle Eocene, or Bridger, are very largely made up of volcanic ash

FIG. 65. — Badlands of Little Dry Creek, Wyo., Bridger stage, middle Eocene. (Photograph by Amer. Mus. Nat. Hist.)

which was partly deposited upon land surfaces, partly showered into water, which may have been in the form of periodical lakes, or *playas*. The quantity of fresh-water shells, and of the scales and bones of fishes and crocodiles indicate some sort of water bodies, but it is not likely that either of the basins was occupied by a single large lake.

The Bridger beds are of soft and friable sandstones and clays which yield readily to weathering, and, consequently, they form a vast badland region, one of the most extensive of all the Tertiary formations.

e. Uinta Stage. — There is some difference of usage in drawing the line between the Eocene and Oligocene because of the gradual transition between them. Here, the Uinta is taken as the summit of the Eocene and the Duchesne River as the base of the Oligocene, though there is much to be said in favour of including the latter in the Eocene. Such border-line problems are many in the stratigraphy of the continental Tertiary deposits. The Uinta is the upper Eocene of the northwestern interior and is named from the Uinta Mountains with which it forms a parallel band, on the south side, in Utah and Colorado. In appearance the beds resemble those of the upper Bridger, upon which the Uinta lies in apparent conformity, and is, in turn, overlain by the Duchesne River.

Climate of the Eocene. — The very rich floras from the Green River Shales, from the Wilcox of the Gulf Coast and from the Eocene of Greenland, show that the climate was warmer than in the Paleocene, and much warmer than at the present day. In Greenland the climate was temperate and very like that of the middle Atlantic States as it is now, and no Arctic ice-cap can have been in existence. The coastal plain of the Southern States had a subtropical climate, which grew warmer from the earlier to the later part of the epoch. In the intermediate region a warm temperate climate prevailed, palms flourishing at least as far north as Montana and large crocodiles abounding over the same area throughout the whole of the epoch. Wyoming especially has yielded many species of these great reptiles which, even better than the palms, prove that the climate must have been much warmer than it is now.

Land-connections in the Eocene. — The lower Eocene fauna of North America is so nearly identical with that of Europe as to demonstrate that communication between these continents was open by way of Asia. Asia was joined to North America by a land-bridge occupying the site of Bering Sea. During the whole epoch this land-bridge persisted and, because of the mild climate, was available for southern mammals. While the connection of Asia with North America continued, that with Europe was interrupted by the establishment of a long narrow sound, which ran from the Arctic to the Black Sea, following the course of the Ural Mountains. If, as seems probable, North and South America were united in the Paleocene, the connection was broken down throughout the Eocene.

3. Oligocene Epoch

The marine Oligocene is but scantily developed on the Atlantic slope, where it is known only in the southeastern states. On the Pacific side marine beds are very much more extensive, especially in Alaska, where they reach the great thickness of 10,000 feet. The continental Oligocene formations are found almost entirely over the Great Plains, in the Dakotas, Nebraska and Colorado. Outlying areas of great interest are known in southern California, eastern Oregon and in the Saskatchewan Province of Canada.

a. *Duchesne River Stage.* — Recently discovered, these beds have not yet been surveyed, nor has their area been determined. The stage in Utah and Colorado, on both sides of the Green River, follows upon the Uinta upon which it rests and in thickness it exceeds 2000 feet. Its fauna, so far as it has been made known, is transitional from Eocene to Oligocene and might almost as well be included in

FIG. 66. — Big Badlands of S. D., White River stage, Oligocene. (Photograph by Field Mus. Nat. Hist.)

one as in the other. The deposits in central Wyoming which have been called Uinta and upon which the lower Oligocene lies unconformably, seem to be referable to this stage and in the Sespé formation (*q.v.*) of southern California the same fauna has recently (1931) been discovered. Fragmentary fossils of this date have also been found in Alberta, Canada.

b. *White River Stage.* — The immense area of badlands carved out of the White River beds covers parts of South Dakota, Nebraska, Colorado and Wyoming. Small outlying areas occur in North Dakota, Montana and Saskatchewan. The formation is of no great thickness, not more than 500 to 600 feet, and consists of very evenly and regularly stratified and indurated clays, with a large admixture of volcanic ash. The ash is sometimes concentrated in snowy white beds of pure volcanic débris. Stream-channels, now filled with cross-bedded sandstone, or fine conglomerate, ramify through the strata at various levels and are the remains of the ancient drainage systems. The deposits were laid down in the temporary lakes, or *playas* which were formed in the seasons of high water over the conjoined flood-plains of the many streams. There were occasional more permanent

FIG. 67. — Big Badlands of S. D., White River stage, upper Brulé substage.
(Courtesy of J. S. Nichols, Esq.)

ponds in which fresh-water shells were preserved, but alligators and fishes are rare. Tooth-marks of rodents on many of the bones show that such bones lay on dry ground before they were buried.

The White River beds are plainly divisible into three substages which have received various names shown in the subjoined table.

White River Stage	Upper, Protoceras-Leptauchenia Beds	Brulé substage
	Middle, Oreodon Beds	
	Lower, Titanotherium Beds	Chadron substage

These subdivisions have great significance in tracing the steps of evolutionary change, for each one records its own steps in that change.

c. *John Day Stage.* — This peculiar name is taken from the John Day River of eastern Oregon, a tributary of the Columbia, which cuts across the beds of this stage. The formation is overlain by the immense flows of the Columbia River lava fields, which cover more than 200,000 square miles of the northwestern states. Consequently the John Day beds are exposed only where the streams have cut cañons down through the thick lava flows, and so the area of the beds is entirely conjectural. As yet, they have not been found outside of Oregon. The John Day is very much thicker than the White River, 2000 feet, or more, and is composed entirely of volcanic débris, which was showered down upon dry land, for no fresh-water shells, or aquatic mammals, or reptiles have ever been found.

This stage has been divided into three substages, which have received no names other than lower, middle and upper, but the distinction is none the less important. The lower subdivision is barren and no fossils have been found in it; the middle substage is richly fossiliferous and contains the typical John Day fauna, while the upper division is probably referable to the Miocene rather than to the Oligocene. The John Day fauna is so peculiar and isolated that much difficulty is felt in attempting to fit it into its proper place in the geological scale. No doubt, there were peculiarities of the environment which are not now determinable; geographical isolation is not at all likely.

Sespé Series. — The Sespé is a succession of continental deposits of great thickness (more than 7000 feet) in southern California, where the continental beds lie unconformably upon marine Eocene and are unconformably overlain by marine Miocene; they probably represent the upper Eocene and the whole Oligocene. The lowest part of the Sespé has as yet yielded no fossils, but some 1500 feet above the base a considerable fauna has been discovered and this is correlated with the Duchesne River of Utah. Near the top of the series a second and very different assemblage of mammals has been brought to light and this is evidently later than the White River, very probably corresponding in time to the barren lower division of the John Day.

Oligocene Climate. — Along the sea-coasts the genial conditions of the Eocene continued through the Oligocene, but in the western interior the continental deposits indicate a definite change to somewhat cooler conditions, palm trees and large crocodiles having disappeared from the northern interior. The difference from the Eocene cannot have been very great, for small alligators continued to live as far north as South Dakota, and the change was probably due to increased altitude, for the sea-coasts were not affected.

Continental Connections. — The land-bridge to Asia remained as during the Eocene, and the likeness of mammals between Mongolia and North America was close during the Oligocene. Asia and Europe must have been reunited, for a large European element appears in the White River fauna, which is evidently immigrant, and the north Atlantic land-bridge, if it ever existed, had been broken down.

4. Miocene Epoch

Marine deposits of this epoch form a narrow belt in the coastal plain of the Atlantic and Gulf region and along the Pacific. The

FIG. 68. — Exposure of Gering formation, Bear-in-the-Lodge Creek, Neb., lower Miocene. (Photograph by Amer. Mus. Nat. Hist.)

Pacific Coast Miocene forms exposures which, though narrow, are of great thickness, from 5000 to 7000 feet and are largely made of the ash which the very active volcanoes showered into the sea.

The continental Miocene is chiefly exposed on the Great Plains, especially in Nebraska, where the entire series appears to be represented and is there called the Arickaree. There are, however, still great difficulties in determining the Oligocene-Miocene boundary and in fitting the aberrant John Day fauna into its place. A thin mantle of Miocene extends, with interruptions, from Nebraska far into Mexico. Indeed, with few exceptions, the Miocene formations are all thin, but slightly or not at all indurated, and of indefinite area, because no survey has as yet mapped the boundaries of the stages and substages, which can be distinguished only by their fossils. No large areas of Miocene badlands are known. Miocene deposits are mostly the work of rivers and the wind, but the "Santa Fé Marl," a thick deposit in New Mexico, is presumably of lacustrine origin.

a. *Gering Stage.* — This formation is exposed to view in South Dakota and Nebraska, but small areas are found elsewhere, especially

FIG. 69. — Bone Hills at Agate Spring, Neb., from the west, Harrison stage, lower Miocene. (Photograph by Amer. Mus. Nat. Hist.)

in central Montana, where it has been called the Fort Logan, and in southeastern Wyoming. The Gering fauna has a large element in common with the John Day, but it is still a question whether the Gering should be considered a distinct stage, or should be included in the Harrison. Much further study is required before these divisions of the Miocene can be clearly demarcated.

b. *Harrison Stage.* — This is plainly divisible into two substages, the upper and lower, between which there is a notable faunal change. The Harrison forms an east and west belt, following Pine Ridge through central Nebraska, and in some localities, as at Agate, mammal bones are found in incredible profusion. In South Dakota the Gering and Harrison lie upon the uppermost beds of the White River

Oligocene, but there, as elsewhere, the difficulty is to find a place for the John Day in the time-scale.

c. Deep River Stage. — The typical locality for this middle Miocene stage is in central Montana, in the valley of the stream variously called Deep Creek and Smith River, where very small exposures, only a few acres in extent, have yielded a considerable fauna. Other small areas, of approximately equivalent date, are scattered over the Great Plains, as at Pawnee Creek, northeastern Colorado, and Snake Creek, Nebraska. In northwestern Colorado, the *Brown's Park* beds, which are scantily fossiliferous, assuredly are referable to the Miocene and apparently to the middle part of that stage. The *Virgin Valley,* of Nevada, is placed here in the scale. Another area is the *Mascall,* of eastern Oregon, where the beds were deposited on the basalt of the Columbia River lava-flows, which cover the John Day. At one point, the whole sequence of beds, the John Day, the basalts and the Mascall, have been folded into a great arch upon the truncated summit of which lie the horizontal, undisturbed strata of the Pliocene. No folding has been observed in the Great Plains area.

d. Valentine Stage. — This name replaces the long-used and familiar "Loup Fork," which has been employed in so many different senses as to have lost all meaning. The Valentine, which, for more than half a century, was always classed as Miocene, has recently, by some excellent authorities, been referred to the Pliocene, but to the present writer (perhaps unduly conservative) the older arrangement seems preferable.

The Valentine, in thin and but slightly indurated beds, covers a vast area of the Great Plains. The material, chiefly fine sands and marls, was accumulated by the action of streams and the wind, except that the Santa Fé Marl of New Mexico, a thick mass, is presumably a lacustrine deposit. This marl is principally very late Miocene, but the uppermost part is Pliocene.

A very different phase of the Miocene is the *Florissant,* of South Park, Colorado, a body of finely laminated shales, made by the showering of volcanic ash and dust into a small lake. Except for their pale brown colour, these are very similar to the buff Green River Shales, of the Eocene, and like them they have preserved great numbers of beautiful impressions of plants and insects, and also a few fishes and birds, but hardly any mammals.

Miocene Climates underwent a notable change in the course of the epoch. In the earlier Miocene the conditions were generally mild and genial, much the same as they had been in the Oligocene. The Florissant vegetation, though without palms, resembles that of the Gulf States at present, and the small alligators of the middle Miocene show that in Nebraska the winters cannot have been severe. On the Atlantic Coast, the marine fauna of the upper Miocene indicates much colder water than that of the lower. In central Europe the climate of the older Miocene appears to have been warmer than in North America, but gradually became cooler and by the close of the epoch palms had disappeared and had been replaced by coniferous forests.

Land Connections. — The Miocene of Mongolia shows so great a diminution of American elements, as to indicate a breaking of the connection between the two continents, and this inference is in harmony with the character of the American lower Miocene faunas, which have very little in common with Europe. In the middle part of the epoch, however, the connection must have been restored, for renewed immigration from the Old World began. The most conspicuous of these migrants from the eastern hemisphere were the earliest of the American representatives of the Proboscidea, or elephant tribe, but there were many others. A possible brief connection with South America is indicated by bones of a †ground-sloth in the Miocene of Nebraska, a very puzzling circumstance.

5. Pliocene Epoch

It is only of very late years that most of the Pliocene formations have been identified and, as yet, they have not been surveyed or mapped. Little can be said, therefore, as to the areal extent and thickness of these subdivisions. They have, however, supplied many most interesting and instructive fossils.

Except in the northeastern part of the continent, the Atlantic coast was shifted to the eastward of its present position. Greenland would seem to have been connected with the Arctic Archipelago and Newfoundland with Labrador, while, from Nova Scotia to southern Virginia, the land extended far beyond its present limits. On the other hand, the sea encroached upon the coast of the Carolinas and Georgia, southern Florida and the north shore of the Gulf of Mexico from Florida to northeastern Texas. Narrow belts of marine deposits mark the limits of this encroachment.

On the Pacific side, the Pliocene is far more extensively developed; some of the thickest Pliocene deposits known in the world are there displayed. Over the Great Plains, from western Texas to Nebraska, the continental Pliocene stages are thinly scattered, and additional Pliocene areas have been found in Florida, New Mexico, Arizona, the Mohave Desert of southeastern California, Nevada, Idaho and Oregon. The Mohave Desert section is the thickest known body of continental Pliocene, the strata of which are steeply tilted, exposing their truncated edges, and making possible a measurement of their thickness without drilling bore-holes through them.

a. Lower Pliocene. — In the preceding epochs there has been a standard succession of strata which could be followed, but, in dealing with the Pliocene, it is necessary to make use of a different procedure, for the stages are so widely scattered and no one section suffices. The immensely thick Pliocene of the Mohave Desert may, some day, furnish the standard section desired, but at present only the basal member, the *Ricardo*, has been identified and named. In the "Panhandle" of Texas is the *Clarendon*, a sandy accumulation, and northeast of this is the *Hemphill*, in the county of that name, which followed the Clarendon in time. In the northern Great Plains, the oldest Pliocene, according to the scale adopted here, is the *Republican River*, of Kansas, which is very fossiliferous, and that is followed by the Upper *Snake Creek* of western Nebraska. In this part of the state, along the Niobrara River, is a great accumulation of Miocene-Pliocene beds, not yet clearly subdivided, the *Devil's Gulch*, which has yielded such a wonderful series of primitive elephants. The *Rattlesnake*, of Oregon, rests on the folded and truncated strata of the middle Miocene Mascall. In Florida, the *Alachua Clays* have been the source of valuable lower Pliocene mammals.

b. Middle Pliocene. — Much the most important middle Pliocene stage is the *Blanco*, again of the Texas Panhandle, which has a fauna of exceptional interest, though, unfortunately, the list of fossils is a very short one. An equivalent formation is the lower part of the *San Pedro* of Arizona.

c. Upper Pliocene. — Very important and abundantly fossiliferous beds of upper Pliocene age form the *Hagerman*, of Idaho, and the upper portion of the San Pedro of Arizona is about the equivalent of this. It will be observed how much more widespread and manifold are the lower Pliocene deposits than those of the middle and upper portions of the series. Indeed, the San Pedro and the Hagerman were discovered but a few years ago. The subjoined table will help to make clear the relations of the principal Pliocene formations.

	IDAHO AND OREGON	W. NEBRASKA	N. KANSAS	TEXAS	FLORIDA
Upper	Hagerman	Devil's Gulch			
Middle				Blanco	
Lower				Hemphill	
	Rattlesnake	Snake Creek	Republican River	Clarendon	Alachua

II. QUATERNARY PERIOD

This period is remarkable for its extraordinary and, as yet, inexplicable climatic vicissitudes. The refrigeration which had gone on progressively through the Pliocene culminated in the glacial conditions of the Quaternary.

1. Pleistocene Epoch

Four Glacial and three Interglacial stages are comprised in the Pleistocene, and the Glacial stages were those in which vast fields of moving ice covered 3,000,000 square miles in North America and 700,000 square miles in Europe. In the Interglacial stages the climate was so greatly ameliorated as to be warmer than it is at present. These violent climatic changes had a profound and far-reaching effect upon mammalian life, leading to great migrations and, eventually, to the greatest and most widespread extinctions in all the history of the class. The causes of the extinctions are not known and climatic changes may have had nothing to do with them.

Whatever the factors in producing it may have been, the refrigeration was world-wide in its effects and consisted essentially in a lowering of the annual average temperature by about 9° F. and a depression of the snow-line by about 1000 metres.

At the times of greatest cold the rain-belt was shifted to the southward of its present limits and great fresh-water lakes were formed in what are now arid regions. The best-known of these are Lake Bonneville in the eastern, and Lake Lahontan in the western side of the Great Basin; Great Salt Lake is the much shrunken remnant of Bonneville. Other and smaller Pleistocene lakes in the arid region have preserved very valuable records of the birds and mammals of the time.

As described in the chapter on fossilization, Pleistocene mammals are found either entirely outside of the glaciated areas, or in the deposits of the Interglacial stages. In the nature of things, one could not expect to find such fossils in the glacial drifts. The European Pleistocene has been carefully subdivided and the succession of its faunas made out, but that has not been feasible in this country and the Pleistocene fauna must be dealt with as a unit.

Aside from caves and fissures, in which the Pleistocene fossils obtained are of the latter part of that epoch, the principal source of such fossils have been deposits, which are believed to have been laid down in the last Interglacial stage. One of these, the *Sheridan*, is a layer of compact, wind-accumulated dust, which covers the Great Plains like a mantle, hill and valley alike. In many parts of the Sheridan are "pockets," which are packed with bones, principally those of horses, whence the formation has been called the "*Equus* Beds." The other is the tar and asphalt deposits of southern California, from which so wonderful an assemblage of mammals has been taken.

2. Recent Epoch

Some geologists speak of a post-Glacial division of the Pleistocene, but the general usage is to consider the Recent as beginning with the final disappearance of the ice, except from Greenland and some Arctic islands and the high mountains. In regions to which the glaciation did not extend the distinction between Pleistocene and Recent is very vague and the line of demarcation must be arbitrarily drawn. In the northeastern part of the continent the Recent was inaugurated by a subsidence of the land, which converted the St. Lawrence into an arm of the sea, marine waters filling the valleys of the Ottawa and Richelieu Rivers and Lake Champlain, and extending almost to Lake Ontario. The rise from that subsidence to the present altitude of the continent marks the beginning of modern conditions, i.e. in the geological, not the historical meaning of the term.

CHAPTER VII

CENOZOIC FORMATIONS OF SOUTH AMERICA

South American Cenozoic formations, both marine and continental, are, in the abundance and fine preservation of their fossil mammals, worthy rivals of those of the northern continent, and they have preserved a similar record of evolutionary development and of geographical and climatic changes. The important mammal-bearing deposits so far made known are almost all in Argentina, especially in the southern provinces, comprised in what was formerly called Patagonia. The late Dr. Ameghino and his brother Carlos, whose services to palæontology are quite inestimable, discovered most of these formations and arranged them in chronological order, naming them in accordance with some characteristic fossil. The geographical names here used were mostly given by the late M. Gaudry, Director of the Paris Museum, and by Dr. G. G. Simpson of the American Museum of Natural History. With few exceptions the Cenozoic formations have not been mapped, but their succession in time has been definitely ascertained and may be regarded as settled.

I. Tertiary Period

No Paleocene deposits, marine or continental, have been found in any part of South America, and, as was pointed out above, the same is perhaps true of North America so far as marine formations are concerned. This probably means that both continents were standing at greater altitudes than at present and that they were then connected by land.

The table on page 115 gives the Tertiary divisions of South America, the terms in parentheses are those given by Ameghino.

1. Eocene Epoch

Most of the South American Tertiary formations are, at present, little more than names, but the order of their succession in time is known and much of their fossil content has been recovered. The series may be grouped into two portions, the pre- and post-Patagonian, for that is the only one of the Eocene, Oligocene and Miocene stages which may be directly compared with a formation in the northern hemisphere, and thus gives a fixed point of departure.

Tertiary	Pliocene	Tarija stage Cape Fairweather Araucanian Entre Rios Chasicó Mayo	{ Monte Hermoso { Catamarca
	Miocene	Friassian Santa Cruz Patagonian Colhué-huapi (†Colpodon Beds)	
	Oligocene	Deseado (†Pyrotherium Beds) Musters (†Astraponotus Beds)	
	Eocene	Casa Mayor (†Notostylops Beds) Rio Chico { Upper Lower	

The supposedly Eocene stages, the Casa Mayor and the Rio Chico, of still undetermined extent, occur in northern Patagonia, in the province of Chubut. The Casa Mayor (the †*Notostylops* Beds of Ameghino) has been the source of an extremely rich and varied fauna, only a small part of which has been described, but enough is already known of it to say that it is of the highest evolutionary interest and importance. The Rio Chico beds underlie those of the Casa Mayor and consist of sandstones and clays of a very different appearance from the tuffs of the Casa Mayor. They have a fauna which is allied to the latter yet distinct from it. Both of these stages, especially the latter, have in them quantities of stratified volcanic ash and dust, deposited by the wind.

2. Oligocene Epoch

The *Musters* and *Deseado* stages are here conjecturally assigned to the Oligocene, though they may be more properly referable to the older Miocene, but, as they contain no mammals in common with the northern hemisphere, direct correlation with the North American Tertiaries cannot be made, and only the most general comparison is as yet feasible. The Musters (the †*Astraponotus* Beds of Ameghino) has been found in the vicinity of the lake of that name, but very little concerning its extent or geological character has been published. The Deseado (†*Pyrotherium* Beds of Ameghino) named from the Rio Deseado, has been much more thoroughly explored. The beds are in scattered patches, which are in the depressions of the deeply eroded and worn surface of the underlying, older formations, some of them Cretaceous. A large and interesting fauna has been obtained from this stage.

3. Miocene Epoch

The Deseado was followed by the *Patagonian*, a succession of marine strata, which demonstrate the submergence of all southern Patagonia and Tierra del Fuego, from the Andes to the east coast, beneath the waters of the Atlantic. The beds are chiefly sandstones and are crowded with fossils, most of them the shells of marine molluscs, but, most fortunately, there are also many well-preserved remains of dolphins, porpoises and whales (Cetacea). These Cetacean fossils, which include fine skulls, permit a direct comparison with the northern hemisphere, for they are very similar to the Miocene Cetacea of North America and Europe. The invertebrate fauna of the Patagonian stage is almost identical with that of certain Tertiary formations in Australia and New Zealand. A similar, but more nearly subtropical, marine fauna is that of Navidad on the coast of Chile, considerably farther north than the Patagonian exposures.

The *Colhué-huapi* (Ameghino's †*Colpodon* Beds) appears to be contemporary with the lower part of the Patagonian, being the continental phase laid down along a coast-line which shifted back and forth, so that marine and continental beds interdigitate.

The *Santa Cruz* stage rests upon the surface of the Patagonian and demonstrates the elevation into land of the whole southern part of the continent, but with initial oscillations, for, according to Hatcher, the lower part of the Santa Cruz is contemporary with the uppermost Patagonian. The Santa Cruz covers a much greater area than any of the other Tertiary formations, extending for hundreds of miles northward from the Straits of Magellan and, at the time of the deposition of these beds, the southern end of the continent must have been broader than at present, for the formation extends out on the bed of the Atlantic to an unknown distance. The tide on that coast has a phenomenal range, and at low water a broad belt of fossiliferous Santa Cruz is laid bare. The beds are very largely made up of volcanic ash and tuffs and there are river-made deposits, with cross-bedded sandstones in the channels, but nothing indicates the presence of lakes, or ponds, for no fossils of fresh-water shells, fishes or aquatic mammals have been found.

The Santa Cruz fauna is very rich in individuals as well as in genera and species, and is more fully known than that of any other stage of the South American Tertiary. The first Tertiary mammals collected in South America were found by Charles Darwin in 1833 along the Rio Santa Cruz, the river which has given its name to the stage. Volcanic activity on a great scale characterized Santa Cruz times, as is shown, not only by the immense extent of the ash-beds, but also by the interbedded lava-flows and by the very much worn and degraded volcanic cones.

The *Friassian* stage has been little explored and is very incompletely known.

4. Pliocene Epoch

With the exception of the Friassian, the deposition of the mammal-bearing formations of southernmost South America came to an end

FIG. 70. — Strata of Catamarca substage, Pliocene, Santa Minaria, Argentina. (Photograph by Field Mus. Nat. Hist.)

with the Santa Cruz. The Pliocene stages are found very much farther north, and in widely separated regions. At no point, yet discovered, are the Pliocene stages, or any two of them, found in superposition and hence their order of succession is somewhat uncertain, especially as the fossils of most of them are very incompletely known.

The oldest Pliocene is believed to be the Mayo, called from the river of that name near Laguna Blanca. The fauna, as reported, is intermediate between the Friassian and the Entrerian. Next follows the Chasicó, named from the Arroyo Chasicó in the southern part of the Argentinian province of Buenos Aires, the fauna of which is in part equivalent to that of the basal Entrerian, in part transitional from the Mayo. The Entre Rios, a succession of alternating marine and fresh-water beds, occurring in the province of Entre Rios, which is between the Paraná and Uruguay Rivers, is placed next above the Chasicó, as indicated by its mammals. A systematic exploration of this region would, almost certainly, have important results.

Much the most extensive and best-known of the Pliocene faunas is that of the *Catamarca* substage, named from the Province of Catamarca in the foothills of the Andes in northwestern Argentina. The Pliocene strata were here involved in the uplift and folding of the Cordillera, and in consequence are harder and more firmly consolidated than those of any other continental Tertiary stages in South America. The re-established connection with North America is shown by the arrival of a raccoon-like animal, the most ancient example of the true Carnivora yet found in the southern continent and a forerunner of the successive waves of migration, which were to continue during the later Tertiary and Quaternary periods.

At some time in the Pliocene, Patagonia was again more or less completely submerged by the sea and marine sandstones, crowded with fossil shells, were laid down upon the worn and eroded surface of the Santa Cruz beds. This is the *Cape Fairweather* stage, named from the point on the Atlantic Coast where the marine Pliocene was first discovered by Hatcher. This typical locality no longer exists, as the sea has destroyed and carried away the cliff in which the Cape Fairweather beds were exposed. Fortunately, Mr. Hatcher found the same formation again in the Andes where it occurs at an elevation of 5000 feet above the sea, proving that since the Pliocene the southern Cordillera, at least, has been raised by that amount. If, as seems altogether probable, the whole of Patagonia was covered by the Pliocene sea, the beds then deposited on the plains have been swept away by erosion, and no traces of them have been found at the lower levels.

The exact position of the Cape Fairweather beds in the Pliocene column is uncertain, but it is reasonable to suppose that the same depression of the land which brought the sea in over Patagonia, also inundated the La Plata estuary. Until a careful comparison between the marine shells of Patagonia and those of the province of Entre Rios shall have been made, it will be impracticable to assign the Cape Fairweather to its proper position in the Pliocene.

The beds of the *Monte Hermoso* substage occupy a small area of the Atlantic coast of Argentina, near Bahia Blanca, and would seem to be of later date than any or all of the Pliocene stages above mentioned; they are overlain by the Pampean deposits of the Pleistocene and contain more mammals of North American type than does the Catamarca formation. The Monte Hermoso is clearly referable to the late Pliocene.

The uppermost Pliocene of South America is the *Tarija* stage, named from a valley in Bolivia. Little has been published concerning the character and extent of these beds, but they have been made famous by the number of beautifully preserved †mastodont skulls which have been found there. Though related to the †*Mastodon americanus* of the northern continent, they are referable to another genus and species, †*Cordillerion andium*, which are characteristic of the plateaus and mountains of western South America.

II. Quaternary Period

In the southern hemisphere the proportion of sea is so much greater, and of land is so much less, that climates are less extreme than in the northern hemisphere, and the climatic changes of the Quaternary were less violent, owing to the moderating effects of the sea.

Pleistocene Epoch

Glaciation in South America was far less extensive than in the northern hemisphere. The Andean glaciers were much longer than at present, and in Patagonia they extended out over the eastern plain, but it remains to be determined whether there was more than one Glacial stage; that the world-wide lowering of temperature affected South America is certain, but little study has yet been given to its results.

The Pampas of Argentina are covered with a mantle of consolidated *loess*, a mass of wind-accumulated dust, harder and more compact than the Sheridan of the northern continent, but otherwise much like that formation. This is the Pampean stage, which seemingly is entirely Pleistocene in date, though the older portion of it may be Pliocene. The Pampean is one of the most remarkable and prolific museums of extinct mammalian life in all the world. It was these fossils which first awakened in Charles Darwin's mind a belief in the possibility of evolution, a problem to which he devoted the remainder of his life. Even in the XVIII Century the great bones had attracted the attention of travellers and in 1799 the skeleton of a gigantic †ground-sloth was sent to Spain and mounted in the museum at Madrid. Cuvier described it and named it †*Megatherium americanum.*

The line between Pleistocene and Recent is very difficult to draw in South America, because of the restriction of the Glacial drifts to the Cordillera and the far south; and therefore there are no fossiliferous deposits which can be definitely called Recent, except in certain caves. The Pleistocene is supposed to end with the Pampean.

Tertiary Climates of South America. — Throughout the entire period the climate was apparently genial, though not uniformly so, that of the Eocene seeming to be cooler than that of the Miocene. The marine faunas of the Patagonian formation, as far south as Tierra del Fuego clearly indicate higher temperatures and warmer waters than prevail in such high latitudes to-day. At Navidad, much farther north on the coast of Chile, the climate might almost be called subtropical, at all events, warm-temperate. In Santa Cruz times, which followed the post-Patagonian upheaval, the climate was warm and apparently arid, for no fossil wood occurs in the strata, and had trees been growing there in any quantity, it is difficult to understand why no fragments of trees or branches should have been buried in the showers of volcanic ash and dust which entombed so many animals. North of the Santa Cruz area, in the provinces of Chubut and Rio Negro, leaf-bearing beds have been found, and there conditions may have been less arid.

In the upper Miocene and Pliocene there is no direct evidence of the gradual refrigeration which was so distinctly marked in the northern hemisphere, though such refrigeration there must have been, for the Pleistocene glaciation did take place, though on a much smaller scale than in the northern hemisphere.

Tertiary Land Connections of South America. — These present a very complicated and difficult problem, concerning which there is great difference of opinion among the naturalists who have dealt with the evidence. Limitations of space prevent any discussion of that evidence here; only the author's own conclusions can be given; but, in fairness, it must be added that some of those conclusions are rejected by eminent authorities.

During the Cretaceous period, at least in the upper Cretaceous, North and South America were connected by land, for the marine fossils show a complete separation of Atlantic and Pacific waters, and, very probably, the connection persisted into the Paleocene, but the absence of deposits of this epoch from South America makes impossible any positive statement on this head. The land-bridge must have been broken down very early in the Eocene, at the latest, and the separation must have lasted through the Miocene, except, perhaps, for a transitory renewal of the connection in the middle Miocene. At all events, the typically South American edentate group of the †Gravigrada, or †ground-sloths, was represented in the lower Snake Creek beds of Nebraska. That is a very puzzling circumstance, which seems to be in conflict with all other evidence at present known. Several possible explanations suggest themselves, but a discussion of them here would be unprofitable. In early Pliocene times the junction of the two continents was re-established and has continued to the present day.

The problem of the West Indian islands is very obscure and no solution that is in all respects satisfactory has yet been suggested. It is probable that all of the Greater Antilles were connected with one another and with Central America in the Pliocene, but, if so, the extreme paucity of mammals in the islands at present is very difficult of explanation.

So far, there is little difference of opinion, for the evidence in support of these conclusions is very strong, but there is no such unanimity regarding the connections of South America with Australia and Africa which are here postulated. There is much reason to believe that the Australian land-bridge was not across the Pacific, but by way of the Antarctic continent, which must have been connected with both Australia and South America in the Miocene epoch, at least. The marine fauna preserved in the Patagonian stage is made up of shoal-water animals, such as were wholly incapable of crossing the deep Pacific and their presence in the Miocene of Australia and New Zealand necessitates a continuous coast-line which, as suggested by the conformation of the sea-floor, was most probably by way of Antarctica. The much warmer climate of the Miocene made the polar continent practicable as a path of mammalian migration, but a very difficult path, for very few creatures were able to use it.

Connection with Africa appears to have been directly across the Atlantic and in tropical latitudes, where that ocean is narrowest. That Africa and South America were parts of the same great land-mass in the Permian period is hardly open to doubt, but the question is: how long did that connection continue? There is much reason to think that in the Cretaceous and early Tertiary periods there was a possibility of communication for land animals and plants between the two continents, but the way of intermigration cannot have been freely open, for so limited a number of land and fresh-water animals were able to take advantage of it.

CHAPTER VIII

GEOGRAPHICAL DISTRIBUTION OF MAMMALS

Zoölogical and botanical geography had been well studied in the pre-Darwinian period, when it was believed that each species of animal and plant had been separately created and placed in the region to which it was exactly fitted. No explanation of the geographical distribution of organisms was either possible or required; it was an ultimate fact, and the study of distribution could be little more than statistical. Yet the data gathered were full of surprises and anomalies, which seemed to be entirely capricious. At first sight, the factor determining distribution seemed to be climate and there can be no doubt that climate is extremely important in this connection, but, evidently, it is far from being the only determining factor. The tropical zones of Australia, Africa and South America have a very similar climate, yet their animals differ most profoundly and radically. The islands of Cuba and Java differ hardly at all climatically, yet their animals are utterly different; they have nothing in common.

The zoölogical and botanical difference between any two regions is not measured by the distance between them; western Europe and eastern Asia are very much alike in these respects and the forests of eastern Asia have much more in common with those of the Atlantic coast of North America than with those of the Pacific coast of the same continent. On the other hand, the narrow strait between the islands Bali and Lombok of the Malay Archipelago, separates two regions of radically different faunas. Under the old conception the geographical arrangement of animals admitted no formulations of general laws.

The acceptance of the theory of Evolution which followed so swiftly upon the publication of Darwin's *Origin of Species* in 1859, demanded an explanation of the facts of animal and plant distribution and failure to find such explanation would be fatal to the theory. Indeed, it was, after the fossil mammals, the data of animal distribution in South America, and, especially, in the Galápagos Islands, that first led Darwin to his great generalization. While much remains to be learned and while many problems still await solution, the evolutionary theory has afforded a satisfactory explanation of the main facts and this explanation, in turn, affords a very strong support to the theory.

A test of Evolution was given in the many instances of "discontinuous distribution," when two areas, inhabited by nearly allied animals, were yet separated by immense distances. A remarkable example of this is afforded by the present distribution of the tapirs. The species of one genus, *Tapirus*, inhabit the Malay Peninsula and the island of Borneo, on the one hand, Central and tropical South America, on the other. The theory of Special Creation offered no explanation of such facts, and, in terms of the theory of Evolution, such discontinuous distribution was to be explained in one of two ways: Either (1) the American and the Asiatic species were developed independently of one another and derived from a different ancestry, or (2) the regions between these widely separated areas once formed a continuous land, inhabited by tapirs throughout. The first alternative of separate derivation may be set aside as altogether improbable and incompatible with all that we have learned as to the manner in which evolutionary development actually has taken place.

Even if we had no knowledge concerning the geological history of the tapirs, the second alternative would be chosen as incomparably more likely. In fact, it is positively known that the tapirs once ranged all across the northern hemisphere, Europe, Asia and North America, whence they migrated into South America, when the junction of the two continents made such migration possible. Finally, they became extinct, at a very late geological date, in all the regions intervening between the areas now inhabited by tapirs.

The two divisions of the camel family, or Camelidæ, present exactly the same problem. One genus, the true camels (*Camelus*) is a native of Asia, the other *Lama*, which comprises the llamas, guanacos, and vicuñas, is native to South America. The geological record shows that the family originated in North America, to which it was confined for ages, and eventually one group migrated to Asia, the other to South America, while both became extinct in North America, though not before historic times, as the term is understood in Europe. Such is the invariable explanation of discontinuous distribution whenever the palæontological record is known.

We have next to consider the nature of the obstacles, or barriers, that prevent the indefinite spread of mammals, and inquire why the continuous land area of the Americas, which extends through more than 125° of latitude, does not everywhere have the same mammals. We have every reason to believe that each group of mammals originated in one area and spread from that as far as circumstances permitted. What is the nature of those circumstances?

The rate of multiplication of animals is so rapid that, under normal conditions, every species is pressing upon the means of subsistence and, if increasing in numbers, must constantly extend its range in search of food. Were there no restraining checks, every species would increase indefinitely in numbers. Were all the young to survive and breed, "even large and slow-breeding mammals, which only have one at a birth, but continue to breed from eight to ten successive years, may increase from a single pair to 10,000,000 in forty years" (Wallace). A species is thus forced to spread from its place of origin, unless stopped by some impassable barrier. The most effective barrier is the sea, a few miles of which will stop the spread of any land mammal. There are some species that swim across straits, as the Guanaco has been seen to cross the Straits of Magellan, but even these bold swimmers have their well-defined limits. A broad, or deep and swift river forms the boundary of many species, as does the Amazon and, in southern Patagonia, the Santa Cruz River limits the southward spread of armadillos.

Important geographical changes, such as the junction of separated lands, or the severance of continuous land-areas by incursions of the sea, have a profound effect upon the distribution of land animals. Lands which have been disjoined, however closely similar their faunas may have been at the time of separation, will, by divergent development, grow more and more unlike in proportion to the length of time that the separation continues. Areas which were separated but a short time ago, geologically speaking, now have nearly identical animals, as is true of Great Britain, which was severed from the European continent in late Pleistocene times. An earlier separation of the great islands of the Malay Archipelago has resulted in a greater, though still slight difference from the mainland, while the long-continued isolation of Australia has made it the most peculiar region of the earth, zoölogically speaking.

The junction of separated regions results in an intermigration from each one into the other, and the completeness of the mingling of the two faunas will depend upon the ease with which the new land-bridge may be crossed. A much larger proportion of species will migrate along lines of latitude, than on the meridians of longitude, because in following latitude no very different climates are encountered, such as are met with along meridians. The Americas have formed a continuous body of land since the early Pliocene and, though a considerable number of northern mammals have established themselves in South America, yet the faunas of the two continents differ very radically. Northern Asia, on the contrary, which was separated from North America, after a long-continued connection, had throughout the Tertiary and still retains a much greater zoölogical similarity to North America.

Climate, especially temperature, is almost as effective a barrier as arms of the sea, though, of course, climate alone does not produce similarity of faunas, as is strikingly shown by the example of tropical South America, Africa and Australia, as mentioned above, but, *within continuous land-areas*, temperature is the most insurmountable barrier to the spread of mammals. "Humidity and other secondary causes determine the presence or absence of particular species in particular localities within their appropriate zones, but temperature pre-determines the possibilities of distribution; it fixes the limits beyond which the species cannot pass" (C. Hart Merriam).

The absence of any animal from a particular land-area is no proof that the climate is unsuitable to that animal. This is shown by the manner in which animals introduced into a country new to them, often run wild and multiply enormously, as rabbits have done in Australia, the mongoose in Jamaica, horses on our western plains and on the Pampas of Argentina, pigs and goats on many temperate and tropical islands.

Topographical features, such as mountain ranges and high plateaus are often important barriers, but this is due rather to the temperature changes caused by altitude than to difficulty in crossing the heights themselves. For this reason ranges of mountains and table-lands extended along meridians of longitude carry a cold temperate, or polar fauna far equatorward of its range in the lowlands. The mountain ranges of North America illustrate this very perfectly because of their great north-south extension. The immense Mexican plateau is zoölogically a part of North America, while the low-lying, tropical coastal lands (*tierras calientes*), as far as southeastern Texas, have Central American affinities. Likewise in South America, the animals of the cold Patagonian plains extend northward along the high Andes into the Tropics.

A different sort of barrier to the spread of a species into a new region is the pre-occupation of that region by one or more other species. The pre-occupants may play so similar a part in the economy of nature as to give the newcomer no opportunity to establish itself. That is a typical case of the struggle for existence, which ends in the "elimination of the unfit." On the other hand, the pre-occupant may be an active enemy, totally different in kind from the invader, as in the case of the Tse-tse Flies (*Glossina*) of Africa. The bite of these flies is fatal to domestic animals, which cannot enter the fly-infested areas, and is often fatal to men. Uganda was almost depopulated of natives because of the "sleeping sickness," which is caused by the bite of *Glossina palpalis*.

Many times in the course of the Tertiary period mammals entered North America either from the southern continent or from Asia, but died out without gaining a lasting foothold here. At this great distance of time it is never possible to determine why a species that succeeded in reaching a new region was unable to maintain itself there. The same phenomenon was repeated in South America and other continents, for it is not at all exceptional. The most probable explanation is that the creatures already in possession of the land were an effective obstacle to the intruders.

The rate of spreading of a species into new areas may be fast or slow, as conditions are favourable or otherwise. Newly introduced insect-pests, such as the Gypsy and Brown-tailed Moths in New England, the Japanese Beetle in New Jersey, the San José Scale in California, often spread with portentous rapidity. This is because the enemies and parasites which kept them in check in their original homes are absent from North America. In some instances it has been possible to import and acclimatize some of these enemies and thus hold down the intruders. Introduced mammals, though multiplying very much more slowly than insects, have often taken possession of great areas at a surprising rate. The few rabbits imported into Australia soon became a menacing plague, because climate and vegetation were favourable and natural enemies were lacking. Darwin tells that horses ran wild at Buenos Aires in 1537, and their descendants were observed at the Straits of Magellan, more than 1500 miles away, in 1580.

Land areas which have recently been raised from beneath the sea must first be taken possession of and covered by vegetation before they are traversed by mammals and such an extension by plants may be a relatively slow process, for many plants will not grow upon a new land until the marine salts have been leached out of the soil. It may be the absence of certain food plants from the newly vegetated land which prevents the crossing by some animals, while others pass freely. In the course of the Tertiary period a great variety of mammals spread from Asia to America, or from America to Asia, but always there were certain groups, often whole families, which failed to cross from one continent to the other. For example, no member of the civets, hyenas, hippopotamuses, true swine, giraffes or oxen (as distinguished from bisons) has ever been found in the Western Hemisphere. Likewise, there are several American families, most of them now extinct, which never reached the Old World.

The existing distribution of mammals is conveniently represented by maps on which are marked the areas, of more or less comprehensiveness, which have similar mammals. The facts of geography require divisions of different orders of importance. Thus, in descending order, the terms *realm, region, subregion, province,* etc., are useful means of expressing the facts. It is usual, first of all, to divide the land surfaces of the earth into three realms, *Notogæa, Neogæa* and *Arctogæa.* Notogæa includes but a single region, the *Australian,* which comprises Australia, Tasmania, New Zealand, New Guinea and adjoining islands, westward to Lombok. The realm and region are characterized by having the only Monotremata now in existence and by a mammalian fauna which, otherwise, is almost exclusively marsupial.

Next to Australia, by far the most peculiar part of the earth is South and Central America, which constitute a realm, *Neogæa,* likewise a single region, the *Neotropical,* to which the West Indies also belong. Arctogæa is far more comprehensive than the other realms, including Africa, Europe, Asia and the greater part of North America. This vast area, which is subdivided into no less than five regions, has a great variety of mammals, and yet, with a certain unmistakable likeness throughout. The three continents of the Old World form an immense, connected land-mass, and the final separation of North America from this great complex is an event of geologically late date.

For reasons that have been explained above, the junction of the two Americas has had comparatively little effect upon the zoölogy of the northern continent except in its tropical portion. The great divisions of zoölogical geography are of very unequal size, for they are determined by the degrees of difference in the mammalian faunas. The degrees of difference are, in turn, a measure of the length of time that lands have been separated, or in the case of connected regions, of the difficulty of communication between them.

The following table gives the major divisions of the earth in terms of mammalian geography.

I. REALM OF NOTOGÆA: *Australian Region.* — New Zealand, Australia, Tasmania, New Guinea and neighbouring islands.

II. REALM OF NEOGÆA: *Neotropical Region.* — South and Central America, lowlands of Mexico, West Indies.

III. REALM OF ARCTOGÆA.
  1. *Malagasy Region.* — Madagascar.
  2. *Ethiopian Region.* — Africa south of the Sahara Desert.
  3. *Oriental Region.* — Southern peninsulas of Asia, Malay Archipelago.
  4. *Holarctic Region.* — N. Africa, Europe, Asia (except southern part), boreal N. America.
  5. *Sonoran Region.* — Remainder of N. America (except lowlands of Mexico and southern Florida).

I. NORTH AMERICA

In this scheme North America, like Africa and Asia, is a composite of two or more regions; the northern half, including nearly all of Canada, belongs to the vast Holarctic Region, which encircles the earth. The Sonoran Region occupies the remainder of the continent, except for the Transition Zone, the lowlands of Mexico and the coast of southern Florida. In these broadly continuous land areas, which are not demarcated by great physical features, boundaries between divisions are not sharply drawn and between the Holarctic and the Sonoran regions lies the *Transition Zone*, where the two faunas intermingle.

Dr. Merriam's arrangement, which deals with North America only, divides the land into a series of transcontinental zones, which he names the Arctic, Boreal, Transition, Upper and Lower Sonoran and Tropical. The very irregular boundaries between zones *follow the lines of equal temperature during the breeding season, May, June and July;* the irregular boundaries are due to topographical irregularities which deflect the isothermal lines.

The Arctic zone is part of a circumpolar area, which is much the same in both Western and Eastern Hemispheres, and in each continent the fauna differs much more from the contiguous zone to the south than it does from the Arctic fauna of another continent. With some local differences, the characteristic Arctic mammals are the Polar

Bear, Arctic Fox, Musk-ox, Barren-ground Caribou, Lemming, Arctic Hare and Marmot. Most, if not all, of these forms are of Old World origin.

The North American portion of the great Holarctic region is variously called the Boreal zone (Merriam) and the Canadian sub-region (Wallace). No difference of principle is involved in this varying nomenclature, for, as Dr. Merriam writes: "It so happens

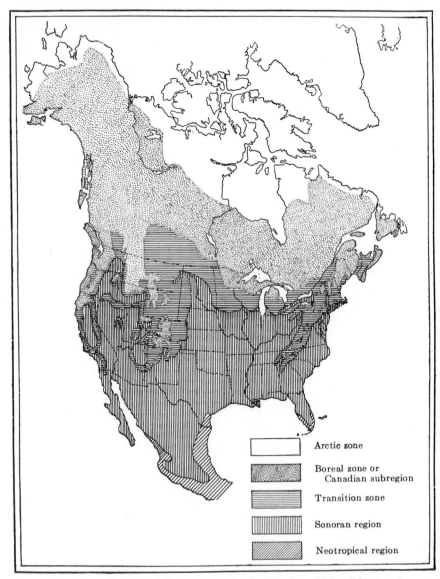

Arctic zone

Boreal zone or
    Canadian subregion

Transition zone

Sonoran region

Neotropical region

FIG. 71. — Zoölogical divisions of North America. (After Merriam.)

that the Boreal element in America resembles that of Eurasia so closely that in the judgment of many eminent authorities the two constitute a single primary region — a view in which I heartily concur." The Canadian, or Boreal subregion of the Holarctic is the great belt of coniferous forest which extends obliquely across the continent from Alaska to New England; its boundary with the Arctic zone is the northern limit of trees and, on the south, it is demar-

Fig. 72. — Polar Bear, *Thalarctus maritimus*. (By permission of N. Y. Zoöl. Soc.)

cated from the Transition zone by a sinuous line which approximately follows the parallel of 45° N. latitude, but extends far to the south along the Appalachian, Rocky and Sierra Nevada ranges of mountains.

On the Pacific Coast, where the Boreal zone reaches to San Francisco, there is a remarkable mingling of species, which, east of the mountains, are in separate zones. The mild and equable climate, with its small annual range of temperature, is suitable for both northern and southern mammals.

The mammals of the Canadian, or Boreal subregion are mostly of Old World origin, and migrated to America in Pliocene and Pleistocene times, but there are some native American elements and even one genus of South American derivation, the Short-tailed, or

Fig. 73. — Musk-ox, *Ovibos wardi.* Two males and female. (By permission of N. Y. Zoöl. Soc.)

Fig. 74. — Arctic Fox, *Vulpes lagopus,* in winter dress. (By permission of N. Y. Zoöl. Soc.)

FIG. 75. — Arctic Fox in summer dress. (By permission of
N. Y. Zoöl. Soc.)

Canada Porcupine (*Erethizon*). Especially characteristic of this subregion, or zone, are the Old World types of deer, none of which
range farther south than the Transition zone. The Wapiti, errone-

ously called Elk (*Cervus canadensis*) is very closely allied
to the European Red Deer, or
Stag (*C. elaphus*) and still
more closely to the Stag of
the Thian Shan Mountains in
Central Asia (*C. eustephanus*).
So great is the resemblance of
the three forms that some naturalists prefer to include them
all in a single species. The
American Moose, which should
be called Elk (*Alce americanus*)
is so near to the Scandinavian
Elk (*A. machlis*) that it is
hardly distinguishable as a separate species, and the Woodland Caribou (*Rangifer caribou*)
is the American representative
of the Lapland Reindeer (*R.
tarandus*).

FIG. 76. — Canada Porcupine, *Erethizon dorsatus*. (By permission of N. Y.
Zoöl. Soc.)

The mistakenly so-called Rocky Mountain Goat (*Oreamnos montanus*) is a peculiar and aberrant form of the chamois subfamily of the antelopes. Mountain Sheep (*Ovis montana, O. dalli,* etc.), are

FIG. 77. — Woodchuck or Marmot, *Marmota monax*. (By permission of N. Y. Zoöl. Soc.)

represented by three or four species, one of which extends into the Sonoran region, as does also the Bison, wrongly named Buffalo (*Bison bison*), which is nearly allied to the European Bison (*B. bonasus*). The latter, called *Wisent* in German, in Cæsar's time ranged through Germany and is described in his account of the Hercynian Forest, but the advance of civilization has almost exterminated it except perhaps in the Carpathians. There are, at present, three very similar kinds of "Buffalo" living in

FIG. 78. — Chipmunk, *Tamias striatus*. (By permission of N. Y. Zoöl. Soc.)

North America, which some naturalists regard as varieties, others as distinct species. The Woodland Bison (*B. bison athabascæ*) is Boreal in distribution, the Plains "Buffalo" (*B. bison*) is chiefly Sonoran and formerly covered nearly all of the Great Plains in vast herds. There are two distinct races, or subspecies, of the Plains "Buffalo," northern and southern forms which were in the corresponding herds. By a curious coincidence, the Union Pacific Railroad followed the previously established line between the two herds. The southern variety is *B. bison bison,* and the northern *B. bison septentrionalis* (J. D. Figgins).

Of the Carnivora, the weasels, martens, Fisher, Mink, Ermine (*Mustela*), the Wolverene (*Gulo*) and the Grey Wolf (*Canis nubilis*) are Boreal, the last three extending also into the Arctic zone. Essentially Boreal, though also entering the Sonoran, are the bears (*Ursus*), red foxes (*Vulpes*), otters (*Lutra*), and Old World shrews (*Sorex*), while the Star-nosed Mole (*Condylura*), the mole-shrews (*Urotrichus*) do not extend south of the Transition zone. Southern invaders in the Boreal zone are the Puma, or "Mountain Lion" (*Felis concolor*), which just enters the subregion, the Canada Lynx (*Lynx rufus*), and one species of skunks (*Mephitis*), the Raccoon (*Procyon lotor*),

Fig. 79. — Mink, *Lutreola vison.* (By permission of N. Y. Zoöl. Soc.)

Badger (*Taxidea americana*) and the American deer (*Odocoileus*).

Many rodents are characteristically Boreal: marmots, or woodchucks (*Marmota*), the Sewellel (*Aplodontia rufa*), lemmings (*Myodes*), jumping mice (*Zapus*), Canada Porcupine (*Erethizon dorsatus*), and the pikas, or "whistling hares" (*Ochotona*). Boreal rodents that enter the Sonoran are the chipmunks (*Tamias*), Beaver (*Castor*), meadow mice (*Microtus*), the Muskrat (*Fiber zibethicus*). The white-footed mice (*Sitomys*) and the wood-rats (*Neotoma*) are southern rodents that extend into the Boreal zone.

Between the Boreal zone, or Canadian subregion, and the Sonoran region is the *Transition Zone,* which has very sinuous boundary lines. It includes most of New England, New York, Pennsylvania, and southern Ontario, southern Michigan and Wisconsin, then, bending northward extends across Minnesota, North Dakota, Manitoba and Saskatchewan. Curving thence southward across eastern Montana and parts of South Dakota and Nebraska, it crosses Wyoming and follows around the Great Basin to the plains of the Columbia River. It extends far to the south along the mountain ranges, following the

FIG. 80. — Fisher, *Martes pennantii.* (By permission of N. Y. Zoöl. Soc.)

FIG. 81. — Beaver, *Castor canadensis.* (By permission of N. Y. Zoöl. Soc.)

Appalachians to northern Georgia, the Rockies to New Mexico and the Sierras to southern California.

"The Transition zone, as its name indicates, is a zone of overlapping Boreal and Sonoran types. Many Boreal genera and species here reach the extreme southern limits of their distribution and many

FIG. 82. — Red Fox, *Vulpes fulvus*.   (By permission of N. Y. Zoöl. Soc.)

Sonoran genera and species their northern limits. But a single mammalian genus (*Synaptomys*) [one of the field mice] is restricted to the Transition zone. . . . A number of species, however, seem to be nearly or quite confined to it" (C. H. Merriam).

The *Sonoran Region* is the most characteristic part of North America; the northern boundary follows, for most of the way, the parallel of 43° N. latitude, but over the Great Plains and the Great Basin, on each side of the Rocky Mountains and the high plateaus, it extends to the 48th parallel. On the south, it includes the table-land of Mexico. Sonoran genera which do not extend into the Boreal zone are the Opossum (*Didelphis*), in the southern part a Peccary, or "Wild Texas Pig" (*Tagassu tajacu*), representatives of a family which are very distinct from the true swine of the Old World, and had a long American history, and an armadillo (*Tatu*). The Prong-horned Antelope (*Antilocapra americana*) is so peculiar and isolated that it is placed in a family of its own, the Antilocapridæ, distinct from all other antelopes. The typical genus of American

FIG. 83. — Wolverene, *Gulo luscus*. (By permission of N. Y. Zoöl. Soc.)

FIG. 84. — Wapiti or "Elk," *Cervus canadensis*. (By permission of N. Y. Zoöl. Soc.)

FIG. 85. — Moose, *Alce americanus*. (Photographed by
A. Austin, Jackson's Hole, Wyo.)

FIG. 86. — Alaska Brown Bear, *Ursus middendorfi*. (By permission of N. Y.
Zoöl. Soc.)

Fig. 87. — Upper figure, European Bison, *Bison bonasus.* Lower figure, American Bison, *B. bison.* (By permission of N. Y. Zoöl. Soc.)

FIG. 88. — Ermine, *Mustela erminea.* (By permission of N. Y. Zoöl. Soc.)

FIG. 89. — Rocky Mountain "Goat," *Oreamnos montanus.* (By permission of N. Y. Zoöl. Soc.)

A

B

C

Fig. 90. — Boreal Mammals. *A*, Black-footed Ferret, *Mustela nigripes.*
B, Otter, *Lutra canadensis.* *C*, Jumping Mouse, *Zapus hudsonius.* (*A* and *B*,
by permission of N. Y. Zoöl. Soc.; *C*, by permission of W. S. Berridge, London.)

deer, *Odocoileus*, which differs in important respects from the deer of the Eastern Hemisphere, is represented by several species, and

FIG. 91. — Kangaroo-rat, *Dipodomys philippsi*.
(By permission of N. Y. Zoöl. Soc.)

three varieties of bison were once extremely abundant, until almost exterminated by human ruthlessness. Bison, Antelope and American types of Deer also reach the Boreal zone.

Carnivora are equally characteristic: the Grey Fox (*Urocyon virginianus*), Coyote, or Prairie Wolf (*Canis latrans*), Timber Wolf

FIG. 92. — Thirteen-lined Spermophile, *Spermophilus tre-decimlineatus*. (By permission of N. Y. Zoöl. Soc.)

(*C. occidentalis*), the Cacomistle (*Bassariscus*), the Coati (*Nasua narica*), Raccoon (*Procyon lotor*), Badger (*Taxidea americana*), three genera of skunks, the Puma (*Felis concolor*), several species of lynx and bears are abundant, though one species each of raccoon, ·skunk, badger, puma and lynx range into the Boreal, where they are manifest intruders. The American types of shrews (*Blarina*) and moles (*Scalops* and *Scapanus*) are characteristically Sonoran, though partially shared with the Boreal.

A great many peculiar rodents inhabit the Sonoran region: cotton-rats (*Sigmodon*), pocket-gophers (*Geomys, Thomomys*), several genera

FIG. 93. — Grey Wolf, *Canis nubilis*. (By permission of N. Y. Zoöl. Soc.)

of the beautiful little kangaroo-rats (*Dipodomys*, etc.), and, while the prairie-dogs (*Cynomys*), the white-footed mice (*Sitomys*), wood-rats (*Neotoma*) and one genus of pocket-gophers (*Thomomys*) are chiefly Sonoran, they have Boreal representatives. The flying squirrels (*Sciuropterus*), true squirrels (*Sciurus*), ground-squirrels (*Spermophilus*), rabbits (*Lepus*), wolves (*Canis*) and otters (*Lutra*) have a very wide range through both Sonoran and Boreal, but they have

FIG. 94. — Kit Fox, or Swift, *Vulpes velox.* (By permission of N. Y. Zoöl. Soc.)

FIG. 95. — Prong-horned Antelope, *Antilocapra americana.* (By permission of N. Y. Zoöl. Soc.)

FIG. 96. — Grey Fox, *Urocyon virginianus.* (By permission of N. Y. Zoöl. Soc.)

FIG. 97. — Prairie Wolf or Coyote, *Canis latrans.* (By permission of N. Y. Zoöl. Soc.)

FIG. 98. — Raccoon, *Procyon lotor*.   (By permission of N. Y. Zoöl. Soc.)

FIG. 99. — Virginia Deer, *Odocoileus virginianus*.   (By permission of N. Y. Zoöl. Soc.)

FIG. 100. — Skunk, *Mephitis mephitis*. (By permission of N. Y. Zoöl. Soc.)

FIG. 101. — Mule Deer, *Odocoileus hemionus*. (By permission of N. Y. Zoöl. Soc.)

FIG. 102. — Badger, *Taxidea americana*. (By permission of N. Y. Zoöl. Soc.)

FIG. 103. — Puma or Mountain Lion, *Felis concolor*. (By permission of N. Y. Zoöl. Soc.)

FIG. 104. — Lynx, *Lynx rufus*. (By permission of N. Y. Zoöl. Soc.)

FIG. 105. — Prairie-dog, *Cynomys ludovicianus*. (By permission of N. Y. Zoöl. Soc.)

many more species in the Sonoran. In fact the Sonoran mammals are much more varied and have a much larger number of species than those of the Boreal zone. A mere list of the genera gives but an inadequate idea of the difference.

FIG. 106. — Grey Squirrel, *Sciurus carolinensis*. (By permission of N. Y. Zoöl. Soc.)

II. SOUTH AMERICA

The Neotropical region, zoölogically so peculiar that it forms the realm of Neogæa by itself, comprises Central and South America and the West Indies. Continental South America is subdivided into two subregions, the Brazilian and the Chilean, which are simply the warmer and cooler parts of the continent. The Central American subregion

FIG. 107. — Opossum, *Didelphis marsupialis*. (By permission of N. Y. Zoöl. Soc.)

includes not only the lands geographically so called, but also the lowlands of Mexico, extending into southeastern Texas, and the coastal strip of southern Florida.

"Richness combined with isolation is the predominant feature of Neotropical Zoölogy, and no other region can approach it in the number of its peculiar family and generic types" (Wallace). Most of the Neotropical fauna is of indigenous origin and derived from a long series of native ancestors, but there is a very important element which has descended from North American immigrants, as is made plain by the palæontological history of the two continents. Many of the immigrants were unable to establish themselves permanently, and died out after a longer or shorter period.

FIG. 108. — Common Marmoset, *Hapale*. (By permission of W. S. Berridge, London.)

Two families of Marsupialia are represented in the Neotropical fauna. The opossums (Didelphyidæ) are very much more numerous and varied than in North America; there are at least three genera, five or six well-marked subgenera, sixteen or seventeen species, some of which are no larger than mice. The opossums are especially numerous in the Brazilian forests. Of particular interest are the two species of the little *Cænolestes*, now confined to Ecuador, Colombia and Peru, which are the surviving remnants of a once very extensive and wide-spread family.

At the present time continental South America has no Insectivora, but in the Central American subregion there are some shrews (*Blarina*) which have entered from the north. In Cuba and Haiti are found two species of a very remarkable insectivore, *Solenodon*, which, strange to say, has its nearest allies in the tenrecs (*Centetes*) of Madagascar, almost the last surviving relics of an ancient group that was nearly world-wide in distribution. As compared with the Old World, the Western Hemisphere has but a small number of Insectivora.

There is no greater contrast between North and South America than that afforded by the Primates. Not including Central America, which belongs to the Neotropical region, North America has no monkeys and has not had them for long ages past, while South America has a great variety of them in the tropical forests. These are very different from the monkeys of the Eastern Hemisphere, most obviously in the prehensile tails which most Neotropical genera possess.

There are two families of Primates in South America; one of these, the Marmosets (Hapalidæ) differs from all other monkeys in several particulars. The most conspicuous of these differences are the long claws on the feet and the non-opposable thumb; the tail is not prehensile. The second family, the Cebidæ, comprises monkeys which

Fig. 109. — Sapajou, *Cebus*. (By permission of N. Y. Zoöl. Soc.)

are superficially like those of the Old World, but there are so many differences, that the relations between the two groups are problematical.

South America has no anthropoid apes and, so far as the palæontological record goes, never has had them.

South America has a remarkably rich and varied assemblage of the Rodentia, both indigenous and immigrant, but the native families and genera are much the more important and conspicuous. All of the autochthonous forms belong to the porcupine-like suborder, or Hystricomorpha, of which South America is still, as it has been for ages, the headquarters. No less than six families and twenty-nine or thirty genera are known, and all of these genera and four of the families are restricted to the Neotropical region. The extreme scantiness of the Hystricomorpha in North America forms a striking contrast to the wealth of species in the southern continent, the Canada Porcupine (*Erethizon*) being the sole genus represented.

Space is lacking for a description of this horde of curious rodents and only a few of the more characteristic types can be mentioned.

Fig. 110. — Brazilian Tree Porcupine, *Coendou prehensilis*. (By permission of N. Y. Zoöl. Soc.)

The two genera of arboreal porcupines (*Coendou* and *Chætomys*) belong to the same family as the North American *Erethizon*, but have long prehensile tails, which are used in grasping and climbing. The very large family of the Octodontidæ has seventeen Neotropical genera in addition to four others which occur in Africa. The Degu (*Octodon*) of Chile, Bolivia and Peru, has the appearance of a large rat with tufted tail. The spiny rats (*Echimys* and *Loncheres*) are not related to the true rats, but are so called from their rat-like appearance; they have numerous horny spikes scattered through the hair of the back. The Coypu (*Myocastor*) is a large aquatic animal, remotely like the northern Muskrat in appearance, and the hutias (*Capromys* and *Plagiodontia*), arboreal forms, occur only in Cuba, Haiti and Jamaica. The chinchillas (*Chinchilla* and *Lagidium*) of

FIG. 111. — Chinchilla, *Chinchilla laniger*. (By permission of W. S. Berridge, London.)

FIG. 112. — West Indian Hutia, *Capromys pilorides*, Cuba. (By permission of N. Y. Zoöl. Soc.)

A

B

C

D

Fig. 113. — Neotropical rodents. *A*, Vizcacha, *Viscaccia*. *B*, Paca, *Agouti paca*. *C*, Rock Cavy, *Cavia rupestris*. *D*, Water-hog or Carpincho, *Hydrochœrus*. (*D*, by permission of N. Y. Zoöl. Soc.; *A*, *B*, *C*, by permission of W. S. Berridge, London.)

the Andes, and the Vizcacha (*Viscaccia*) of the Argentine plains, look somewhat like rabbits, but have long, bushy tails.

The cavies, to which the familiar, misnamed Guinea-pig (*Cavia porcellus*) belongs, are a very characteristic family.   Beside the cavies, it includes the Mara, or "Patagonian Hare" (*Dolichotis*), a large, long-legged, long-eared and short-tailed creature, and the Water-hog,

Fig. 114. — Coypu, *Myocastor coypu*. (By permission of N. Y. Zoöl. Soc.)

or Carpincho (*Hydrochœrus*), an aquatic animal, as its name implies, and much the largest of all existing rodents; it equals an ordinary pig in size.   The Carpincho is confined to the warmer regions, as far south as Argentina.   The heavy Paca (*Agouti*) and the slender-limbed Agouti (*Dasyprocta*) make up another family in which there is a most regrettable confusion between the vernacular and technical names. Altogether, this assemblage of the porcupine-like suborder of the Rodentia is most remarkable and in no other region of the earth is anything like it to be found.

The immigrant rodents, which are so plainly of northern origin, are represented in the Neotropical region by a much smaller number of families and genera than occur in North America.   The pikas (*Ochotona*) are entirely absent and there are very few species of rabbits, one of which is found in Brazil and which is separated by a very wide interval from that in Costa Rica.   Of the squirrel-like division, only the true arboreal squirrels occur and of these there are many species; the ground-squirrels, chipmunks, marmots, prairie-dogs and beavers

are wanting. Of rats and mice there is but one family. The vesper,
or white-footed, mice (*Sitomys*) have invaded South America and
have there given rise to a number of peculiar genera, the northern
ancestry of which is, nevertheless, unmistakable. Examples are the
groove-toothed mice (*Rheithrodon*) and the fish-eating rats (*Icthy-
omys*). Other families of rats and mice which abound in the northern
hemisphere are absent, such as the voles, or meadow-mice, the muskrats, jumping-mice, kangaroo-rats and pocket-gophers. The immigrant groups thus have only one family each in the Neotropical region.

Fig. 115. — Agouti, *Dasyprocta aguti*. (By permission of N. Y. Zoöl. Soc.)

The Carnivora are all of immigrant origin and they were the first
of the northern orders to make their appearance in South America.
The beasts of prey which were indigenous to the Neotropical region
and were supplanted by the northern invaders, were all marsupials,
some of great size and power. Since the invasion took place, there
has been time for extensive differentiation and the development of
genera and species peculiar to the new environment.

The Canidæ almost all belong to genera which are not found
elsewhere, and form a considerable assemblage. There are no true
wolves or foxes, but several species of fox-like wolves, with bushy
tails, take their places and are common in the plains areas. A very
peculiar type is the Brazilian Bush-dog (*Icticyon venaticus*), a heavy,
short-legged and short-tailed animal, which, it has been alleged,

Fig. 116. — Brazilian Bush-dog, *Icticyon venaticus*. (From J. Murie.)

Fig. 117. — Short-eared Wolf, *Canis microtus*. (By permission of
N. Y. Zoöl. Soc.)

finds its nearest ally in the Dhole, or "Wild Dog," of India, both being regarded as having descended from a Miocene genus of North America. There are grave objections, however, to this view.

The weasel family (Mustelidæ), so numerous and diversified in the northern hemisphere, is rather scantily represented in South America. There are no badgers and but few skunks (*Conepatus* and

FIG. 118. — Fox-like Wolf, *Cerdocyon gracilis*. (By permission of W. S. Berridge, London.)

Spilogale); true weasels are absent, but their place is taken by the Grison (*Galera vittata*) and Tayra (*Tayra tayra*) and, in the far south, by *Lyncodon patagonicus* and finally, there are two or three species of otters (*Lutra*).

The raccoons (*Procyon*) have a very wide range in South as in North America and the curious, long-snouted coatis (*Nasua*), which just enter the Sonoran region, are typically Neotropical. The bears (Ursidæ) are a characteristically northern family and hardly enter the southern hemisphere at all. Except for its northwestern corner, Africa has no bears and South America has but one genus, with perhaps two species. This is the Spectacled Bear (*Tremarctos ornatus*) of the highlands of Peru and Chile, an obviously northern form, which has followed down the mountain ranges into South America.

The cat family (Felidæ) is rather numerously represented. The pumas (*Felis concolor*) range from the Boreal zone of North America throughout the Neotropical region almost to the Straits of Magellan.

FIG. 119. — Spectacled Bear, *Tremarctos ornatus*. (By permission of N. Y. Zoöl. Soc.)

There are numerous local varieties, but they are all much alike. The Jaguar (*Felis onca*), which extends from Texas to Argentina, is a large spotted cat, much like the Leopard in appearance, but more massive and heavily built. The Ocelot (*F. pardalis*, Arkansas to Paraguay) is smaller and streaked and blotched rather than spotted, and, in addition there are several small felines, spotted, clouded and solid-colour, but no lynxes. The latter are essentially northern animals, even more so than the bears, and have no representatives in the southern continents.

Hoofed animals are not numerous in the Neotropical region and are almost all artiodactyls. The only existing Perissodactyla of the

FIG. 120. — Little Skunk, *Spilogale putorius*. (By permission of W. S. Berridge, London.)

whole Western Hemisphere are the tapirs (*Tapirus* and *Tapirella*) of Central and tropical South America, a very remarkable contrast to the ancient faunas, especially those of North America, as will be shown in the sequel. The Artiodactyla are more numerous, though still very scanty in comparison with those of the Old World, and even North America, which is but poorly provided with these

FIG. 121. — Argentine Skunk, *Conepatus gibsoni*. (By permission of W. S. Berridge, London.)

FIG. 122. — Tayra, *Tayra tayra*. (By permission of
W. S. Berridge, London.)

animals, is much richer in them than is the Neotropical region, where,
indeed, all of the hoofed animals are the descendants of comparatively
late immigrants from the north and none is truly autochthonous,
though some peculiar forms have arisen. The peccaries (*Tagassu* and
Pecari), or wild pigs, range from Texas through Central and South
America, to Paraguay. Of especial interest are the members of the

FIG. 123. — Kinkajou, *Potos caudivolvulus*, Central
America. (By permission of W. S. Berridge, London.)

Fig. 124. — Ocelot, *Felis pardalis.* (By permission of N. Y. Zoöl. Soc.)

Fig. 125. — Jaguar, *Felis onca.* (By permission of N. Y. Zoöl. Soc.)

FIG. 126. — *Solenodon cubanus*. (From Brehm.)

FIG. 127. — Collared Peccary, *Tagassu tajacu*. (By permission of N. Y. Zoöl. Soc.)

camel family (Camelidæ) which differ so widely from the true camels of Asia. The Guanaco (*Lama huanacus*) forms great herds in Patagonia and Tierra del Fuego and extends along the Cordillera to Ecuador and Peru, where it is associated with the Vicuña (*L. vicunia*),

Fɪɢ. 128. — Guanaco, *Lama huanacus*. (By permission of N. Y. Zoöl. Soc.)

a smaller and more slender species, which does not range south of Bolivia. The Andes afford a pathway by which mammals of the south temperate zone extend their range to the Equator.

The true ruminants (suborder Pecora) are represented in the Neotropical region only by the deer (Cervidæ) of which there are several genera, all of them of the North American, as distinguished from the Old World type. Some of these deer are so peculiar that they must have had a long South American ancestry. The white-tailed, or Virginia Deer (*Odocoileus virginianus*) of the northern

United States is a comparatively large animal, which is much smaller in Florida and the Southwest. The type extends through Mexico and Central America to Guiana and Peru, the Neotropical forms being so small and having such weak antlers, that they are referred to different species. Another type is the Marsh Deer (*Blastoceros paludosus*) of eastern South America which has short stout antlers, each beam with a

Fig. 129. — Vicuña, *Lama vicunia*. (By permission of N. Y. Zoöl. Soc.)

double bifurcation. There are other species of the genus, such as the Pampas Deer of Argentina (*B. bezoarticus*). In western Patagonia and in the Andes and Peru are two species of a genus which has the preposterous name of *Hippocamelus*, surely a *reductio ad absurdum* of the "law of priority." The antlers of these deer are simply forked. Their vernacular name is Huemul.

Peculiarly Neotropical are the little "brockets," which hardly exceed a height of two feet at the shoulder, and have simple, spike-like antlers not more than three inches long. The genus, named *Mazama*, has several species, one of which ranges as far north as the Mexican state of Puebla. "The smallest of all deer is the Chilian pudu (*Pudua pudu*), a creature not much larger than a hare, with almost rudimentary antlers" (Lydekker).

Old World types of deer, the Wapiti, Moose and Caribou, and the antelopes, sheep and bison, all of which abound in North America, are altogether wanting in the Neotropical region.

The xenarthrous Edentata, with the exception of one armadillo which has invaded Texas, are entirely confined to the Neotropical region. The order, which was once far more numerous and diversified

Fig. 130. — Florida Deer, *Odocoileus virginianus osceola*. (By permission of N. Y. Zoöl. Soc.)

than it is at present, comprises three groups of animals so strange and bizarre that they seem more like fabulous creatures than real mammals. In external appearance, the three suborders are very different from one another, but they are united by profound similarities of structure, and undoubtedly form a natural assemblage.

One suborder is that of the sloths (Tardigrada), shaggy, arboreal animals, with short and rounded, almost monkey-like head and no tail. Their very long legs and hook-like feet make them nearly helpless on the ground, but are very useful for hanging from the branches of trees, for these creatures are strictly arboreal. Indeed the sloths and the bats are the only mammals which habitually hang in a suspended position.   In the tropical forests are two genera of sloths, between which the most obvious difference is that in one the fore-foot has three toes (*Bradypus*) and in the other two (*Cholœpus*).

The suborder Vermilingua, or anteaters, includes entirely toothless animals.   The great Ant-bear (*Myrmecophaga jubata*), which may

FIG. 131. — Marsh Deer, *Blastoceros paludosus,* female. (By permission of N. Y. Zoöl. Soc.)

reach a length of seven feet, including the tail, has an extremely long and slender head, long, shaggy black and white hair and an immense, bushy tail.   The fore-feet are armed with huge, sharp-pointed claws, which are used for tearing open the hills of termites, the so-called "white ants," and also serve as very effective weapons, for the Ant-bear can successfully defend itself, even against the Jaguar.   In walking the claws are curved inward and the animal rests its weight on the outer edges of the fore-feet, while the hind-feet are plantigrade, the sole of the foot and the heel resting on the ground.

The Collared Anteater (*Tamandua*) is much smaller than the great Ant-bear and is mainly arboreal in habits.   It has a short-

FIG. 132. — Wood Brocket, *Mazama nemorivagus*. (By permission of W. S. Berridge, London.)

FIG. 133. — American Tapir, *Tapirus terrestris*. (By permission of W. S. Berridge, London.)

haired, black body, with a median white stripe down the back, white neck and limbs, a colour-pattern which makes the animal seem to be wearing a close-fitting and sleeveless black jacket. The tail differs from that of the Ant-bear in being short-haired. The little Two-toed Anteater (*Cyclopes didactylus*), which is hardly larger than a rat, has a prehensile tail. Both suborders, the sloths and the anteaters, are forest animals, and tropical, or subtropical in distribution; they are not found west of the Andes, or south of Paraguay.

The Dasypoda, or armadillos, are the third existing suborder of the Edentata, and differ entirely in appearance from the hairy sloths

FIG. 134. — Two-toed Sloth, *Cholœpus didactylus*. (By permission of W. S. Berridge, London.)

and anteaters, being very short-legged and having, for the most part, but little hair, though covered with a very complete armour, head, body and tail, bony scutes, or ossifications in the true skin, with horny scales over these. The long-snouted head is protected by a shield, which is made up of numerous, horn-covered, bony scutes, joined by their edges, and the tail is encased in a tubular sheath of more or less regular rings, each ring of bony plates and horny scales. The body-shield, or *carapace*, which covers back and sides, consists of anterior and posterior bucklers, in which the scutes are immovably fixed together, and, between the bucklers, is a series of movable, overlapping bands, the number of which varies in the different genera.

In the little Pichiciago (*Chlamyphorus truncatus*) the head and body are covered with rectangular plates of horn, the bony scutes being small and thin. The carapace has no bucklers and consists of some twenty transverse rows of plates; it is attached only along the middle

Fig. 135. — Three-toed Sloth, *Bradypus tridactylus*. (By permission of N. Y. Zoöl. Soc.)

line of the back and, beneath it, is silky white fur. The rump is covered with a solid plate of bone, over which are thin scales of horn; this plate is almost vertical in position and its lower border is notched for the tail. The armour of this little subterranean creature is, thus, altogether exceptional in the suborder.

The armadillos are all more or less burrowers in habit and omnivorous in diet, eating roots, worms, insects, etc.; the extraordinary

FIG. 136. — Collared· Anteater, *Tamandua tetradactyla.*
(By permission of N. Y. Zoöl. Soc.)

FIG. 137. — Ant-bear, *Myrmecophaga jubata.* (By permission of N. Y. Zoöl.
Soc.)

rapidity with which they can burrow into the ground is almost the only way in which they can escape from their enemies, but, in one genus, *Tolypeutes*, the animal can roll itself into a ball, completely

FIG. 138. — Nine-banded Armadillo, *Tatu novemcinctus.* (By permission of N. Y. Zoöl. Soc.)

protected by mail all around it.   The armadillos are much more varied than the anteaters, or sloths, and have a far wider geographical range, from Texas to Patagonia.   Seven or more distinct genera of the suborder occur in the Neotropical region and, among them, there is

FIG. 139. — Six-banded Armadillo, *Dasypus sexcinctus.* (By permission of N. Y. Zoöl. Soc.)

great difference in size.   The Great Armadillo (*Priodontes*) of Brazil, is a yard or more in length, while the little *Zaëdyus*, of Patagonia, is not so large as a rabbit, and smallest of all is the Pichiciago, which is about five inches long.

The fauna of the Central American subregion is not so rich and characteristic as that of Brazil and, to a certain extent, is transitional to that of the Sonoran region of North America. Several Sonoran

FIG. 140. — *Cænolestes obscurus*, somewhat reduced; surviving remnant of a Miocene family of marsupials. (From W. H. Osgood.)

genera extend into Central America which are not known to pass the Isthmus of Panama; such are shrews, a fox and one of the pocket-mice.

The islands of the West Indies offer problems of zoölogical geography which are exceedingly puzzling and have, as yet, found no satisfactory solution. The most striking feature of Antillean zoölogy is the extreme paucity of its mammals, which is in extraordinary contrast to the wealth of the Malay Archipelago, the islands of which are as rich in mammals as equal areas of the Asiatic mainland. Java and Cuba are of nearly the same size and have very similar tropical climates, yet, while Java has some ninety species of mammals, Cuba has but four, the curious insectivore *Solenodon* and three species of the rodent genus *Capromys*. Puerto Rico has, at present, no indigenous land mammals other than bats. The explanation of this poverty of the Antillean fauna is yet to be found, chiefly because the geological history of the islands is still so incompletely known.

The geographical distribution of animals has many features that seem capricious and paradoxical; many of them seem inexplicable, yet enough is already known to justify the conclusion that the existing distribution is the necessary and inevitable outcome of a long series of past changes, climatic, geographical and evolutionary, and that where existing facts of distribution cannot be explained, it is always because the history of the species involved is known imperfectly, or not at all. Even with our incomplete knowledge, the geographical distribution of animals, especially of mammals, affords some of the most convincing proofs as to the truth of the Theory of Evolution.

CHAPTER IX

SUCCESSIVE MAMMALIAN FAUNAS OF NORTH AMERICA

The natural way to tell a story is to begin at the beginning and go on to the end, but to deal in that manner with the many assemblages of mammals which have, in turn, inhabited the Western Hemisphere, has the great drawback of beginning with a time when everything is completely unfamiliar to the reader. There is, therefore, a real practical advantage in reversing the order of the narrative, starting with the end and thus proceeding from the more to the less familiar. The foregoing chapter gave a sketch of the more characteristic mammals which now inhabit the Americas and we may now take a step backward into the early Recent, when a considerable number of Pleistocene mammals were still surviving. In fact, some geologists refer this early Recent to a post-Glacial part of the Pleistocene, but the difference of usage is merely a matter of names and has no great significance.

I. QUATERNARY FAUNAS

The Pleistocene is here regarded as having ended with the final disappearance of Glacial ice from continental North America and the post-Glacial is termed the Early Recent.

1. Recent

The mammals now in existence, together with those which have been exterminated by human agency, constitute what may be called the modern, or Late Recent fauna. Going back in time, however, more and more survivals from the Pleistocene are encountered and those survivals were much more numerous and persisted till a much later time than is commonly understood. The American †Mastodon (†*Mastodon americanus*) survived into the historic period and most of the skeletons displayed in so many museums are long post-Glacial in date. The most prolific source of these skeletons has been the valley of the Hudson River, which in Pleistocene times was buried deep under the ice. The only known skeleton of the curious †Stag-moose (†*Cervalces*) was found in shell marl beneath a bog in northern New

177

FIG. 141. — †Stag-moose, †*Cervalces scotti.* (Restored from a skeleton in Princeton Univ. Mus.)

178

Jersey, far to the north of the terminal moraine and, therefore, post-Glacial in date. A cave in New Mexico has yielded the skeleton of a small †ground-sloth (†*Nothrotherium*) now in the Yale museum, which has been described and figured by Professor Lull. This skeleton cannot be of great antiquity, for the ligaments and much of the skin still adhere to the bones. Professor Romer, of Harvard University, has described the skull of the great †Camel-llama (†*Camelops*) with much of the soft parts still attached, which was found in a cave in Utah. Large, extinct species of peccary and bison and the †Giant Beaver (†*Castoroides*) have been found in post-Glacial deposits and, no doubt, others remain to be discovered.

2. Pleistocene

In Europe it has been possible to arrange the successive Pleistocene faunas, Glacial and Interglacial, in chronological order, but that arrangement has not yet been practicable in this country, though differences in time between the fossils of certain localities have been demonstrated. It will be necessary, therefore, to treat the North American Pleistocene fauna as a unit, though distinctive Glacial and Interglacial faunas are indicated. Pleistocene mammals in North America are found almost entirely in those parts of the continent to which the Glacial ice did not extend, for glacial drift is nearly barren. The occurrence of caribou in southern New England, of musk-oxen in Idaho, Kentucky, Arkansas and Texas, and of the Walrus on the coast of Georgia, is proof of a climate much colder than the present, but it is not possible to refer these remains to any particular Glacial stage. Most of the Pleistocene mammals, so far known, have been found in Interglacial deposits, though it is seldom possible to say to which of the three Interglacial stages they belong.

The richly fossiliferous localities represent all parts of the continent south of the ice-limit and of the Alaskan lowlands, which were not glaciated. Over all of this vast area, from the Atlantic to the Pacific and from Pennsylvania to Florida, Texas and Mexico, there is a remarkable uniformity in the mammals, but the effects of climate are to be noted and the differing habitats of forest and open grassland were important factors. The most prolific sources of the fossils are the Sheridan loess of the Great Plains and the tar-pits of southern California. Florida also has yielded important, though more fragmentary, remains. In the eastern half of the continent caves and fissures have been the principal sources of fossils, such as those at Port Kennedy, on the Schuylkill above Philadelphia; at Franktown,

LION

SLOTH (FRONT AND SIDE VIEWS)

ANTELOPE

GIANT SLOTH (FRONT AND SIDE VIEWS)

BISON

SABRE-TOOTH TIGER

WOLF

CAMEL

AMERICAN MASTODON

HORSE

IMPERIAL MAMMOTH

FIG. 142. — Outline restorations of the chief mammals of the Rancho La Brea tar-pits, Pleistocene. Scale uniform, about $\frac{1}{75}$ natural size. (From Osborn.)

Pennsylvania; Cumberland, Maryland; and the Conard Fissure in Arkansas. Caverns in the Appalachian Mountains have supplied some valuable material.

It is very probable that nearly or quite all of the mammalian genera now in existence were included in the Pleistocene faunas, but not all the species, as new ones have undoubtedly arisen since that time. There was, in addition, a host of forms that have disappeared from the Western Hemisphere, or even have vanished from the earth altogether in the great extinctions which followed the Pleistocene over three-fifths of the land surface of the world, leaving what Wallace called a "zoölogically impoverished world." Many genera and families and even whole orders were completely swept away and these extinctions were, from the human point of view, a great benefit, for the earth is a much safer and pleasanter abode for Man than it was before the change. Great size is very characteristic of many Pleistocene mammals and it is just the hugest, fiercest and most bizarre forms that have disappeared.

To modern eyes the North American Pleistocene fauna (treating it as a unit) is a very strange one and includes many elements which are now confined to Asia, Africa or South America, together with many which have entirely disappeared. Most surprising, perhaps, in an American landscape is the presence of numerous and varied proboscideans, of which two very distinct groups, the †mastodonts and the true elephants, co-existed in the same regions. The American †Mastodon (†*Mastodon americanus*) was much the most abundant of the proboscideans, especially in the forested regions east of the Mississippi and of the Pacific Coast; apparently it was rare in the Great Plains. The species ranged southeastward from Alaska, over southern Canada, all the United States and northern Mexico. The †Mastodon differed from the true elephants in having much simpler grinding teeth and a much lower and flatter head; in the male there was a small median tusk in the lower jaw, which must have been concealed in the lip. The creature was thickly covered with long coarse hair, black or brown in colour, as is proved by the hair associated with several skeletons. It was the smallest of the Pleistocene Proboscidea, seldom attaining a height of nine feet, six inches.

Three genera and six or seven species of true elephants roamed over Pleistocene North America, all of which belonged to the subdivision of the †mammoths, typified by the Siberian †Mammoth (†*Mammuthus primigenius*) which ranged from the south of France across Europe and Asia to Kamchatka and from Alaska south-

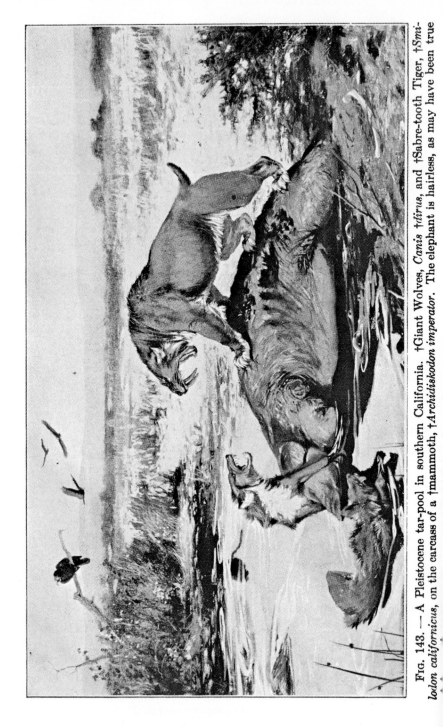

Fig. 143. — A Pleistocene tar-pool in southern California. †Giant Wolves, *Canis* †*dirus*, and †Sabre-tooth Tiger, †*Smilodon californicus*, on the carcass of a †mammoth, †*Archidiskodon imperator*. The elephant is hairless, as may have been true

182

eastward to New England. Palæolithic Man in Europe made many remarkably skilful and life-like representations of the †Mammoth; wall paintings in the caves of the Pyrenees and the south of France, and incised outlines on ivory or stone still remain to prove the animal's presence in Pleistocene Europe. The frozen elephant carcasses which have been found in Siberia belong to this species, and show that it was clothed with wool beneath long coarse hair. (Fig. 168, p. 276.)

The †Mammoth was a cold-country animal and did not extend far to the south, where its place was taken by species of the nearly allied genus †*Parelephas*, †*P. jeffersoni*, the most widely spread of these, ranged all over the United States, south to Florida and the table-land of Mexico. This was a much larger animal than the Siberian †Mammoth, standing 11 feet high, and may, or may not, have been covered with hair; there is no means of determining.

Still a third genus of mammoth-like elephants was the remarkable †*Archidiskodon*, of which there were at least three species. One of these is a variety of the Italian †*A. meridionalis*, which has not been found east of Nebraska. The other species, †*A. imperator* and †*A. maibeni* were of gigantic size, the former reaching the almost incredible height of 13 feet, six inches and the latter was even taller. These enormous creatures have been found chiefly to the westward of the Mississippi, though also extending to Florida and southward to the city of Mexico. (Fig. 170, p. 279.)

Perissodactyla were represented in the North American Pleistocene by tapirs and many species of horses, but not by rhinoceroses, which had died out in the Pliocene. Tapirs were to be found along the Pacific Coast and in the eastern forest, but apparently not in the Great Plains. Two species have been named, *Tapirus* †*haysii*, a larger and heavier one, and a smaller form which seems to be identical with the living *T. terrestris* of Central and South America.

There were at least ten species of the existing genus *Equus*, but the familiar species *E. caballus*, to which all the domestic breeds of horses belong, has not been found. The smallest known species, *E.* †*tau* of Mexico, about equalled a Shetland Pony in size. In marked contrast was *E.* †*giganteus*, of Texas, the largest of American species, which exceeded the heaviest modern draught-horses in size. Of other Texan species, one, *E.* †*scotti*, resembled the zebras in its proportions and another, *E.* †*semiplicatus*, was more ass-like.

The forest-horse of the eastern states, *E.* †*pectinatus*, was of moderate size, about 14 hands in height. Another very small species, *E.* †*fraternus*, which was particularly abundant in the southeast, ranged north into Pennsylvania and west to Nebraska. The Great Plains must have supported immense herds of horses and their multitudinous bones and teeth have suggested the name of *Equus Beds* for the Sheridan formation. The most abundant of the Plains species, *E.* †*complicatus*, of cow-pony size, extended down nearly or quite to the Gulf of Mexico.

On the Pacific Coast, *E.* †*pacificus*, which was second only to *E.* †*giganteus* in size, was associated with the much smaller and more abundant *E.* †*occidentalis*. Of this species, complete skeletons have been obtained from the tar-pits of Rancho La Brea. This horse of medium size (15 hands) was remarkable for the very simple pattern of its grinding teeth and for its deer-like slenderness of limb.

In view of the thriving condition, the diversity and abundance of the Pleistocene horses in America, their complete disappearance before the European discovery is a very puzzling circumstance.

There was a far greater variety of Artiodactyla than there is now; some were indigenous, and descended from a long line of American ancestry, others seem semi-indigenous, and descended from immigrants of middle Tertiary date, but most of them were late migrants from the Eastern Hemisphere, where the immense group of the true ruminants passed through most of its evolutionary history and where its headquarters still are.

Indigenous were the peccaries, or American pigs, which, though chiefly South American at present, still persist in Texas. In the Pleistocene they extended all across the continent and as far north as central New York, and were represented by two genera, both extinct. One of these, †*Platygonus*, had much longer legs than existing peccaries and was, in several respects, more advanced and specialized. Indigenous also were the great llamas, which extended even into Alaska. True camels (*Camelus*) have not been found, but the immense †*Camelops*, was, in a measure, intermediate between the two subfamilies and was much taller than the Asiatic camels; a very small member of this family has been reported, but not yet described, from the caves of New Mexico.

The typical American deer (*Odocoileus*) were, to all appearances, derived from immigrants which came to North America in the Miocene. The Virginia and Black-tailed species are familiar "modern instances" of this group. In the Pleistocene they differed little from their state at present. The Old World Stag, or Wapiti (*Cervus*), the Caribou (*Rangifer*) and the Moose (*Alce*) were immigrants of so late a date that they have undergone but little modification. The isolated

†*Cervalces*, a moose with some stag-like characteristics, is much of an enigma, though it was probably a Pleistocene migrant from Asia, as was also the chamois-like antelope misnamed the "Rocky Mountain Goat" (*Oreamnos montanus*). No sheep have yet been found in the American Pleistocene.

The Prong-buck (*Antilocapra americana*), a very peculiar type of antelope, was probably derived from migrants which came from

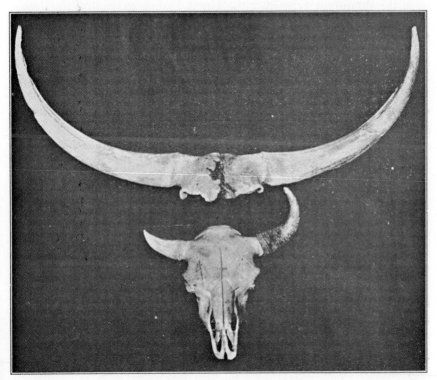

Fig. 144. — Horn-cores of bisons. Upper figure, †Giant Bison, Pleistocene, *B.* †*latifrons*. Lower figure, modern "Buffalo," *B. bison*, with left horn-sheath in place. (Amer. Mus. Nat. Hist.)

the Old World in the Miocene. At present there is but a single species, but in the Pleistocene there was a considerable group of allied genera, and several of these, like †*Ilingoceros*, had the twisted horns of the "strepsicerine" antelopes of Africa and Asia. A remarkable four-horned member of this family, †*Tetrameryx*, was common in the Southwest. Another genus of the same family was the little †*Capromeryx*, not more than two feet high, which must have resembled the tiny Dik-dik (*Madoqua*) of Africa, though the latter have hairy noses. The existing Musk-ox (*Ovibos moschatus*) is the last survivor of a group of immigrants from Asia, which have been found on both the Pacific and Atlantic slopes, of which the typical genus was †*Prepto- ceras*. In the Glacial stages the true musk-oxen (*Ovibos* and †*Symbos*) retreated southward before the advance of the ice, reaching as far as Arkansas.

In the forested regions east of the Mississippi, the most abundant of the ruminants were the deer, but there were some bisons, which were the dominant type over the Great Plains, extending to Alaska. The existing Bison (*B. bison*) in its two varieties of the Plains (*B. bison bison*) and the Woodland Bison (*B. bison athabascæ*) is the surviving remnant of a vastly greater and more diversified assemblage. No less than seven species have long been known and to these Dr. Figgins has lately added two more (*B.* †*rotundus* and *B.* †*angularis*) and a new genus, †*Stelabison*. Most of these species were larger than the existing "Buffalo" and some were gigantic. For example, *B.* †*crassicornis* of Alaska, and *B.* †*latifrons*, found throughout the Mississippi Valley, had a spread of horns of over six feet!

This great assemblage of hoofed animals, †mastodons, elephants, peccaries, llamas, deer, antelopes, bison, tapirs and horses, were the prey of a horde of Carnivora, many of them much more formidable than any now existing, which included both native and immigrant stocks. The smaller beasts of prey, such as raccoons, badgers, weasels, otters, etc., seem to have been very much as at present, it was among the cat, dog and bear families that the terrible destroyers were found. Most conspicuous and abundant of these were the †sabretooth cats (†*Smilodon*) often called "tigers," but for no particular reason. Several species of the genus were spread all over the United States and Mexico, even ranging far into South America, but the only North American species of which the skeleton is completely known is †*S. californicus*. An incredible number of these have been collected from the tar-pits of Rancho La Brea. The whole subfamily (†Machairodontinæ), now extinct, was especially characterized by the upper canine teeth, which are great recurved scimitars, with serrate edges, for stabbing.

There was also an enormous true cat, *Felis* †*atrox*, which may well be called the †American Lion; it exceeded by a quarter the dimensions of the largest species of the family now in existence. These magnificent creatures, which have been found in California and in the South, apparently, at least, were very much less numerous than their †sabretooth rivals and, unlike the latter, they were of immigrant stock. The smaller true cats, the pumas and lynxes, were very much like their modern successors, but, so far as can be judged, they were relatively less numerous than at present.

As characteristic of the Pleistocene as the †sabre-tooth cats, were the great †dire wolves (*Canis*, or †*Ænocyon dirus*) which were larger than any existing American wolf and ranged all over the

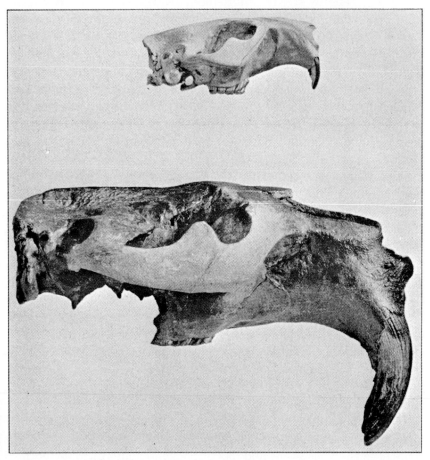

Fig. 145. — Skulls of beavers on same scale. Upper figure, Recent Beaver, *Castor canadensis*. Lower figure, †Giant Beaver, Pleistocene, †*Castoroides ohioensis*. (Field Mus. Nat. Hist.)

country to Florida and Mexico. They are the most abundant fossils in the California tar-pits, even outnumbering †*Smilodon*. The massive teeth of this species, fitted for crushing bones, would suggest habits more or less like those of the hyenas. The existing Grey Wolf, Coyote, Red Foxes, were all present in the Pleistocene, but appear to have been much less common than the †Dire Wolf.

Of the bears, there were two natural groups, one of which, comprising the Black and Grizzly Bears, was very much as at present and migrated from Asia at a very late period. The other group, so far as known at present, was peculiar to the Western Hemisphere and was derived from immigrants which entered North America early in the Pliocene. These were the †Short-faced Bears (†*Arctotherium*), which were very large, equalling, or even surpassing the great Brown and Kadiak Bears of Recent Alaska. The jaws are so much shortened that the skull has an appearance not unlike that of a bull dog, and the teeth indicate habits more strictly carnivorous than in the typical bears. The modern Spectacled Bear of South America (*Tremarctos*) is allied to the short-faced group. Scanty remains of a colossal bear have been found in Nebraska, far exceeding in size any other known member of the family. Presumably, it belonged to the short-faced section.

The Rodentia, or gnawing animals, are very inadequately represented among Pleistocene fossils, as is true also of the small and delicate mammals generally. No doubt all the Recent genera of North American rodents were in existence in the Pleistocene and, in addition, there were several large, peculiar, or exotic forms which have since disappeared from the continent, or have become altogether extinct. The †Giant Beaver (†*Castoroides ohioensis*) was a northern form, found only, as yet, in Nebraska, Michigan, Indiana, Ohio and New York, and was as large as a Black Bear. This genus, though seemingly of indigenous origin, had highly complex grinding teeth, which were very like those of the South American Capybara (*Hydrochœrus*) though there was no relationship between the two, except as all rodents are interrelated. The Capybara itself was likewise present in the North American Pleistocene, though not extending beyond South Carolina. Another immigrant from the Neotropical region, the Short-tailed, or Canada Porcupine (*Erethizon dorsatus*) was common all over the country in the Pleistocene and has thriven and maintained its foothold until the present day, with a Boreal and mountainous distribution.

Of all the huge and strange creatures which inhabited North America in the Pleistocene, undoubtedly the most bizarre were the xenarthrous Edentata, which began to invade the continent from south America in the early Pliocene, or even in the Miocene. Most of these belonged to the extinct orders of the †ground-sloths (†Gravigrada) and the †Glyptodontia, which might well be called †Giant Armadillos, were not that term already in use for a living Brazilian species. Four genera of †ground-sloths were in North America during the Pleistocene, with some different ranges. †*Mylodon*, of very massive proportions, with short heavy legs and formidable claws, was principally an open country animal and was most abundant along the Pacific slope and over the Great Plains from Nebraska to Mexico, but extended also into the eastern forests, as far north as Pennsylvania.

A second genus, †*Megatherium*, comprised animals larger and more ponderous than an elephant, but with much shorter legs and very massive tail. The species of this genus though occasionally ranging as far north as New Jersey, are mostly confined to the southern states and Mexico. Another †ground-sloth, first described and named by Thomas Jefferson in 1797, †*Megalonyx*, was much smaller than †*Megatherium*, which it resembled in general appearance, and was most frequent in the eastern forests, though it also occurred in the Mississippi Valley and California. The most complete skeletons yet obtained were found in N. E. Ohio and in a cavern in Tennessee. One of these is mounted in the museum of the Ohio State University at Columbus. The fourth of the North American †ground-sloths was †*Nothrotherium*, a much smaller animal than those mentioned above, which is remarkable for the extreme slenderness of the fore-legs, that look like those of the existing Ant-bear (*Myrmecophaga*). So far as at present known, †*Nothrotherium* was confined to California and the Southwest, New Mexico, Texas, Old Mexico and South America.

The †Glyptodontia, enormous, armadillo-like creatures, were encased in a solid carapace, the thick plates of which were immovably joined to one another at their edges. The long tail was sheathed in heavy rings of bony plates. The †glyptodonts were entirely southern in distribution, Mexico, Texas and Florida. Armadillos, the only group of existing edentates to be represented in the North American Pleistocene, were confined to the South. An extremely large extinct animal (†*Chlamytherium septentrionale*) was associated in Florida with the modern *Tatu*.

Summing up, it may be said that the Pleistocene fauna of North America was remarkably rich, abundant and varied and was characterized by many very large animals. The open roads of migration from Asia and South America brought together a great assemblage of Old World and Neotropical types, which, mingled with the many indigenous groups, made up a fauna of far more comprehensive and cosmopolitan character than is the existing one. This fauna contained substantially all the genera of mammals now living in this continent, together with many groups no longer represented here. The most conspicuous elements of the fauna were †mastodonts, true elephants, llamas, peccaries, antelopes of extinct kinds, musk-oxen, a great variety of huge bison, many species of horses, †sabre-tooth cats, immense lion-like cats, †dire wolves, †short-faced bears, †ground-sloths, †glyptodonts and armadillos; truly a most wonderful list.

II. Tertiary Faunas

1. Pliocene

In spite of the remarkable progress which has, of late years, been made in the stratigraphy and palæontology of the Pliocene of North America, that part of the history remains the most incompletely known of all the Tertiary epochs. The material is widely scattered and is, in most localities, scanty and fragmentary; nevertheless, a fairly adequate conception of Pliocene mammalian life may now be gained. There was, of course, considerable change and development among mammals in the course of the epoch, the Pliocene grading into the Miocene below and the Pleistocene above almost imperceptibly. The fauna of the Hagerman lake-deposits in Idaho is very typical of the upper Pliocene, though the list of genera is a short one and evidently includes but a small fraction of the mammals then living in North America.

In making up these faunal lists the treatment of negative evidence becomes very important. Because certain mammals are absent from a given series of beds, it must not be immediately inferred that those mammals did not exist at that time and place. This may, or may not, have been true; the failure to find certain fossils may have been due to the conditions of fossilization, or to the accidents of collecting. On the other hand, negative evidence cannot be ignored as unimportant, for when properly evaluated, it is quite as significant as positive evidence, but it must be carefully considered in the light of all relevant facts.

Aside from certain deposits of questionable date, no bones belonging to the modern genus *Equus* have been found, even in the latest Pliocene. The equine genus characteristic of the upper Pliocene is †*Plesippus*, in which, as the name implies, the modern stage of development was almost attained, but the grinding teeth have a somewhat simpler pattern. †*Plesippus* was the first of the equine genera in which the limb-bones had acquired the sturdy proportions seen in Recent horses, all the preceding genera having remarkably slender, deer-like legs. One species of Pleistocene horse, *Equus* †*occidentalis*, of California, retained the slenderness of limb char-

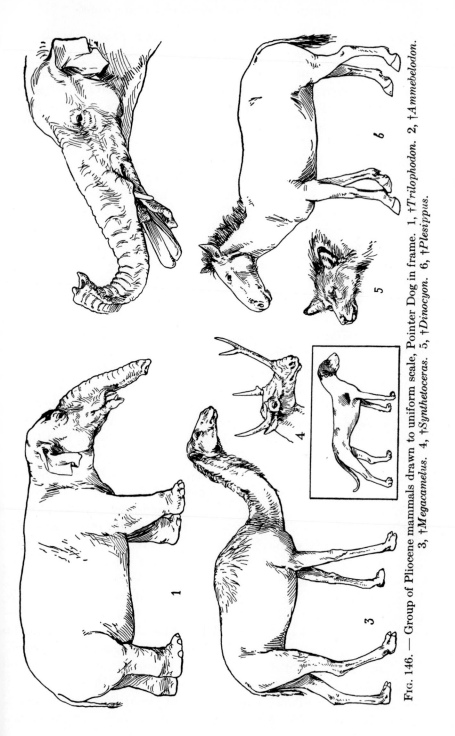

Fig. 146. — Group of Pliocene mammals drawn to uniform scale, Pointer Dog in frame. 1, †Trilophodon. 2, †Ammebelodon. 3, †Megacamelus. 4, †Synthetoceras. 5, †Dinocyon. 6, †Plesippus.

acteristic of most Tertiary equines which preceded †*Plesippus*. In one respect, there was a very strong contrast between the horses of the Pliocene and those of the Pleistocene, namely, that in the former there was no such variety of species as we have found in the latter.

Tapirs have not been found and this is an instance in which negative evidence is very probably misleading, for these animals existed in North America before and after the upper Pliocene.

Remains of artiodactyls are scanty and fragmentary; peccaries, llamas, deer (the latter of uncertain reference) have been found and antelopes of the peculiar American family, Antilocapridæ, were common in Oregon and Nevada. A genus of this group, †*Sphenophalos*, is of great interest as having the *bony horn-core* obscurely forked, not merely the horny sheath, as in *Antilocapra*. A colossal camel-like animal (†*Megacamelus*) was discovered in the upper Pliocene of Arizona; it is a gigantic llama rather than a camel. Bison and musk-oxen, so abundant in the Pleistocene, had apparently not yet arrived in America.

None of the true elephants has, as yet, come to light, a very striking difference from the Pleistocene and an even stronger contrast with the latter is afforded by the astonishing number and variety of the †mastodonts which have been found in the middle and upper Pliocene, especially of Nebraska. No doubt these grotesque beasts were as common elsewhere as on the Great Plains, but only there were the conditions of fossilization so favourable. †*Stegomastodon*, in a sense intermediate between †mastodonts and elephants, was common in Texas, and in Nebraska the prevailing forms were the long-jawed, four-tusked genera †*Trilophodon*, †*Rhynchotherium*, etc.

Most remarkable of all were the "†shovel-tuskers" and "†scoop-tuskers" (†*Ammebelodon* and †*Platybelodon*). In the former the lower jaw was immensely elongated (as much as six feet) and the lower tusks flattened and narrowed, presumably for digging. In †*Platybelodon*, which is also found in Mongolia and elsewhere in the Old World, the lower tusks were immense, wide scoops. It is difficult to imagine what such creatures can have looked like in life. In addition to this host of long-jawed and four-tusked proboscideans, there were some short-jawed, two-tusked genera (†*Pliomastodon*) which were forerunners, if not direct ancestors, of the †Mastodon (†*Mastodon americanus*) which was so characteristic of the Pleistocene. All this astonishing horde of long- and short-jawed †mastodonts were immigrants from Asia; few, if any, new genera arose on American soil.

The list of Pliocene Carnivora is quite varied, though evidently still very incomplete. The characteristic middle Pliocene †*Borophagus*, may have continued through the whole epoch; it is difficult to decide from extant specimens whether an allied genus may have replaced it. Much the best material has been obtained in the lower Pliocene of Texas (Clarendon and Hemphill stages). †*Borophagus*

Fig. 147. — †Horned Gopher, †*Epigaulus hatcheri*, lower Pliocene, Neb. (Restored from a skeleton in U. S. Nat. Mus.)

was one of the dog family, a short-faced wolf, with massive, hyena-like teeth. There were true cats so modern in type as to be referable to the Recent genus *Felis*, and †sabre-tooth cats which may have belonged to the European genus †*Machairodus*, but the known material is insufficient to make this reference at all certain. Otters of the modern genus *Lutra*, were present and also an allied form, †*Lutravus*, which shows some likeness to the Neotropical Grison (*Galera vittata*) and there were other members of the weasel family (Mustelidæ) not yet named.

The rodent fauna, so far as it has been ascertained, is of very modern character; there were rabbits, ground-squirrels, pocket-gophers, †horned gophers, deer-mice, hamsters, etc. Doubtless many rodents remain to be discovered.

In very decided contrast to the Pleistocene, the upper Pliocene had but few of the South American edentates. So far as is at present known, there was only the very large †ground-sloth †*Megalonyx* and one Texan †glyptodont †*Glyptotherium*.

The fauna of the lower Pliocene is much more completely known than that of the upper and, in particular, the Snake Creek stage of Nebraska has yielded a long list of finely preserved mammals. The Rattlesnake stage of Oregon, the Ricardo of southern California, the Clarendon and Hemphill of Texas and the Alachua of Florida give supplementary information, but, except for the Texan beds, the material from these deposits is more fragmentary.

The scarcity of Proboscidea is a great contrast to the upper Pliocene, when they were so abundant. They were mostly of the long-jawed, four-tusked kind (†*Rhynchotherium*, †*Trilophodon*), but the short-jawed type, without lower tusks and having a low, flat skull, (†*Pliomastodon*) was also represented.

The large representation of Perissodactyla compensated, in a measure, for the relative scantiness of the Proboscidea. Rhinoceroses were especially abundant, several genera of the hornless and small-horned kinds surviving from the Miocene. As usual, tapirs are rare as fossils, but they have been found. Horses were well represented and by three genera, in particular. One of these, †*Protohippus*, survived from the upper Miocene and is of great interest in the history of the equine family; it has the hypsodont (or high-crowned) grinding teeth, both in the deciduous and in the permanent series, but the crown was relatively hardly more than half as high as in the modern *Equus*. In stature †*Protohippus* was about equal to a Virginia Deer, which it further resembled in the very slender, graceful limbs. The feet, both fore and hind, had three toes.

The horse which especially characterizes the lower Pliocene is †*Pliohippus*, which differs from †*Protohippus* chiefly in the loss of the phalanges, so that the feet are as completely single-toed, or mono-dactyl, as in modern horses. The splint-bones, however, are much longer and less reduced than in the latter. †*Hipparion*, which is very like †*Protohippus*, except in having a slightly different pattern of the grinding teeth, made its way into Asia, where it is everywhere characteristic of the lower Pliocene, and extended its range to the south of France. Finally, the Miocene browsing horse, †*Hypohippus*, which had low-crowned, rooted molars without cement, persisted into the Pliocene. An enormous species of this genus was found in Nebraska; it was the last survivor of a long line.

Artiodactyla were numerous and varied, but conspicuously less so than in the corresponding formations of the Old World. Peccaries (†*Prosthennops*) with long snouts and simpler teeth than in the modern genus, were common. Almost the last of the peculiar and characteristic North American family of the †Merycoidodontidæ (†"oreodonts" in the vernacular) is the lower Pliocene †*Pronomotherium*, in which the facial part of the skull is so short and deep as to give it a curious likeness to the skull of an anthropoid ape. In the living animal, however, such likeness would be destroyed by the proboscis which †*Pronomotherium* undoubtedly had. The camel tribe passed through most of its evolutionary history in North America, though that continent never had any true camels, which arose in Asia from an immigrant American ancestry. In the lower Pliocene were ancestral types (†*Procamelus*) of moderate size and an immense llama (†*Pliauchenia*) which was much smaller, however, than the colossal †*Megacamelus* of the upper Pliocene. The last of the †gazelle-like camels (†*Rakomylus*) occurs here.

The ruminants, especially, were not nearly so numerous or so diversified as those of the Eastern Hemisphere. Hornless deer-like animals (†*Blastomeryx*) were not improbably the ancestors of the American types of deer (*Odocoileus*) but the horde of deer-like genera in the lower Pliocene died out and left no successors. The remarkable †*Merycodus*, which had simply forked, or even branching antlers, may have given rise to the prong-bucks (*Antilocapridæ*). These two genera are the most abundant of the lower Pliocene. A fantastic creature with four horns (†*Synthetoceras*), which was found in the Clarendon of Texas, is the last of a long series that goes back to the Oligocene.

Carnivora of several families are a conspicuous element in the lower Pliocene fauna. True cats and †sabre-tooths were present, but the fossils are rare and ill-preserved, so that little is known of them. Bear-like animals (? †*Indarctos* and †*Hyænarctos*) have been reported from the Pacific Coast and were the earliest American members of the family, which came from Asia. Much more characteristic of the lower Pliocene is the multitude of the Canidæ, large and small. There were ancestral wolves (†*Tomarctus*) and many species of the aberrant and strange forms that have been called "†bear-dogs" and "†hyena-dogs," but as these terms have been widely misunderstood as implying a relationship, it will be better to use "†bear-like" and "†hyena-like," terms which are meant to express a merely superficial resemblance.

The principal †hyena-like dog, †*Ælurodon*, is an unmistakable canid, but its teeth are very like those of hyenas and probably indicate a likeness in habits of feeding. Of the †bear-like dogs, †*Amphicyon*, †*Dinocyon* and †*Hemicyon* also occur in Europe; some of the species were of enormous size, rivalling the largest of modern bears. The weasel family (Mustelidæ) is represented by many imperfectly known species, most of which do not seem to have any close relationships with modern forms.

Rodents are common and several of the Recent families are known, such as the rabbits, pocket-gophers, †land-beavers and mice, but especially characteristic are the †horned gophers (†*Epigaulus*), surely the strangest looking rodent of all time.

South American edentates had begun to invade North America and †ground-sloths of no great size have been found in Oregon and Nebraska; the elevation of the Isthmus of Panama and the junction of the two continents were having their effects.

The middle Pliocene fauna, typically found in the Blanco of Texas, is not so well known as that of the upper, or the lower division; it has a greater abundance of the Proboscidea than the latter and is marked by the final appearance of the rhinoceroses in America and by the seemingly complete extinction of the long-lived †oreodont family.

The Pliocene of North America may be briefly characterized by the steady modernization of its horses and the dying out of the †oreodonts and rhinoceroses, the variety of its camel-llama types, some of which are of gigantic size, and above all by the extraordinary multitude of Proboscidea, which came in from Asia in the upper Pliocene. Most of these belong to the long-jawed and four-tusked †mastodonts, but some of the short-jawed kinds had also arrived. The first appearance of American bears and a great increase of †deer-like and †antelope-like genera are also characteristic.

2. Miocene

The boundary between Pliocene and Miocene has been repeatedly shifted, because the passage from one to the other is gradual, without hiatus. Even yet, there is some difference of usage in drawing the line. Dr. Simpson, for example, regards the Valentine as the lowest Pliocene, while to me, the whole character of the fauna seems Miocene.

As we go backward in time, existing genera gradually disappear

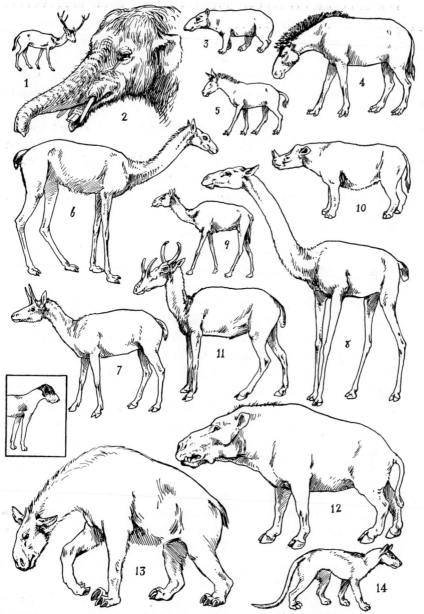

FIG. 148. — Miocene mammals drawn to scale, with a pointer dog, in frame, for comparison. 1, †*Merycodus*. 2, †*Trilophodon*. 3, †*Merycochœrus*. 4, †*Hypohippus*. 5, †*Merychippus*. 6, †*Oxydactylus*. 7, †*Dromomeryx*. 8, †*Alticamelus*. 9, †*Stenomylus*. 10, †*Diceratherium*. 11, †*Syndyoceras*. 12, †*Dinohyus*. 13, †*Moropus*. 14, †*Daphœnodon*.

and their place is taken by ancestral forms and by such as died out without leaving descendants. More and more, therefore, with increasing antiquity, it becomes necessary to use the vernacular names of groups in a broad and comprehensive sense. Family names are now generally used by palæontologists to mean genetic series and, in that sense, many of them go back to the Eocene for their known beginnings.

The upper Miocene Rodentia are numerous and varied and include many of the Recent families, but all the genera are different. Rabbits, rats and mice, squirrels, marmots, †beaver-like burrowers, pocket-gophers and the extraordinary †mylagaulids, including the horned species, are relatively common. There can be little doubt that many rodents are still to be discovered.

The Carnivora were much like those of the lower Pliocene, except that the †hyena-like dogs were less numerous, but the †bear-like genera (†*Amphicyon*, †*Hemicyon*, †*Dinocyon*), including some very large species, were abundant. So far, no member of the main line of wolf descent has been found in the upper Miocene, but, almost certainly, this lack is merely another instance of the failure of preservation, or of discovery. Nothing that can be considered as ancestral to the foxes has yet been found anywhere in the upper Miocene of any continent. Members of the weasel family (Mustelidæ) are numerous, martens, otters, badgers and a large form suggestively like the Wolverene (*Gulo*) are known, but most of these forms, while related to the modern genera, would seem not to have been their direct ancestors. †Nimravines (†*Pseudælurus*) were present, but not abundant. Raccoons (Procyonidæ) are somewhat doubtful and bears entirely absent.

Miocene Proboscidea are comparatively rare in this country, which is in striking contrast to the multitude of these animals in the Pliocene. Miocene proboscideans are relatively small and are long-jawed, four-tusked genera (†*Trilophodon* and †*Tetralophodon*) of the †buno-mastodonts. Short-jawed genera existed in the middle Miocene and, no doubt, in the upper section also.

Of the Perissodactyla, four families were represented in the American upper Miocene, the horses, tapirs, rhinoceroses and the marvellous, clawed †chalicotheres; the last-named, however, were rare and at the point of extinction in America. Of the tapirs, little more can be said than that they were present in the fauna and were intermediate in character between those of the Oligocene and those of the Pleistocene. Rhinoceroses are very abundant, and numerous skeletons of this group have been collected. Apparently, most of these upper Miocene genera were not descended from American stocks, but were Old World migrants. They belonged to the same genera as those of the lower Pliocene and were either hornless (†*Aphelops*, †*Peraceras*) or had a very small horn on the tip of the nose (†*Teleoceras*). Some were remarkably long-bodied and short-legged, with much the same proportions as a hippopotamus, while others had longer legs and feet.

Most abundant of all were the horses, and the typical upper Miocene horse is †*Protohippus*, which continued into the lower Pliocene; it was a small, three-toed animal with very slender legs. †*Hypohippus*, which also continued into the Pliocene, was a three-toed browsing horse, with rooted, low-crowned teeth. A closely allied form is †*Anchitherium* of the French Miocene, which appears to have been a migrant from America. †*Hypohippus* has a very large and deep depression on each side of the face, which probably lodged an extension, or *diverticulum*, of the nasal organ.

Much more abundant in the upper Miocene were the Artiodactyla, yet very inferior in number and diversity to those of Europe. Especially conspicuous were the camel-llama tribes (suborder Tylopoda), which for a very long period were entirely confined to North America. The typical upper Miocene genus is †*Procamelus*, which was apparently an ancestor common to both camels and llamas, and of this genus there were several more or less well-defined species. The characteristically North American family of the †oreodonts had begun to decline and was not destined to continue beyond the lower Pliocene. Several genera, however, are found in the upper Miocene; among them was the grotesque, ape-like †*Pronomotherium*, which was the final step in the evolution of the short-faced, proboscis-bearing type. This family displayed great variety in the structure of the skull, but were remarkably conservative with regard to that of the body, limbs and feet. Another upper Miocene genus was †*Merychyus*, which had a short, deep skull, with high-crowned (hypsodont) teeth that were fitted for grazing. Its limbs are more slender and the feet narrower than in most other members of the family. The hornless deer (†*Blastomeryx*) and the "†deer-antelopes" (†*Merycodus*) were conspicuous elements in the fauna and peccaries of primitive type were common.

An especially characteristic feature of the later Miocene faunas was the large number of mammals, belonging to several different orders, which had the hypsodont, or persistently growing type of grinding teeth; many of the horses, camels, ruminants and rodents displayed this structure and, as was first pointed out by Kowalevsky, the explanation is probably to be found in the spread of grasslands at the expense of the forests. Because of the minute particles of silica which they contain, the grasses are very abrasive and rapidly wear down the teeth of grazing mammals. In adaptation to this new source of abundant and nutritious food-supplies, many different mammals developed a form of tooth which was fitted to compensate by growth for the loss through abrasion.

The middle Miocene 'covers small, widely-scattered areas in Oregon, where it is called the *Mascall*, in northeastern Colorado, the *Pawnee Creek*, in Nebraska, where the *Sheep Creek* and the lower part of the *Snake Creek* are referred to this time, and in central Montana, where the *Deep River* beds are especially typical. Except for the Snake Creek area, the list of fossil genera is comparatively short and it is evident that it affords a more than usually inadequate picture of the life of that time. Small animals are particularly rare, except in the Snake Creek, where a considerable number of fragmentary remains of *rodents* have been found. These are rabbits, squirrels, beavers, pocket-gophers, rats and mice and the extraordinary extinct family of the †Mylagaulidæ, which we have already met with in the upper Miocene and lower Pliocene, including the bizarre horned †*Ceratogaulu3* (or †*Epigaulus*).

Middle Miocene Carnivora are very numerous and varied, but as they all belong to extinct genera, it is difficult to characterize them in vernacular terms, a difficulty which increases in direct proportion to the geological antiquity of the genera. Of the dog family, the great aberrant bear-like †*Amphicyon* and †*Dinocyon*, of which there were several species in each genus, were associated with ancestors of the modern wolves (†*Tomarctus*). Primitive raccoons and many mustelines were represented, as was also a †nimravine (†*Pseudælurus*), but, as yet, no †sabre-tooth has been found.

Hoofed animals were, as a matter of course, much the commonest fossils. Probably the last of the extraordinary clawed perissodactyls, or †Ancylopoda, to be found in the Western Hemisphere were those of the upper and middle Miocene. In the middle section two tribes of the suborder coexisted; the American †*Moropus*, so common in the lower Miocene, continued into the middle, though in greatly reduced numbers, and along with this was the European †*Macrotherium*, an immigrant. The suborder has not been found in this continent later than the upper Miocene, but in Asia it persisted until the Pleistocene.

Of the normal, hoofed perissodactyls (Chelopoda) rhinoceroses

FIG. 149. — A †land-beaver, †*Palæocastor*, showing spiral burrows, lower Miocene.

were much less common than they had been in the lower Miocene, though there was little variety then, only the small-horned †*Teleoceras* being found.   To all appearances, the indigenous American stocks of rhinoceroses largely died out in the middle Miocene, †*Teleoceras* and the other genera of the upper Miocene and lower Pliocene being seemingly immigrants from Asia.

The characteristic middle Miocene horse is †*Merychippus*, several species of which are very common fossils. This genus is an unusually interesting transitional form. †*Merychippus* is just what an animal ancestral to the later horses might be expected to be like. Two other horses occur in the middle Miocene, one, †*Desmatippus*, is somewhat of a puzzle, for it has been found only in the Deep River beds in association with †*Merychippus*, though it is much more primitive than the latter. The permanent teeth are low-crowned and rooted, but have a thin deposit of cement in the valleys, and the enamel-crests have a crenellated outline. Structurally, †*Desmatippus* comes between †*Merychippus* and the lower Miocene †*Parahippus*, but there seems to be no place for it in the strata as a real member of equine genealogy, unless there was a hiatus in time between the upper Harrison and the middle Miocene in which †*Desmatippus* was evolved.

The persistently conservative, three-toed †*Hypohippus*, with its brachyodont, rooted grinding teeth, began its separate existence in the middle Miocene and continued into the upper Pliocene. The horses of this genus could not have grazed, but browsed upon leaves and other soft vegetable tissues.

Artiodactyla were the dominant order of ungulates; peccaries, camels, antelopes and deer, using these terms in the most comprehensive sense. The characteristic cameline genus is †*Protolabis*, an obvious ancestor of the upper Miocene †*Procamelus;* the grinding teeth are not so high-crowned as in the latter, the incisors less reduced and the long bones of the feet (metapodials) are separate, not forming cannon-bones. The size of the middle Miocene animal is smaller †*Alticamelus* of this formation was an astonishing creature, having the great height, extremely long neck and fore-limbs of the modern giraffes, which it must have resembled in habits.

The hornless, deer-like †*Blastomeryx* and aberrant deer †*Dromomeryx* and the antelopine †*Merycodus* are characteristic. It would seem that every formation must have its incredibly fantastic creature and, for the middle Miocene, the choice lies between the giraffe-like †*Alticamelus* and the grotesque cervid, †*Cranioceras*, in which, beside the pair of horns over the eyes, a third one grew out of the occipital crest in the middle line. The characteristically North American family of the †oreodonts (†Merycoidodontidæ) which came to an end with the lower Pliocene, was flourishing in the middle Miocene. Of the proboscis-bearing genera, both †*Merycochœrus* and †*Pronomotherium* were present, but in the latter the peculiar development had not reached such an extreme as is seen in the upper Miocene and lower Pliocene species. The grazing, slim-legged †*Merychyus* was common and the similar, but heavier †*Ticholeptus* is characteristic of the Deep River, which Cope named the †*Ticholeptus* Beds. The supposedly aquatic †*Cyclopidius* was the last known survivor of the †*Leptauchenia* series, which goes back to lower White River times.

The middle Miocene is notable for the fact that in it are found the most ancient known American proboscideans. The fossils are rare, scanty and fragmentary, and it is difficult to classify them, but there would seem to be two distinct tribes represented; one of the long-jawed, four-tusked kind and the other (†*Miomastodon*) of the short-jawed type, with very simple grinding teeth, which led up to †*Mastodon americanus* of the Pleistocene.

The subdivisions of the lower Miocene are still in some doubt, so far, at least, as to the names which should be applied to them. Provisionally, the fourfold division of the Upper and Lower Harrison, the Gering and Monroe Creek (Lower Rosebud) will be here adopted. Though the two divisions of the Harrison have very distinct faunas, they will be treated together for the purposes of this succinct chapter, for they have a great deal in common. The lower Miocene faunas are almost entirely indigenous in the sense of being derived from American ancestry. The immigrant forms are so few as to suggest that the way of migration from the Old World had, in some manner, been rendered difficult. In harmony with this suggestion is the fact that in the Miocene of Mongolia the American element was greatly diminished.

As in the Miocene generally, the small mammals are very inadequately represented, the conditions of deposition being unfavourable to their preservation. The Rodentia, which are quite numerous, though seldom well-preserved, are directly continuous with those of the Oligocene and, at the same time, more or less distantly connected with the modern rabbits, squirrels, beavers, sewellels, pocket-gophers and kangaroo-rats.

Carnivora were numerously represented, especially the dog family

(Canidæ), for, in addition to very primitive wolves, there are several aberrant genera, which held over from the John Day through the Gering, but not into the Harrison. The †nimravines (†*Pseudælurus*) and the †sabre-tooth cats probably were a development of native lines. Several large mustelines, one of which was in many ways like the Wolverene, were of Old World origin. Of particular interest is the genus †*Phlaocyon*, which is taken to be the beginning of the raccoon family (Procyonidæ) and, if rightly interpreted, indicates the derivation of that family from primitive dogs.

Four families of Perissodactyla were represented in the lower Miocene. The prevalent and exceedingly common rhinoceros among the fossils is a small animal with a transverse pair of horns on the nose of the male (†*Diceratherium*), the female was hornless. This genus is a survival from the Oligocene and was apparently the last of the native lines, the ancestry of which may be traced back into the Eocene. Tapirs are very rare in the lower Miocene, when they were smaller and lighter than their successors.

Individually, horses are exceedingly abundant in the lower Miocene, but there is no great variety among them and nearly all the fossils are referable to the single genus †*Parahippus*, which is intermediate in size and structure between the middle Miocene †*Merychippus* and the upper Oligocene †*Miohippus*. One very long-legged species is separated by some authorities as a distinct genus and called †*Kalobatippus*, the "†stilt horse," which must have been a very peculiar-looking creature when in life.

The suborder †Ancylopoda, or perissodactyls with claws, was more numerous in the lower Miocene of North America than at any other time before or after. The first-named genus of the group was the German †*Chalicotherium*, whence the family name of †Chalicotheriidæ and the vernacular term †chalicotheres, which is used for the suborder. The lower Miocene genus is †*Moropus*, which is as grotesque a creature as could be well imagined and, indeed, in advance of experience, no one ever did imagine such a beast. The American history of the †chalicotheres runs from the middle Eocene to the end of the Miocene, or, perhaps, to the early Pliocene, but only in the lower Miocene were these incredible monsters at all common. †*Moropus* was a very large animal, with elongate neck and back sloping to the rump.

Artiodactyla were even more numerous and diversified than the perissodactyls. †*Dinohyus* was the latest and largest of a series called the "†giant pigs," which ran through the Oligocene and the lower Miocene. †*Dinohyus* must have stood six feet high at the shoulder.

Peccaries of a more primitive type than those of the upper Miocene and the Pliocene completed the list of suillines.

The †oreodonts existed in great variety, though except in size, and in the character of dentition and skull, they were not very different from one another, having much the proportions of peccaries and swine, with short necks, legs and feet, long bodies and tails. The most abundant of the lower Miocene genera are †*Merycochœrus*, which had a short proboscis, and †*Promerycochœrus* with long face; the last of the †anthracotheres, †*Arretotherium*, occurs in the Harrison.

A family which had been very abundant in the Oligocene, the †Leptomerycidæ (or †Hypertragulidæ) continued into the Miocene with both of its branches, one of which ended in the lower Pliocene. The little †*Hypertragulus*, which must have been much like the chevrotains, in appearance, and the even smaller †*Nanotragulus* have not been found after the lower Miocene, but the extraordinary, four-horned †*Syndyoceras* was an even more incredible creature than its Oligocene forerunner. The first of the deer-like †*Blastomeryx* species dates from this time and was doubtless a newly arrived migrant from Asia.

Three distinct lines of the camel-llama tribe are found in the lower Miocene. (1) There was what may be called the main stem which led to the modern forms of camels and llamas, and was typified by †*Protomeryx*, which did not much exceed a sheep in size. (2) The still smaller †gazelle-like camels (†*Stenomylus*) are so called because of the length and great slenderness of their legs, not because of any relationship with the antelopes. (3) There was a series which would seem to have been ancestral to the extraordinary †giraffe-like camels (†*Alticamelus*) of the Middle Miocene, exemplified by the large, and long-necked, but lightly and slenderly built †*Oxydactylus*.

Miocene mammals are so numerous and varied that it is difficult to sum up the successive faunas in a paragraph. The most abundant Carnivora belong to the dog family, of which the †bear-like and †hyena-like dogs are much the most numerous, and some of the †bear-like forms were of immense size: †*Dinocyon*, largest of known dogs, was as big as a Polar Bear. The many large mustelines would seem not to have been ancestral to any of the modern genera, but rather to have

belonged to sidelines. Cats were relatively rare, a great change from
the Oligocene.

There was a great variety of hoofed animals; in the course of the
epoch the horses acquired hypsodont teeth and increased in size
and in approximation to the modern type. The native stocks of
rhinoceroses largely died out with the lower Miocene, but migrants
from the Old World replaced them. The first proboscideans to reach
North America were the four-tusked †mastodonts of the middle
Miocene. Artiodactyls were the most numerous and diversified of
hoofed animals. The last of the †giant pigs were those of the lower
Miocene and the family of the †oreodonts reached its culmination
in the middle of the epoch. The earliest American deer and antelope
appeared in the Miocene and peccaries continued throughout, but
are nowhere common as fossils.

3. Oligocene

The aspect of the Oligocene mammalian faunas differs much in
accordance with the direction from which they are approached. If
one reaches them after a study of the Eocene, they seem to have a
very modern aspect, caused by the almost complete disappearance of
the archaic types of mammals which had been characteristic of the
Paleocene and persisted through more or less of the Eocene. Further
there was the development of orders which are still in existence
such as the Carnivora, Artiodactyla and Perissodactyla. The last
named group, which had been preponderant during the Eocene, in
the Oligocene yielded first place to the Artiodactyla. On the other
hand, if approached from the Miocene side, Oligocene mammals seem
very ancient and primitive, even though many of the genera, so far
as can be judged, were directly ancestral to families which are still
flourishing. Oligocene genera differ so much from their modern successors that terms like "horses," "rhinoceroses," "camels" must
be understood in an even more comprehensive sense than in the
foregoing pages.

a. *John Day Stage.* — About the John Day fauna there is much
that is puzzling, for it is so peculiar and unlike the faunas of the
Great Plains as to indicate some radical difference of habitat. Perhaps, as Osborn has suggested, it was an assemblage of forest-living
animals, contrasting in many ways with the contemporary fauna
of the open grasslands. Nearly all the mammalian genera of the
John Day would seem to have been of indigenous origin; a few are
doubtful and none is an indisputable immigrant.

Of the Carnivora there were but three families and one of these, the Mustelidæ, was but scantily represented. †Sabre-tooth cats were numerous and varied, but the true cats are not known to have reached America before the Pliocene. There are, however, two genera, †Archælurus and †Nimravus, which Cope, their discoverer, called "the false sabre-tooths," but which may turn out to be referable to the Felinæ. By far the most abundant and diversified of the carnivorous families was that of the dogs (Canidæ), which were mostly of small or moderate size. One species of †Temnocyon (†T.alti-genis) approximates the size of the modern Grey Wolf. The variety among the genera of the family is quite remarkable; long-faced and short-faced types and early stages of the †bear-like and †hyena-like dogs, as well as ancestors of the existing wolves and dholes (Cyon) may be distinguished, a truly wonderful assemblage.

The Rodentia were much more numerous and varied than they had been before, and included primitive and ancestral genera of the rabbits, rats, mice, squirrels, beavers, gophers and the earliest distinguishable representatives of the sewellels (Aplodontidæ), a curious modern family of rodents, peculiar to the Pacific Coast region.

The remainder of the John Day fauna consisted of artiodactyls and perissodactyls, the latter much diminished from the lower Oligocene and Eocene. The commonest rhinoceroses were those with a transverse pair of horns on the nose (†Diceratherium), but the American hornless †Subhyracodon continued and was destined to end before the lower Miocene. Of the horses, there was a single genus, †Miohippus, which was intermediate in size and structure between †Mesohippus of the White River and †Parahippus of the lower Miocene. Tapirs are rare and little known. The presence of the clawed †chalicotheres has been demonstrated, but the material is too scanty to show how they differed from their successors of the lower Miocene.

Artiodactyls were very numerous and of many different kinds. Ancestral peccaries are relatively common and well preserved and are of great evolutionary interest. The †giant-pigs, or †entelodonts, were very large, but had not attained such immense size as had those of the subsequent lower Miocene. The †oreodonts, individually very numerous, were in smaller variety than during the Miocene. Characteristic is †Promerycochœrus, an animal not unlike a Wild Boar in size and appearance; it was probably the beginning of the proboscis-bearing series which culminated in the ape-like †Pronomotherium of the Miocene. The commonest John Day representative of the family is †Eporeodon, which was in the less aberrant line of descent.

The †Agriochœridæ, a family allied to the †oreodonts, were comparatively short-lived, extending only from the upper Eocene to the John Day inclusive. In structure and probable habits they are extremely problematical. They were distinguished by powerful cat-like claws instead of hoofs. The †agriochœres were clawed artiodactyls just as the †chalicotheres were clawed perissodactyls. In both instances the dentition, purely herbivorous in type, seems to be entirely incompatible with claw-bearing feet.

The camel family representative in the John Day is still incompletely known, but the genus seems to be the same (†*Protomeryx*) as that in the lower Miocene. Another artiodactyl family of doubtful relationships is the †Leptomerycidæ, very small creatures which must have had much the appearance of the chevrotains or "mouse-deer" of present day Java. The common John Day genus is †*Hyper-tragulus*.

As noted in Chapter VI, the Sespé formation in the Coast Range of southern California is a continental deposit of more than 7000 feet in thickness, which rests upon marine Eocene and is, in turn, overlain by marine Miocene and thus probably represents the whole Oligocene. In the upper part of the Sespé occurs a fauna which appears to be that of the lower John Day and is older than those of the upper and middle parts of the stage which occur in Oregon. Here are found the only examples of †*Leptauchenia* which have been obtained in the Pacific Coast region. This fauna is, in general, transitional from the typical John Day downward to the White River.

b. White River Stage. — The great Badlands of this stage, which cover such wide areas of South Dakota, Nebraska, Wyoming and Colorado, represent the middle part of Oligocene time, the faunas of which are the best-known of the North American Tertiary, and have few rivals in the world for the extraordinary abundance and complete preservation of their fossil mammals. There are three well-defined substages, each with its own faunal characteristics, but in this brief résumé it will not be necessary to emphasize these distinctions. It is evident that a way of migration existed to and from Asia, for the White River contains a much larger proportion of Old World elements than does the John Day.

Marsupials, then as now, were restricted to the opossums (†*Pera-therium*) of which there were several species, some very minute.

Insectivora were relatively abundant; some of these were the last survivals of an Eocene family; others, such as the hedgehogs, moles and shrews, were probably immigrants.

Fig. 150. — *1*, †*Archæotherium. 2*, †Ancestral camel, †*Poëbrotherium. 3*, †*Mer-ycoidodon. 4*, †*Agriochærus. 5*, Ancestral horse, †*Mesohippus. 6*, †*Hoplophoneus. 7*, †*Bothriodon. 8*, †*Hyænodon. 9*, †Cursorial rhinoceros, †*Hyracodon. 10*, †*Pro-toceras. 11*, †Pair-horned rhinoceros, †*Diceratherium.* For scale see Fig. 154.

The primitive flesh-eaters known as †Creodonta, which had completely dominated the Eocene and Paleocene, had their last American representatives in the White River, where the sole surviving genera, †*Hyænodon* and †*Pterodon*, had come from the Old World. In Europe these animals continued into the Miocene, but in North America they have not been found in beds later than those of the White River. In the United States there are several species of the single genus †*Hyænodon*, of very different sizes, from a small fox to a large bear. Their powerful crushing and shearing teeth

FIG. 151. — White River †brontothere, †*Brotops robustus*. Drawn to same scale as Fig. 150.

suggest carrion-feeding habits, for their short legs and weak feet seem to indicate that they were not swift runners and not very efficient in the capture of living prey. In the White River of the Canadian Province, Saskatchewan, there is a very large species of †*Hemipsalodon* that may be different from †*Pterodon*, which has not been found in the United States in later than Duchesne River time.

Coincident with this decline of the †Creodonta was the rise of the true Carnivora, of which three families are found in the White River, those of the dogs, cats and mustelines. The dogs (Canidæ) were not nearly so diversified as were those of the John Day, but two tribes were already clearly differentiated, the larger (†*Daphœnus*) were very early, perhaps the earliest of the †bear-like series, and smaller weasel-like dogs (†*Pseudocynodictis*) with very long bodies and tails, the phylogenetic position of which has been the subject of much debate. †*Brachyrhynchocyon* was the forerunner of the †short-faced dogs of the John Day. No true cats (Felinæ) have been found, but †sabre-tooths are relatively common and of these there are three distinct types. One, †*Dinictis*, is much more primitive; the second, †*Hoplophoneus*, is a far more powerful and specialized animal. In the third, †*Eusmilus*, the scimitar-like canines and the protective flange

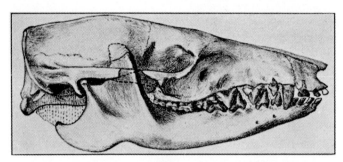

Fig. 152. — Skull of a small insectivore enlarged, †*Ictops dakotensis*, White River stage. (Morrill Mus. Univ. Neb.; from Scott and Jepsen.)

of the lower jaw reached what appears to be an extreme exaggeration and then this series died out.

In strong contrast to the Oligocene of Europe, the weasel family (Mustelidæ) is very poorly represented, only two genera (†*Bunælurus* and †*Mustelavus*) being at all well known.

The final member of the edentate-like North American †*Palæanodonta*, which can be traced back to the Paleocene, is somewhat doubtfully represented by the little †*Epoichotherium*, which had simple cylindrical teeth.

The Rodentia form a great contrast to those of the Eocene, far exceeding the latter in number and diversity; nine families and nineteen genera have been described, as many families as are living in North America to-day, though there are now seventy-five genera. Of the nine existing families only four (five, if the rabbits are included) have been found in the White River and the others are survivals of Eocene types. The White River rodent fauna is thus a mixture of old and new. (A. E. Wood.)

Hoofed animals, though in bewildering variety, were restricted to two orders, artiodactyls and perissodactyls. The latter no longer held the predominant position which had been theirs throughout the Eocene, but they had not yet suffered any actual loss, for no less than six perissodactyl families (as here reckoned) were still represented in the White River fauna. The Eocene family of the

†Brontotheriidæ reached its culmination in size and fantastic variety in the lower substage of the White River and then died out. In that substage is found a marvellous abundance of those great beasts, some of them of elephantine stature and bulk. In the Oligocene the family was common to North America and Asia and some species even spread into southeastern Europe.

Rhinoceroses were very common in the White River fauna, which included three American tribes, or series, derived from Eocene an-

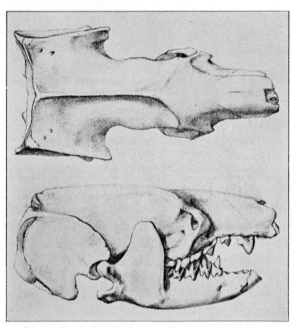

FIG. 153. — Skull of a small insectivore enlarged, †*Apternodus gregoryi*, allied to the West Indian *Solenodon*. Upper figure, top view. Lower figure, side view. (Mus. Comp. Zoöl. Harvard Univ.; from Scott and Jepsen.)

cestors. These three series are here regarded as families of the Rhinoceroidea. One of these families, the †Hyracodontidæ, or †thyracodonts, was of rather small, slender, long-necked, long-legged animals with narrow feet, and looked more like horses than rhinoceroses, except for their heavy, ungraceful heads. These were lightly built, cursorial animals, which have not been found later than the White River, or outside of North America.

The second series, that of the rhinoceroses proper (Rhinocerotidæ), comprised animals which in size and proportions were much like tapirs, though thoroughly rhinocerotic in the structure of every tooth and bone. Nearly all of the White River rhinoceroses were without horns, but in the uppermost substage are found those in which incipient paired horns mark the beginning of the †*Dicera-therium* type.

The third family (†Amynodontidæ) is made up of massive, long-bodied animals, with short necks, legs and feet, the entire structure of which is suggestive of aquatic habits; the large canine tusks are very like those of a hippopotamus. The †Amynodontidæ, which originated in the North American Eocene, also spread into Asia and thence into Europe.

Horses are very numerous in the White River beds nearly all belonging to the characteristic genus †*Mesohippus,* of which many species have been named. From the earlier to the later beds of the stage, there is a distinct increase in size, though the largest species did not exceed a sheep in stature. In detail, these little animals differed widely from modern horses, yet, with all the differences, there is an unmistakably equine character about the skeleton. In the upper levels the John Day horse, †*Miohippus,* makes its appearance.

White River tapirs, though rare as fossils, are better known than those of other Tertiary stages. The genus, †*Protapirus,* is apparently the same as that of the Old World and included animals which were much smaller than the existing species and of decidedly more primitive character. The bones of the muzzle indicate that the proboscis, if present at all, must have been in an incipient condition. An aberrant genus is †*Colodon,* in which the canines are reduced or absent. These were slender, long-legged animals, with very narrow feet; they are quite horse-like in appearance, but the teeth show that they were nearly related to an Eocene family.

Finally, the clawed †chalicotheres were represented in the fauna, but by fossils which are so rare and so fragmentary that little can be said concerning them.

In abundance of individuals the artiodactyls far surpass the perissodactyls in the White River badlands, though the number of families is but little greater. Much the commonest of these families is the unfortunately named †Merycoidodontidæ (or †Oreodontidæ). For a vernacular form "†oreodonts" is often retained, because it is so much less cumbrous, though according to the rules of nomenclature the term has no standing. The family is, so far as is yet known, exclusively North American in distribution and lasted from the upper Eocene to the lower Pliocene inclusive. In the White River, several species of †*Merycoidodon*, of varying sizes, were very numerous; indeed they are much the commonest of all fossils in that formation. A very peculiar †oreodont series, seemingly derived from †*Limnenetes* of the Chadron, appears in the uppermost part of the White River stage, where small and very small species of the genus †*Leptauchenia* are numerous. These curious animals had large vacuities in the bones of the face, exceedingly large auditory bullæ and hypsodont grinding teeth. The position of the nostrils, orbits and auditory tubes is like that of a miniature hippopotamus and strongly suggests aquatic habits. (Fig. 227, p. 366.)

The related, claw-footed †Agriochœridæ are very much rarer and are less common than in the John Day. The same genus, †*Agriochœrus*, occurs in both stages.

An immigrant group that gained but a brief foothold in America was the European family †Anthracotheriidæ, of which a surprising number of genera and species occur in the White River; in size and appearance these animals were like long-snouted swine.

Peccaries are not uncommon, though well-preserved fossils are very rare. At least two species of the genus †*Perchœrus* occur.

The "†giant pigs" (†Entelodontidæ) which reached their maximum size in the lower Miocene, are very abundant in the White River and are represented by species of very different stature. The family was first recognized in Europe and they reached America from Asia. No ancestors of the group are known in the American Eocene, though allied aberrant relatives are found there, which died out without descendants.

Of the camel family there were two tribes in the White River, one represented by the llama-like †*Poëbrotherium* which was an animal of very slender build and somewhat taller than a sheep, with hind legs considerably longer than the fore. †*Poëbrotherium* appears to have been ancestral to the modern camels and llamas. The other tribe, typified by †*Eotylopus*, is as yet of unknown significance; it may, perhaps, have given rise to the aberrant camels of the Miocene.

An extinct family, the †Leptomerycidæ, formed a group of small ruminant-like genera, the relationships of which are obscure and have been much disputed. †*Leptomeryx* and †*Hypertragulus* must have resembled the chevrotains, or "mouse-deer." †*Hypisodus* was a little creature, no larger than a rabbit, which, like †*Poëbrotherium*, was one of the very few Oligocene genera that had hypsodont, grazing teeth. Much like a gazelle in size and proportions was †*Protoceras*, the male of which had a grotesque head, with two pairs of horn-like protuberances from the skull and long recurved upper canine teeth. It is probable that †*Protoceras* will prove to be the ancestor of the even more grotesque †*Syndyoceras* of the Miocene and †*Synthetoceras* of the Pliocene, an astonishing series of nightmare-like creatures. A little artiodactyl †*Leptochœrus*, has been for more than seventy years an unsolved enigma, for the rare specimens found have been fragments of jaws with a few teeth unlike any other American genus or family. The recent discovery of an incomplete skull, of the allied genus †*Stibarus* now in the museum of Rapid City, South Dakota, makes possible a preliminary solution of the problem. The little creature, which did not exceed a Jack Rabbit in size, was probably one of the many immigrants from Asia and seems to have been distantly related to the †Dichobunidæ of Europe. Its possible connections with the American Eocene genera, †*Bunomeryx*, and †*Homacodon*, have yet to be determined.

   c. Duchesne River Stage. — Almost everything that is known of the Duchesne River formation and its fossils is due to the labours of the late Mr. O. A. Peterson and his associates of the Carnegie Museum, Pittsburgh. The strata of this stage, some 1400 feet thick, occur in northeastern Utah, where they lie, in apparent conformity, upon the top of the Uinta Eocene. Some writers prefer to assign the Duchesne River to the Eocene and there is much to be said for this course, but the character of the scanty fauna as a whole, is more decidedly Oligocene. Fossils are rare in these beds and the list of genera so far obtained is rather short, but it gives a fair conception of the life of that time and it may confidently be expected that future discoveries will add much to the fauna as at present known.

   In the Sespé formation of California the lower fossiliferous horizon has yielded a number of fossil mammals which agree well with those from northeastern Utah and indicate a very similar fauna.

   The Duchesne (as it may be called for brevity's sake) genus of Insectivora (†*Protictops*) belongs to an American family which died out in the White River. †Creodonta are represented by three genera, †*Hyænodon*, †*Pterodon*, and †*Hessolestes*, of which the first two are immigrants and belong to European genera. †*Hyænodon* has been found both in Utah and California, †*Pterodon* only in California. †*Hessolestes* is the last known representative of a family (†*Mesonychidæ*) which dates back to the American Paleocene and to the Eocene and Oligocene of Mongolia. True Carnivora have been obtained from the Duchesne; fragments indicate the probable presence of early dogs.

Rodentia obtained, as yet, represent squirrel-like forms, fore-runners of White River genera and a very interesting genus †*My-tonolagus*, which is the most ancient rabbit known in North America.

Artiodactyla are represented by fewer genera than the Peris-sodactyla, but, under the circumstances, when the fauna is mani-festly so little known, this fact may or may not be significant. A small suilline which may be referable to the Bridger genus †*Helohyus*, has been found, and also several †agriochœrids. One of these, †*Mes-agriochœrus*, appears to be in the line of descent between †*Pro-tagriochœrus*, of the upper Eocene and the White River †*Agriochœrus;* the Uinta genus †*Dichobunops* may also persist, but this is doubtful. †Oreodont remains, too incomplete for certain reference, have been obtained. The camel-llama series is represented by †*Poabromylus* and the White River genus †*Leptomeryx* here occurs for the first time.

The known Perissodactyla indicate several different lines, most of which continued into the White River and some even to the pres-ent day. Of the horses little more can be said than that they were present in the fauna. A tiny but unmistakable little tapir (†*Heter-aletes*) occurs, as do also two of the rhinoceros families and, al-most certainly, the third one will eventually turn up. The White River genus, †*Hyracodon* itself, appears to have been already in existence and a genus, †*Mesamynodon*, intermediate between the Uinta †*Amynodon* and the White River †*Metamynodon*, is character-istic. Most significant of all, perhaps, is the presence in relatively large numbers of a †brontothere which belongs to a genus, †*Teleodus*, that was first discovered at the base of the White River beds.

The mammals of the Oligocene epoch, with one possible excep-tion (*Sciurus*), all belonged to extinct genera and most of the fam-ilies have likewise disappeared. Except for the huge †brontotheres of the basal White River and the †giant pigs, there were no really large animals in the Oligocene; some were of moderate size, but the mammals were mostly small, some very minute. Few of the archaic types of mammals, so common in the Eocene, survived; only the two immigrant †creodonts, †*Hyænodon* and †*Pterodon* continued.

All the hoofed animals were either artiodactyls or perissodactyls; †oreodonts, †entelodonts, camels and †leptomerycids of one series, and horses, tapirs, three families of rhinoceroses, and the †bronto-theres, of the other, were characteristic. Among the Carnivora, the dog family was wonderfully diversified, especially in the John Day, and †sabre-tooth cats were common, but the other carnivorous families were either rare or absent from North America. The Rodentia steadily increased in numbers, diversity and relative importance throughout the epoch and were most numerous and varied in the John Day.

4. Eocene

Though the Eocene passes by slow gradations into the Oligocene, both faunally and stratigraphically, it is, as a whole, in very strong contrast to that epoch and its mammals bear the stamp of a much higher antiquity. During the very long lapse of time between the beginning and the end of the Eocene, development was ceaselessly in progress and the cumulative effect of all these changes was very great. In part, the change consisted in the elimination of the archaic groups and, in part, in the higher development of those families and orders which were destined long to survive.

a. Uinta Stage. — The Uinta is typically developed south of the mountains of the same name, on both sides of the Green River in Colorado and Utah. It is divisible into three substages, called, in ascending order A, B and C, and grades downward almost imperceptibly into the Bridger, or middle Eocene. The substage A contains several Bridger genera, which disappeared in the succeeding substages. The Duchesne River fauna is still so incompletely known that few significant comparisons can be made with it, though such genera as have been found indicate very clearly its transitional nature.

A very marked difference between the Uinta and White River faunas lies in the character of the predaceous mammals. In the Uinta the sole representatives of the Carnivora were small primitive dogs (†*Prodaphœnus* and †*Procynodictis*), which seem, so far as they are known, to be ancestral to those of the Oligocene. The contrast with the preceding Bridger in regard to the beasts of prey is equally great, for the Bridger had many and varied members of the primitive suborder †Creodonta and the Uinta very few. The hyena-like †Mesonychidæ were represented by a genus †*Harpagolestes*, which included very large animals. The only other †creodont family, the †Oxyænidæ, had two representatives, †*Oxyænodon* and †*Apatælurus*, the latter a remarkable counterpart of the †sabre-tooth cats, with flanged lower jaw.

The small mammals, Insectivora and Rodentia, of the Uinta are still very imperfectly known; of the latter, the typically Eocene genus

†*Paramys*, a squirrel-like animal, is known, as is also a problematical genus which resembles the jumping mice (†*Protoptychus*).

A very peculiar archaic order, that of the †Tæniodonta, had its last representative in the Uinta, where the persistent Bridger genus, †*Stylinodon*, made its final appearance.

Another survival of an archaic group was †*Eobasileus*, holding over from the Bridger, which was the final representative of the suborder †Dinocerata and the order †Amblypoda, which throughout the lower and middle Eocene had been the most conspicuous and among the commonest of the mammals.

Perissodactyls were still very numerous, though less dominant than they had been in the Bridger. The horses were represented by a genus †*Epihippus*, which had simpler teeth and was smaller and lighter than the White River †*Mesohippus*. All three families of the rhinoceroses were represented and by genera which seem to be directly ancestral to those of the Duchesne and the White River. †*Prothyracodon* was the forerunner of †*Hyracodon*, †*Amynodon* of †*Metamynodon* and †*Eotrigonias* of †*Trigonias*. Of the †brontotheres, a single genus is known, †*Protitanotherium*, an animal of moderate size with short nasal "horns." Whether this single form gave rise to all the bewildering variety of grotesque monsters found in the lower White River, it is too early to say. Small tapirs (†*Isectolophus*) are rarely found.

The feature that especially characterizes the Uinta fauna is the abundance and variety of the Artiodactyla. This was something entirely new in the history of North America, for in the middle and lower Eocene of this continent artiodactyls were extremely rare and of no great variety, whereas in Europe, and no doubt in Asia, the Eocene had an abundance of this order. The †entelodonts were, it is believed, the final members of a series that began in the lower Eocene and, though related to their White River successors, cannot well have been ancestral to them, and were too small to deserve the name of "†giant pigs." The genus common to the Bridger and Uinta is †*Achænodon*.

There was a great variety of ruminant-like animals, some of which were obviously ancestral to White River genera, while others are extremely difficult to classify. The †oreodonts find their first known representatives in the several species of the Uinta †*Protoreodon* and the †agriochœres were relatively more important than at any subsequent time. There were two series of these strange clawed artiodactyls, for the transformation of the hoofs had begun. One of these (†*Protagriochœrus*) was obviously ancestral to †*Agriochœrus* of the White River and John Day; the other, †*Dichbunops*, is an aberrant side branch that speedily died out.

The first of the camel family, so far as is yet known, appeared in the Uinta (†*Protylopus*), a little creature hardly so large as a Grey Fox, but of the greatest interest. Several other genera were associated with these, some of which (†*Leptotragulus*) seemingly gave rise to the †Leptomerycidæ of the White River and subsequent stages, while others appear to have died out without leaving successors.

The Uinta—Duchesne—White River—John Day—Gering together form a series so closely connected that boundary lines seem arbitrary and the successive steps of evolutionary change in the various families are preserved with unusual completeness. The great influx of Artiodactyla differentiates the Uinta sharply from all preceding time.

b. Bridger Stage. — Although the Bridger fauna passes upward gradually into that of the Uinta, the two assemblages are very different, and the Bridger departs so widely from the corresponding faunas of Europe as to indicate a breaking of the land-connection which had existed during the lower Eocene. The three outstanding characteristics of the Bridger fauna are: (1) the great rarity of the Artiodactyla; (2) the overwhelming preponderance of the Perissodactyla and especially of the †brontothere family; and (3) the conspicuousness of the grotesque, elephant-like †Dinocerata, which died out in the Uinta. In all the other mammalian orders there are definite Bridger features, but the most striking characteristics of the fauna are those enumerated above.

Of the very scanty Artiodactyla, there are three groups: (1) the †entelodonts, which are collaterally related to the "†giant pigs" of the Oligocene and Miocene, but differ so much from these in their short broad heads and in the reduced premolars, that they must be regarded as a separate branch of the same family. (2) Fragmentary remains of the much smaller, pig-like animals probably represent the earliest known peccaries and were very near to the common ancestor of the Old World and New World swine. (3) A very interesting, though problematical genus is the little four-toed †*Homacodon*, which appears to be referable to a European family and was possibly an early member of the camel-llama series.

The difference between the Bridger faunas and those of the middle Eocene of Europe has already been mentioned and in nothing is this distinction more strongly marked than in the Artiodactyla, which were so abundant and varied in Europe, so few and far between in America. At no time before, or after, were the perissodactyls so dominant as they were in the Bridger. It is true that in certain

Fig. 154. — Some characteristic mammals of the Bridger Eocene reduced to a uniform scale, with a pointer dog, in frame, for comparison. *1*, Primitive rhinoceros, †*Hyrachyus eximius*. *2*, †*Tritemnodon agilis*. *3*, †*Patriofelis ferox*, and *4*, †*Dromocyon velox*, †creodonts. *5*, Primitive rodent, †*Paramys delicatior*. *6*, †*Uintatherium alticeps*. *7*, †Brontothere, †*Mesatirhinus superior*.

families, such as the horses and rhinoceroses, development went far beyond the state reached in the middle Eocene, and in the Oligocene as many perissodactyl genera are known as in the middle Eocene.

It is in the *relative* abundance of species and individuals that the dominating position of the Bridger perissodactyls is so conspicuous, and in these respects no other group of mammals was at all comparable.

In form and proportions Bridger perissodactyls were all much alike, and the distinction of families and genera is made almost entirely on the teeth. None of these animals were large, but were prevailingly of medium and small size, some of them very small. The existing tapirs represent the maximum size attained by perissodactyls at that time, and most genera were much smaller. Except for the ancestral horses, the perissodactyls of the Bridger are frequently called "tapiroid"; not that more than a few of them are related to the tapirs, but because they have a superficial likeness to those animals. The Perissodactyla of the time may be compared to a lake from which many separate streams arise, the families all having a common source and not yet widely separated, but following divergent courses which grow farther and farther apart. These animals all have elongate heads, rather short necks, very long bodies and tails, short legs and feet. With the exception of one genus (†*Triplopus*) they all have four digits in the manus and three in the pes.

By far the most abundant of the families, both individually and generically, is that of the †brontotheres, which are much smaller and more numerous and varied than those of the Uinta, and without horns, though incipient horns appear in some genera from the uppermost part of the stage. There are two tribes of the family, distinguished by the upper molar teeth; in one tribe, typified by †*Palæosyops* (the commonest of Bridger mammals) these teeth are low, broad, and with the outer wall with blunt cutting edges; the other is exemplified by †*Telmatherium*, which has the upper molars much higher, the outer wall more erect, and with more trenchant edge. The latter group seems to be that which was ancestral to the †brontotheres of the Uinta and White River, though the †*Palæosyops* tribe was far more abundantly represented.

Bridger horses (†*Orohippus*) are considerably smaller than their Oligocene descendants, had a more primitive type of dentition and retained four toes in the manus.

Of the three rhinoceros-like families, two were undoubtedly present in the Bridger: ancestors of the cursorial †hyracodonts (†*Hyrachyus*, †*Triplopus*) are abundant and, indeed, †*Hyrachyus* is very near to the common ancestor of all three lines. †*Colonoceras* was a prematurely horned member of this group. The aquatic family was represented by the Uinta genus †*Amynodon; Eotrigonias,* of the true rhinoceros group has also been found in the Bridger.

A tribe of the †Hyrachyidæ, sometimes made a separate family (†Helaletidæ) are more tapir-like and contain possible ancestors of the tapirs; the skeleton of †*Helaletes* is much lighter and more slender than that of †*Hyrachyas.*

The most ancient and least specialized of the claw-footed †chalicotheres (†*Eomoropus*) occurs in the Bridger.

Nearly every one of the Tertiary stages had some relatively large and grotesque mammals, which were more or less confined to a single stage, or to two or three successive stages and then died out without leaving descendants. The Bridger monsters, included in the suborder †Dinocerata, may be traced from late Paleocene throughout the Eocene, Clark Fork to Uinta inclusive, but it was in the Bridger that they reached their culmination of size, strangeness of appearance and relative abundance. Except for the head, the †dinocerates resembled small elephants, and from the narrow, elongate skull rose three pairs of bony protuberances, of which the pair on the nasals may have borne solid, rhinoceros-like horns.

The Bridger had many predaceous mammals, but no true Carnivora, unless it should be preferred to assign the family †Uintacyonidæ to the Fissipedia. That family is on the border line between †Creodonta and Fissipedia and may be assigned with almost equal propriety to either suborder. All the other predaceous families belong unquestionably to the ancient and archaic group of the †creodonts. The Bridger †Uintacyonidæ include several genera of small animals (†*Uintacyon,* †*Miacis,* †*Vulpavus,* etc.), none of which exceeded a fox in size. Another family (†Oxyænidæ) was made up of larger animals (†*Patriofelis* and †*Protopsalis*) the latter almost as large as a lion.

A very interesting and long-lived family of †creodonts, that of the †Hyænodontidæ, is represented in the Bridger by several small animals (†*Sinopa,* †*Tritemnodon,* etc.), which must have resembled weasels and martens in appearance. Though related to them, these genera cannot have been ancestral to the Oligocene †*Hyænodon* and †*Pterodon,* which were immigrants from Asia. All of these families agreed in general appearance; they all had large heads, long bodies and very long tails, short legs and weak feet, which were plantigrade in gait. Another family, the †Mesonychidæ, were quite different from this type, for though they had the large heads and small brains of the other †creodonts, they had much longer legs and digitigrade feet, giving them something of the appearance of long-tailed hyenas. The Bridger genera (†*Mesonyx*, †*Dromocyon*) were of moderate size, about equalling a wolf in stature.

In short, the Bridger †Creodonta attained the summit of development of these archaic beasts of prey, in diversity and numbers, not in size, for †*Mesonyx* was much smaller than its Uinta successor, †*Harpagolestes*, but after the Bridger the group rapidly declined and

FIG. 155. — Head of †tillodont, †*Tillotherium fodiens*, Eocene, Bridger stage. (Restored from a skull in Peabody Mus. Yale Univ.)

gave place to the much more efficiently equipped Fissipedia, which developed so remarkably in the Oligocene and Miocene.

Bridger Rodentia are markedly less varied than those of succeeding Tertiary stages. Almost all the fossils collected belong to the squirrel-like †*Paramys*, which ran through the whole Eocene, but there are also a few small, mouse-like forms.

The Bridger had a considerable number of Primates, in the form of lemurs, or primitive monkeys, of which the best known genus is †*Notharctus*. At no subsequent time have primates been found in North America, north of the Neotropical region, and the suggestion that the South American monkeys were derived from the Eocene genera of the Sonoran region is improbable.

A suborder of the Edentata, the †Palæanodonta, was remotely related to the suborder Xenarthra of South America. In the Bridger these northern edentates are rare; they must have resembled the smaller modern armadillos in size and proportions. The only known genus of this stage is †*Metacheiromys*.

Two very puzzling archaic orders, the †Tillodontia and †Tæniodontia, held over, as it were, from the earlier Eocene, but did not persist into the Oligocene. Though not related to the rodents, the †tillodonts must have had much the appearance of gigantic rodents, for they had similar enamel-faced, chisel-like incisor teeth which continued to grow throughout life, but the size of these animals (which were as large as a Black Bear) makes it unlikely that they can have been rodents. The grinding teeth, on the other hand, suggest those of Insectivora.

The †Tæniodontia, so called from the vertical bands of enamel on their teeth, continued through the Bridger and into the Uinta, a series which runs back into the Paleocene. The Bridger and Uinta genus, †*Stylinodon*, had simple cylindrical and rootless teeth, which were sheathed in enamel. These strange creatures had so many resemblances to the †ground-sloths that they have sometimes been referred to the Edentata.

Even this summary account suffices to show how rich and diversified the Bridger fauna was. So far as is at present known, it contained 10 orders, 24 families and 51 genera; of these, 9 genera and 22 families persisted from the lower Eocene; no new orders were added in the Bridger.

c, d. Wasatch Stage.— The old and familiar term Wasatch has been employed in so many different senses that it can now be used only in a comprehensive way for the whole lower Eocene, and including Gray Bull and Wind River. The Wind River fauna is a mixture of middle and lower Eocene types and has but few elements peculiar to itself. The †tapir-like †*Heptodon*, the primitive †uintathere †*Bathyopsis* and the most ancient †brontotheres, †*Lambdotherium* and †*Eotitanops*, are the most important of the characteristic genera. This fauna contains the most ancient members of many Bridger genera and the last of many Gray Bull forms; the fossils are, to a large extent, very fragmentary, though some finely preserved material has been obtained.

The *Gray Bull* [1] *Fauna* is very rich and very characteristic and different from any other American assemblage of mammals. On the

---

[1] This is the stage which has often been called the Wasatch, a term which now has a different sense, Messrs. Granger and Jepsen having shown that it can no longer be used as the name for a stage.

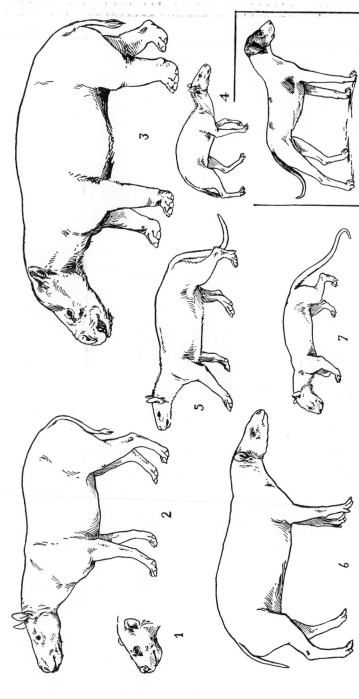

FIG. 156. — Characteristic lower Eocene mammals on a uniform scale, with pointer dog, in frame, for comparison. 1, †*Ectoganus*. 2, †*Eotitanops*. 3, †*Coryphodon*. 4, †*Hyracotherium*. 5, †*Phenacodus*. 6, †*Heptodon*. 7, †*Oxyæna*.

other hand, its resemblance to the corresponding fauna of Europe is so remarkably close as almost to amount to identity; the families and genera are nearly all the same, the species usually different. The Gray Bull is especially marked by the first appearance of the Perissodactyla, perhaps also of the Artiodactyla, though the latter

FIG. 157. — Head of †tæniodont, †*Ectoganus simplex*, lower Eocene, Gray Bull stage. (Restored from a skull in U. S. Nat. Mus.)

or their closely related ancestors may have been present in the Fort Union. In addition, there are certain orders of great antiquity, Paleocene and even Cretaceous, which have persisted to the present day, such as marsupials, insectivores, primates and rodents, which were in the Gray Bull. Finally, a third element, consisting of archaic, primitive groups, typically Paleocene in character, continued into the lower Eocene in force and then died out at various subsequent stages, the Wind River, the Bridger, the Uinta and even the White River.

There is reason to believe that the most ancient American Rodentia were those of the Paleocene, but the first determinable ones are those of the Gray Bull, which belonged to a single family, now extinct, but were most like the squirrels. The family, †Ischyromyidæ was conspicuous in the White River and the Gray Bull genera, †*Paramys* and †*Sciuravus*, continued throughout the Eocene, the former having first appeared in the Paleocene.

Artiodactyla, which may have been present in the Fort Union, were assuredly so in the Gray Bull, but the fossils are very rare and fragmentary. The earliest pig-like animals (†*Eohyus*) and †entelodonts (†*Parahyus*) and perhaps also the beginning of the camel line (†*Bunophorus*) have been identified. Perissodactyla were much more common, though far less so than they became in the Bridger. The most abundant of these is the most ancient known member of the horse family, †*Hyracotherium*,[1] of which there were several species, not larger than a small fox, or a domestic cat. These most interesting little creatures, though so different from modern horses, have something unmistakably equine about them and are connected with the existing genera by a completely graded series of intermediate forms.

The most ancient known tapir is believed to be †*Heptodon*, an animal no larger than a Coyote, but the reference is doubtful, because the distinction between the perissodactyl families, other than that of the horses, was still vague and uncertain; they were all very much alike.

Insectivora were relatively abundant and were represented by three or four families, some of which resemble the existing aquatic insectivores of west Africa, while others are more like European hedgehogs.

Primates were varied in character, but all of them were small, lemur-like animals, similar in character to those of the Bridger. One genus, †*Tetonius*, was remarkably like the modern Tarsier (*Tarsius spectrum*) of the Malay Archipelago, and its very large eye-sockets suggest similar nocturnal habits.

Numerically, the archaic groups, which were derived, with more or less modification from Paleocene families, much surpassed the progressive modern orders and thereby gave the fauna its mixed transitional nature. These archaic groups, especially characteristic

---

[1] This genus has long been called †*Eohippus*, the †"Dawn Horse," in America, a term which has become widely familiar. Unfortunately it must give place to the name previously applied to the same genus in England by Sir Richard Owen.

of the Paleocene and even of the late Cretaceous, died out, as we have seen, in the successive stages of the Eocene and Oligocene.

Except for the border-line family of the †Uintacyonidæ, the position of which is debatable, all of the lower Eocene beasts of prey belonged to the suborder †Creodonta, of which there was a great variety, both in size and habits. The differences are indicated by the character and manner of wear seen in the teeth. The families are for the most part the same as those found in the Bridger, while the genera are all different. The terrestrial, digitigrade and blunt-clawed family of the †Mesonychidæ is represented by much larger animals (†*Pachyæna*) than the Bridger genera, a reversal of the common rule, for in most genetic series the animals increase in size with the progress of time.

The †oxyænids (†*Oxyæna*) were smaller and lighter than their successors of the Bridger, but otherwise like them. An allied family, the †Palæonictidæ, are also found in Europe. The genus †*Palæonictis*, first discovered in France, was of short-legged, stocky, long-bodied animals with large heads and very long heavy tails. The earliest member of the †hyænodont family (†*Sinopa*), reached its acme of development in the Bridger, but had many species in the Gray Bull, of small, light and evidently agile type, while of the problematical †Uintacyonidæ, there was a crowd of small, fox-like, weasel-like and civet-like genera, which, no doubt, preyed upon small mammals, lizards and birds. The last of the Paleocene †Arctocyonidæ, which was also a European family, was the Gray Bull genus †*Anacodon*, which had grinding teeth like those of bears, though the flange of the lower jaw indicates a sabre-like upper canine, an extraordinary combination.

The most abundant Gray Bull fossils are those of archaic hoofed animals, which came to an end with the Wind River, and of these the conspicuous genus was †*Coryphodon*, first discovered and named in England. This genus first appeared in late Paleocene time in North America. The †coryphodonts, of which there were many species, were the largest mammals of their time, resembled small elephants in their proportions, and were much heavier than tapirs; the formidable canine tusks were more hippopotamus-like. Their brain capacity was extraordinarily small. The †uintatheres, so characteristic of the Bridger, have not been found in the Gray Bull, but, as they existed before and after that time, they were assuredly present in the lower Eocene.

Another very primitive ungulate order is that of the †Condylarthra, which was well represented in the Gray Bull, in which the characteristic genus is †*Phenacodus*, one of the last surviving members of a group which was ancestral to most, if not all, of the other ungulate orders, and connected the clawed and hoofed cohorts. †*Phenacodus* itself did not give rise to any later group, as it was on the point of extinction. Another family of supposed †Condylarthra, the †Hyopsodontidæ, has had a chequered career, having been referred to no less than four different mammalian orders. Originally believed to be allies of the pig-like artiodactyls, they were next assigned to the Primates, next to Insectivora, and finally to the †Condylarthra, where their stay may not be very prolonged. Such fluctuations of opinion are not a sign of incompetence on the part of palæontologists, but rather a proof of how closely the mammalian orders were approximating one another in the lower Eocene. The genus †*Hyopsodus*, from which the family is named, is found abundantly in all of the Eocene stages from the Gray Bull to the Uinta inclusive, but the great majority of the fossils found are fragments of the lower jaw, with a few teeth.

Very surprising was the discovery, announced a few years ago, of a genus (†*Arctostylops*) of the South American †notoungulate order, the †Entelonychia. The same group has also been found in Mongolia, but both in Asia and in North America these fossils are very rare and they are a difficult problem in animal geography.

The North American edentate suborder, the †Palæanodonta, was represented in the Gray Bull fauna, the genus †*Palæanodon* being the forerunner of †*Metacheiromys* of the Bridger.

The problematical orders, †Tillodontia and †Tæniodontia, the relationships of which are so obscure, were, relatively speaking, flourishing in the lower Eocene. †*Esthonyx*, the Gray Bull †tillodont, was much smaller than the Bridger genera and its incisors were only beginning to take on the chisel-like (or *scalpriform*) character. The †tæniodont genera, †*Ectoganus* and †*Psittacotherium*, had already acquired the scalpriform incisors and rootless grinding teeth.

Opossums were the only marsupials of North America in the lower Eocene, as they are to-day. The remarkable group of the †Multituberculata, most long-lived and wide-spread of mammalian orders, had its latest known representative in the Gray Bull, the genus †*Eucosmodon* holding over from the Paleocene.

So far as it has been ascertained, the Gray Bull mammalian fauna was made up of 12 orders, 24 families and 46 genera. Of these,

5 orders, 8 families and 3 genera persisted from the Paleocene; the others were new.

5. Paleocene

By G. L. Jepsen

Four faunal zones or horizons have been differentiated in the terrestrial sediments of the Paleocene, and their sequence has been established in the 3300 foot thick Fort Union formation in the Big Horn Basin of Wyoming, where they are all exposed. Using this complete section as a standard, all of the other Paleocene strata which have yielded important collections of fossil mammals in North America are correlated in the following table: —

FORT UNION FORMATION, WYOMING	CORRELATIVES		
Clark Fork...............	Plateau Valley,* (Colo.)		
Silver Coulee.............	Tiffany, (Colo.)	Bear Creek, (Mont.)	Paskapoo, (Alberta)
Rock Bench..............	Torrejon, (N. Mex.)	Lebo, (in part) (Mont.)	
Mantua..................	Puerco, (N. Mex.)		

* The " beds " may be in part equivalent to the Tiffany.

The Puerco and Mantua faunas contain 7 orders, 9 families and about 25 genera; the Torrejon, Lebo and Rock Bench together have 7 orders, 20 families and 54 or more genera represented. In the Silver Coulee and its equivalents there are 8 orders, 12 families and about 25 genera; and the Clark Fork has yielded 9 orders, 17 families and 23 genera. In all, 14 orders and more than 30 families and 100 genera of mammals have been recovered from the Paleocene of North America.

These earliest Tertiary faunas are composed of archaic families, of which few still survive; but about one-half of the Paleocene orders are alive to-day, notably the marsupials, insectivores, edentates, rodents, carnivores, primates and (of questionable presence in the Tiffany and Bear Creek) the bats and the Dermoptera. Many of the Paleocene families of these orders, and in some cases the orders themselves, are difficult to distinguish from each other. In part this situation is due to the incompleteness of the fossil specimens. Even the carnivores and ungulates, so distinct now, were very similar then; and some of the †Condylarthra were very like the Eocene artio-dactyls.

In addition to the †Condylarthra another archaic hoofed group, the †Amblypoda, is prominent in Paleocene fossil collections. The extraordinary †*Barylambda*, an animal of medium stature, but massive build, is a characteristic member of the Plateau Valley fauna. In the Clark Fork fauna †*Coryphodon*, very characteristic of the Wasatch, made its first appearance, as did †*Probathyopsis*, earliest known representative of the †Dinocerata. These genera were giants in comparison with most of the very small Paleocene mammals and achieved the size of modern tapirs.

Flesh-eaters were many and varied, but all of them were †creodonts, from which primitive group the modern carnivores probably developed, through the family †Uintacyonidæ. The †Arctocyonidæ, with bear-like molars, were chiefly Paleocene in range.

A conspicuous group throughout the Paleocene was the order †Multituberculata. Of all mammalian orders, this was the longest-lived, for it endured at least from the upper Triassic to the lower Eocene inclusive; no other order has a comparable longevity. The †multituberculates were pre-eminently a Mesozoic group, but their persistence through Paleocene time was not a mere survival of stragglers; they still had sufficient vitality to develop further and, in a sense, the Paleocene may be called the time of their culmination.

Contrary to the belief held a few years ago, the late Paleocene faunas are not sharply distinguished from those of the Eocene. The discoveries of new collecting localities and of new specimens in the old classic areas have considerably altered the conception that the lowest Eocene (Gray Bull) witnessed a sudden and vast faunal influx.

The distinction which is most easily used in the field is the presence of the Perissodactyla in the Eocene, and their complete absence in the Paleocene.

In summary, it may be said that the Paleocene faunas were primitive and archaic, retaining many Mesozoic features and possessing very little that has survived, except in its very modified descendants, to modern times. The first condition precedent to the great expansion and diversification of the Mammalia was supplied by the extraordinary development of the modern type of vegetation in the upper Cretaceous, thus assuring abundant food supplies. The second essential precondition was the disappearance of the great predatory reptiles, notably of the †dinosaurs, which coincided with the close of the Mesozoic era. Then, for the first time, mammals had a free field for development, without having to meet the competition of formidable enemies. The extraordinary way in which mammals and birds both took advantage of the great opportunity, is one of the marvels of geological history.

CHAPTER X

SUCCESSIVE MAMMALIAN FAUNAS OF THE NEOTROPICAL REGION

I. Quaternary Faunas

1. Recent

Little is yet known of the Recent, as distinguished from the modern, fauna of South America, but there is clear evidence that several Pleistocene genera persisted into Recent times. The †mastodont (†*Cordillerion*) which was killed and eaten by Indians in Ecuador, as described in Chapter XII, was certainly living in historic times. The great †ground-sloth, †*Neomylodon*, of which the skull, excrement and large pieces of hair-covered skin were found in a Patagonian cave, must have been alive in the Recent epoch, as were the associated large cat and horse, both belonging to extinct species. No doubt many other such instances remain to be discovered.

2. Pleistocene

The Pampas of Argentina are a wonderful museum of Pleistocene mammals such as is found nowhere else in the world, with the exception of the California tar-pits. This is supplemented by very rich collections, though of more fragmentary material, gathered from Brazilian caves, and from deposits in Ecuador and Bolivia. The fauna is far stranger than the corresponding one of North America and differs more radically from that of modern times, since it includes a much larger proportion of extinct families and orders. For the present, the fauna must be treated as a unit, though it will eventually be subdivided into zones.

Like the modern fauna, that of the Pleistocene is plainly divisible into two assemblages: (1) the immigrants from the north, which reached South America in successive waves of migration, the first of which arrived in the early Pliocene, and (2) the indigenous element, which had a very long evolutionary history in the Neotropical region. It may be safely assumed that all the existing genera of South American mammals were present there in the Pleistocene. True, not all of

FIG. 158. — Some of the commoner Pampean mammals, reduced to a uniform scale, with a pointer dog, in the frame, to show the relative sizes. *1*, †*Dœdicurus clavicaudatus*. *2*, †*Glyptodon clavipes*, †glyptodonts. *3*, †*Macrauchenia patachonica*, one of the †Litopterna. *4*, †Pampas Horse, †*Hippidion neogœum*. *5*, †*Toxodon burmeisteri*, a †toxodont. *6*, †*Megatherium americanum*. *7*, †*Mylodon robustus*, †ground-sloths.

them have yet been found, just as is also the case in North America, but it is not to be expected that any fossil fauna should fully and completely represent the life of its day.

South American Pleistocene Carnivora, like those of to-day, were all of northern ancestry. The †short-faced bears (†*Arctotherium*) were first discovered in the Pampean beds before they were found in the United States, but none of the true bears (*Ursus*) is known, living or fossil, in the Neotropical region, the Spectacled Bear of the Andes (*Tremarctos*) being more nearly allied to †*Arctotherium*. Of the cat family, the †Sabre-tooths (†*Smilodon*) were as common as in North America and were first discovered in the Brazilian caverns. The great lion-like cats (*Felis* †*atrox*) of California and the Mississippi Valley were absent, but species nearly allied to the modern Puma, Ocelot and Jaguar were common. The South American fox-like wolves (*Cerdocyon*) and the Brazilian Bush-dog (*Icticyon*) were much as they are now, and strange to say, there was a dog which seems referable to the same genus (*Cyon*) as the modern Dhole, or Wild Dog, of India.

As is still true, the weasel family was less numerous and varied than in North America; extinct species of skunk (*Conepatus*), tayra (*Tayra*) and otter (*Lutra*) were present, but no badgers, minks, martens or wolverenes.

The Rodentia were of mixed origin, but the known immigrants are few: the mice, rats and rabbits were of northern origin and also a meadow mouse (*Microtus*), but the latter failed to gain a permanent foothold and died out. The great majority of Pleistocene rodents belonged to the porcupine-like group, or Hystricomorpha, and were the descendants of long-established South American families, such as are still flourishing in the region, but most of the Pleistocene *species* are extinct. Several extinct West Indian genera from Cuba, Puerto Rico and Anguilla were allied to the capybaras.

The monkeys were entirely Neotropical in type and several of the modern genera, such as *Cebus* and *Callithrix*, and a very large extinct genus (†*Protopithecus*) have been found in the Brazilian caves, but not in the Argentine Pampas. These were apparently treeless, as they still are.

The hoofed animals were extremely abundant and varied and of both immigrant and indigenous origin, the latter all extinct now. The Perissodactyla included horses and tapirs, but not rhinoceroses, which have never been found in the Neotropical region. The tapirs ranged much farther south than they do now, extending to Argentina. Of the horses, there were some species of the genus *Equus*, all with somewhat simpler teeth than the true Horse (*E. caballus*) and with some resemblance to asses. There was also a group of four extinct genera peculiar to South America, but derived from a northern ancestry. The best known of these are †*Hippidion* and †*Onohippidium*, which had most exceptional features of the skull (not visible externally, however); the head was large and clumsy, the neck relatively short, the limbs heavy and the feet short. †*Hyperhippidium*, a small Andean horse, had remarkably short feet, like those of the "Rocky Mountain Goat," well adapted to mountain climbing.

The Artiodactyla were much more varied than the perissodactyls and comprised peccaries, numerous deer, all of South American type, and two species of antelopes have been reported from Brazil, immigrants which failed to establish themselves, for there are now no Neotropical antelopes. There were also many species of llamas, which then extended into Brazil and were not, as at present, confined to the colder parts of the continent.

Only a single elephant tooth, belonging to Jefferson's †Mammoth (†*Parelephas jeffersoni*) and collected in French Guiana, has ever been found in all South America, but †mastodonts were common. Two very distinct types have been found; one †*Cordillerion*, a highland genus, which extended down the Andes to Chile and Bolivia; the other, †*Cuvieronius*, was especially characteristic of the plains. Both genera were distinctly of North American and Old World ancestry, and the path of migration through California and Nebraska, Texas and Central America has been traced. The practically complete absence of the true elephants from South America is, perhaps, to be explained by their inability to cross the tropics in considerable numbers. The elephants of North America were northern forms.

The indigenous hoofed animals which dwelt in Pleistocene South America have not been found outside of the Neotropical Region; so far as is known, Nicaragua is the northernmost point of their range. The Pleistocene genera were the last representatives of groups, already on the wane, which were numerous in the Tertiary, but died out, one by one, in the successive stages.

An extremely peculiar creature, †*Macrauchenia*, first discovered by Charles Darwin, was the last survivor of an order, the †Litopterna, which had played a conspicuous rôle in the South American Tertiary. †*Macrauchenia* was a long-necked, small-headed animal, larger and much heavier than a camel, to which it bore a superficial resemblance. Another indigenous group, the †Typotheria, found its last representative in the Pampean †*Typotherium*, an animal somewhat larger than a pig. It had chisel-like, incisor teeth so like those of the Rodentia that the creature was once referred to that order. †*Toxodon*, type of the suborder †Toxodonta, was also discovered by Charles Darwin, who said that it was "Perhaps one of the strangest animals that ever lived." †*Toxodon* was a ponderous beast, about as large as a rhinoceros, with fore-limbs much shorter than the hind. As Darwin

pointed out, the position of eyes, ears and nostrils was such as probably to indicate aquatic habits.

In the Neotropical Region of to-day, the xenarthrous Edentata
are the most striking and characteristic feature of the mammalian
fauna, and this fact was far more conspicuously true in the Pleistocene.
Of the three existing suborders, tree-sloths, anteaters and armadillos,
the first two are but scantily represented in the fossils, as is apt
to be true of forest-dwellers, but armadillos were very abundant both
in Brazil and Argentina. Most of the existing genera have already
been found, and in addition there were several extinct ones. One of
these, †*Chlamydotherium*, which also invaded Florida, was relatively
gigantic, much larger than any recent species.

Few more fantastic mammals than the †Glyptodontia have ever
existed; the short deep head, with its covering casque of thick bony
plates, the huge thick-walled carapace, the enormous bony tail-
sheath, the short legs and heavy feet, with their broad hoofs must
have given the creatures rather the appearance of gigantic, long-
tailed tortoises than that of mammals. In length, they varied from
six to twelve feet, including the tail. In the various genera, the skeleton and carapace did not differ greatly, but there were great differences in the form and size of the tail-sheath. In †*Glyptodon*, for example, the sheath is composed of overlapping bony rings, each with
prominent spines; in †*Sclerocalyptus* the hinder half of the tail was a
tube made up of co-ossified plates, while in †*Dædicurus* the end had an
immense club-like expansion which was set with great horn-like
spikes. In comparison with the bewildering variety of South American
†glyptodonts, the few that made their way into North America were
but an insignificant company.

Much the same statement applies to the †ground-sloths, of which
the Neotropical region had an incomparably greater number of
genera and species; ten, or more, genera have been found in the
Pampean.

The Pleistocene mammalian fauna of South America was far
stranger and contained a much larger proportion of extinct types
than that of North America; the †ground-sloths and †glyptodonts,
the †litopterns, †typotheres and †toxodonts, and the antelopes,
horses and †mastodonts, the †giant rodents and monkeys have all
disappeared from the Neotropical region, or vanished entirely from
the earth.

The Pleistocene mammals of the West Indies form as puzzling an
aggregate as does the Recent fauna. The mammals that then existed

in the islands indicate a land connection with Central America at some time in the later Tertiary. Whether the islands were, or were not, connected with the mainland, they must have been joined with one another. Cuba, Haiti, Puerto Rico and the Leeward Islands as far east as Anguilla, formed a continuous land, from which Jamaica had been separated earlier. Admitting a junction with the mainland, the question immediately arises: why did so few mammals cross over? Compared with the Pleistocene fauna of Brazil and Argentina, that of Cuba and Puerto Rico is extremely meagre. The West Indian Pleistocene has yielded no hoofed animals of any sort, and no Carnivora. Several genera of small †ground-sloths were present in the islands, all peculiar and all belonging to the South American family of the †Megalonychidæ. No other edentates have been found. Beside bats, the only other abundant group of mammals is that of the Rodentia, which included many large and peculiar genera with highly complex teeth and belonging to South American families more or less nearly allied to the capybaras. A very primitive genus of the Insectivora, †*Nesophontes*, is common to Cuba and Puerto Rico.

The outstanding feature of the West Indian Pleistocene fauna is its inexplicable poverty.

II. Tertiary Faunas

From South America has been obtained almost as full, detailed and uninterrupted a story of mammalian evolution as has been deciphered in the northern continent. While some parts of Neotropical history have been very completely studied and illustrated, a much larger part still awaits a thoroughgoing examination. In sending me tentative faunal lists of the principal pre-Santa Cruzian formations, Dr. Simpson writes, under date of May 31, 1933: "I had hoped to have at least the *Notostylops* fauna all done by now, but it is a tremendous job and after three years I feel that I am just well started on it. The others I have hardly had time to touch yet."

The Pleistocene mammals of South America have been obtained, for the most part, from the middle regions of the continent, southern Brazil and the Argentine Pampas, and the fossiliferous Pliocene mostly occurs in the same general area, except Brazil, in northern, eastern and western Argentina and Bolivia. The more ancient formations, Eocene to Miocene, are all in the far south, in what is unofficially called Patagonia, and thus lack several groups of mammals and reptiles which were assuredly present in other parts of the continent, where warmer and moister climates and extensive forests prevailed. So far as can be inferred from known fossils, Tertiary Patagonia would seem to have been a country of arid, or semi-arid plains, devoid of forests and with singularly few reptiles, or amphibians, and, even along the few water-courses, trees were scanty, but the climate was distinctly warmer than at present. A very large proportion of Tertiary sediments is made up of volcanic débris, chiefly fine ash, and is more or less regularly stratified by wind or water.

1. Pliocene

The Pliocene of South America has uncertain limits both above and below, but the number of the faunas and the order of their succession are sufficiently clear. The latest Pliocene, that of the Tarija Valley in Bolivia, has yielded a fauna which is manifestly incomplete, even more so than usual, for it lacks nearly all the small mammals. The families represented are those of the Pleistocene and the genera are the same, but many species are different and the animals were somewhat smaller and less advanced. The differences are so slight, however, that some authorities include these beds in the Pampean. In the Tarija 35 species have been identified. †Mastodonts, tapirs, several genera of the peculiar South American horses, peccaries, deer, many llamas, †glyptodonts, armadillos, †ground-sloths of four different genera, bears, wolves, skunks, cats, †sabre-tooths and a few rodents, make up a fauna which is in strong contrast to that of preceding Pliocene stages with regard to the very much larger proportion of immigrants from North America which it contains.

a. *Araucanian Stage.* — The Hermosean of the Atlantic Coast, near Monte Hermoso, and the Araucanian of the Argentine provinces of Catamarca and Tucuman, may be considered together, as there are but minor differences between them. The outstanding feature of these faunas is the insignificance of the immigrant element; a raccoon (†*Amphinasua*), one of the dog family, a rabbit and an unidentified artiodactyl are all that are known at present. These faunas are indigenous in overwhelming proportions, and it is a hopeless undertaking to attempt giving any real conception of these strange animals to the non-professional reader, for almost all the genera belong to extinct families, even extinct orders and, in the modern world, there is nothing with which they can be instructively compared.

True Carnivora were almost entirely absent and their place was taken by large predaceous marsupials, as it had been in all the preceding Tertiary stages, though they are rare in the Catamarca, obviously by an accident of fossilization. One of these marsupials, †*Thylaco-*

smilus, is the most astonishing imitation of a †sabre-tooth tiger that can be imagined. The upper canines were converted into great recurved scimitar-like tusks and equally large protective bony flanges were developed on the lower jaw, yet the creature is an unmistakable marsupial. This remarkable discovery was made and recently announced by Mr. E. S. Riggs of the Field Museum of Natural History in Chicago. Opossums, it is superfluous to mention, for they are abundant in South America to-day and have been so throughout the entire Tertiary history of the continent.

The xenarthrous Edentata were represented by numerous genera, nearly all of which are extinct. Together with many armadillos of ordinary size, there were some gigantic ones (†*Chlamydotherium*) very much like those of the Florida Pliocene. There were many †glyptodonts (†*Sclerocalyptus*) which, though much larger than their Miocene ancestors, were considerably smaller than their Pampean descendants.

†Ground-sloths, or †Gravigrada, like the †glyptodonts, are intermediate in size between the Pleistocene and Miocene genera; they belonged to all three families of the suborder, but mostly to the †mylodonts and †megatheres, the †megalonychids being very few. This is a most noteworthy change from the Miocene, when the great majority of the †ground-sloths were of the †Megalonychidæ. Tree-sloths (Tardigrada) and the anteaters (Myrmecophagidæ) have been found, though they are very rare, no doubt because Catamarca was then unforested.

Of the very numerous Rodentia, only the rabbit (†*Argyrolagus*) was an immigrant from the north, all the others belonging to autochthonous families. Some of these rodents were relatively extremely large and one (†*Megamys*), a member of the chinchilla family was gigantic, as large as a rhinoceros and the largest of known rodents. The great abundance of the cavy family (Caviidæ) is characteristic of the South American Pliocene.

With the exception of the little artiodactyl, all the hoofed animals belonged to the native orders, now extinct. Both families of the †Litopterna occur in these faunas, and the Pampean genus †*Machrauchenia,* was already distinct as such, but the species were smaller than those of the Pleistocene. The last survivors of the second †litoptern family, the †proterotheres, are found in the Monte Hermoso beds. The genus, †*Epitherium,* was wonderfully, though but superficially, like those of the Tertiary three-toed horses of North America.

The predominant hoofed animals of the Neotropical Pliocene

were the †Notoungulata and the suborder †Toxodonta was the most numerous, forerunners of the massive brutes of the Pampean. One genus (†*Trigodon*) had the interesting peculiarity of a single median horn on the forehead, like that of a rhinoceros. Horned animals were a rarity among the indigenous Neotropical ungulates and nearly all of the known examples belong to the †Toxodonta. Another suborder, the †typotheres, was quite abundantly represented both by medium-sized and by very small animals, some (†*Pachyrukhos*) no larger than a rabbit.

Monkeys must have been present in the Neotropical Pliocene, but none have been reported, probably for the same reason that ant-bears are so uncommon, namely, that the known faunas were those of treeless plains.

b. Entre Rios Stage. — The Paraná, or Entrerian, named from the Argentine province of Entre Rios, has yielded what are supposed to be the most ancient of immigrants from the north, which are assigned to the dog, bear and raccoon families, but the fossils are fragmentary and the identifications doubtful. Otherwise, the beasts of prey were all marsupials of various sizes.

The list of edentate genera is a very long one, but consists almost entirely of armadillos, †glyptodonts and †ground-sloths. Of the latter, all three families were represented.

The hoofed animals all belonged to the indigenous Neotropical orders, the †typotheres and †toxodonts being especially abundant and varied. Both families of the †Litopterna were represented, the †Macrauchenidæ by smaller and less specialized genera than those of the Catamarcan beds.

The Rodentia were very numerous and diversified, but all belonged to the Hystricomorpha. The agouti, coypu, vizcacha, cavy and chinchilla families were abundant and most of the genera are extinct.

The uppermost Miocene is the Friassian, named from the Rio Frias, of western Patagonia and other localities in the same general region, which Kragliévich regarded as representing three substages. These beds have not been mapped and their relations to older formations can be determined only by a comparison of their fossils. These indicate that the Friassian is later than the Santa Cruz, but not very much so, geologically speaking. The fauna is mostly composed of new species of Santa Cruz genera, many of which appear here for the last time, but there were also new genera derived from Santa Cruz and older forms by modification. The region in which these beds occur is, primarily, along the base of the Andes from the south of the Argentinian province of Neuquén to the south of the Chubut province. The fossiliferous localities are scattered and the various subdivisions are named from the rivers along which they are found. Kragliévich has proposed the following arrangement.

Friassian
{
Mayorensian substage
Friassensian substage
Colloneuvenian substage
}

The Colloneuvenian fauna differs very little from that of the Santa Cruz. The Friassensian contains many Santa Cruzian genera, with others which are of later type; the Mayorensian is basal Pliocene.

The Pliocene faunas of the Neotropical region, save the very latest of them, were almost free from the immigrant mammalian genera which became so numerous in the Pleistocene. There were, however, sufficient of these immigrants to indicate that the Isthmus of Panama had been raised above the sea and that the way of migration between the two continents was open, though seemingly difficult. The Pliocene faunas were composed almost altogether of indigenous orders and suborders; predaceous marsupials and opossums, hystricomorph rodents, †ground-sloths, †glyptodonts and armadillos; hoofed animals of the †toxodont, †typothere and †litoptern groups were the abundant forms. Numerically, these faunas were very rich and of a truly extraordinary degree of isolation, so completely different are they from those of any other known region.

2. Miocene

The isolation of the Neotropical Region, which was so marked in the Pliocene, was even more complete in the Miocene and renders any correlation with the Miocene subdivisions of the northern hemisphere exceedingly difficult, because of the lack of elements common to both northern and southern continents. Fortunately, the marine Patagonian stage, with its whales and porpoises, so like those of the Miocene of the eastern United States, offers a fixed point of departure from which correlation may be carried upward into overlying and downward into underlying beds, although in a somewhat loose and inexact manner.

a. Friassian Stage. — Though separated by an interval of land-elevation the Santa Cruzian and Friassian faunas are very nearly alike and many Santa Cruz genera appeared for the last time in the

Friassian. The species seem to be very generally different, but in these faunas any satisfactory discrimination of species is extraordinarily difficult; the genera, on the other hand, are almost all distinct and easy to determine. Such typical Santa Cruz genera as †*Astrapotherium*, †*Nesodon*, †*Adinotherium*, †*Prozaëdius*, †*Propalæohoplophorus*, represented by different species, appear for the last time in the Friassian; others continued on to various stages of the Pliocene and still others were new, as, for example, †*Prototrigodon* and †*Megathericulus*.

b. Santa Cruzian Stage. — This is the best-known and most thoroughly studied of all the South American Tertiary stages and its beds, largely made up of stratified volcanic ash, rest upon the marine sandstones of the Patagonian. The fossils are unusually well preserved and so many complete skeletons have been collected that further discoveries of great importance are hardly to be expected.

To eyes accustomed to the Tertiary mammals of the northern hemisphere, the first encounter with the Santa Cruz fossils is bewildering; it is like landing upon another planet, with radically different animals. All the *orders* familiar to us are lacking; there are neither proboscideans, artiodactyls, perissodactyls nor true carnivores, and, of the rodents, only the porcupine-like group is to be found. The abundant fossils are those of edentates, †ground-sloths, †glyptodonts and armadillos, — of the indigenous orders of hoofed animals, — †toxodonts, †typotheres, †homalodotheres, †litopterns, †astrapotheres, almost all of which are entirely unknown in any other continent. The place of the Carnivora was taken by predaceous marsupials, much like the existing "Tasmanian Wolf" in size and structure, and numerous smaller kinds which played the part of foxes, weasels, martens, etc. Opossums were present, though apparently not very numerous, and a great variety of herbivorous marsupials of which the little Andean *Cænolestes* is the last survivor.

Insectivora, which are not at present found in continental South America, were represented in the Santa Cruz by small animals (†*Necrolestes*) which have been referred to the golden moles (Chrysochloridæ) of South Africa, but this reference is doubtful.

Santa Cruz Edentata were incredibly abundant, especially the †ground-sloths, or †Gravigrada, a group which dominated the Neotropical region from the Miocene to the end of the Pleistocene. The great majority of the Miocene genera belonged to the family †Megalonychidæ, which underwent great reduction and is but scantily represented in the Pampean beds. The early †mylodonts and †meg-

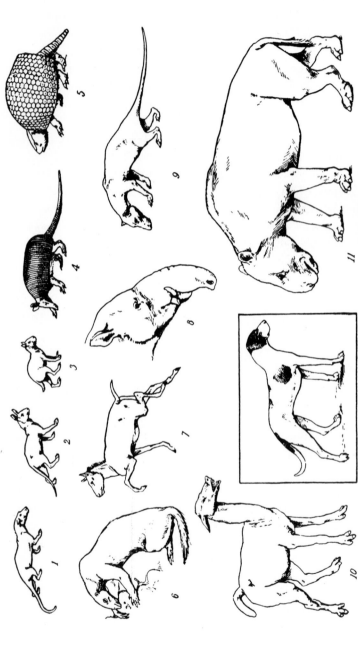

FIG. 159. — Diagram to illustrate the comparative sizes of the Santa Cruz mammals, within the rectangle, to give the scale. 1, †*Cladosictis lustratus*, predaceous marsupial. 2, †*Protypotherium australe*, †typothere. 3, †*Eocardia excavata*, rodent. 4, †*Stegotherium tesselatum*, armadillo. 5, †*Propalaeohoplophorus australis*, †glyptodont. 6, †*Hapalops longiceps*, †ground-sloth. 7, †*Thoatherium minusculum*, †litoptern. 8, †*Astrapotherium magnum*, †astrapothere. 9, †*Prothylacynus patagonicus*, predaceous marsupial. 10, †*Theosodon garretorum*, †litoptern. 11, †*Nesodon imbricatus*, †toxodont.

atheres are very much less common in the Santa Cruz beds, but became preponderant in the Pliocene and Pleistocene. All of the Santa Cruz †ground-sloths were small animals, some very small, in striking contrast to the massive and colossal brutes of the Pampean.

The †glyptodonts were likewise small, hardly one-tenth of the size of the great moving fortresses so characteristic of the Pleistocene of both continents. Santa Cruz †glyptodonts preserved many fea-

FIG. 160. — Restoration of †*Eocardia*, probable Santa Cruz ancestor of the modern Patagonian "Hare," *Dolichotis*. (From a skeleton in Princeton Univ. Mus.)

tures of their armadillo ancestry and displayed most interesting transitional features.

Armadillos were extremely abundant and diversified, but almost all of them belonged to families which were aberrantly specialized and did not give rise to any of the existing genera. One genus (†*Stegotherium*) had a long, slender, almost toothless bill and its head must have looked very much like that of an anteater. In another genus (†*Peltephilus*) two of the bony scutes covering the skull were converted into sharp-pointed horns.

The Primates are excessively rare in the Santa Cruz. No doubt this scarcity is due to the treeless condition of Miocene Patagonia, as is also true of the lacking tree-sloths and ant-bears. The Santa Cruz monkeys are clearly of Neotropical type and are referable to the existing family of the Cebidæ. The only well-defined genus is †*Homunculus*.

The great wealth of hoofed animals in the Santa Cruzian stage all belonged to three orders, †Notoungulata, †Astrapotheria and †Litopterna. Of the three suborders of the †Notoungulata, the †Toxodonta, †Typotheria and †Entelonychia, the †toxodonts were much the commonest fossils, and the most abundantly represented genus is †Nesodon, a structural, if not an actual ancestor of the Pampean †Toxodon, and like the latter, it was discovered by Charles Darwin. †Nesodon was a heavily built animal about the size of a tapir, with relatively large head and remarkably small feet. The much smaller, but otherwise similar, †Adinotherium would seem to have had a single small frontal horn, and, if so, was one of the very few horned genera of the indigenous South American hoofed mammals.

A second suborder, the †Typotheria, very numerously represented, comprised small and very small animals, which were remarkably rodent-like in appearance, but which were true ungulates nevertheless. The third suborder, the †Entelonychia (represented chiefly by †Homalodotherium), very much less common, included relatively large animals in which the hoofs had been converted into claws, much as in the †Ancylopoda of the northern hemisphere. The structure of these strange creatures, which were far too large to have been burrowers, suggests habits of digging with the fore-feet.

The †Astrapotheria and †Entelonychia were much the largest of Miocene Neotropical mammals. The former had large canine tusks, very like those of a hippopotamus, but the creature evidently had a proboscis, slender legs and very short, five-toed feet much like those of an elephant. The group is in no way related to the Proboscidea, except as all ungulates are related to one another. There is but a single well-defined genus in the Santa Cruz, †Astrapotherium, from which the order takes its name.

Both families of the †Litopterna were common; the horse-like †Proterotheriidæ apparently reached their acme of development in the Santa Cruzian stage and were never again to be so varied and abundant. In the Pliocene their decadence was very obvious and they did not extend into the Pleistocene. The common Santa Cruz representative of the †Macrauchenidæ, †Theosodon, seems to have been directly ancestral to those of the Pliocene and Pleistocene and was much smaller and less specialized.

The Santa Cruz fauna is composed of moderate sized, small and minute mammals. Except for one species of †Astrapotherium, hardly a single member of the fauna can be called large and this is in remarkable contrast to the mammals of the supposedly Oligocene Deseado formation.

c. Colhué-huapi Stage. — This is the formation called by Ameghino the †*Colpodon* Beds (couches à †*Colpodon*) and is, in part, contemporary with the marine Patagonian, of which it is, to some extent, a terrestrial phase. The fauna is decidedly, but not radically, different from that of the Santa Cruz, to which it was plainly ancestral, but several gaps remain to be filled by future exploration.

Marsupials, both the opossums and the predaceous, thylacine-like forms were common and there were many genera of the Cænolestidæ.

A very striking and conspicuous difference from the Santa Cruz is in the very much smaller number of the †ground-sloths, both individually and generically. The only family represented is that of the †Megalonychidæ, of which but two genera have, so far, been found. The †glyptodonts were likewise fewer in number and variety, but the armadillos were much the same.

Rodentia also were much less diversified and abundant than in the succeeding stage and only four families of the hystricmorphs have been reported; the tree-porcupines, the spiny rats, the chinchillas and, questionably, the cavies. In view of the great abundance of the cavies in the Pliocene, this paucity is a notable difference.

As usual, the bulk of the fauna is made up of hoofed animals, which include different genera of the families and orders which abound in the Santa Cruz, but also a number of prematurely specialized genera, in which the hypsodont, or high-crowned teeth are thickly covered with cement and, in some of the †toxodonts, the lower teeth are deceptively horse-like, but these precocious types did not persist into the Santa Cruz. Forerunners of the normal †toxodonts, as they may be called, †*Pronesodon* and †*Proadinotherium*, differed but little from their Santa Cruzian successors, and the other suborders of the †Notoungulata, the †Typotheria and the †Entelonychia, were abundant. The †Astrapotheria and the two families of the †Litopterna differed little from the Santa Cruzian species.

The discovery of the Santa Cruz monkey, †*Homunculus*, in the "*Colpodon* Beds" has recently been reported by Rusconi.

3. Oligocene

Down to the Patagonian and its more or less contemporary stage the Colhué-huapi, the application of the Tertiary divisions, as established in Europe and North America, can be made with considerable confidence, but for the four preceding stages, the Deseado, Musters, Casa Mayor and Rio Chico, the correlation becomes uncertain. All that can be definitely asserted is that these four stages are included between the Cretaceous below and the Miocene above. It is customary to class the Deseado as Oligocene and the other three as Eocene, but such an arrangement can be only tentative. So far, it would appear, no Paleocene has been found in South America.

Deseado Stage. — This fauna is almost as well known as that of the Santa Cruz, although the material is not so complete or so well preserved. In one respect it departs from a very general rule, many of its species being larger than their successors. Almost always the genera of families which increase and thrive grow larger with the progress of time, but in the earlier Deseado and the succeeding Santa Cruz, this relation is reversed.

Beside the difference in size of the animals, the Deseado fauna differs conspicuously from the Santa Cruzian in the absence of monkeys and in the very much smaller number and variety of the rodents and edentates. †Ground-sloths are rare, but one genus, †*Octodontherium*, was a far larger animal than any known Miocene member of the suborder. †Glyptodonts are likewise rare as fossils and are known only from fragmentary remains. Armadillos were the only abundant edentates and were even more common than in the Miocene; no less than eleven genera (some of them of doubtful validity) have been named, and three of these persisted into the Santa Cruz.

Deseado rodents, so far as can be judged from the fossils, were much less numerous and diversified than in the Miocene for only two families are represented, the chinchillas and the tree-porcupines, and these are the most ancient South American rodents that have, as yet, been discovered.

Marsupials, very like those of the Santa Cruz, but with fewer genera, were the only beasts of prey. One genus, †*Pharsophorus*, was much larger than any known Miocene marsupial and may fairly be called gigantic. Many small members of the Cænolestidæ were present.

Much the greatest number of Deseado fossils are those of the native orders and suborders of Neotropical hoofed animals. So far as diversification is concerned, the Deseado would appear to be the time of culmination of the highly characteristic South American order, the †Notoungulata, of which no less than nine families are distinguishable. Especially abundant were the †Toxodonta, which included not only the ancestors of the Miocene genera, but also numbers of prematurely specialized forms, which had high-crowned (hypsodont), cement-covered teeth, and in which the lower molars had a deceptively horse-like pattern (†Rhynchippidæ and †Notohippidæ). Next in frequency of occurrence, were the †Typotheria, of which many genera likewise had the hypsodont, cement-covered teeth.

This multiplication of grazing animals, with hypsodont, cement-covered teeth, is a very interesting parallel to the similar development which appeared in so many rodent, artiodactyl, perissodactyl and proboscidean families of the Miocene in the northern hemisphere, but the adaptation to grazing habits took place much earlier in South than in North America, from which fact it might be inferred that the extension of grasslands occurred much sooner in the southern continent. In both suborders these genera with highly complicated teeth died out at the close of the Deseado stage.

A †toxodont family, the †Leontiniidæ, which was especially characteristic of the Deseado, had a minute horn, or perhaps a pair of them, on the tips of the nasal bones, but this family also disappeared before the beginning of the Miocene. There were likewise many of the small animals which were precursors of the abundant Santa Cruz species. One relatively large form, †Eutrachytherus, was not only much bigger than any known Miocene †typothere, but was more akin to the ancestry of the Pampean †Typotherium.

The third suborder of the †Notoungulata, that of the strange, claw-bearing †Entelonychia, had very large representatives in the Deseado, †Asmodeus being fairly gigantic and greatly surpassing the Miocene †Homalodotherium.

The mysterious order of the †Astrapotheria likewise had very large members in the Oligocene. †Parastrapotherium greatly exceeded in size the species of †Astrapotherium common in the Santa Cruz, though the rare †A. giganteum may have been as large.

A very paradoxical and debatable group, the order †Pyrotheria found its highest development and its final end in the Deseado, though it may be traced back to the Casa Mayor. The Oligocene member of the group, †Pyrotherium, was a large, heavily built animal, with very short and massive limbs, and long, narrow skull. It probably had a proboscis and the dentition is much like that of the Oligocene proboscideans of Egypt, but with two pairs of upper and one pair of lower incisor tusks. So characteristic is this genus of the Deseado that Ameghino named the formation the "†Pyrotherium Beds."

Finally, the †Litopterna had representatives of both families in this fauna, but the distinction between them was not so clearly marked as it was in the Santa Cruzian stage. Working backward in time, or downward through the strata, it looks as though the two families were converging to a common ancestry.

Of this wonderful assemblage of hoofed mammals, comprising six distinct groups, whether of ordinal or subordinal rank, nothing remains in the modern world. Not only are all the species, genera and families extinct, but the orders and suborders as well; two of the suborders, the †Toxodonta and †Typotheria, were still thriving in the Pampean stage, when the last member of the †Litopterna, †Macrauchenia, came to its end. Except for a very few and doubtful forms in the Eocene of Mongolia and North America, none of these six groups has ever been found outside of the Neotropical region.

4. Eocene

The oldest three stages of the South American Tertiary, the Musters, Casa Mayor and Rio Chico, in descending order, are generally referred to the Eocene and this is probably the correct correlation, at least for the two last-named. The Musters stage, on the other hand, may prove to be lower Oligocene rather than Eocene.

a. Musters Stage. — This stage, which is equivalent to the †*Astraponotus* Beds of Ameghino, contains a fauna which is obviously related to that of the succeeding Deseado, yet very distinct from it. Much remains to be done in the way of describing existing collections before this fauna can be understood in detail, but its character may already be defined in general terms.

The only beasts of prey were marsupials and one of these, a forerunner of the Deseado †*Pharsophorus*, was relatively large. Cænolestids were comparatively rare and opossums have not been reported, but this lack is manifestly an accident of preservation.

The Edentata diminished steadily backward from the Santa Cruz, a somewhat absurd way of putting it, but one occasioned by the reversed order in the narrative which is here employed. In the Musters stage only the armadillos are at all common, and even of them but a single family is represented. †Glyptodonts were present, but very rare, and no evidence of the †ground-sloths has yet been obtained, though the group must already have been in existence in some other part of South America.

The primitive hoofed mammals known as the †Condylarthra, so characteristic of the Paleocene and early Eocene of North America, are believed to have been a part of the Musters fauna, yet the known material does not suffice to draw a clear line between the †Condylarthra and the †Litopterna; though both families of the latter are probably represented, the distinction cannot yet be made from known fossils.

The †Notoungulata were the most abundant and diversified elements of the fauna. There were many genera and species of the suborder †Entelonychia of which, †*Periphragnis* was the largest. This genus seems to have been the direct ancestor of †*Asmodeus*, of the Deseado stage and †*Homalodotherium*, of the Santa Cruz. The †Typotheria were the most diversified of the †notoungulate suborders; all of them were small animals and most of them had the hypsodont, rootless and cement-covered teeth already noted in the succeeding pre-Santa Cruzian stages.

A somewhat surprising feature of the Musters fauna is the apparent absence of the †Toxodonta except of the horse-like family of the †Notohippidæ, though it remains to be determined whether this absence was, or was not, due to the conditions of fossilization. The †Astrapotheria were continued by the little-known †*Astraponotus*, used to designate the stage, and †*Propyrotherium* was intermediate between †*Pyrotherium* of the Deseado and †*Carolozittelia* of the Casa Mayor.

Three features of the Musters fauna are in the strongest contrast to that of the Santa Cruz: (1) the absence or great rarity of the normal †toxodonts, (2) the absence of the †ground-sloths and (3) the presence of many †Typotheria with cement-covered teeth.

b. Casa Mayor Stage. — This fauna, though in large degree ancestral to that of the Musters stage, is yet so much more primitive as to suggest that a considerable hiatus in time separated these two stages, an interval much longer than that between the Deseado and the Musters. The Casa Mayor fauna is here referred to the older, but not the oldest Eocene, and is extraordinarily rich in species, genera and families, so much so that Ameghino conjectured that the stage might be divisible into several substages. So far, however, such a subdivision has not proved to be feasible.

The Casa Mayor fauna is made up of small and very small animals; only one genus can fairly be called large and, of the others, the largest about equalled a full-grown pig in size. Furthermore, these mammals are primitive in structure; but few have the hypsodont, or cement-covered teeth so frequent in the later formations, and there is but a limited number of ordinal and suborbinal groups represented in the fauna. Insectivora, Rodentia and Primates are entirely wanting and, of the Edentata, only the armadillos are known to occur. One genus of armadillos, †*Utaetus*, is of exceptional interest, for it is the only known example among the Xenarthra in which a remnant of enamel has been found; on the tips of unworn teeth there are caps of enamel.

While indigenous in the sense of being ancestral to later faunas, the Casa Mayor shares some mammalian and reptilian groups with other regions, such as the †Condylarthra, the Marsupialia, the alligators and boa-like snakes, showing an intermigration in the Paleocene, or older Eocene, which was not repeated until the Pliocene.

The marsupials were numerous and varied and relatively more important than they were in subsequent times; the opossums would seem to have been derived from the Cretaceous of North America. The cænolestids and allied families were numerously represented and, apparently, filled the rôles of the smaller rodents. The predaceous kinds, †Borhyænidæ, were mostly small and distinctly more primitive than their successors of the later stages, but there is one very surprising exception to this statement. The carnivorous genus †*Arminiheringia* comprised animals approximating a lion in size and, in some respects, more specialized than any of the Miocene members of the family.

Many of the hoofed animals appear to be referable to the northern hemisphere order of the †Condylarthra, though more complete material may show this reference to be untenable. †Notoungulata were many, most of them being primitive members of the †Typotheria, though ancestral representatives of the †Entelonychia were also common. The largest hoofed mammal of the stage is †*Thomashuxleya*, an animal about as large as a swine, and at present the most completely known. This genus would seem to have been the direct ancestor of †*Asmodeus* and †*Homalodotherium;* it is interesting to note that the transformation of hoofs into claws had not yet taken place. The †Entelonychia were more varied and important in this stage than in any of the subsequent ones. No member of the †toxodont family has been found in these beds, a notable difference from all subsequent formations, including the Pampean. †Astrapotheria are well represented and in †*Albertogaudrya* we have what seems to be the small, primitive ancestor of †*Astrapotherium* itself.

The †Pyrotheria likewise were already distinguishable as such; so far as it is known, †*Carolozittelia* may be considered as ancestral to †*Pyrotherium*. The †Litopterna were apparently already differentiated as an order, but it is still doubtful whether the two families had been separated.

c. *Rio Chico Stage.* — Of this recently discovered fauna, Dr. Simpson, its discoverer, says: it "appears to be closely related to that of the Casa Mayor, probably being directly ancestral to the latter, but to consist of distinctive and more primitive species and genera."

TERTIARY REPTILES OF PATAGONIA

Something should be said of Patagonian Tertiary reptiles, because of the light which they throw upon the problems of geography and climate. Reptiles are inexplicably rare in the Tertiary formations of Patagonia, a sharp contrast to the abundance of them in the Tertiary beds of North America. In the Santa Cruz no reptiles other than a few fragments of lizard jaws have ever been found. The Deseado has yielded the extremely interesting horned tortoise †*Meiolania*, elsewhere known only from Australia. No reptiles have been reported from the Colhué-huapi, or the Musters, but Dr. Simpson has discovered two very significant reptiles in the Casa Mayor, one a gigantic snake, †*Madtsoria*, and the other a small alligator, †*Eocaiman*. The snake finds its nearest known ally in †*Gigantophis*, of the Egyptian Eocene, and the alligator appears to be the common ancestor of the Recent South American genera *Caiman* and *Jacare*. †*Eocaiman* is related to the early Tertiary alligators of North America in a way that "strongly suggests that these North and South American alligatoroid genera are a distinctive group of common geographic and zoölogic origin" (Simpson, Amer. Mus. Novi., No. 623, p. 8). Of the great snake he says: "that South America was not an isolated continent" in the late Cretaceous or early Paleocene, when the radiation or dispersal of the Boa-like snakes took place. Both of these reptiles give strong evidence that in early Eocene times the climate of central Patagonia must have been subtropical.

CHAPTER XI

PREFACE TO THE HISTORIES OF THE MAMMALIAN ORDERS. MODES OF EVOLUTION: EXTINCTION AND MIGRATIONS OF MAMMALS

Throughout this book the theory of Evolution is taken for granted and no attempt is made to present the evidence for it. The manner in which the evolutionary process is conceived to have acted is dealt with in the final chapter, but something must be said on that subject in a preliminary way, in order to give the reader a conception of how the genealogical, or *phylogenetic*, series are put together. Phylogeny (or tribal genesis), as has been well said, is the most inexact of the sciences, because it has such a large subjective element and depends so much upon the judgment of the individual naturalist.

It is for this reason that palæontologists differ so often and so radically in the answers which they give to phylogenetic questions, for their fundamental preconceptions are so irreconcilable, that one regards as quite impossible what another believes to be usual and normal. For example, the late Professor W. D. Matthew, a justly eminent authority, derived both the true cats and the †sabre-tooths from primitive Oligocene representatives of the latter. To the present writer that view has always seemed untenable and he would derive both subfamilies from a much more ancient common ancestor.

Even if considerations of space did not forbid discussion of this problem, it would be manifestly unsuitable to this book. The author must, therefore, content himself with expressing his own opinion and, where that is disputed, stating the fact of dissidence and, in important instances, summarizing rival views. Such a dogmatic treatment of phylogenetic problems is an unfortunate necessity; polemical discussions must be confined to technical publications for professional readers.

The difficulties involved in the solution of phylogenetic problems are manifold, of many different kinds. The most obvious and most frequent is the lack of necessary material, where the needed fossils have never been found, or are so fragmentary that any interpretation of them can be but tentative. This difficulty is slowly diminishing through the continual advance of discovery, though one cannot venture to hope that it will ever be substantially removed.

A second difficulty is the opposite of the first, an "embarrassment of riches," when there are so many possible ancestors of a given group at a given stage, that it is impracticable to decide between them. Still a third class of difficulties are geographical, to determine how largely a given series of animals has been developed in a particular region and how far development has been interrupted by immigration. A very pertinent illustration of this difficulty is afforded by the history of the horses, using that term to mean the whole equine family, from its earliest known beginnings. It has been generally believed that this history has been recorded in the western Tertiary deposits of North America in an exceptionally clear and detailed manner. Yet midway in the story a formidable difficulty arises: for reasons that cannot be explained here, some leading authorities are convinced that the later genera of the West cannot have been descended from the earlier ones of that same area, but were migrants from some other region, more probably North American than Asiatic.

The root of this geographical difficulty lies in uncertainty concerning the manner in which the evolutionary process operates. What were the kinds of change that actually happened in the past and what were the kinds that never did happen? Were there exceptional kinds of change that sometimes, though rarely, took place and other kinds that were normal and usual? These, and others like them, are questions that cannot yet be answered with any assurance. Sometimes the demonstrable modes of development are themselves extremely misleading, producing fallacious results. It has been proved, for example, that certain structures have arisen, entirely independently, in two or more groups of animals, and, in such cases, the possession of such structures is no proof of relationship. How is one to decide, unless the history of each group is fully known, whether those identical structures have been independently acquired, or were due to a common inheritance? The decision can generally be made by comparison of the totality of structure, for there is no reason to believe that the same group of mammals was ever derived from more than one line of ancestry. If any such derivation ever actually took place, it must have been so rare as to be negligible in a general view.

When it is possible to make out a genetic series of several genera, succeeding one another in chronological order, and fulfilling all the conditions of direct development from ancestor to descendant, the result is much more satisfactory both to writer and to reader, than if it must be said: "this genus, *A*, is not directly, but only collaterally ancestral to that, *B*." Or, expressed in another way, "*A* is a structural, but not an actual, ancestor of *B*." A structural ancestor is a preceding form, which, in most points of structure, fulfils the conditions of a true ancestry, but is, at the same time, so specialized in some particular, as to exclude it from the direct line.

The existing Monotremata, the Duck-billed Mole (*Ornithorhynchus*) and Spiny Anteater (*Tachyglossa*) of Australia are, by far, the most primitive of modern mammals, reproducing by means of eggs and retaining many characters of their reptilian ancestry, which all other mammals have lost. Nevertheless, upon this foundation of primitiveness are superposed so many specializations of head and feet as to make it impossible to consider them as ancestral to any other known mammals. On the other hand, their primitive characteristics enable us to judge what the ancient, truly ancestral Monotremata were like.

That in most phylogenetic series, as at present constructed, many or all the members are structural rather than direct ancestors of succeeding members, is what would naturally be expected. When two successive rich and diversified mammalian faunas are compared, it is found, as a rule, that the later one is not to be derived from the whole of the earlier one, but that, so far as we are able to judge, most of the earlier genera died out without leaving descendants and that the newer fauna was derived through divergent evolution from a relatively small number of genera in the preceding one. Nearly always, in addition, the newer fauna was recruited by immigration, sometimes on a very large scale, as in the lower Eocene, sometimes bringing a smaller proportion of migrants, as in the White River, and again with very few, as in the John Day.

Thus the chance of finding the few, real ancestors, in any fauna, of a subsequent assemblage among the multitude of "structural ancestors" and of types that left no descendants, is obviously small and, for that reason, the palæontologist must often satisfy himself with these substitutes for the actual ancestors, hoping that the progress of discovery will eventually bring the true ancestors to light, as it often has done before.

This distinction between "real" and "structural" ancestors rests upon the conception of the evolutionary process which a given naturalist holds and, as this conception varies much among students of the subject, the distinction between "real" and "structural" must vary accordingly. The fundamental postulate upon which the genealogies set forth in the following chapters are founded is, that the mode of development is direct and continuous, not to be symbolized by a zig-zag line, nor having gaps, where considerable changes took place abruptly, *per saltum*. The course of evolution here regarded as the normal one is by *divergent* development, by which one ancestral genus gave rise to several descendant groups, though only less important is *parallel* development, in which several related groups follow parallel lines of change, often keeping remarkably even pace with one another throughout all their changes. *Convergent* development, according to which the descendants are more nearly alike than were their ancestors, has certainly often taken place, so far as single characters, or an associated group of correlated characters, are concerned, but, according to present information, has never, or most rarely, resulted in an identity of the entire organism. The horse-like †Litopterna (family †Proterotheriidæ) of South America are a remarkable instance of convergence, for with all their resemblances, they were not remotely related to the true horses, for they were not even perissodactyls. An astonishing case of convergence is the great marsupial †sabre-tooth, †*Thylacosmilus* of the South American Pliocene, which imitates the true †sabre-tooth cats in the most bewildering fashion, yet remains an unmistakable marsupial. This wonderful discovery was made and recently announced by Mr. E. S. Riggs, of the Field Museum, Chicago. All these cases of convergence and every other known case, it should be emphasized, are readily to be distinguished from real relationships, though not all palæontologists would admit this.

One limit of error is given by the chronological succession, which prevents attempting to derive an earlier genus from a later one, but even chronology may sometimes be misleading, because of the ever-recurring incompleteness of the geological record. A genus, for example, may give off a stem which becomes truly ancestral to later genera and, at the same time, some species of the genus may long persist with relatively little change, and continue along with its descendants, just as a man may go on living among his children and grandchildren. In some instances our only knowledge of the ancestral genus is derived from those later survivals, as is illustrated in the strange †Dinocerata, extinct since the Eocene.

Bridger $\left\{\begin{array}{l}\text{Upper} — †\textit{Eobasileus}\\ \text{Middle} — †\textit{Uintatherium}, †\textit{Elachoceras}\\ \text{Lower} — \text{Barren}\end{array}\right.$
Wind River — †*Bathyopsis*
Clark Fork — †*Probathyopsis*

If the lower Bridger member of this series were known, it almost certainly would prove to be †*Elachoceras,* or some very similar form, and it must be considered as a structural ancestor until the actual ancestor from the lower Bridger is brought to light.

These are the postulates upon which the succeeding chapters are founded, but, needless to say, they make no claim to finality. They are generally accepted by palæontologists as a working hypothesis, but the advance of knowledge and new discovery will assuredly modify them, perhaps sweep them away altogether, "as with a flood."

Extinction of Animals

This is a phenomenon which has recurred in an unimaginable number of instances throughout the recorded history of the earth, and, most frequently, in what seems to us to be a sudden manner and on a vast, even a world-wide scale. The apparent suddenness is no doubt largely illusory, and has been caused by long gaps in the geological record. One of the most remarkable and conspicuous of the wholesale extinctions is that which took place at the end of the Mesozoic Era, when the great reptiles that had long dominated land, sea and air, and had swarmed in all continents and in every sea, were wiped out with what looks to us like startling abruptness, and simultaneously all over the world. Between the Mesozoic and the following Cenozoic Era there was an almost universal hiatus in sedimentation and, for an indeterminate length of time, no record was made. Before the hiatus, the †dinosaurs, †pterosaurs, †plesiosaurs, etc., had been abundant; after it they had all disappeared. The suddenness and simultaneity are more or less deceptive, but the vast extinctions are none the less real.

The problem of extinction has been discussed by many writers; in fact, ever since Cuvier and William Smith first proved that innumerable species, belonging to all classes of animals and plants, had actually vanished from the earth. Lamarck, the first of scientific evolutionists, maintained that no species had ever become extinct save by the agency of Man. By that he meant that all the species of former ages were still represented in the modern world by their transformed descendants. This doctrine was revived in our time

(1910) by the late Professor Steinmann, of Bonn, but it involves such manifest absurdities that the conception has been rejected by palæontologists with almost complete unanimity.

Notwithstanding all this discussion, extinction remains an unexplained mystery, for all the instances which we have witnessed have been occasioned by human agency. The great Alaska Sea-cow (†*Rhytina*) the †Moas, gigantic birds of New Zealand (†*Dinornis*, etc.), the †Dodo (†*Didus*) and other birds and mammals have been exterminated through the careless greed of Man. The so-called Buffalo (*Bison*), vast herds of which once covered the Great Plains, was barely saved from destruction by the intervention of the United States and Canadian governments. But all these "modern instances" throw no light upon natural extinctions, as to which we can only speculate.

Many causes of extinction have been suggested, such as changes of climate, the onset of new infectious diseases, the "struggle for existence" in competition with better adapted rivals, or enemies, and many others. It is probable that nearly all of the suggested factors, and many more that have not been thought of, have been real agents in the process, yet the combined operation of the various causes is not understood.

Though it would be unprofitable to speculate as to the causes of extinction, much may be learned as to the manner in which species have actually been exterminated. For this purpose, the most useful field of study is afforded by the vast extinctions which, during and after the Pleistocene epoch, decimated the mammals over three-fifths of the land-surface of the globe, only tropical Africa and Asia escaping. The ascertained facts show (1) that the extinctions were not sudden, but gradual, and (2) that they were not universal, but, at first local, and spreading gradually from local centres. Even to-day, some of the extinctions remain partial and incomplete. The Musk-ox, for example, formerly extended across Siberia as far west as Great Britain, and became extinct in the Old World, but has managed to keep a foothold in the extreme north of the New. Of this partial extinction a great many examples might be cited, of groups once distributed all over the northern hemisphere, which died out much earlier in Eurasia than in America, or *vice versa*. Throughout the Oligocene, Miocene and Pliocene, the †sabre-tooth cats ranged all around the northern hemisphere, but nowhere entered the southern. In the Pleistocene they had almost or altogether disappeared from the Old World, while reaching the acme of their development in numerical abundance, size and power in the Western Hemisphere and extending their range throughout South America.

This partial extinction is a common and well-recognized phenomenon, for all the instances of "discontinuous distribution," a few of which were mentioned in Chapter VIII, are cases of partial extinction; the two expressions mean almost the same thing. The tapirs (cited in Chapter VIII) were once spread all over the northern hemisphere, and the Asiatic Tropics and South America as well. Now they are found only in Malaya, Central and South America, a typical example of partial extinction and discontinuous distribution. The rhinoceroses and the elephants, the giraffe family, the opossums and many other mammalian groups now occupy areas incomparably smaller than those over which they were formerly spread, and similar arrangements may be detected in the various stages of the Tertiary.

Many, if not all, of the Pleistocene and post-Pleistocene extinctions were gradual, not sudden. The fauna entombed in the Los Angeles tar-pits and in the Sheridan loess of the Great Plains is now believed to be that of the last Interglacial stage and was the most magnificent assemblage of mammals for abundance, diversity, size and power in the whole recorded history of North America. How large a proportion of this wonderful fauna survived the rigours of the Wisconsin, or final Glacial stage, cannot yet be told, but a very considerable number of genera, now extinct, did survive for longer or shorter periods, dying out now here and now there, until they vanished altogether. It was long taken for granted that, when stone weapons were found in association with the bones of Pleistocene mammals, the presence of Pleistocene Man in America was thereby proved. The reasoning was fallacious, for many Pleistocene mammals were in existence only a few centuries ago, in what is called "historic time" in the Old World.

Several skeletons of the American †Mastodon have been found in bogs, covered by only a few inches of peat, with more or less of the hair and recognizable contents of the stomach preserved. Such fossils can be of no great antiquity, and they all occur in post-Pleistocene deposits, laid down after the complete disappearance of the Glacial ice. The †ground-sloth skeleton (†*Nothrotherium*) found in a New Mexico cavern, which has ligaments and fragments of skin adhering to it (see page 179) must be of very modern date, as is also the skull of †*Camelops*, with its attached skin, obtained by Professor A. S. Romer from a cave in Utah. There are many other instances of the survival of Pleistocene mammals into modern times, but it is not necessary to enumerate them.

Similar facts are true of South America, as told in Chapter VIII; most significant of these are the large pieces of hair-covered skin of an extinct †ground-sloth found in a Patagonian cave. Finally may be mentioned the most remarkable case of all. In Ecuador was found in 1929 the skeleton of a †mastodont of South American type (†*Cordillerion*) which had manifestly been killed by the Indians, who had built a circle of fires around the carcass for the more convenient roasting of the flesh, and had even removed the ribs of one side and made fires within the body-cavity. Quantities of broken painted pottery and stone implements were left in the camps, which, together with the skeleton, were buried by a landslide from the bluff at the foot of which the victim had been killed. Dr. Spillmann, of Quito, has described this remarkable find which he dates near the beginning of the Christian Era.

These and other similar facts show that in many cases, at least, extinction was gradual, not sudden, and began as a local phenomenon in scattered areas, from which it spread until it became complete, or was arrested as a partial extinction. Though important and instructive, such facts tell us little as to the causes of extinction.

MIGRATIONS OF MAMMALS

In Chapter VIII, on the Geographical Distribution of Mammals, the necessity of postulating the "doctrine of specific centres" was explained. According to this doctrine, every species of mammal originated in some particular area and spread from there until it was arrested by some impassable barrier, climatic or geographical. A species which is increasing its numbers presses hard upon the means of subsistence and each generation must go farther from the starting point in search of a food supply. Such unconscious and unintentional spread has been given the ill-chosen and unfortunate name of "migration," as though it were analogous to the annual migration of birds, of which every one has heard.

In the case of insect-pests, most of them introduced from abroad at known dates, it has been possible to determine their rate of spread with much accuracy. The Colorado Potato-beetle, the San José Scale, the Gypsy and the Brown-tail Moth, the Japanese Beetle, and the Japanese Mantis have all been studied from this point of view and the results confirm those hypotheses deduced from the geological history of mammals, that the so-called migration is an unconscious spread of successive generations in search of food, and that it continues until some obstacle puts a stop to it.

It is the great changes of climate and of the connections between the various continents that give such importance to the slow spread of mammals. In the course of the Cenozoic Era North America has been successively joined to and separated from South America, Asia and, perhaps also, directly with Europe. Europe and Asia are now so broadly connected as to make the former merely a peninsula of the latter and to justify the term "Eurasia" for the immense land-mass which together they constitute. During a longer or shorter portion of the Eocene epoch a long, narrow sound, extending from the Arctic to the Mediterranean, cut Europe off entirely from Asia.

The Tertiary land connections of Africa and of South America are not so clearly indicated and are still under debate, yet there is strong reason to believe that both of these continents and Australia were at one time joined by land-bridges with Antarctica and that Africa and South America were joined by a transatlantic isthmus in the early Tertiary.

Whenever land-masses, formerly separated by the sea, were joined together by an upheaval of the sea-bottom and had been taken possession of by vegetation, land-mammals began to spread in both directions, so that each land contributed more or less extensively to the fauna of the other. This spread must have been a relatively slow process, in the course of which most species would undergo more or less extensive modification, so as to give rise to different species in the newly invaded land. At several times in the Tertiary period the mammals of North America and Europe were closely alike, and at other times very different, thus registering the making and severing of the land-connection. In the lower Eocene (Wasatch) the mammals of the two continents were almost identical, so far as the genera are concerned, the species are nearly all different, having undergone such modification in passing from one continent to the other as to require specific distinction.

Of all barriers to the spread of land-animals the most effective are wide arms of the sea, but hardly less so are differences of climate, especially of temperature. For that reason migrations along parallels of latitude were practicable for a much larger proportion of the mammals involved than those along the meridians of longitude. Bearing in mind the mild climates that prevailed during most of the Tertiary period, the land-bridge across the site of the present Bering Sea and Strait, notwithstanding its sub-Arctic position, accounts for the extraordinary similarity of the earlier Tertiary mammals of North America and eastern Asia.

Much more difficult and therefore more incomplete were the intermigrations along lines of longitude, which led through different climates, impassable to many species, though practicable for others. For example, when North and South America, which had long been separated by a sea and had developed mammalian faunas of extraordinary difference, were at length united at the end of the Miocene epoch, intermigration in both directions began. Several northern mammals made their appearance in the Pliocene of South America and southern genera in that of North America, but only a very small proportion of the mammals characteristic of each continent found their way into the other. Between the two warm-temperate zones extended the Tropics, which acted as a vast sieve, holding back most mammals and allowing but a relatively small number of climatically adaptable species to pass through.

So great is the importance of migrations, so called, that the history of mammals is quite unintelligible unless such wanderings be taken into account. Some naturalists, it is true, have adopted a sceptical attitude in regard to these migrations, but the palæontological evidence for them is entirely convincing to those who have examined it. In general, it may be said that the apparently sudden and unheralded appearance of animals in a region where older formations contain no fossils ancestral to those animals, is evidence of immigration from some other region, which may or may not be known. For example, the early and primitive types of elephants appeared in the middle Miocene of North America and the lower Miocene of Europe. In neither continent have more ancient formations yielded anything which can be regarded as having been ancestral to the elephants. Unless the theory of Evolution is entirely illusory, these animals must have originated in some other region, from which they spread into Europe and North America, and that region was, at first, only conjectural. Subsequent discoveries showed the unknown region to be North Africa, for in Egypt the elephant line could be traced back to the Eocene, where it is represented by small and extremely primitive animals.

Mammalian migrations sometimes involved whole faunas, a very striking example of which began in the latest Paleocene and continued into the lower Eocene. The Torrejon fauna was made up almost entirely of archaic types, some of which were like those of the later Cretaceous and were not ancestral to any existing families, and, except for a few Insectivora and probable Primates, this assemblage had no representatives of any existing Placental *order*. Then followed the great immigration of which the effects first appeared in the Clark Fork and the succeeding Gray Bull. This completely transformed the character of mammalian life and brought in primitive and ancestral forms of horses, rhinoceroses, tapirs, †brontotheres, camels, deer, pigs and Carnivora.

The same story applies to Europe and the close similarity between the lower Eocene mammals of Europe and North America is due to an immigration in both directions, presumably from Central or Northeastern Asia. Though the most striking of known examples, this late Paleocene and early Eocene invasion is far from unique. A comparison of the contemporary mammals through all the Tertiary stages, reveals the times when Europe, Asia and North America were connected by continuous land, and when this immense area was broken up into two or even three continents.

The partial interchange of mammals between North and South America in the early Pliocene is another very conspicuous example of the tendency of land animals to spread into regions newly made accessible by the upheaval of sea-bottoms. The separation of the two Americas in the Miocene epoch was registered in the extraordinary and profound difference of their mammals, and the faunally unique Australian Region owes its peculiarity to its long-continued isolation.

CHAPTER XII

HISTORY OF THE PROBOSCIDEA

Modern elephants are confined to southern Asia, the Malay Archipelago, and the warmer parts of Africa, and only two genera, *Loxodonta* and *Elephas*, survive from the multitude that, from the middle Miocene to the end of the Pleistocene, ranged over all the continents, save only Australia. The long and extremely complex story of proboscidean development is one of the most fascinating chapters of mammalian history and has slowly been deciphered by the labours of many eminent naturalists, beginning with the work of Cuvier at the close of the XVIII Century. Professor H. F. Osborn's splendid monograph on the Proboscidea, of which the first volume has been recently published (Aug. 1936) and which crowns the labours of thirty years, has done more to put this wonderful chronicle into a clear light than all the previous studies of the subject. This chapter is principally derived from Osborn's great work, the advance sheets of which I had the privilege of studying. Even with this guide, however, much remains obscure and must await future discoveries for elucidation. There are gaps in the narrative which, for the present, can be bridged by nothing more substantial than conjecture.

Most of this astonishing evolution took place in the Old World and more, or fewer, of the newly developed types reached North America in wave after wave of immigration. There is some evidence, not at all conclusive, of movement in the opposite direction, but, if such emigration actually took place, it was of entirely subordinate importance. The land-bridge which, during nearly the whole Cenozoic Era, occupied the site of Bering Sea, was the path of these migrations and made North America effectively a part of Asia, the mild climates of the Tertiary periods and of the Interglacial stages rendering the bridge accessible even to southern mammals. In the Eocene and Oligocene epochs eastern Asia was zoölogically much more akin to North America than it was to Europe.

As will be seen later, the Proboscidea originated in Africa, to which continent they were long confined. In the lower Miocene they migrated to Europe and Asia, rapidly spreading to North America, where they made their earliest known appearance in the middle Miocene. Thereafter, as new forms arose, they spread with surprising rapidity and most of them, sooner or later, extended into North America, though several groups, for some unknown reason, failed to cross the bridge. In the late Pliocene, the proboscideans entered South America and covered the whole continent from the Guianas to Argentina and Bolivia. The Pliocene and Pleistocene were the time of the greatest diversification and geographical expansion of the Proboscidea, when they ranged over all of Arctogæa and Neogæa, a most striking contrast to the present order of things.

Of the four suborders into which Osborn divides the Proboscidea, two, the †Mastodontoidea and Elephantoidea, entered the Western Hemisphere and only the latter survives to the present day.

Osborn's classification, which he revised and changed only a few weeks before his lamented death, is here adopted, though certain changes in terminology have been made, in order to bring the names of families and subfamilies into harmony with the accepted rules of zoölogical nomenclature. Where there is such difference of practice, Osborn's names are added in parenthesis. In the interests of intelligibility, the names of the principal Old World groups are given and distinguished by bold-faced type, Old World subfamilies by italics.

Order PROBOSCIDEA

Suborder I, †**Mœritherioidea,** the most ancient and primitive of known proboscideans: Eocene and Oligocene of North Africa.

Suborder II, †**Deinotherioidea:** upper tusks wanting; lower jaw and tusks curved downward and backward. Miocene and Pliocene of Old World.

Suborder III, †Mastodontoidea: mostly with both upper and lower tusks; grinding teeth low-crowned and rooted, with few transverse enamel ridges. Eocene to Pleistocene of Eastern Hemisphere mid-Miocene to post-Pleistocene of North America, Pliocene to post-Pleistocene of South America.

Suborder IV, Elephantoidea: grinding teeth very large, with progressively higher and more numerous ridges, covered with cement masticating surface showing many plates of alternating dentine enamel and cement. Jaws much shortened and lower tusks wanting. Skull high and dome-shaped.

In his latest revision, Osborn divided the †Mastodontoidea into four families and fifteen subfamilies. These, with the necessary changes of names, are as follows:

SUBORDER †MASTODONTOIDEA †MASTODONTS

FAMILY A. †MASTODONTIDÆ
1. †*Palæomastodontinæ*
2. †Mastodontinæ
3. †*Zygolophodontinæ*
4. †*Stegolophodontinæ*

FAMILY B. †TRILOPHODONTIDÆ
(†Bunomastodontidæ)
5. †Rhynchotheriinæ (†Rhynochorostrinæ)
6. †Trilophodontinæ (†Longirostrinæ)
7. †Gnathabelodontinæ
8. †Amebelodontinæ
9. †Tetralophodontinæ
10. †Cordillerioninæ (†Notorostrinæ)
11. †*Pentalophodontinæ* (†Brevirostrinæ)

FAMILY C. †STEGOMASTODONTIDÆ (†Humboldtidæ)
12. †Stegomastodontinæ (†Humboldtinæ)

FAMILY D. †SERRIDENTIDÆ
13. †Serridentinæ
14. †Platybelodontinæ
15. †Notiomastodontinæ

SUBORDER ELEPHANTOIDEA, ELEPHANTS

FAMILY ELEPHANTIDÆ
1. †*Stegodontinæ* — †Transitional
2. *Loxodontinæ* — African Elephants
3. †Mammuthinæ — †Mammoths
4. *Elephantinæ* — Indian Elephants

The Proboscidea are very isolated among hoofed animals and display in their structure a curious mixture of great specialization in teeth and skull, with extreme conservatism in body and limbs. Aside from the skull, the skeleton is primitive and retains almost the same condition as that found in the most ancient known genera of the order. Great increase in size and weight took place in most of the subfamilies and such increase required certain readjustments in the skeleton, but the changes involved are not radical. Professor E. H. Barbour, who has been struck by the incongruous association of highly specialized teeth and skull, with primitive body, limbs and feet, says of the proboscideans: "Their bodies underwent no fundamental progressive changes, but remained generalized and of one pattern. In the case of the skull, it is a wholly different matter. The latter with its jaw, grinding teeth, admirable tusks and remarkable proboscis, exemplifies vigorous progressive changes and consequent specialization." "In the Proboscidea the molar teeth furnish the chief diagnostic characters and all stages of their progressive development are known. They grade insensibly from two grinding ridges in the earliest to as many as thirty in the later elephants."

Of the external features, the most conspicuous is the proboscis, which gives its name to the order. This organ is a great prolongation of the nose, with the nostrils opening at the end, and in modern elephants, with a finger-like tip, which can pick up minute objects.

Suborder Elephantoidea

Family 1. Elephantidæ

In this family the dental formula is: $i \frac{1}{0}$, $c \frac{0}{0}$, $p \frac{0}{0}$, $m \frac{3}{3}$, and is supplemented by the milk-premolars, $dp \frac{3}{3}$. These perform the functions

Fig. 161. — Head of Indian Elephant, *Elephas maximus*, showing small ears. (By permission of N. Y. Zoöl. Soc.)

of the true premolars, which have been altogether suppressed and are not even formed in the jaws. The latest species in which germs of the permanent premolars were formed, is †*Archidiskodon planifrons*, of the upper Pliocene of India.

The single upper incisor of each side, believed to be the second of the original three, is a long, massive, bluntly pointed tusk, which continues to grow throughout life and is nearly unique among mammals; only the Narwhal, a whale, has a similar tusk. In the true elephants, enamel is confined to the tip of the tusk, which is the earliest part formed.

The grinding teeth have a structure, which, though characteristic, is not unique, several other mammals imitating them more or less closely. Such a tooth consists of a number of very high enamel ridges, each enclosing a body of dentine. The valleys between the ridges are filled up with cement, which also spreads over and encloses

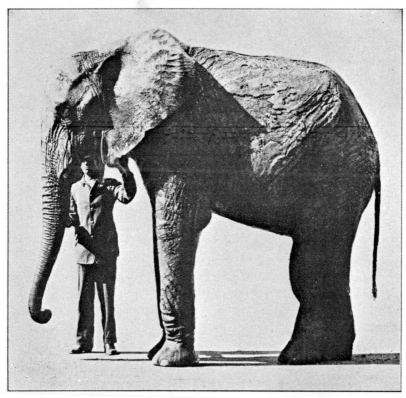

FIG. 162. — African Elephant, *Loxodonta africanus*. (By permission of N. Y. Zoöl. Soc.)

the entire tooth, so that, in the unworn state, no ridges are visible. When the covering of cement has been worn away from the masticating surface and the enamel ridges truncated by attrition, that surface is seen to be made up of alternating plates of dentine, enamel and cement, which, because of their different degrees of hardness, wear unequally, thus keeping the surface rough. These teeth are extremely hypsodont, even more so in the Indian genus (*Elephas*) than in the African (*Loxodonta*). The grinders increase from before backward in size and in the number of component enamel ridges. In the Indian Elephant (*Elephas maximus*) the number of enamel ridges of the six grinding teeth (i.e. including the milk-premolars) is: 4, 8, 12, 12, 16, 24. In the African elephants (*Loxodonta africanus*) the ridges are fewer and of different shape; the formula is: 3, 6, 7, 7, 8, 10 and these animals are far more primitive in teeth and cranium than the elephants of Asia and America.

The manner in which the teeth are erupted in the elephants is altogether exceptional; they come in obliquely from behind, the upper

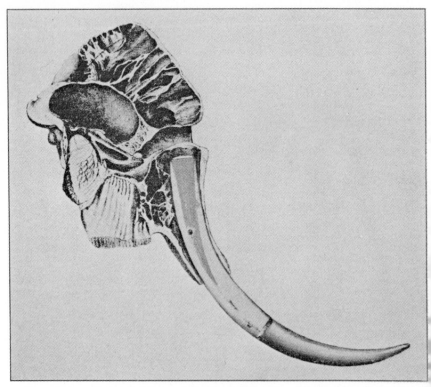

FIG. 163. — Vertical section of skull and left tusk of Indian Elephant, showing cancelled bone around brain-case and oblique replacement of upper molars. The small black circle in the tusk is a leaden bullet. (From R. Owen, 1845.)

ones moving forward and downward, the lower ones forward and upward. The tooth is thus obliquely truncated and, in its slow advance, it pushes out the one ahead of it and takes its place. Thus, there are, ordinarily, but four teeth in use at the same time, one on each side, above and below, though, for a time, one tooth and part of another may be in use together. The oblique wear, abrading first the anterior part of the tooth, results in so reducing its height that, by the time the tooth is fully in place, the front part is worn

down to less than half of the vertical height of the hinder part. This
method of eruption is made necessary by the very short jaws and
the great size of the teeth. At the same time it renders possible the
very long life of these great creatures, for a herbivorous mammal
cannot long outlive its teeth.

The elephant skull is a very remarkable and exceptional structure, for it has unusual functions. It must, in the first place, support
the enormous weight of the
tusks, which may be as much
as 500 pounds, and wield
these ponderous weapons with
ease and swiftness. The tusks
are employed, not only as
weapons, but also in digging
roots and uprooting trees, for
which a tremendous leverage
is required. In the second
place, it must carry and use
the immense grinding teeth,
which form such an effective
masticating mill. It must,
thirdly, afford attachment to
and carry the proboscis, which
is so long and heavy and yet
is so wonderfully mobile and

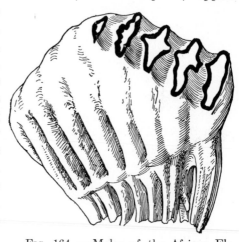

Fig. 164. — Molar of the African Elephant, *Loxodonta africanus*, showing the oblique mode of wear. Heavy black lines indicate enamel enclosing areas of dentine,
cement covering the whole tooth.

such an efficient implement for so varied uses. Fourthly, it must
afford the surface necessary for the powerful muscles of the jaws
and neck. Finally, it must fulfil the usual purposes of the mammalian
skull in carrying and protecting the brain and higher sense-organs.

In order to obviate the necessity of enormous additional weight,
the huge skull must be lightened, so far as is possible, without losing
the required strength. All the bones of the skull are immensely
thickened and, at the same time, lightened by the development of a
great number of communicating cells, or sinuses, and thus the brain-
chamber is, as it were, hidden away in the middle of the great cranium. This explains the difficulty of killing an elephant by shooting
him in the head, for the bullet must reach the brain and that shot
requires much knowledge and skill.

A remarkable and characteristic feature of the elephantine skull
is its great vertical height in comparison with the extreme shortening
of the antero-posterior diameter, as though the front and back sur-

faces had been violently approximated. Different species show different ratios of length and height, but in all true elephants, the skull is very high and very short. Compared with the †mastodonts, with their long, low skulls, this is a very notable change. That this transformation was gradual cannot be doubted, but the stages of phylogenetic development are yet to be discovered.

The premaxillaries have become mere sheaths for the great tusks and, in existing elephants, have an almost vertical position. The nasal bones are greatly abbreviated and the anterior nasal opening is shifted to the top of the skull, above the posterior opening, so that the nasal canal passes vertically or horizontally through the head, an arrangement that is correlated with the possession of a long proboscis and is very rare among land animals, though normal in the Cetacea, or whales, dolphins, porpoises, etc.

In the elephants the neck is very short, proportionally, the body long, capacious and very massive; the neural spines of all the vertebræ, even those of the loins, are inclined backward. The shoulder-blade is very large and has a prominent acromion and long metacromion. The hip-bones (pelvis) are greatly expanded, in adjustment to the width of the abdomen and its immense mass of viscera. The limbs are long, massive and columnar and their upper segments, especially the thigh, are much elongated. The knee-joint is thus brought down below the body to the relative position of the hock-joint in a horse, or cow. In unguligrade mammals, which walk on their hoofs, the knee-joint is covered and concealed by the great muscles of the flank, while in the elephants the knee is exposed and free from the body. In the latter, therefore, the leg seems to bend in a direction opposite to that seen in horses, cattle, deer, etc. Plantigrade animals, generally, such as bears, raccoons, monkeys and Man, have the exposed knee-joint.

The bones of the fore-arm have exceptional proportions; the ulna is extremely massive and, except at the lower end, the radius is much more slender, thus reversing the proportions usual among hoofed animals. The thigh-bone has a smooth, hemispherical head, with no pit for the round ligament; the shaft which, in most mammals, is cylindrical, is so flattened, that its breadth much exceeds its thickness, and there is no third trochanter. The bones of the lower leg are separate and relatively short; the fibula, though stout, is much less heavy than the massive tibia.

All the long bones are devoid of marrow-cavities, the place of which is taken by spongy bone, through which the marrow is disseminated. In this manner the strength of the bone is increased without augmenting its diameter. Several extinct groups of large and bulky hoofed mammals acquired this same structure, when they had gained a certain bulk and weight and, in these groups, the change to the filled-up marrow cavities may be observed to accompany the increase of body-weight; it has taken place independently in at least three orders of ungulate mammals.

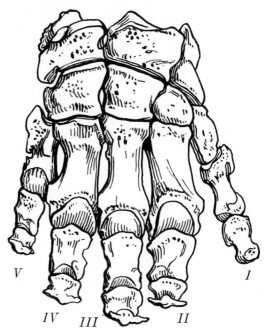

FIG. 165. — Right manus of the Indian Elephant, *E. maximus*.

The feet of elephants are extremely broad and short and the three median digits, Nos. II, III and IV, are far larger and heavier than the laterals, Nos. I and V. These feet are digitigrade in attitude, but not in function, for the weight, as shown in Professor Max Weber's section (Fig. 166) is carried upon a pad of elastic tissue, which, with the very thick skin, forms the sole of the foot. The hoofs are mere horny excrescences on the periphery of the columnar foot and are nails rather than hoofs. Very similar feet are possessed by hippopotamuses and rhinoceroses, though with fewer digits. The proboscideans have five digits in manus and pes, but not all of them have hoofs; in the Indian and West African species, the number of hoofs is five in the front foot, four in the hind, while in the East African species there are four and three respectively.

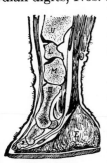

FIG. 166. — Vertical section through the manus of the Indian Elephant. *U*, lower end of ulna. *L*, lunar. *M*, magnum. *III*, third metacarpal. *1, 2, 3*, phalanges. *E*, pad of elastic tissue. (After M. Weber.)

In the adults of elephants now living, the skin is entirely naked, but the young calf has a considerable quantity of hair and in one race, or subspecies, from the Malay Peninsula, the calf, in some instances, at least, is densely covered with thick and partly bristly hair. This subspecies has been named *E. maximus hirsutus*. The naked elephants of to-day are adapted to life in warm climates, though the Indian species is reported to be extremely sensitive to the direct heat of the tropical sun and therefore chooses a habitat of dense forests. Formerly, there were cold-country genera and species, which were thickly clothed with hair and completely protected from cold.

Subfamily †*Mammuthinæ*, †*Mammoths*

Before the great extinctions which followed the Pleistocene, North America had several kinds of true elephants, but they all belonged to the †mammoth subfamily; the genus *Elephas*, as restricted by Osborn, is not known to have entered the Western Hemisphere. South America had many †mastodonts, but, so far, only a single elephant tooth, belonging to one of the † mammoths (†*Parelephas jeffersoni*) found in French Guiana, has been reported from all that continent. This suffices to show that the true elephants did make their way into South America, but they were unable to maintain a foothold there. As the †mammoths, the only North American elephants, were pre-eminently of northern origin and most of them were unable to penetrate the Tropics in any considerable numbers, they thus failed to establish themselves in South America.

Pleistocene North America had three genera of the †mammoth subfamily, †*Mammuthus*, †*Parelephas* and †*Archidiskodon*. The Siberian †Mammoth (†*M. primigenius*) is the best-known of all fossil mammals, for several complete carcasses have been found in the permanently frozen gravels of northern Siberia. The animal was very familiar to the Palæolithic men of the Pyrenees and the south of France, who left many admirable representations of the great beast which they assiduously pursued. These are paintings on cavern-roofs, incised drawings (one very famous drawing is incised on a fragment of the creature's own tusk), carvings in ivory and bone, all of which are so accurate and spirited, that they give a very lifelike conception of the animal. A frequent feature of these figures is a high, dome-shaped head, set off by a deep notch from a similar hump at the withers. This very strange characteristic has been adopted by Osborn and Knight in their restorations and is reproduced in the figure (Fig. 167) which I owe to the kindness of Mrs. Harrington. Granting the accuracy of this feature, unique among elephants, it must have been due to an accumulation of fat and was probably seasonal, for not all the cave-paintings show it and it has not been observed in the Siberian carcasses, though these have very high, dome-like skulls. Pfitzenmayer's drawing (Fig. 168) shows an alternative restoration of this species. The proboscis had no finger-like tip, but had two lips of nearly equal size, as is shown in the Berezovka †Mammoth and in certain cave drawings.

Fig. 167. — Restoration of †Mammoth, †*Mammuthus primigenius*, Pleistocene, showing dome-like head, presumably a seasonal accumulation of fat. (From a painting by Mrs. Blanche Harrington.)

†*Mammuthus* was typically an Arctic animal and was thoroughly protected against cold. Beneath the extraordinarily thick skin was found a layer of fat, as much as three inches thick in places. The entire animal was covered with a dense growth of fine, woolly hair, about an inch long, and an outer coat of long, coarse, dark-brown hair, which may reach a length of 20 inches. Observers report that the hair is more like that of the Musk-ox in appearance than that of any other known animal. The tail is shorter than in existing elephants and ended in a tuft of stiff bristles.

The head of the †Mammoth is relatively larger than in Recent elephants, permitting the marvellous growth of the tusks, which sometimes attained a length of 16 feet. The body is relatively short and this shortness, together with the downward slope of the back toward the rump, gave the animal a decidedly different appearance from that of other known elephants.

Notwithstanding the abundance of material, no detailed comparison of the skeleton of the †Mammoth with that of other members of the family has yet been made, but the facts already known justify the generic separation of †*Mammuthus* from *Elephas:* the principal

Fig. 168. — Restoration of the Berezovka †Mammoth, †*Mammuthus primigenius*, showing two-lipped trunk. (Modified from Pfitzenmayer.)

difference between the two, so far observed, is in the structure of the hind-foot. Curiously enough, the authorities who have described the latest find, known as the "Berezovka †Mammoth," give different accounts of the pes. Salensky (1904) says that the foot of the †Mammoth is four-toed. Herz (1902) reports five digits in the manus, four in the pes. Pfitzenmayer's account (1906) is as follows: "Metacarpal I and metatarsal I bear no phalanges; the remaining four metacarpals and metatarsals bear only two; the ossification of the third (or terminal) phalanx takes place only in entirely full-grown examples, while, in younger individuals, such as the Berezovka Mammoth, it is rudimentary and cartilaginous" (p. 523).

Although the word "mammoth" bears the connotation "gigantic," the elephant so named was not very large, seldom exceeding a

FIG. 169. — Restoration of the Columbian †Mammoth, †*Parelephas columbi*, from a skeleton in the American Museum of Natural History.

277

height of nine feet, six inches at the shoulder; the largest Indian elephants are taller by a foot.

In the Siberian carcasses have been preserved the contents of the stomach and, in the mouth, wads of substances masticated, but not swallowed. From these materials the food-plants eaten by the †Mammoth have been microscopically determined. These plants were of kinds still growing in Arctic Siberia; in summer time they consisted almost entirely of grasses, and, in winter, of coniferous twigs and leaves.

The Siberian †Mammoth, †*Mammuthus primigenius*, was a late arrival in North America, appearing in the Pleistocene. It was preeminently a northern animal, ranging all across the Holarctic Region in circumpolar distribution. In North America it extended from Alaska to New England along the Glacial ice-front, which it followed up as the ice retreated northward, but, in the cold Glacial stages it ranged into Florida. In American species of †*Mammuthus* the enamel plates of the molar teeth become more numerous and excessively thin.

A second representative of the †mammuthine subfamily, the Columbian †Mammoth (†*Parelephas columbi*), which has often been confused with †*Mammuthus*, is the immigrant form of a series which traces back to the Pliocene of Italy through the species †*P. jeffersoni*, of the Mississippi Valley, and †*P. washingtoni*, of the Pacific Coast. This genus, in which the teeth have fewer and thicker enamel plates than those of the Siberian animal, had a more southerly range than the latter, †*P. columbi* being especially common in the southeastern United States, South Carolina, Georgia and Florida.

A third genus of the †mammoths is the remarkable †*Archidiskodon*, in which the grinding teeth are of a more primitive pattern than in the other two genera of the subfamily, the enamel ridges being lower, thicker and less numerous than in the teeth of †*Mammuthus*, or †*Parelephas*. The skull, however, agrees closely in type with those of the genera just named. The genus was an immigrant and a variety of the Italian †*A. meridionalis* has been found in Nebraska. In North America, representatives of †*Archidiskodon* extended along the Pacific Coast and across the Great Plains to Texas and Mexico and southeastward into Florida. The genus gave rise to two magnificent indigenous species in this country, by far the largest of all known American proboscideans, †*A. imperator* and †*A. maibeni*, which much exceed modern elephants in size. According to Osborn, the shoulder-height of the various species may be estimated as follows:

Elephas maximus — 10 ft. 6 in.   †*Archidiskodon imperator* — 13 ft. 6 in.
Loxodonta africanus — 11 ft. 4 in.   †*A. maibeni* — 14 ft.

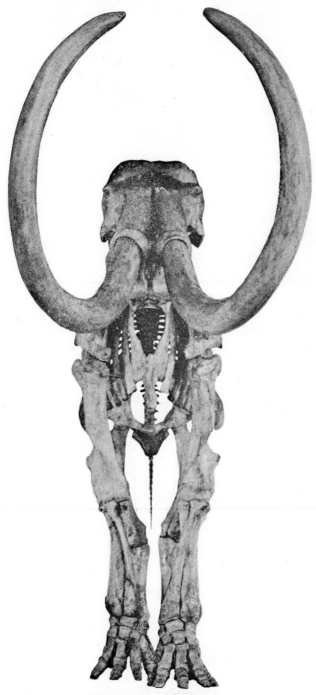

Fig. 170. — Nebraskan †Mammoth, †*Archidiskodon meridionalis nebrascensis*, Pleistocene of Angus, Neb. (Col. Mus. Nat. Hist.)

279

No true elephants, as distinguished from †mastodonts, have been found in the American Pliocene. Even in the Old World, where they unquestionably originated, elephants are not known to occur before the upper Pliocene — the time and place of their origin are still un-

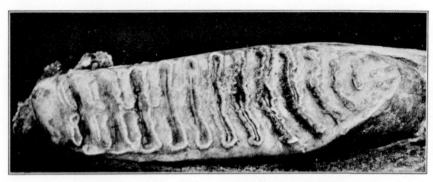

Fig. 171. — Masticating surface of lower molar of †*Archidiskodon*, much reduced, Pleistocene of Neb. (Col. Mus. Nat. Hist.)

known. Very probably they were derived from †mastodonts through some such intermediate form as the Indian †*Stegodon*.

SUBORDER †Mastodontoidea, †MASTODONTS

Osborn's final classification of the †Mastodontoidea is, so far as the American groups are concerned, as follows, with the necessary changes of family and subfamily names.

FAMILY I, †MASTODONTIDÆ — True †Mastodons.
SUBFAMILY †MASTODONTINÆ
   †*Miomastodon*, †*Pliomastodon*, †*Mastodon*

FAMILY II, †TRILOPHODONTIDÆ (†Bunomastodontidæ Osb.)
SUBFAMILY 1. †RHYNCHOTHERIINÆ (†Rhynchorostrinæ Osb.)
   †*Rhynchotherium*, †*Blickotherium*, †*Aybelodon*
   2. †TRILOPHODONTINÆ (†Longirostrinæ Osb.)
   †*Trilophodon*, †*Megabelodon*
   3. †GNATHABELODONTINÆ
   †*Gnathabelodon* — "Shovel-jawed " †longirostrines
   4. †AMEBELODONTINÆ — "†Shovel Tuskers "
   †*Amebelodon*
   5. †TETRALOPHODONTINÆ
   †*Tetralophodon*, †*Morrillia*
   6. †CORDILLERIONINÆ (†Notorostrinæ Osb.) S. A.
   †*Cordillerion*

FAMILY III, †STEGOMASTODONTIDÆ (†Humboltidæ Osb.)
SUBFAMILY †STEGOMASTODONTINÆ,
†*Stegomastodon,* †*Eubelodon,* †*Cuvieronius S. A.*

FAMILY IV, †SERRIDENTIDÆ
SUBFAMILY 1. †SERRIDENTINÆ
†*Serridentinus,* †*Ocalientinus,* †*Serbelodon*
2. †PLATYBELODONTINÆ
†*Platybelodon,* †*Torynobelodon*
3. †NOTIOMASTODONTINÆ S. A.
†*Notiomastodon*

Family 2. †*Mastodontidæ*

Another and very distinct family of proboscideans which inhabited North America from the middle Miocene through the Pleistocene and into the Recent, is that of the †Mastodontidæ. The genus †*Mastodon* and species †*M. americanus* are particularly abundant and well known, for several complete and many partial skeletons have been obtained. Beside the one taken from a tar-pit at Rancho La Brea, the finest of these skeletons were found in the Hudson River valley, in areas that had been covered by the ice of the last Glacial stage. These animals survived into Recent and even historic times. The species extended across the continent to California, but would seem to have been most abundant in the eastern forests, for the teeth show it to have had browsing rather than grazing habits.

Of the known eastern skeletons, the most perfect is the famous "Warren †Mastodon," which was discovered in 1845 near Newburgh, N. Y., and, since 1906, has been in the American Museum of Natural History. The determinable contents of the stomach were found within the ribs of this and several other reported skeletons and consisted of finely cut twigs of coniferous trees, especially hemlock and spruce. No hair was found with the Warren skeleton but was obtained in connection with three other specimens, two in the state of New York and one in Indiana. Dr. J. C. Warren writes: "Judge Miller, in describing the discovery and appearance of a skeleton at Shawangunk, Ulster County, [N. Y.] says that, 'around and in the immediate vicinity were locks and tufts of hair of a dun brown, of an inch and a half to two inches and a half long and, in some instances, from four to seven inches in length.'" No mention is made of the soft wool undercoat which the †Mammoth possessed and, presumably, the †Mastodon was not adapted to so severe a climate as that of northern Siberia.

FIG. 172. — The American †Mastodon, †*Mastodon americanus*, Pleistocene. (Restored from a skeleton in Princeton Univ. Mus.)

The most characteristic feature of †*Mastodon* is to be found in the grinding teeth (Fig. 173), which are simple, low-crowned and rooted and consist in the unworn state of three or four enamel-covered ridges and with no cement in the valleys between the ridges; each ridge is bisected by a very narrow and not very deep cleft. The valleys between the ridges are almost free from conules and, hence, no trefoils are developed by wear. The three milk-premolars took over the function of the permanent premolars, which were formed within the jaws, but not erupted. As the grinding teeth are so much smaller than those of the true elephants, as many as twelve teeth, three on each side, above and below, might be in simultaneous use, but, ordinarily, the actual number was eight. The teeth came into place vertically upward and downward, as is usual among mammals, for there was no necessity for the obliquely forward movement made requisite by the great size of the cheek-teeth in the true elephants.

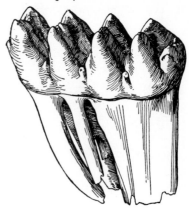

FIG. 173. — Last lower molar of the American †Mastodon.

The long tusks are parallel and have a moderate upward curvature, but in old males they became very massive and much more strongly curved. The females had lost all trace of the lower tusks, but, in the males, short tusks are retained. In †*M. americanus*, of the later Pleistocene and post-Glacial time, the lower tusk is single and is inserted in the median line of the mandible; occasionally, however, there is a symmetrical pair of small tusks in the lower jaw. In †*M. moodiei*, from the older Pleistocene of Nebraska, the paired lower tusks would seem to be constant and, with the beak of the mandible, they are bent downward. That they were used, is shown by the worn tips, but their chief interest is as vestiges of the large and functional lower tusks which were displayed by the Tertiary ancestors of the genus.

In the genus †*Mastodon*, the jaws are much abbreviated and the mandible resembles that of the true elephants. Otherwise, the skull, while essentially proboscidean in structure, is much less specialized and differs notably in form from the elephant skull. In †*M. americanus* the cranium is much lower and flatter and less dome-shaped than in the elephants, but in †*M. moodiei* it is higher and much more elephant-like. The interpretation of the difference in cranial form between the two species of †*Mastodon* can only be guessed at, until genetic

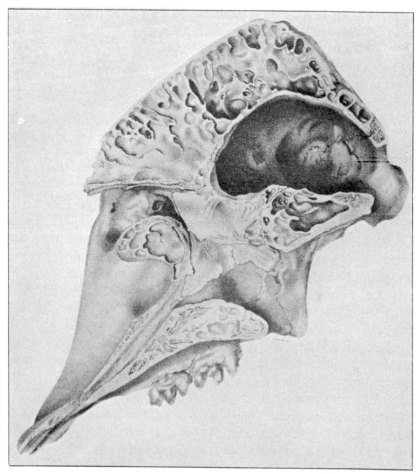

Fig. 174. — Vertical section through skull of the American †Mastodon, tusk not shown. Compare with Fig. 163. (From J. C. Warren.)

series of both shall have been discovered. In †*M. americanus* the skull is less shortened antero-posteriorly, so that the forehead and premaxillary tusk-sheaths are directed more upward, less forward. The cranial bones are considerably thickened and filled with cellular tissue, but this development is far less extreme than in the Elephantidæ.

The skeleton of the body and limbs resembles that of the true elephants so closely that no particular description is called for, other than to note the relatively long body and short, massive limbs.

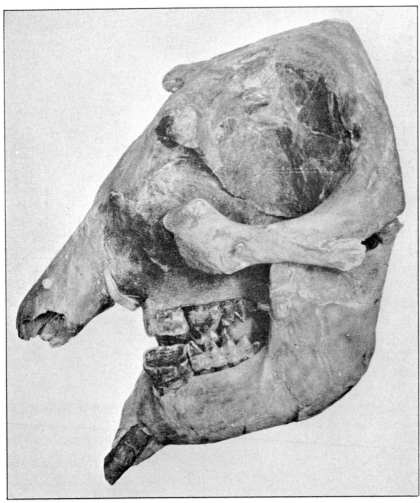

Fig. 175. — Skull of †*Mastodon moodiei*, lower Pleistocene, showing vestigial lower tusk. (Morrill Mus. Univ. Neb.)

It is a question still unsettled, whether the American †Mastodon was an immigrant, or of indigenous origin, as the evidence seems to support both hypotheses impartially. The genus †*Mastodon* and its putative ancestors are found on both sides of the Pacific, teeth of the †*M. americanus* type occurring as far west as European Russia and Hungary.

In the Pliocene of California has been found the extremely interesting skull of †*Pliomastodon*, which, in almost all respects, might well be the ancestor of †*Mastodon*. There are, however, certain specializations in the skull of the California species, †*P. vexillarius*, which seem to make it improbable that that species could have been directly ancestral to †*Mastodon*. Perhaps, the less known species from Nebraska, or that from Florida may have been the direct ancestor sought for. At all events, the California skull very nearly shows what the required ancestor must have been. It is far more primitive than that of †*Mastodon*, being remarkably low and elongate; the upper tusks are large and upcurved and, apparently, have no enamel band. If any lower tusks were present, they must have been very small.

The Miocene member of the series, †*Miomastodon*, as yet known only from teeth found in the middle Miocene deposits of Colorado, Nebraska and Nevada, is one of the most ancient of American Proboscidea. The grinding teeth resemble those of †*Mastodon* in having no conules in the valleys and, therefore, no trefoils are formed by abrasion; the transverse enamel-ridges, which in †*Mastodon* are divided only by the very narrow median cleft, are, in †*Miomastodon*, composed of conical cusps which are incompletely fused together; each tusk retains a band of enamel running from end to end.

The family of the †Mastodontidæ would seem to have had its beginning, so far as is yet known, in †*Palæomastodon* from the upper Eocene of Egypt, and was undoubtedly derived from long-jawed ancestors, which had two pairs of tusks, upper and lower, of subequal length. In this Egyptian genus the molar teeth are crested rather than tubercular, yet the formation of the crests from confluent tubercles is plainly to be seen; there are no conules in the valleys and therefore no trefoils in the abraded teeth. As previously pointed out, the proboscideans entered Europe and Asia from Africa in the lower Miocene and reached North America in the middle Miocene, the genus †*Miomastodon* being one of these earliest immigrants. Whether the series †*Miomastodon* — †*Pliomastodon* — †*Mastodon*, developed on American or Asiatic soil, is still an open question. If †*Mastodon* was an autochthonous, American form, as is entirely possible, then it must have sent out migrants, which ranged across Asia into eastern Europe.

Compared with other proboscidean series, this one of †*Palæomastodon* — †*Mastodon* is relatively unimportant. The discovery in Colonial times of these huge bones attracted the fascinated interest of American and European scholars and, subsequently, in the XIX Century, the finding of so many finely preserved skeletons has given to this limited group a disproportionate significance. In reality, it is but a slender branch of the great tree.

Family 3. †Trilophodontidæ
(†Bunomastodontidæ, Osb.)

It is unfortunate that Osborn's term for this family is inadmissible under the rules of zoölogical nomenclature, for it is accurately descriptive. The family was far more extensive, widely ramified and diversified and universally distributed than the †Mastodontidæ proper, for it had representatives in every continent, Australia alone excepted. Of the seven subfamilies into which Osborn divides the group, six had representatives in North America and six (only partly the same subfamilies) are long-jawed, sometimes extravagantly and grotesquely so, and two are short-jawed, a character which, to all appearances, was acquired quite independently of the true †mastodons, which are also short-jawed.

In North America the Pliocene was the time when these strange creatures were most numerous and varied and were especially abundant over the Great Plains. An astonishingly numerous representation of the family has been found in Nebraska, resulting in the magnificent collection in the Morrill Museum of the State University at Lincoln. Professor E. H. Barbour, director of the museum, reports: "It is doubtful whether any like area boasts of like numbers, for wherever ground is broken in Nebraska, the sand hills excepted, proboscidean bones may be expected."

The first distinctive feature of the †Trilophodontidæ, as a whole, lies in the character of the grinding teeth, in which the transverse ridges are composed of conical cusps, only partially fused together, and small cusps, or conules, appear in the valleys between the ridges, or crests, so that, after a period of abrasion, single or double trefoils of enamel are produced. The appearance of these teeth is, thus, very different from the simple pattern of enamel seen in the †Mastodontidæ, though, as in the latter, the teeth are very low-crowned, forming roots and ceasing to grow as soon as they were erupted.

The second characteristic of the family is the extraordinary elongation of the lower jaw, though in some of the subfamilies this was subsequently very much reduced. The skull is long and low, with the premaxillary sheaths of the upper tusks presenting upward

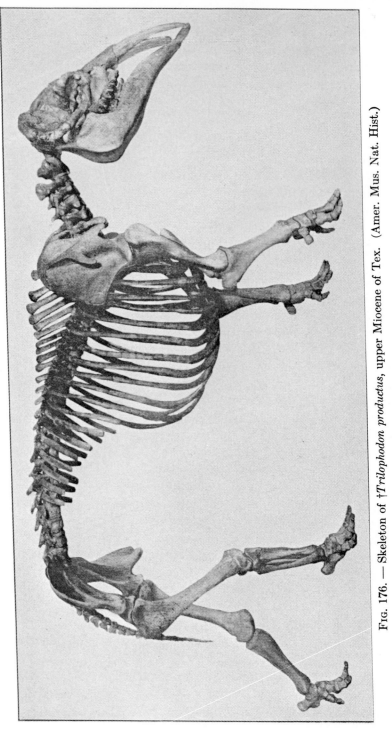

Fig. 176. — Skeleton of †*Trilophodon productus*, upper Miocene of Tex. (Amer. Mus. Nat. Hist.)

instead of forward, as they do in the true elephants, and the development of the cellular structure in the cranial bones is much less advanced than in the latter.   In stature, the †trilophodonts were relatively small, the largest known Pliocene species, †*Trilophodon gigantsus*, being only seven feet high, while others do not exceed five feet, but they often have extremely massive limbs.

AMERICAN †TRILOPHODONTS

Limitations of space render it impossible to deal in any but a very cursory manner with the six subfamilies of this group which

FIG. 177. — Head of upper Miocene †mastodont, †*Trilophodon productus*, showing the chisel-like lower tusks. (Restored from a skull in Amer. Mus. Nat. Hist.)

are represented in the Western Hemisphere.   The central stem of the family is the †longirostrine section (subfamily †Trilophodontinæ) in which the mandible attains incredible lengths.   This group made its most ancient known appearance in the early Miocene of France. The animal which Cuvier named †*Mastodon angustidens* and is now called †*Trilophodon angustidens*, is a species which had a very wide range, and closely similar species migrated to North America, where

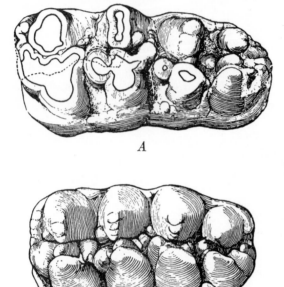

they became very abundant. The subdivisions of this long-lived, widespread and much diversified family are made chiefly in accordance with the shape of the lower jaw, or mandible, and the character of the inferior tusks. The mandible may be long, or short, with straight, or strongly decurved rostrum, or "beak" and the mandibular tusks vary greatly in shape, or, in a few groups, they are altogether wanting.

Of Osborn's seven subfamilies of the †Trilophodontidæ, one has not been found in America and, of those that do occur here, the †longirostrine group (subfamily †Trilophodontinæ) with extraordinary, elongated lower jaws, is the most abundant and it ranged over the continent north

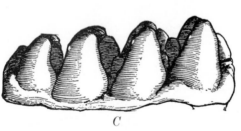

Fig. 178. — Last lower molar of †*Trilophodon productus*. *A*, partly worn. *B*, grinding surface of unworn tooth. *C*, same tooth in side view. (From Osborn.)

of Mexico. Fossil remains of the subfamily are most frequently found in the Great Plains region, especially in Nebraska, but that is probably due to conditions of preservation. No continental Pliocene deposits are known east of the Mississippi River, except in the southeast. †Trilophodonts may have been as numerous in the eastern forests as on the Great Plains, but there is no way of deciding whether they were or not. As before mentioned, in this subfamily the rostrum attained extravagant lengths, sometimes as much as six feet, equalling or surpassing the height of the animal. Lower tusks are usually present and of triangular or cylindrical shape, but in the remarkable †*Megabelodon* the mandibular tusks are wanting and the tip of the rostrum is expanded and spatulate, whence the name of the "Spoonbill †Mastodonts." Professor Barbour to whom we owe the discovery of these bizarre creatures, interpreted the "spoonbill" as being "presumably for the attachment of a coarse, heavy, gristly

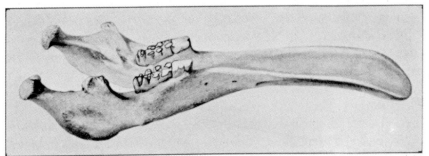

FIG. 179. — Oblique view of lower jaw of †*Gnathabelodon thorpei*, Pleistocene of Neb. (From Barbour and Sternberg.)

pad, usable perhaps in tearing leaves and twigs from branches," or it may have been a horny digging apparatus.

A more extreme development of this type of mandible is displayed by the †*Gnathabelodon* of Barbour and Sternberg and described in 1935. The describers formed a separate subfamily for this genus and Osborn agreed with the classification. In this very elongate mandible with decurved rostrum, as in †*Megabelodon*, the terminal portion is deeply concave, forming a shovel with a thin edge. Such a jaw can only have been used as a mud digger, perhaps scooping up aquatic plants from shallow ponds. The difficulty in comprehending these strange rostra and the equally paradoxical tusks, presently to be mentioned, is occasioned by the fact that no animal in the least like these Pliocene proboscideans is now living and we are therefore confined to speculation, never a very satisfactory means of acquiring knowledge.

In most genera of the †Trilophodontidæ the lower tusks are well developed and straight, but in †*Amebelodon* the ends of the tusks are broad and spade-like, from which they have been called "†Shovel Tuskers." As all the proboscideans, of whose habits anything is known, have used the tusks in digging, there can be no doubt that the "shovel tusks" were especially efficient in such work, digging in firm soil, while the scoops, whether of mandible or tusks, were probably employed in soft mud.

The subfamily †Rhynchotheriinæ is not certainly known outside of North and Central America, though some fragmentary remains, found in Egypt and India, have been referred to it and, almost certainly, the group originated in the Old World. These genera display two peculiar modifications of †longirostrine structure: (1) the sharp, downward bending of the mandibular beak in a manner which suggested the Old World †Dinotherium to the famous English palæontologist, H. Falconer. Consequently, he named a jaw from Mexico †Rhynchotherium. (2) The second peculiarity is the presence of enamel bands on the lower tusks. †Rhynchotherium was one of the earliest proboscidean immigrants to America and the genus continued for an unusually long period, from the middle Miocene to the Pleistocene. Two other genera of the subfamily have been described, both of them distinguished by slender jaws, †Blickotherium, of Nebraska, Mexico and Honduras, and †Aybelodon, as yet known only from Honduras. No member of this subfamily has been found east of the Mississippi, but the group ranged from Montana to California and southward to Texas, Mexico and Central America.

An Old World subfamily (†Pentalophodontinæ) is characterized by the great shortening of the lower jaw and suppression of the lower tusks, as in the true †Mastodonts, but with such different molars as to show that the abbreviation took place independently.

A remarkable subfamily, immigrant from Asia, is that typified by the genus †Tetralophodon. The genus was first discovered in Germany, then traced eastward through Persia, India, Java and China to North America, where it has been found in Nebraska, Kansas and Texas. The American species seem to form a progressive series, culminating in †Morrillia of the Nebraskan upper Pliocene.

In the Old World species of †Tetralophodon, the lower tusks are of variable lengths, and are longest in the Persian form, but in the American species, these tusks are reduced or absent. In all, the lower jaw is much shorter than in †Trilophodon, in which it often has such grotesque length. The first and second molars of †Tetralophodon have four enamel crests instead of three and the last molar has progressively from five to eight. As in †Trilophodon, the grinding teeth are very low-crowned, but they become higher in the American species, until, in †Morrillia, they may almost be called subhypsodont,

Fig. 180. — Lower jaw of †*Amebelodon fricki*, "†Shovel Tusker," Pliocene of Neb. (Morrill Mus. Univ. Neb.)

with ridges appressed and nearly parallel-sided, and the valleys filled with cement. No other known member of the †Mastodontoidea had teeth which so nearly approximated those of the true elephants as did the molars of †*Morrillia*. It is possible that this genus may have been a stray migrant from that part of Asia, not yet identified, where the true elephants were in the early stages of their development.

As previously reiterated, the true elephants never gained a foothold in South America, but †mastodonts were numerous in the Pleistocene of that continent and belonged to three different families. The †Trilophodontidæ are represented there by †*Cordillerion*, which has a subfamily to itself and resembles the true †mastodons in having a short, tuskless lower jaw. That they entered South America from the north, might have been inferred *à priori*, but the inference has been confirmed by the discovery of these animals in Central America, Mexico, Texas, Arizona and California, discoveries which indicate the path of migration. There can be no doubt that this, like all other groups of proboscideans, was of Old World origin, though its immediate ancestry has still to be recovered. Remotely, the subfamily was probably of †longirostrine stock. The only known genus, †*Cordillerion*, covered the western part of South America in Pleistocene and late Pliocene times and, as has been seen, it probably persisted into the modern, historic period.

†*Cordillerion*, originally named †*Mastodon andium* by Cuvier, was especially adapted to life on the high Andean plateaus, ranging from Ecuador to Bolivia. The premaxillaries are very broad, so that the tusks are widely separated; the tusks have a peculiar spiral twist and a broad enamel-band is, as it were, wound spirally around each one. The grinding teeth are narrow, with three or four cross-crests and median conules in the valleys, which, on abrasion, display single trefoils. The rostrum of the mandible, though without tusks, is moderately prolonged and is probably an inheritance from †longirostrine ancestors and, as in those ancestors, the cranium is low and flattened. The species of this genus are relatively rather small, in adaptation to life in the highlands.

Family 4. †*Stegomastodontidæ*

(†Humboldtidæ Osb.)

This family includes two North American genera and one South American genus and these, though assuredly descended from Asiatic ancestors, cannot yet be connected with any Old World forms and it remains to be determined how far their peculiarities were acquired after they had entered the Western Hemisphere. The South American genus, †*Cuvieronius*, was first named †*Mastodon humboldti* by Cuvier and is common in the Pampas of Argentina, but rare in the

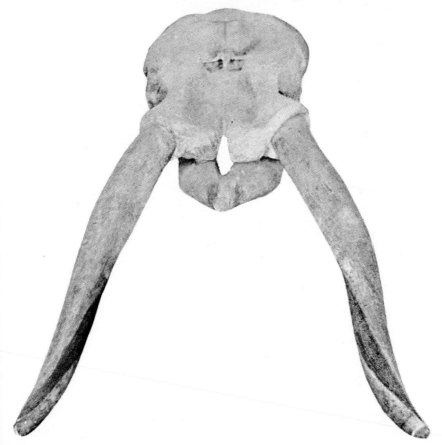

FIG. 181. — Front view of skull of †*Cordillerion andium*, lower Pleistocene of Tarija, Bolivia. (Field Mus. Nat. Hist.)

mountainous regions. †*Cordillerion* was the genus of the highlands, †*Cuvieronius* of the low-lying plains. The latter genus comprised larger animals and had a higher, more domed and elephant-like cranium than the North American †*Mastodon americanus*, and the lower jaw is much abbreviated and without any trace of tusks. The upper tusks are simply curved, are devoid of enamel-bands and the grinding teeth have double trefoils.

The North American genus, †*Stegomastodon* appears to be nearly

allied to †*Cuvieronius,* though the relationship cannot well be other
than collateral, nor can the former genus be derived from any immediate ancestry yet known in Asia or Europe. The grinding teeth
are very complicated because of the addition of numerous conical
cusps filling up the valleys, and the deposition of cement between
the cones. Except those of †*Morrillia,* the grinders of †*Stegomastodon*
have attained a higher degree of complexity and specialization than
those of any other known member of the †Mastodontoidea. The

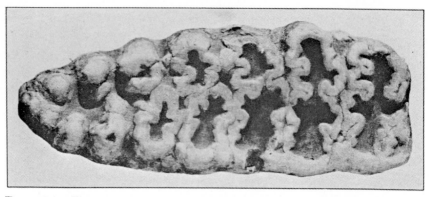

FIG. 182. — Third lower molar of †*Stegomastodon aftoniæ,* lower Pleistocene of
Iowa. (From a cast of the type specimen in Amer. Mus. Nat. Hist.)

lower jaw is abbreviated and without tusks and the upper tusks are
rather short and very massive. This genus has been found only
in the Pleistocene of California and from Iowa and Nebraska to Texas
and Arizona.

The second North American genus which should probably be
included in the †Stegomastodontidæ is †*Eubelodon,* of the Nebraska
Pliocene, of which Professor Barbour has figured a very fine skeleton.
In this animal the upper tusks have the primitive downward curvature seen in the †trilophodonts, and have lost the enamel-bands; the
narrow grinding teeth display double trefoils. The lower tusks have
disappeared, but the beak of the mandible is prolonged and bluntly
pointed and, in length is intermediate between †trilophodont and
†stegomastodont types. The limbs are relatively short, but very
massive, actually, as well as proportionally, heavier than in modern
elephants.

Family 5. †*Serridentidæ*

The terminological history of this group is peculiar; its first appearance in palæontological literature was as a species of †*Mastodon,* the

†*M. serridens* of Cope. In 1923 Osborn raised it to the rank of a genus, which he called †*Serridentinus*, subsequently making it the type of a subfamily and finally, in 1935, establishing the family. On the other hand, several palæontologists decline to admit the family, or even the genus, but merge them with the †trilophodonts, to which they are obviously closely allied and to which they ran a parallel

Fig. 183. — Lower molar, oblique view, of †*Serridentinus*, Brown Co., Neb.
(Neb. State Mus.)

course. In this already overcrowded book, it is impossible to discuss disputed questions and it must suffice to say that Osborn's example is here followed and the †Serridentidæ accepted as a family, with three subfamilies. The differences of this family from the longirostrine †Trilophodontidæ are: (1) The shifting of the trefoils from the middle to the sides of the grinding teeth, internal on the upper, external on the lower molars, and (2) the less elongated mandible in most, if not all, of the species, (3) the generally smaller size.

Like the †trilophodonts, the †serridentines originated in the Old World, first appearing in the Miocene of Europe and thence spreading through Asia into North America, where they were rare in the Miocene, but abundant in the Pliocene. They extended their range southeastward into Florida and southward into Central America, eventually reaching South America, where they gave rise to a peculiar subfamily, the †Notiomastodontinæ.

The †serridentines are less diversified than the †trilophodonts, since there are but three subfamilies of them as compared with seven. Each of these groups, however, finds a parallel among the †trilophodont subfamilies. The subfamily †Serridentinæ resembles the longirostrine †trilophodonts, though the mandible is less prolonged. The †"shovel tuskers" of the †trilophodonts (subfamily †Amebelodontinæ) are even exceeded in extravagant grotesqueness by the †"scoop tuskers," or †Platybelodontinæ of the †Serridentidæ, in which the upper tusks are reduced to very small size, the mandible is sharply constricted in front of the cheek-teeth and then very widely expanded to make room for the broad, flat and sharp-edged lower tusks, which are marked with longitudinal ribs of enamel. Obviously, these tusks formed a very efficient digging implement, paralleled by the narrower spade-like tusks of †Amebelodon and by the scoop jaw of †Gnathabelodon.

The genus †Platybelodon (from which the subfamily name is taken) was first discovered in the Caucasus and subsequently in the Pliocene of Mongolia and, some years later, in that of Nebraska. In spreading to America, †Platybelodon underwent such an amount of modification as to require a new generic name, and Professor Barbour called it †Torynobelodon. These astonishing †"scoop tuskers" are among the strangest of the many grotesque creatures which palæontology has brought to light.

Finally, there is the South American †Notiomastodon of Cabrera, as yet the only known member of its subfamily, which, like †Cuvieronius, was an animal of the Pampas and which resembled both of the other South American †mastodonts in having a short lower jaw without tusks. The upper tusks are turned downward and outward, not spirally curved, and have an enamel-band. The lower molars have trefoils arising from the external cusps.

Though the South American genera of †mastodontoids, †Cordillerion, †Cuvieronius and †Notiomastodon, belong each to a different family, they all agree in having the abbreviated, elephant-like lower jaw, which is without tusks. There can be little doubt that the shortening of the mandible, and consequent loss of tusks, took place separately and independently in †Cordillerion and †Notiomastodon, as it did in the other families and subfamilies of short-jawed proboscideans, the true †Mastodontidæ, the brevirostrine †trilophodonts (an Old World group), the †Stegomastodontidæ and the true elephants. Within the order, this abbreviation of the jaws was an oft-repeated tendency.

The origin of the Proboscidea long remained a mystery; they appeared unheralded and with seeming suddenness in the lower

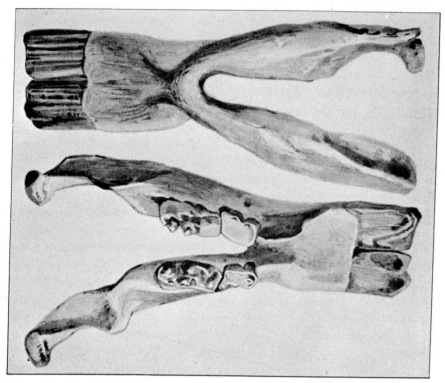

FIG. 184. — Upper and lower views of mandible of †*Torynobelodon barnumbrowni*, upper Pliocene of Neb. (From Barbour.)

Miocene of Europe and the middle Miocene of North America and in neither continent was any hoofed mammal known in the Oligocene or Eocene which, by any stretch of the imagination, could be regarded as ancestral to those intruders. Obviously, they must have been immigrants from some region not identified and Africa seemed to be the most likely place of origin. This hypothesis was confirmed by the discoveries of the late C. W. Andrews, of the British Museum, who found in the Oligocene and Eocene of the Fayûm, in Egypt, proboscideans that were much more ancient and primitive than any that had previously been known.

†*Palæomastodon*, from the upper Eocene of Egypt, has already been considered (p. 286) as a probable ancestor of †*Mastodon*, and in †*Phiomia*, of the Egyptian Oligocene, we have a probable ancestor of the †trilophodonts, which played so conspicuous a rôle in the later Tertiary of the northern hemisphere; †*Phiomia* comprises much smaller and more primitive animals than the Miocene and Pliocene genera, but displays an unmistakable likeness to them. In the Egyptian genus, the short and sharp-pointed upper tusks have a downward curvature and each has a broad band of enamel on its external side; the lower tusks are short, straight and horizontally directed. The molar teeth have three enamel crests, each of which is plainly formed by the apposition of conical cusps, and small conules arise in the valleys and these, when abraded, give rise to trefoils. The premolars are smaller and simpler than the molars and succeeded the milk-premolars vertically, as in mammals generally, and as was likewise true of †*Palæomastodon*.

The skull is already characteristically proboscidean, with nasal bones much shortened and rostrum of the lower jaw greatly extended. Except for its much smaller size, this skull might almost pass for that of one of the Miocene †longirostrines. Little is known of the skeleton, but the vertebræ and limb-bones of the nearly allied †*Palæomastodon*, so far as they have been discovered, are very like those of the smaller elephants, except that the metacarpals are slender and elongate, though the carpals are of the proboscidean block-like shape.

The most ancient and, by far, the most primitive proboscidean that has yet been brought to light is †*Mœritherium*, of the Egyptian Eocene, which was not ancestral to †*Palæomastodon* or †*Phiomia*, but is rather to be regarded as a collateral offshoot from the very early proboscidean stock; it probably was of amphibious habits. Nevertheless, it gives valuable information concerning the earlier stages of development through which the actual ancestors of the order passed.

†*Mœritherium* was a rather small animal, little larger than the Wild Boar, and had lost fewer teeth than any of the subsequent genera, having the formula: $i \frac{3}{2}, c \frac{1}{0}, p \frac{3}{3}, m \frac{3}{3} \times 2 = 36$. The second incisor above and below ($i \frac{2}{}$ and $i \frac{}{2}$) is enlarged and faced with enamel and they opposed each other much as do the chisel-shaped incisors of rodents. The tusks of later proboscideans could not have been derived from these specialized teeth, unless our conceptions of the manner in which evolutionary changes took place are altogether

wrong. The other incisors and the upper canine are very small and were evidently in process of suppression. The molars have four conical tubercles each, arranged in two transverse pairs and these are manifestly the beginning of the transverse enamel ridges, which appear, in one form or another, in all of the succeeding proboscidean genera. The premolars are smaller and even less complex than the molars and succeeded their predecessors in the normal mammalian fashion.

The skull has a remarkably long cranial and short facial region, the eye-sockets being very far forward in the face. Though the nasal bones are short, there can have been no proboscis, as is made clear by all the bones of the muzzle. The cranium is very long and narrow and of a cylindrical shape that reminds one of the skull of many Insectivora and the brain-capacity is incredibly small. However, the head was made broad by the greatly expanded zygomatic arches. Such bones of the skeleton as have been found, notably those of the limbs, are very proboscidean in character, but with one significant exception. The pelvis, or hip-bone, which, in all the Miocene and subsequent members of the order, is so strongly expanded and everted, is, in †*Mœritherium*, very narrow and more carnivorous than proboscidean in shape.

Few mammalian orders have had so remarkable a history of diversification and wide dispersal, as has the great elephant order, or Proboscidea, and, while much remains to be done, the outlines of the wonderful story have already been sketched, thanks chiefly to the Herculean labours of Henry Fairfield Osborn. Present day conditions give scarcely a hint of the panorama which palæontology has unrolled.

CHAPTER XIII

HISTORY OF THE ARTIODACTYLA

I. RUMINANTIA

Though this order can be traced back to the lowest Eocene and was long outnumbered and overshadowed by the perissodactyls, it has steadily risen in numbers, diversity and importance, culminating in the Recent epoch. At present the Artiodactyla are much the most numerous of hoofed animals, far outnumbering all other ungulates combined, and they are so widely diversified as to appear, when superficially examined, an arbitrary group. Hippopotamuses and swine seem to have little to do with antelope, deer, oxen or camels, but a study of their structure shows that they all form an unmistakably natural assemblage of truly interrelated forms, however diverse their external appearance.

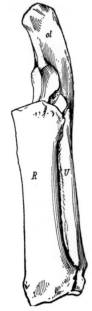

Fig. 185. — Left fore-arm bones of the Domestic Pig, *Sus scrofa*. *R*, radius. *U*, ulna. *ol*, olecranon.

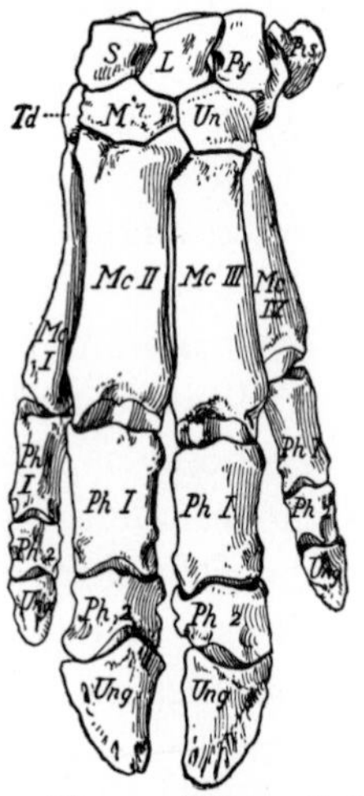

From the geographical point of view the Artiodactyla are a characteristically Old World group and they passed through their principal development in the Eastern Hemisphere, though they have ranged into every continent except Australia. Beside many extinct groups there are several existing families of the order which have never found their way to the Americas, such as true swine, hippopotamus, chevrotains, or "mouse-deer," true oxen and giraffes.

Fig. 186. — Left manus of Pig. *S*, scaphoid. *L*, lunar. *Py*, pyramidal. *Pis*, pisiform. *Td*, trapezoid. *M*, magnum. *Un*, unciform. *Mc I*, second, *Mc II*, third, *Mc III*, fourth, *Mc IV*, fifth, metacarpals. *Ph*, phalanges. *Ung*, ungual.

It is unnecessary to enumerate all the characteristics of the artiodactyls; a few diagnostic features will suffice for the purposes of this book.

As the name of the order implies, the digits are usually present in even numbers, two or four, though primitively there were five, which no artiodactyl now possesses. Whatever the number of digits, the plane of symmetry of the foot passes between the third and fourth digits (i.e. of the original series of five). The third and fourth digits are each asymmetrical, but together they form a symmetrical pair. For this reason the Artiodactyla are sometimes called Paraxonia and the Perissodactyla Mesaxonia. The mesaxonic foot, in which the plane of symmetry bisects the third digit, may be reduced to a single toe, as in the horses, but no artiodactyl ever had less than two digits. The term "cloven-hoof," which so well describes the *appearance* of the ruminant foot (deer, antelopes, sheep, oxen, etc.) must not be taken to mean that a single hoof has been divided. Certain "mule-footed" domestic swine of Texas and Louisiana are described as having a single median toe, but, in this case, it is only the ungual phalanges that have coalesced, while the other phalanges remain separate.

The most characteristic single feature of artiodactyl structure is the ankle-joint; the ankle-bone, or astragalus, has a double pulley, the upper and lower ends having a somewhat similar shape. The lower end is strongly convex and rests almost equally upon the cuboid and navicular, which are deeply cupped to receive it. This type of astragalus

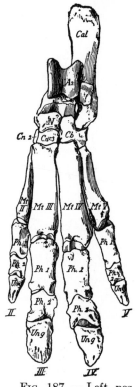

Fig. 187. — Left pes of Pig. *Cal*, calcaneum. *As*, astragalus. *N*, navicular. *Cb*, cuboid. *Cn 2*, *Cn 3*, second and third cuneiforms. *Mt II–V*, second to fifth metatarsals. *Ung*, ungual.

occurs in all known artiodactyls, even the most ancient and primitive, and *in no other mammals whatever*, though some †creodonts approach it. The calcaneum, or heel-bone, has a prominent articular convexity which supports the fibula, and its lower end is very narrow and fits into a step cut, as it were, in the cuboid, which is thus as peculiar and characteristic as are the astragalus and calcaneum.

In all known artiodactyls the articulations between successive vertebræ in the lumbar and posterior dorsal regions are very complex, a structure which, among perissodactyls, is approximated only by the horses. In almost all artiodactyls the number of trunk-vertebræ (or dorso-lumbars) is 19, in the perissodactyls 23 or more. Still another diagnostic difference between artiodactyls and perissodactyls is in the pattern of the molar teeth, which, in almost all perissodactyls, have transverse crests, but in artiodactyls, teeth with such crests are very rare. In the latter there are two fundamental types

of molar form; in one, exemplified by the pigs, the grinding surface is made up of conical cusps, primarily in two pairs, the *quadritubercular* tooth. This molar pattern is called *Bunodont*. In the other type the cusps have a crescen-

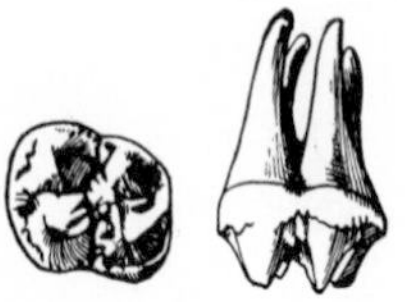

FIG. 188. — Bunodont upper molar of peccary, *Tagassu*.

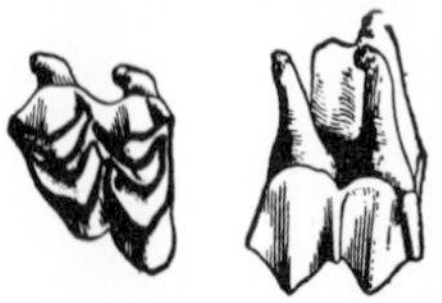

FIG. 189. — Selenodont upper molar of deer, *Odocoileus*.

tic shape, whence the name *Selenodont*. Between these two types are many transitions, the quadritubercular tooth being the primitive and original form from which the selenodont was derived. In the most ancient of artiodactyls there occurs a still more primitive type of molar, the *tritubercular*, which is the common starting point for all types of mammalian dentition.

In the Artiodactyla the premolars are always smaller and simpler than the molars, but in a very few genera the last lower premolar is molariform and the last upper one partially so.

There should also be mentioned, as exclusively characteristic of all known artiodactyls, the form of the last lower milk-premolar ($dp\,\overline{4}$) which has three pairs of cusps, conical or crescentic.

A very general difference between artiodactyls and perissodactyls, so far as existing forms are concerned, is to be found in the character of the muzzle. In perissodactyls the nose and upper lip are covered with skin like that on the rest of the head, hairy or hairless, as may be. Nearly all Recent artiodactyls have a hairless, glandular nose, kept moist by the secretions, such as the Carnivora have. In the swine, both pigs and peccaries, the snout is a very characteristic hairless disc, perforated by the conspicuous, circular nostrils, but the Hippopotamus has no glandular area. Camels and llamas resemble the perissodactyls in having the nose hairy to the edge of the nostrils. A few ruminants, such as the Moose (*Alce*), sheep and some antelopes, have almost or entirely lost the glandular area, but these are obviously cases of reduction. It is hardly necessary to add that nothing is known, in this respect, of the extinct forms.

Existing Artiodactyla fall very naturally into four suborders, or three, as may be preferred, but this mode of subdivision is altogether insufficient to provide for the great horde of families and genera, which from the Paleocene onward spread throughout Arctogæa. The classification and systematic treatment of this diverse multitude present problems of the greatest difficulty and complexity. So widely ramifying and so little understood are the interrelationships of the artiodactyl families that no satisfactory arrangement of them has been devised.

In the scheme of classification it is desirable, as Frechkop has suggested to express the fact that the Artiodactyla divide naturally into two groups, which nearly, but not exactly, coincide with the bunodont and selenodont types of molar teeth. For these sections his terms *Ruminantia*, and *Non Ruminantia* may be adopted. The Ruminantia include the suborders Tylopoda, Tragulina and Pecora; the *Non Ruminantia* the †Palæodonta, †Ancodonta and Hyodonta. These non-ruminating groups, except the Hyodonta, swine and hippopotamuses, are now extinct.

It is now a frequent practice to include the Pecora and Tragulina in the same suborder, but this is to be deprecated. No doubt the Tragulina represent a primitive stage through which the Pecora once passed, but the latter have progressed so far beyond that stage, that the separation is desirable. The tragulines agree with the Tylopoda in having a three-chambered stomach and a diffuse placenta, while all existing Pecora have a four-chambered stomach and a cotyledonary placenta.

The present artiodactyls in the American faunas are, for the most part, of nearer or more remote Old World origin, only two of the families, the llamas and the peccaries, being fairly described as indigenous, for their history may be traced through the Eocene of North America. The deer, antelopes, musk-oxen, sheep and bison are descended from Asiatic immigrants, which arrived at various times from the middle Miocene to the late Pleistocene and differ from their Old World relatives in a degree which corresponds to the date of their arrival in the Western Hemisphere. For some of the families information is much more complete than for others, concerning which little has yet been learned. The conditions under which the various groups lived determined, in large degree, their abundance as fossils.

The following provisional scheme of classification is, with slight modification, that propounded by the late Professor W. D. Matthew (1929), which is a decided advance over earlier plans. Only American groups are included in the table; the exception is indicated by brackets.

ORDER **ARTIODACTYLA.**
  SECTION A. NON RUMINANTIA.
    SUBORDER I. †**Palæodonta,** Ancient and Primitive Families.
      FAMILY   1. †LEPTOCHŒRIDÆ.
      FAMILY   2. †DICHOBUNIDÆ.
      FAMILY   3. †ENTELODONTIDÆ, "†Giant Pigs."
    SUBORDER II. **Hyodonta,** Swine-like Animals.
      FAMILY   4. TAGASSUIDÆ, American Swine.
    SUBORDER III. †**Ancodonta,** Extinct Genera.
      FAMILY   5. †ANTHRACOTHERIIDÆ.
  SECTION B. RUMINANTIA, Ruminants.
    SUBORDER IV. **Tylopoda,** Camels, etc.
      FAMILY   6. CAMELIDÆ, Camels and Llamas.
      FAMILY   7. †LEPTOMERYCIDÆ.
          FAMILIÆ INCERTÆ SEDIS.
      FAMILY   8. ?†MERYCOIDODONTIDÆ.
      FAMILY   9. ?†AGRIOCHŒRIDÆ.
  [SUBORDER V. **Tragulina,** Chevrotains.]
    SUBORDER VI. **Pecora,** Sheep, Antelopes, etc.
    SUPERFAMILY CERVICORNIA.
      FAMILY 10. CERVIDÆ, Deer.
    SUPERFAMILY CAVICORNIA.
      FAMILY 11. ANTILOPIDÆ, Antelopes.
      FAMILY 12. ANTILOCAPRIDÆ, Prongbucks.
      FAMILY 13. †MERYCODONTIDÆ, †Deer-antelopes.
      FAMILY 14. BOVIDÆ, Oxen, Bison, Sheep, Goats.

The inverted chronological order of treatment requires that the subordinal and family groups be dealt with in quite a different succession from that given in the table, but the families will retain the same numbers.

SECTION B. RUMINANTIA

SUBORDER VI. **Pecora.** TRUE RUMINANTS

The Pecora exemplify the highest degrees of artiodactyl development and are now the dominant group of hoofed mammals, far exceeding in abundance and diversity all other groups combined. In the

Pecora the stomach is four-chambered and on the placenta the villi, which in other artiodactyls are diffusely scattered over the surface, are grouped in tufts, or "cotyledons."

In all of the Pecora the fore-arm bones are co-ossified, the ulna greatly reduced, and in the hind-leg nothing remains of the fibula except the lower end, the "malleolar" bone, which is wedged in between tibia and calcaneum. The median metapodials (III and IV) are co-ossified to form cannon-bones, which have a very characteristic shape; the pulley-like articulations for the phalanges are parallel, not divergent (as they are in the Tylopoda), and the carinæ, or keels, which fit into grooves of the phalanges, encircle the whole articular surface, front and back, while in all other artiodactyls, whether they have cannon-bones or not, the keels are confined to the posterior side. The lateral digits in the Pecora are either absent or, more generally, vestigial.

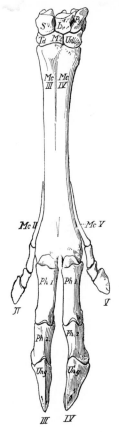

Superfamily CAVICORNIA. *Hollow-horned Ruminants*

In the "hollow-horned" ruminants the horns are the sheaths of the horn-cores, which are bony outgrowths of the skull and are always permanently attached; save in a few instances, the horn-cores are a single pair, but fossil members of the group are known with two pairs, or even with three horns, and a living Indian antelope (*Tetraceros*) has two pairs. The horn-cores are usually simply conical and unbranched and with a single exception, the Prongbuck (*Antilocapra*), the horny sheath is permanent, growing from year to year and unbranched. The Prongbuck, or Prong-horned Antelope,

FIG. 190. — Left manus of Patagonian Deer, *Hippocamelus bisulcus*. *S*, scaphoid. *L*, lunar. *Py*, pyramidal. *Td, M*, co-ossified trapezoid and magnum. *Un*, unciform. *Mc II* and *V*, rudimentary second and fifth metacarpals. *Mc III* and *IV*, cannon-bone. *Ph 1, 2*, first and second phalanges. *Ung*, ungual phalanx.

has a short branch of the horny sheath which is annually shed and renewed. In many of the ruminant groups the females have no horns, and, if the females do possess them, the horns are usually smaller than in the males; a notable example of this is the Big Horn, or Rocky

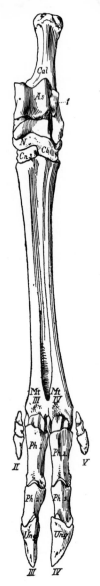

Mountain Sheep. There is great variety in the shape and size of the horn among the Cavicornia. Oxen and bison have simply curved horns, and in some domestic breeds of cattle the horns are enormously long, as they were in several extinct bison. Some of the buffaloes, like the Philippine Carabao, have immense horns. In sheep, the rams at least, the horns are in a spiral curve; in antelopes the horns are usually long and straight, or lyrate, and often they are spirally twisted, as in the "strepsicerine" genera and in certain extinct relatives of the Prongbuck.

Except the Prong-horned Antelope, which seems to have had an American ancestry of considerable length, the Cavicornia of North America are migrants from the Old World in late Pliocene or Pleistocene times. South America never had any Cavicornia, except for the brief incursion of antelopes in the Pleistocene, which were unable to maintain their footing and speedily died out.

Family 14. Bovidæ, Oxen, Bison, Sheep, Etc.

†*Preptoceras*, †*Euceratherium*, †*Symbos*, †*Boötherium*, Pleist. *Ovibos*, Pleist. and Rec. *Bison*, Pleist. and Rec. *Ovis*, Rec.

The only members of the ox-tribe which ever reached America are the various species of bison, which in this country are so generally misnamed "buffaloes." In the Pleistocene there were a large number of species of the genus *Bison*, which roamed the continent from Alaska to Florida and Mexico and of which one species, *B. bison*, still exists, thanks to the protection afforded by the American and especially the Canadian governments. The bisons differ from the true oxen in the form and structure of the skull, shape and position of the horns and in the great shoulder hump, which is made by the very long spines of the anterior dorsal vertebræ, and this makes the line of the back slope steeply from withers to rump. The hair of the Bison is short

FIG. 191. — Left pes of Patagonian Deer. *Cal*, calcaneum. *As*, astragalus. *N, Cb*, co-ossified navicular and cuboid. *Mt III, IV*, cannonbone. *f*, fibula facet. *Cn3*, ectocuneiform.

and woolly on the body and hind quarters, very long and shaggy on the head and neck.

No less than seven species of Bison have been found in the Pleistocene of North America, all of which must have been immigrants, for no Pliocene ancestry of them is known. It is not necessary to assume that all of these species existed at the same time, though they may have done so. One of the earliest and by far the largest of these species was the gigantic *B.* †*latifrons*, of which a skull in the American Museum measures six feet from tip to tip of the horns. This huge creature was spread from Ohio to the Gulf of Mexico and westward into Kansas and Texas. (See Fig. 144, p. 185).

Another gigantic species, *B.* †*crassicornis*, dwelt in Alaska, together with the smaller *B.* †*occidentalis*, which extended as far south as Kansas. The latter species is larger than the existing *B. bison* and the spines of the dorsal vertebræ, which form the hump, are unusually long. Much the same statement applies to the Californian *B.* †*antiquus*, the bones of which are so abundant in the tar-pits of Rancho La Brea, outnumbering all the other artiodactyls of the same locality (deer, antelopes, peccaries and camels). A skeleton of this bison in the Los Angeles Museum measures six feet at the shoulders and some of the vertebræ of the hump have spines 27 inches long. Though commonest in California, *B.* †*antiquus* ranged as far east as Kentucky, where remains of it were first discovered in the Big Bone Lick.

One Old World species of bison, *B. bonasus*, survives in the Caucasus under rigid protection. Cæsar's account of the Hercynian Forest shows that in his time bison were common in Germany and Belgium. Indeed the word *Bison* is a latinized form of the German *Wisent*, which is also mentioned in the Niebelungenlied.

At the present time four or five species of sheep (*Ovis*) dwell in the mountains of the western part of the continent from Alaska to Mexico. The males of the Big Horn, or Rocky Mountain Sheep (*Ovis canadensis*) have immense, spirally coiled horns, but in the ewes the horns are nearly straight. The other species differ but little from the Big Horn and may have been locally developed from some Asiatic immigrant. The Big Horn occurs in the North American Pleistocene, but no sheep is found in any deposits of an earlier date. By far the greatest number of species of wild sheep are dwellers in the high mountains of Asia, one species extending into southern Europe and one into north Africa.

Several genera, the systematic position of which is debatable,

FIG. 192. — †Medium-horned Bison, B. †antiquus, Pleistocene of Rancho La Brea. (From a skeleton in Los Angeles Mus.)

are represented to-day by the so-called Musk-ox (*Ovibos moschatus*), which is now exclusively North American, but in the Pleistocene extended across Asia and Europe as far west as Great Britain. The Musk-ox, which now occurs only in the farthest north, is a heavy, short-legged animal, three and a half to four feet in height; the body is covered by a dense coat of woolly hair, overlain by a thatch of long

FIG. 193. — Restoration of †*Preptoceras*, a musk-ox-like animal from the Californian Pleistocene. (From a skeleton in Univ. Cal. Mus.)

straight hair, which form much the same kind of protection against extreme cold as was possessed by the †Mammoth or †Woolly Elephant (†*Mammuthus primigenius*). The horns are very broad at the base, expecially in old males, covering the top of the head, but not quite meeting in the middle line; the horns proper curve downward and then upward and forward. The series of the true musk-oxen cannot, at present, be traced back of the Pleistocene, but there is reason to think that it originated in the early Pliocene of central Asia.

In the Pleistocene North America possessed four other genera of musk-ox-like animals, all of which are now extinct. In †*Symbos* the bases of the horns meet and unite in the middle line of the head, forming a casque of horn-covered bone, but the horns themselves are smaller than in *Ovibos*. †*Symbos* has been found from Alaska to Arkansas, for it shifted its range according to the climatic changes of the Glacial and Interglacial stages.

The second genus, †*Boötherium*, is much rarer than †*Symbos* and has been found only in Kentucky and Nebraska. This animal had no casque on the head, as the bases of the horns are not enlarged. The other genera, †*Euceratherium* and †*Preptoceras*, occur in caves in California, the latter also in Texas. These forms are of great interest because they show affinities to the musk-oxen on the one hand, and on the other to sheep and certain antelopes, such as the Takin (*Budorcas*) of India and Tibet, and thus tend to connect the problematical musk-oxen with other Cavicornia and indicate central Asia as the probable place of origin.

Family 11. Antilopidæ, Antelopes
Oreamnos, Rec.

The only true antelope found in North America to-day is the mistakenly named "Rocky Mountain Goat" (*Oreamnos montanus*) which is one of the chamois group of mountain antelopes and which has no near relatives in this continent and is not known before the Pleistocene; it is thus a late migrant from Asia. This paucity of antelopes is in very striking contrast to the Eastern Hemisphere and especially to Africa, which has more than 80 species of this family. India also has many antelopes, including the curious four-horned *Tetraceros*.

Family 12. Antilocapridæ, Prongbucks

In his great work on late Tertiary antelopes and deer, Mr. Frick divides the Antilocapridæ into two groups, which he calls respectively the Pronghorns (Antilocaprini) and the Pronglets (†Merycodontini), which are here treated as families. Mr. Frick's explorations, especially in Nebraska, New Mexico and California, have resulted in the discovery of an astonishing wealth and variety of genera and species referable to this family, in addition to those which had previously been known in the Pleistocene. This superabundance of strange and more or less fantastic forms has vanished almost completely, the Pronghorn being the only survivor.

ANTILOCAPRIDÆ

Antilocapra, Rec. to Pleisto. †*Capromeryx*, †*Tetrameryx*, †*Hayoceros*, Pleisto. †*Ilingoceros* Pleisto. and Plio. †*Proantilocapra*, †*Plioceros*, †*Osbornoceros*, †*Sphenophalos*, Plio.

It is obviously impossible to give more than a very brief outline of this horde of species; Mr. Frick's treatise on the later Tertiary

FIG. 194. — Tiny, †four-horned prongbuck, †*Capromeryx*, Pleistocene of Rancho La Brea. (Drawn from a skeleton in Los Angeles Mus.)

pronghorns and deer of North America runs to over 600 pages, eloquent of the immense body of his material. However, the figures which he has kindly permitted me to use, make brief accounts practicable.

The animal variously called Prongbuck, Pronghorn and Pronghorned Antelope (see Fig. 95, p. 145) holds a very isolated position, being the only living member of its family. As had been predicted on *à priori* grounds, recent discoveries have shown it to be the last survivor of an extremely numerous and varied group which flourished in the Pleistocene, but were even more abundant in the upper Miocene and lower Pliocene of western North America and in no other known region.

The Pronghorn differs from all other existing Cavicornia in the character of its horns, which are branched and deciduous, being annually shed and replaced, while the bony horn-cores, which arise directly over the orbits, are simple and unbranched. Another characteristic of this genus is its strictly didactyl feet, for the lateral digits have disappeared without leaving a vestige. The grinding teeth are completely hypsodont.

In the Pleistocene the family was much more numerously represented; in addition to *Antilocapra* itself, which was already in existence, there was a wide variety of allied forms. The group has been most numerously found in the Great Basin and Pacific Coast regions, but extended far over the Great Plains and southward into Mexico. Some of these animals (†*Ilingoceros*, Fig. 196, *E*) had spirally twisted horn-cores like those of the strepsicerine antelopes of Africa, to which these fossils were, at first, supposed to be referable. There were several four-horned genera, commonest of which was the little †*Capromeryx*, of which entire skeletons have been recovered from the tar-pits of Rancho La Brea, and more fragmentary remains have been found in widely distributed localities, from Nebraska southward. This pygmy pronghorn, less than two feet high at the shoulders, has hypsodont, grazing teeth, and remarkably long, slender legs. Over each eye-socket arises a pair of parallel horns from a common base, of which the posterior one may be the longer.

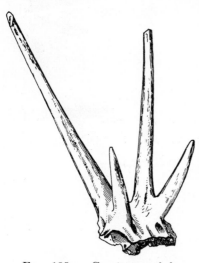

Fig. 195. — Cranium and horn-cores of †four-horned antelope, †*Tetrameryx schuleri*, Pleistocene of Tex. (From Lull.)

A second four-horned genus of the Pleistocene is †*Tetrameryx*, which was a larger animal than †*Capromeryx*, smaller than the modern Pronghorn, though of somewhat heavier proportions; it would seem not to have been so swift a runner. In this genus the horns are much longer than in †*Capromeryx* and those of each pair are divergent, not parallel.

Still a third Pleistocene four-horned type is †*Hayoceros*, which may be described as having an anterior pair of pronged horns, externally like those of *Antilocapra*, and a posterior pair of much longer and more slender horns, which were unbranched, tapering and pointed, and with a decided backward inclination.

The Pliocene had an even greater wealth of pronghorns than had the Pleistocene and among them there appear to be certain direct ancestors of the Recent genus; †*Proantilocapra*, found in Nebraska, differs little from the latter (Fig. 196, *B*) but †*Sphenophalos nevadanus*, known only from fragmentary remains, may have been an earlier ancestor. In this animal the horn-core is broad and bifurcate at the tip, with low anterior blunt prong and higher posterior one. The horny sheath covering such a core must have been deciduous, as otherwise growth would have been impossible. Though the horn-core of *Antilocapra* is unbranched, the pronged horn of this animal and its deciduous habit have long been interpreted as the last remnant of a bifurcate horn-core such as †*Sphenophalos* has, and the discovery of the latter is confirmatory of such an interpretation.

The older Pliocene of New Mexico has yielded a genus, †*Plioceros* (Fig. 196, *C*), which may also have been in the direct line of descent and the forerunner of †*Sphenophalos*. In †*Plioceros* the horn-cores are shorter and broader than in the modern Prongbuck and conspicuously bifurcate; of the two branches, the hinder one is the longer.

A lower Pliocene genus, of New Mexico, †*Osbornoceros* (Fig. 198, *B*), represents a side-branch of this group, which cannot have been in the ancestral line and which had a much greater resemblance to the true antelopes than any other known member of the family. Here the horn-cores are relatively very long and slightly twisted, with a backward and outward curvature, which must have given the horns the appearance of those of such a modern antelope as the African *Tragelaphus* and, at first sight, it would seem that †*Osbornoceros* must have been a true antelope. Such a reference is, however, forbidden by the position of the horns, which arise directly over the orbits as they do in all of the *Antilocapridæ*, while in all the *Antilopidæ* the horns are placed much farther back.

The subfamily cannot as yet be traced beyond the lower Pliocene, the †*Merycodontidæ* replacing it in the Miocene. Especially to be emphasized are the abundance and variety of the prongbucks in the Pliocene, which were somewhat diminished in the Pleistocene and reduced to a single genus in the Recent.

Family 13. †*Merycodontidæ*, †*Deer-like Antelopes* — †*Pronglets (Frick)*

This family stands on the verge of two sections, Cervicornia and Cavicornia, but is not certainly referable to either, and its members

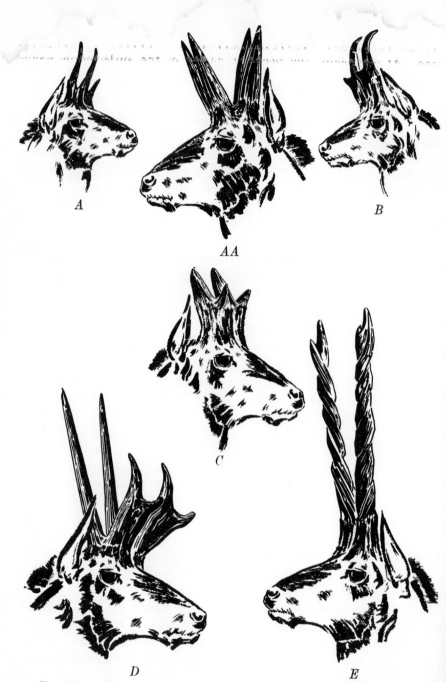

FIG. 196. — Pronghorns of Pleistocene and Pliocene. *A*, †*Capromeryx furcifer*, Pleistocene of Neb. *B*, †ancestral pronghorn, †*Proantilocapra platycornea*, upper Pliocene of Neb. *AA*, †four-horned prongbuck, †*Tetrameryx onusrosagris*, Pleistocene of Ariz. *C*, †*Plioceros crucensis*, Pliocene of N. M. *D*, †*Hayoceros falkenbachi*, Pleistocene of Neb. *E*, †*Ilingoceros alexandræ*, Pliocene of Nev. (Restored by J. M. Guerry; from Frick.)

display paradoxical characters which are very difficult of interpretation. At first sight, the deer-like nature of the antler-horns seems unquestionable, but the teeth are very different from those of any known deer. Not only are the grinding teeth hypsodont (a few deer have high-crowned teeth) but they closely resemble, even in minor details, those of the Pronghorn Antelope. Many of these antler-like appendages show the "burr," or roughened ring around the base of the horns and this has been regarded as proof that the antler-like horns must have been deciduous. It seems necessary to assume either that these appendages were periodically shed, or that they remained covered with hair and skin, "in the velvet," until full growth had been attained. It has been suggested that these branching appendages were sheathed in horn, but conditions of growth make this unlikely and the surface texture of the bone is rather that of an antler than a horn-core. The principal genera of the family are in the following list.

†Merycodontidæ

†*Merriamoceros,* †*Meryceros,* †*Paracosoryx,* †*Paramoceros,* †*Ramoceros,* low. Pliocene, †*Cosoryx,* up. Miocene, †*Merycodus,* mid. and up. Miocene.

As appears from the table, the lower Pliocene was the time of greatest development and diversification of this family, the restored heads of which are shown in Figs. 197 and 198, and give an adequate conception of the extraordinary variety displayed by the antler-forms of the Pliocene. Most curious and aberrant of them all is †*Merriamoceros* (Fig. 198, *A*), from the Mohave Desert, in which the short beam expands at the end into a disc, or shallow cup, for it is slightly concave, around the margins of which are small knobs, or abortive tines, such as are seen on the palmate antlers of certain deer. It seems out of the question that such an "antler" can have had a horny sheath.

In †*Paracosoryx,* several species of which are displayed in Fig. 197, the antlers are simply furcate, but the beam differs greatly in length in the various species: in †*P. savaronis* (*AA*) the beam is very short, in †*P. wilsoni* (*B*) it is very much longer, and in †*P. alticornis* (*BB*), it reaches an exaggerated length. In †*Meryceros* (Fig. 197, *A*) the antler is very like that of †*P. savaronis,* furcate and with short beam. †*Paramoceros* has three tines instead of two and the two species shown in Fig. 197 differ in the length of the beam, which is short in †*P. brevicornis* (*C*), long in †*P. alticornis* (*BB*). In †*Ramoceros* (*E*) the antler divides dichotomously twice, giving four tines, though one of

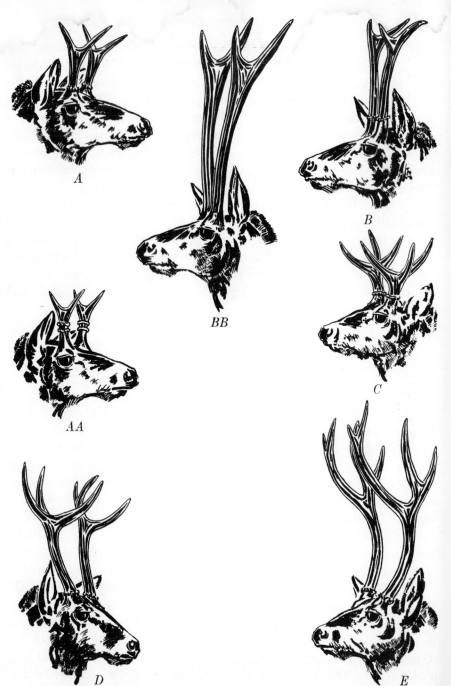

Fig. 197. — †Deerlike antelopes. *A*, †*Meryceros warreni*, Pliocene of Neb.
AA, †*Paracosoryx savaronis*, Pliocene of Neb. *B*, †*Paracosoryx wilsoni*, Pliocene
of Neb. *BB*, †*P. alticornis*, Pliocene of Cal. *C*, †*Paramoceros brevicornis*, Pliocene
of Cal. *D*, †*P. marthæ*, Pliocene of N. M. *E*. †*Ramoceros ramosus*, Pliocene of N. M.
(Restored by J. M. Guerry; from Frick.)

318

these is very short. In all the preceding genera the beam is straight, or nearly so, but in †*Ramoceros* it has a decided forward curvature.

With the Pliocene all these genera come to an end and no representative of the family has been found in the Pleistocene, nor are they known to occur in any other continent.

In the upper and middle Miocene are found several species of the genus †*Merycodus*, from which the family is named. The proportions of the skeleton indicate that these were singularly beautiful and graceful little animals. In appearance they must have resembled deer, the proportions of head, body and limbs being much as in the European Roebuck (*Capreolus*), but the teeth were far more like those of the Pronghorn Antelope. The horns, or antlers, whichever they were, of †*Merycodus* are, for the most part, simply furcate and short-beamed, but in one middle Miocene group of species the beam is much longer and divides into three tines, giving it a strong resemblance to a deer's antlers. The legs of †*Merycodus* are relatively long and very slender and the feet have typically pecoran cannonbones; the lateral digits are somewhat more reduced than in the deer, but not so completely as in the pronghorns. In both manus and pes the second and fifth digits have lost their metapodials, but retain very small phalanges in full number.

Three radically different views have been propounded concerning the relationships and systematic position of the †merycodonts. According to one opinion these animals were †ancestral deer and, if that conception is adopted, the group is to be included in the Cervidæ. The second view regards them as †ancestral pronghorns and its acceptance would involve the reference of the †merycodonts to the Antilocapridæ. A third opinion makes the †deer-like antelopes a side-branch of the antilocaprine stock, given off when this stock had not long been separated from the cervid stem and which came to an end in the Pliocene, leaving no descendants in the modern world. This conclusion, which is here adopted, requires the formation of a separate family for the †merycodonts, since they cannot be properly included in either the Cervidæ or the Antilocapridæ.

None of the Cavicórnia succeeded in establishing themselves in South America, though antelopes did actually reach that continent, as is shown by Pleistocene fossils found in the Brazilian caverns. Pronghorns, bison, sheep and musk-oxen would seem to have been unable to cross the Tropics, for none of them has been found south of the Mexican plateau.

Superfamily CERVICORNIA. *Antlered Ruminants*

This group includes two families, the deer and the giraffes, but inasmuch as none of the latter ever reached the Western Hemisphere, it will be unnecessary to take them into consideration.

Family 10. Cervidæ, Deer

Cervus, Alce, Rangifer, Pleisto. to Rec. *Odocoileus* Pleisto. to Rec. N. and S. A. *Blastoceros, Mazama, Pudu*, Pleisto. to Rec. S. A. †*Cervalces*, Pleist. †*Cranioceras*, †*Sinclairomeryx*, †*Drepanomeryx*, low. Plio. †*Procranioceras*, †*Dromomeryx*, †*Matthomeryx*, mid. Mio. †*Aletomeryx*, †*Blastomeryx*, low. Mio.

In nearly all existing species of deer the male is provided with "antlers," solid outgrowths from the skull, which have no horny sheath and are periodically shed and renewed. A few modern deer have no antlers, such as the Musk-deer (*Moschus moschiferus*) and the Chinese Water-deer (*Hydropotes inermis*). In the muntjaks (*Cervulus* and *Elaphodus*) the antlers are very small and simply forked, but in most deer the antlers grow larger and more elaborately branched with each annual renewal, until an astonishing size and complexity are attained. Usually the beam and branches (or tines) are cylindrical, tapering to a point, but in some, as the Moose (*Alce*), Fallow Deer (*Dama*) and the gigantic misnamed †"Irish Elk" (†*Megaceros*) the antler is broad and flat and is then said to be "palmate." In the Reindeer and Caribou (*Rangifer*) the female has antlers, though smaller and less branched than in the male.

Many years ago Sir Richard Owen pointed out the inverse relation between horns and tusks in the ruminants, those species which are without horns or antlers mostly having long, sabre-like upper canine tusks, while in the horned and antlered tribes the upper tusks are either completely lost, or, less commonly, reduced to a vestigial condition. In the hornless chevrotains, Tragulina, Musk-deer (*Moschus*), Water-deer (*Hydropotes*) and in the small-antlered muntjaks (*Cervulus, Elaphodus*) the upper canines are formidable weapons, and the little Indian Muntjak, or Barking Deer (*Cervulus muntjak*), can defend itself successfully against dogs by the use of these needle-sharp tusks. In all other deer the tusks have been lost, or, as in the Wapiti (*Cervus canadensis*), reduced to vestiges.

Something must be said of the manner in which the antlers are developed. From the frontal bones arise two cylindrical, solid and skin-covered bony projections, the *pedicles*, which differ much in length in the various genera, but are always permanent, never shed with the antlers. When new antlers are to be formed a hairy knob appears on the summit of each pedicle and grows rapidly into the form characteristic for the species; simple spikes are formed the first year, becoming larger and more branched with each renewal. So long as growth continues, the antlers remain skin-covered and are then said to be "in the velvet," and are abundantly supplied with blood-vessels. When growth is nearly completed a rough ring of bone, the *burr*, is deposited around the base of the antler, just above its junction with the pedicle. When growth ceases the blood-vessels shrivel, the

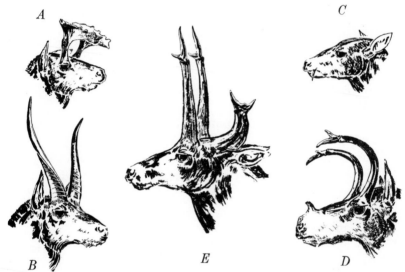

Fig. 198. — Late Tertiary deer and pronghorns. *A*, †*Merriamoceros coronatus*, Pliocene of Cal. *B*, †*Osbornoceros osborni*; Pliocene. *C*, hornless deer, †*Parablastomeryx gregorii*, lower Miocene. *D*, †four-horned deer, †*Sinclairomeryx sinclairi*, lower Pliocene of Neb. *E*. †three-horned deer, †*Procranioceras skinneri*, middle Miocene of Neb. (Restored by J. M. Guerry; from Frick.)

velvet dries and peels off the completed antlers, the animal assisting by rubbing the antlers against tree-trunks.

In the breeding-season the bucks fight for the possession of the does, using the antlers as weapons, but after the rutting time has passed, the bone which connects antler and pedicle is resorbed and the antler, with the burr, loosens and drops off. The whole structure and process of development are pre-eminently characteristic of the deer family, though, as was pointed out in the preceding section, the †Merycodontidæ exhibit some remarkable and puzzling analogies to the deer in their antler-like horns, as here interpreted.

It was shown in Chapter VIII that North American deer form

two strongly contrasted groups, the northern and the southern. In the northern group the deer are so like those of the Old World that some naturalists refer them to the same species, and the genera are obviously the same. These are the Wapiti (*Cervus*), mistakenly called Elk, the Moose (*Alce*) and the Caribou, or Reindeer (*Rangifer*). None of these has been found in America in deposits older than the Pleistocene, nor anything that could be ancestral to them; they were all very late immigrants from Asia.

At least one Pleistocene genus, the †Stag-moose (†*Cervalces*) was different from any now living. The only known skeleton, now in the Princeton Museum (Fig. 141, p. 178), is of post-Glacial date, but other remains have been found in Pleistocene deposits. The skeleton of †*Cervalces* is very much like that of the Moose; the bones of the neck, trunk and limbs are almost identical in the two genera, but skull and antlers are very different. The nasal bones are much less shortened than in the Moose, an indication that the proboscis-like muzzle was less inflated. The antlers are unique, though in a general way like those of *Alce*, they are much less palmated and they have, in addition, a great trumpet-like plate of bone on the lower side of each antler; this plate is not known in any other member of the Cervidæ. †*Cervalces* has not been found in the Old World, yet it must have originated there from the same stock as the Moose and accompanied the latter in its migration to North America.

The southern American deer (*Odocoileus*) include several species which are, in many details of structure, so different from any of the Old World genera as to imply that they must have been descended from a long line of American ancestry, little of which has yet been made known. In the Eastern U. S. the Virginia, or White-tailed Deer (*O. americanus*) is abundant, becoming smaller in the South. The Arizona White-tail (*O. couesii*), is a very small variant of the Virginia group. The Mule Deer and Columbian Deer (*O. hemionus* and *O. columbianus*) are Western and Pacific Coast forms. The vernacular name of "Black-tailed Deer" is used for both of these species.

The deer of the genus *Odocoileus* ultimately, of course, were derived from Asiatic migrants. Probable as this inference seems, it is not yet supported by the evidence of the fossils, for nothing is known of this series in America before the late Pliocene, but the desired ancestors may eventually be found. In the early Pliocene and the Miocene Mr. Frick has recently brought to light a remarkable series of strange and grotesque cervids, which cannot have given rise to any of the existing deer, but constitute an altogether aberrant side-branch of the family. Several of these genera had been previously known, but were believed to be referable to antelopes or pronghorns. Examples of this reference are †*Dromomeryx*, of the middle Miocene, and †*Cranioceras* and †*Drepanomeryx*, of the lower Pliocene. The lower Pliocene was the time of greatest development and none of the genera, so far as is known, extended its range into the middle Pliocene. Two of the Miocene deer, †*Blastomeryx* and †*Aletomeryx*, belong in a different category

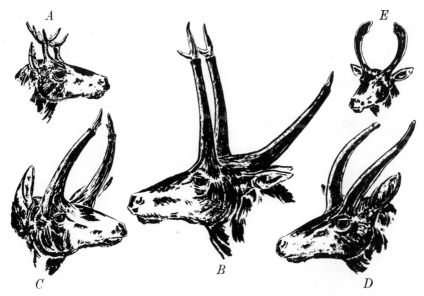

Fig. 199. — Late Tertiary deer. *A*, †*Aletomeryx gracilis*, lower Miocene. *B*, †three-horned deer, †*Cranioceras granti*, lower Pliocene. *C*, †*Dromomeryx whitfordi*, middle Miocene. *D*, *Matthomeryx matthewi*, middle Miocene. *E*, †*Drepanomeryx falciformis*, lower Pliocene. (Restored by J. M. Guerry; from Frick.)

and may, perhaps, have some significance in the development of the modern American deer.

What especially characterizes these extraordinary creatures is the very small size of the antlers and the relatively enormous development of the pedicles, which form, so to speak, the shaft of the spear, with the antler as the spear-head. The pedicles do not arise so directly over the orbits as they do in the pronghorns and in some genera they are between the ears. These aberrant deer are shown in Figs. 198, *D* and *E*, and 199, *B—E*; in time they range from middle Miocene to lower Pliocene, inclusive. The muntjaks have very elongate pedicles and small antlers, but these conditions are immensely exaggerated in the American group and three- and four-horned genera appear among them. Antlers, though confidently inferred, have not yet been found.

A conspicuous three-horned type is †*Cranioceras*, from the lower Pliocene of Nebraska (Fig. 199, *B*), in which there is an anterior pair of very high, nearly straight, pedicles and a posterior median pedicle, which grows out of the occiput and slants steeply backward. Each pedicle is surmounted by a small antler. Apparently the direct forerunner of this grotesque creature was †*Procranioceras*, of the middle Miocene, which differs from its Pliocene descendant chiefly in the shape of the posterior, unpaired horn. This is much shorter, thicker and less divergent than in †*Cranioceras*, having, in fact, a forward curvature.

In the first edition of this book †*Dromomeryx* (Fig. 199, *C*), of the middle Miocene, was described as "the most ancient American cavicorn yet known," but it turns out to be one of the aberrant deer. Another middle Miocene genus of this group is †*Matthomeryx* (Fig. 199, *D*) in which the very elongate pedicles slope backward and have much the appearance of lyrate antelope horns, and the antlers seem to be on the point of disappearance, or, perhaps, they have never developed. In the lower Pliocene occurs †*Drepanomeryx* (Fig. 199, *E*) in which the antlers have disappeared (if they ever were formed) and the pedicles, which arise far back between the ears, are flattened, incurved and scimitar-shaped; this is the extreme development, in one direction, within this group.

Perhaps the most grotesque in all this bizarre assemblage is †*Sinclairomeryx*, of the lower Pliocene (Fig. 198, *D*), a "four-horned" deer. The principal pair of pedicles arise somewhat behind the eyes and instead of being straight and tapering, as they are in †*Cranioceras*, are much more slender, cylindrical, and strongly curved forward. The accessory pair are very short and arise from the nasal bones.

It was noted above that two of the Miocene genera, †*Aletomeryx* and †*Blastomeryx*, differed notably from the aberrant deer just described. The former, †*Aletomeryx*, is represented by an entire skeleton (Fig. 200) and restoration in the Peabody Museum of Yale University, collected in the lower Miocene of Nebraska. In this animal the pedicles are longer than in most modern deer, but relatively less so than in the muntjaks, the short antler has no beam, but divides into tines. Very possibly, this genus may have been one of the ancestors of *Odocoileus*, but the hiatus between the lower Miocene and the upper Pliocene is too great to admit of positive statements.

On the other hand, †*Blastomeryx* (Figs. 198, *C*, 201), which occurs throughout the Miocene, fills all the requirements of a deer ancestor and much resembles the modern hornless deer, such as the Musk-deer (*Moschus*) and the Chinese Water-deer (*Hydropotes*). This genus, likewise, is known from complete skeletons in the Yale and

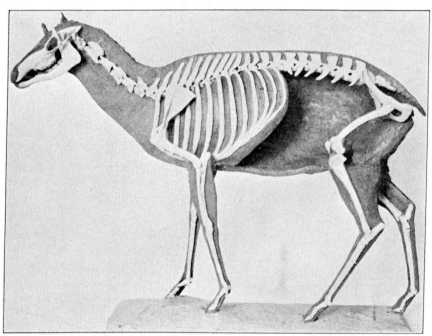

FIG. 200. — Skeleton of †*Aletomeryx*, a primitive deer with short pedicles, lower Miocene. (Restored by Prof. R. S. Lull; Peabody Mus. Yale Univ.)

American Museums. This is hornless and, like all such modern deer, it has long, sharp-pointed and sabre-like tusks. †*Blastomeryx* continued throughout the Miocene with little change. In the lower Pliocene a species, †*B. marshi*, has small, incipient horns and upper canines, which, though functional tusks, are smaller than in the Miocene species. In the latter the tusks are broader and stouter and very similar to those of the Asiatic muntjaks, and there is no sign of horns. The bones of the limbs and feet are much like those of the modern *Odocoileus*, and in the fore-foot the lateral digits are preserved in very reduced form.

There is one great difficulty in the way of regarding †*Blastomeryx* as the ancestor of *Odocoileus* and that is the necessity, on such an assumption, of accepting the independent origin of antlers in the American genera. The problem is complicated by the antler-like horns of †*Merycodus*, which appears to be more nearly related to the pronghorns than to the deer. It seems incredible that so elaborate and complicated an apparatus as the deer-antler, with its provision for annual renewal, could have arisen independently more than once. If there was no such dual origin, it follows that the deer of both Eastern and Western Hemispheres must have had some common

FIG. 201. — Lower Miocene †thornless deer, †*Blastomeryx advena*. (Restored from a skeleton in Amer. Mus. Nat. Hist.)

ancestry, which had developed deciduous antlers, however simple in form.

In the absence of knowledge it is vain to speculate on this topic; the problem must be solved by recovering the successive steps of development in Asia and in North America.

South American deer, the only representatives of the Pecora to maintain a lasting foothold in that continent, were evidently derived from the north by immigration, for they all belong to the *Odocoileus* group. Several species of deer, some of them extinct, have been found in the Pleistocene of the Pampas, but none as yet in the Pliocene. It seems very probable, however, that deer had reached South America in the Pliocene, as is implied by the diversity and degree of specialization which has been attained by the Neotropical members of the family.

SUBORDER IV. **Tylopoda.** CAMELS, ETC.

As now existing, this suborder comprises only the single family of the Camelidæ, camels and llamas, and the extinct families which are here grouped with it are, by most palæontologists, assigned elsewhere. To me, on the other hand, it seems probable, though by no means demonstrated, that this suborder played a very important rôle in the Western Hemisphere, largely taking the place that was held by the Pecora in the Old World, and diversifying into several other families which flourished in the Oligocene and Miocene and died out in the lower Pliocene. All of these families made their first known appearance in America in the Uinta, or upper Eocene, coming from some region not yet identified. No member of the suborder ever possessed true horns, or antlers, though in one series fantastic bony outgrowths of the skull were developed which had some likeness to horns and may be so called for convenience. Though related to the Pecora, the Tylopoda have been separated from them since the upper Eocene.

Although probably of remotely Old World origin, the camels were for ages confined to North America, where, with the horses, they were the most abundant and characteristic mammals. In each successive stage from the Uinta to the Pleistocene, horses and camels are the commonest fossils, probably because they lived in great herds on the open grasslands. In many respects the horses and camels followed parallel courses of evolution, keeping remarkably even pace with each other, and eventually vanishing from this continent at about the same time.

Family 6. Camelidæ, Camels and Llamas

Though for ages the only home of this family, North America has no members of it now, Asia being the home of the true camels and South America of the llamas. The table includes only the genera which have at one time or another lived in the Western Hemisphere.

CAMELIDÆ

Lama, Pleist. to Rec., S. A. †*Camelops*, Pleist. †*Megacamelus*, low. Plio. †*Pliauchenia*, up. Mio. to mid. Plio. †*Procamelus*, up. Mio. and low. Plio. †*Rakomylus*, low. Plio. †*Stenomylus*, low. Mio. †*Alticamelus*, mid. Mio. to low. Plio. †*Protolabis*, mid. and up. Mio. †*Oxydactylus*, low. Mio. †*Protomeryx*, up. Olig. to low. Mio. †*Pseudolabis*, low. Olig. †*Poëbrotherium*, mid. Olig. †*Eotylopus*, do. †*Protylopus*, up. Eoc.

Within the limits of this family there were several tribes, all of which would seem to have been derived from the upper Eocene genera. There was (1) the main stem, the development of which may be almost continuously traced through common ancestors of camels and llamas to the gigantic llama-like forms of the Pliocene and Pleistocene. (2) The browsing, †giraffe-like camels were a branch that began in the Oligocene, reached its culmination in the middle and upper Miocene and ended in the lower Pliocene. (3) A second branch was that of the little †gazelle-like camels. The latest of this line is the lower Pliocene genus, †*Rakomylus*, which was an extraordinary beast; until recently only the lower jaw and teeth were known, but a skull, now in the Frick collection, has lately been found and will be described in the near future. The lower teeth are sufficiently remarkable; the molars are greatly extended in the antero-posterior direction and extremely narrow transversely and, at the same time, they are completely hypsodont. It is evident that these teeth have undergone a great change from the lower Miocene †*Stenomylus*, but the steps of that change have yet to be revealed, for in the long interval between lower Miocene and lower Pliocene no connecting links have yet been found. †*Stenomylus* has brachyodont teeth and in its genealogy there is a hiatus and therefore this genus cannot yet be connected with an Oligocene ancestry. (4) Finally, there was a short branch consisting at present of a single genus, †*Pseudolabis*, which seems to have left no descendants and the ancestry of which is unknown.

Thus, for the main stem and the †*Alticamelus* branch, the successive steps of development are reasonably well known, while the †*Stenomylus* and †*Pseudolabis* branches cannot yet be brought into close connection with the others.

At the present time only two genera of the family are in existence, *Camelus*, the true camels of Asia, and *Lama*, the Guanaco and Vicuña of South America; the Llama and Alpaca are domesticated forms. The ancestors of the Asiatic and South American genera migrated to those continents in the Pliocene and the family finally became extinct in North America in post-Glacial times. In the Pleistocene there were several large members of the group which were neither camels nor llamas, but, in a sense, intermediate between them.

In *Camelus* the first and second upper incisors have been lost, but the third remains, and is a large, sharp-pointed tooth, as are also the first upper premolar and both canines; all these strong, spike-like teeth make a formidable lacerating apparatus. Behind

$p^{\underline{1}}$ is a long gap, $p^{\underline{2}}$ being suppressed; $p^{\underline{3}}$ and $^{\underline{4}}$ are relatively small grinding teeth. The molars are selenodont (i.e. made up of four crescents) and high-crowned, but not extremely hypsodont. The lower incisors are large and shovel-like, the canine is an upright tusk and there are but two premolars.

The dental formula is: $i\frac{1}{3}$, $c\frac{1}{1}$, $p\frac{3}{2}$, $m\frac{3}{3} \times 2 = 34$.

The skull is long and the facial portion is abruptly narrowed, which gives a triangular shape when the head is seen from above. The orbits are completely encircled in bone and the sagittal and occipital crests are very prominent. The tympanic bullæ are large and filled with spongy bone. The condyle of the lower jaw is hemispherical and not, as in other hoofed mammals, semi-cylindrical, and the hinder end of the jaw has a peculiar, hook-like process.

The neck is very long and the cervical vertebræ have the remarkable peculiarity that the canal for the vertebral artery perforates the neural arch instead of the transverse process, as in almost all other mammals. The canal is thus concealed from view except when the vertebra is looked at from an end. The odontoid process of the axis is spout-shaped as it is, with very few exceptions, in all long-necked ungulates.

Legs and feet are very long; as in giraffes and horses the humerus has two bicipital grooves separated by a bicipital tubercle. The two fore-arm bones are co-ossified. The femur is so long that the knee-joint is visible externally, which gives the hind-leg an exceptional appearance. As in the Pecora, nothing remains of the fibula except the malleolar bone.

There are but two digits in each foot, fore and hind, the 3rd and 4th of the original five, the metapodials of which unite to form cannon-bones. The tylopodan cannon-bone differs in a very characteristic way from that of the Pecora; the two lower ends are everted and separated by a V-shaped notch, while the keels of the articular surfaces are confined to the posterior side and invisible from the front. The ungual phalanges are very different from those of the Pecora in being small and nodular, and the hoofs, which do not support the body-weight, are hardly more than nails. Under the other phalanges there is a broad pad of elastic tissue upon which the weight rests. From this pad comes the name of the suborder, Tylopoda, or "cushion-feet."

The teeth and skeleton of the llamas resemble those of the camels much more closely than would be expected from a comparison of the external appearance alone. The absence of humps, the long, pointed ears, the woolly hair, the smaller size and much lighter and more graceful proportions make the llamas look very different from the true camels, but dentition and skeleton are very nearly alike in the two genera. The dental formula is: $i\frac{1}{3}$, $c\frac{1}{1}$, $p\frac{2}{2}$, $m\frac{3}{3} \times 2 = 32$; the single upper incisor is $i\frac{3}{}$, the third of the original series, and the upper canine is recurved and much smaller than in the camel; the spike-like first upper premolar of the latter has been lost and the re-

Fig. 202. — Great †camel-like Llama, †*Camelops hesternus*, Pleistocene of Rancho La Brea. (Restored from a skeleton in Los Angeles Mus.)

maining premolars, $p\frac{3}{}$ and $\frac{4}{}$, have been greatly reduced in size. In the skull the brain-case is relatively larger and more rounded and the sagittal and occipital crests are much less prominent. Save for its smaller and lighter proportions, the skeleton is very like that of the true camels. Thus the existing members of the family form two well-defined tribes, or subfamilies, each of which is characteristic of a different continent.

Using the term to designate the family as a whole, camels were numerous and varied in the Pleistocene, when they ranged from Alaska to Florida, but only one species, †*Camelops hesternus*, from the tar-pits of La Brea, is at all well known. This is a very large animal which measured seven feet to the shoulders, and eight feet to the top of the head in the ordinary standing position. While more llama-like than camel-like in certain structural features, †*Camelops* differs in other respects from both *Lama* and *Camelus*, and has left no descendants. The discovery of a skull of this species, near Fillmore,

FIG. 203. — †*Procamelus elrodi*, a large camelid from the upper Miocene. (Restored from specimens in Carnegie Mus.)

Utah, with dried flesh still adhering to it, proves that these animals persisted into Recent times (A. S. Romer).

Pliocene camels are of several kinds, including †*Camelops* itself. Especially characteristic were certain colossal creatures which attained a height of 15 feet, towering above the largest elephants. †*Megacamelus*, from Arizona, and †*Colossocamelus*, from Nebraska, are the best known of these. In the Blanco (middle Pliocene) are found some very large, llama-like animals (†*Pliauchenia*) which cannot have been ancestral to any existing species, for they have but one premolar in each jaw. Another gigantic cameline creature was †*Megatylopus gigas*, of the lower Pliocene.

The most ancient true camels yet known are those of the Pliocene of India, which evidently arose from modified migrants from North America. The most ancient typical llamas are those from the Pliocene of South America, obviously of northern origin. In North America, on the other hand, the many Pliocene representatives of the family, mostly of large size, were neither one thing, nor the other, but on the whole rather more llama-like. These North American genera were the little modified descendants of Miocene forms, which were the common ancestors of both true camels and llamas.

The upper Miocene †*Procamelus*, if not actually one of these common ancestors, is very near to it, and serves to show what that progenitor must have been. †*Procamelus* has lost only the first and second upper incisors and has the formula: $i \frac{1}{3}, c \frac{1}{1}, p \frac{4}{4}, m \frac{3}{3} \times 2 = 40$. The remaining incisor, $i \frac{3}{}$, the canine and the first premolar, together with the lower canine, form just such a lacerating apparatus, though smaller, as has the modern *Camelus*. †*Procamelus* has a less capacious brain-case and a much longer face than the existing members of the family, while the limb- and cannon-bones are entirely modern in character. That the feet were already provided with pads, is shown by the shape of the ungual phalanges.

The middle Miocene representative of this main stem of the family is †*Protolabis*, which is decidedly smaller and more primitive than †*Procamelus;* the upper incisors are but partially reduced and the metapodials are separate, not united to form cannon-bones, though the digits are already reduced to two in each foot. The ungual phalanges are pointed and shaped very much as in deer and antelopes, from which fact it may be inferred that these animals were without pads and walked upon functional hoofs.

In the lower Miocene and upper Oligocene the characteristic cameline genus is †*Protomeryx*, which is one degree less advanced than †*Protolabis*, for it retains all the teeth, but the first lower premolar is caniniform and spaces appear behind the true canine and the first premolar in both jaws.

The White River camel, †*Poëbrotherium*, is very completely known, for several entire skeletons of it have been obtained. The largest species, †*P. labiatum*, is about as tall as a sheep, but much more slender, and has a small, pointed, unmistakably llama-like head, long neck and body and short tail, and elongate, very slender limbs and feet. The teeth are present in unreduced number, 44 in all, and

Fig. 204. — †Ancestral camel, †*Poëbrotherium labiatum*, White River of S. D.

the anterior ones, incisors, canines, and first premolars are slightly spaced apart, but the long interspaces, which are seen in the Recent genera, are not present, and were gradually acquired through the Miocene and Pliocene stages. The canines are very small and trenchant, not tusk-like, but were not waning; on the contrary, they grew larger with each successive stage. The lower incisors are small, simple, nearly erect and chisel shaped, very different from the large, procumbent, shovel-like teeth which characterize the modern genera.

The second and third premolars are much extended anteroposteriorly and are narrow, sharp-pointed, trenchant cones, very like those of several other families of primitive artiodactyls. The upper molars are still low-crowned, but the lower ones are beginning to assume the hypsodont character. All the molars have four crescentic cusps each.

The skull of †*Poëbrotherium* at once suggests its cameline affinities by its shape and by the characteristic narrowing of the facial region, but it differs from the modern genera in many details, the most obvious of which are the incompletely closed orbit, the shallow, slender jaws and the very large, hook-like process on the angle of the mandible, which, in greatly reduced form, is also present in Recent camels and llamas. A modern feature may be seen in the very large auditory bullæ, filled with spongy bone. The neck is relatively long, though not nearly so much so as in the modern genera, and the neck-vertebræ, except the 6th, had already acquired the tylopodan peculiarity of having the canal for the vertebral artery perforate the neural arch. The odontoid process of the axis is neither peg-like, nor spout-like, but of an intermediate shape, flat on the upper and convex on the lower side. The body is long and light and the tail short.

The hind-legs are considerably longer than the fore, raising the rump above the withers and indicating a leaping gait. Such proportions are frequently found among the primitive members of both artiodactyls and perissodactyls, and is conspicuous in the Tragulina, the little "mouse-deer," which are by far the most primitive of existing ruminants.

The limbs of †*Poëbrotherium* are exceedingly slender; the humerus has a single bicipital groove; the fore-arm bones are co-ossified, and in the lower leg the shaft of the fibula has been lost, the lower end persisting as a "malleolar bone," and the upper end co-ossified with the tibia. The feet had already attained the stage of development which continued through the upper Oligocene and lower Miocene. There

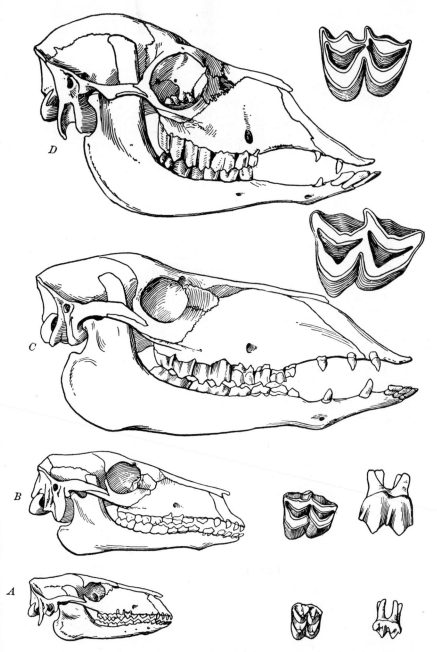

FIG. 205. — Diagram to illustrate the development of the skull and molar teeth in the camel tribe, in ascending geological order. *A*, †*Protylopus petersoni*, Uinta Eocene. *B*, †*Poëbrotherium wilsoni*, White River (after Wortman). *C*, †*Procamelus gracilis*, upper Miocene (after Cope). *D*, *Lama huanacus*, the modern Guanaco.

were, namely, no cannon-bones, but the digits had been reduced to two in each foot, the III and IV, only small nodules of bone representing the upper ends of the 2nd and 5th metapodials. The ungual phalanges are slender, pointed and deerlike, demonstrating the absence of pads on the feet.

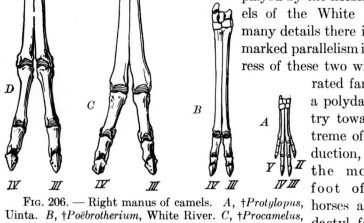

The Pecora, it will be remembered p. 307), were much later in ridding themselves of the lateral digits, and even to-day most members of that suborder retain some vestiges of them; only a few, like the Pronghorn, have no trace of them remaining.

It is interesting to note how nearly equal was the rate of development displayed by the horses and camels of the White River. In many details there is a clearly marked parallelism in the progress of these two widely separated families from a polydactyl ancestry toward the extreme of digital reduction, ending in the monodactyl foot of modern horses and the didactyl foot of Recent camels. Many

FIG. 206. — Right manus of camels. A, †*Protylopus*, Uinta. B, †*Poëbrotherium*, White River. C, †*Procamelus*, upper Miocene (after Cope). D, Recent Guanaco.

years ago the famous Swiss palæontologist, Rütimeyer, noted the osteological resemblances of horses and camels, but did not endeavor to account for them. The discoveries made since Rütimeyer's day have sufficiently proved that these similar characteristics were independently acquired in each family by parallel developments.

At the base of the White River occurs the enigmatical genus, †*Eotylopus*, undoubtedly a very primitive member of the camel family, but its relations to the preceding and succeeding genera are very problematical. If, as may well have been the case, it was directly ancestral to the Miocene camels, then †*Poëbrotherium* was not, and *vice versa*, for the two will not fit into the same series. In brief, one of these two genera was directly, the other collaterally, ancestral to the camels of the subsequent stages, but it is not yet feasible to say which of these alternatives is to be preferred. The older view,

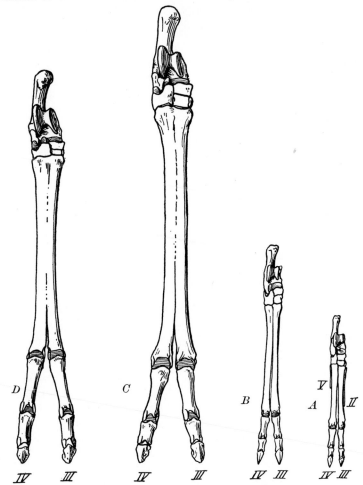

Fig. 207. — Right pes of camels. A, †*Protylopus*. B, †*Poëbrotherium*. C, †*Pro-camelus* (after Cope). D, Guanaco.

that †*Poëbrotherium* is the ancestor sought, is here provisionally accepted, though this view is by no means free from difficulties.

In †*Eotylopus* the dentition is unreduced, and the teeth are arranged in continuous series, without diastemata; the canines are larger than the adjoining teeth and of the normal caniniform shape, while the incisors have broad, spatulate crowns. The premolars are not so compressed and trenchant, or so extended antero-posteriorly as in †*Poëbrotherium*, and the molars are very low-crowned and relatively broad. The skull is proportionately shorter than in the genus last-named, but the auditory bullæ are similar. The neck is short; the ulna and radius are co-ossified and of the fibula, only the two ends remain. The manus has very slender but complete lateral digits, the 2nd and 5th, while in †*Poëbrotherium* only nodular remnants of the metacarpals are retained.

In the Duchesne River beds only a single camel, †*Poabromylus*, has so far been discovered, and that is still very incompletely known. Though of greater geological antiquity, it is more advanced and nearer to †*Poëbrotherium* than is the White River †*Eotylopus*. In †*Poabromylus* the lower premolars are of compressed-conical, trenchant shape and the lower molars are not so high-crowned as in †*Poëbrotherium*, but are otherwise like them, and, as in the latter, the lower jaw is very slender; the upper teeth are not known. So far as it goes, this Duchesne River genus is intermediate in character between †*Poëbrotherium* and the Uinta †*Protylopus*, but is distinctly nearer to the former, while †*Eotylopus* is nearer the latter.

Much the best known of the upper Eocene camels is †*Protylopus*, a little creature hardly larger than a Jack Rabbit. The teeth of each jaw are in continuous series and the canines are but slightly longer than the incisors; the premolars are not so prolonged antero-posteriorly as in †*Poëbrotherium*, but are of similar shape; the molars are very low-crowned and broad and the crescents are thick, a primitive character. The skull is almost a miniature copy of that of †*Poëbrotherium*, but in a number of details is decidedly less advanced. The most significant of these differences is in the character of the auditory bullæ, which are small and hollow, not filled with cancellous bone.

The neck, concerning which information is particularly desirable, is almost the only part of the skeleton which is still unknown. The fore-limb is considerably shorter than the hind, making the withers lower than the rump, as is true of so many primitive ungulates. Ulna and radius are still entirely separate and the shaft of the fibula, though hardly more than a thread of bone, is complete. In the manus there are four functional digits, of which the median pair are not very much larger than the laterals, but in the hind-foot the lateral digits (II and V) are extremely slender, but retain all three phalanges, which formed tiny dew-claws.

In brief, two tylopodan series would seem to have been derived from †*Protylopus*, one, †*Poabromylus*, of the Duchesne, and †*Poëbrotherium*, of the White River; the other, of which the Duchesne

Fig. 208. — Gigantic †giraffe-like camel, †*Alticamelus altus*, from the middle Miocene of Colo. (Restored from specimens in Amer. Mus. Nat. Hist.)

member has not yet been found, is †*Eotylopus*, of the lower White River, the position of which within the family is still uncertain.

Next, should be mentioned the problematical genus †*Pseudolabis*, from the uppermost White River, as to the immediate ancestry and possible descendants of which nothing is known. The lower teeth have not been found and the formula for the upper series is: $i \frac{3}{}$, $c \frac{1}{}$, $p \frac{4}{}$, $m \frac{3}{}$; the third incisor, canine and first premolar are spike-like, as in the true camels. "The skull is remarkably modernized for an Oligocene camel, resembling the Middle Miocene types. The genus apparently represents a side-line of cameline descent, of which we know nothing further" (Matthew).

In addition to the main stem of cameline descent, a brief sketch of which has been attempted in the foregoing pages, there were two very interesting side-branches, each highly specialized in a different way. Of these, the first is the group of browsing, or †giraffe-like camels, a term that must not be taken to imply any relationship with the giraffes, but merely a certain superficial likeness in form. The culminating genus of this series, †*Alticamelus*, persisted into the lower Pliocene, when it died out without leaving descendants, but it underwent little change after the middle Miocene, the time of its first recorded appearance.

†*Alticamelus* comprises very large animals, with relatively small heads and low-crowned teeth, not adapted to grazing. They have extremely long necks, made so by the elongation of five of the cervical vertebræ (2nd to 6th, inclusive); the legs are so very long that they give an absurdly stilted and rickety look to the skeleton, but there is no such inequality in the length of the fore- and hind-limbs as may be seen in the Giraffe, in which the fore-legs are much the longer, making the back slope down from withers to rump. This great elongation of neck and limbs fitted these grotesque creatures for browsing on trees, and the description given by Flower and Lydekker of the appearance and habits of the modern African Giraffe is, no doubt, largely applicable to †*Alticamelus*. "To produce the extremely elongated neck, the seven cervical vertebræ are proportionately long, which gives a somewhat stiff and awkward motion to the neck. . . . The Giraffe feeds almost exclusively on the foliage of trees . . . for browsing on which its prehensile tongue and large free lips are especially adapted."

The first recorded appearance of †*Alticamelus* is in the middle Miocene. In these middle Miocene species we already find cannon-bones in both fore- and hind-feet and the reduced, nodular, ungual

FIG. 209.— Lower Miocene †giraffe-like camel, †*Oxydactylus longipes*. (Restored from a skeleton in Carnegie Mus.)

341

phalanges, which indicate nail-like hoofs and the presence of elastic pads in the feet.

A very probable direct ancestor of †*Alticamelus* is †*Oxydactylus*, of the lower Miocene. This was a considerably smaller animal than its descendant and had shorter, more slender neck and limbs. There are no cannon-bones, the metapodials of both manus and pes remaining separate. The ungual phalanges are slender and sharp-pointed (whence the name of the genus), and these show that the hoofs were

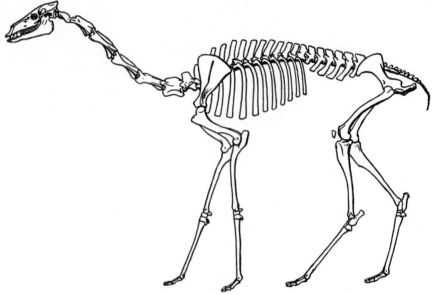

FIG. 210. — Skeleton of †*Oxydactylus longipes*, lower Miocene. For restoration, see Fig. 209. (From Peterson.)

like those of antelopes and deer, and that the elastic pads characteristic of all existing Tylopoda had not yet been acquired.

The †giraffe-like camels cannot be followed back into the Oligocene with any degree of assurance, but this is probably because of fragmentary material. In the John Day and White River is a genus, †*Paratylopus*, which may be the ancestor sought, for it has molars of lower crown than those of †*Poëbrotherium*, from which this genus further differs in the spacing apart of the anterior teeth, the canine-like form of the first premolar, above and below. These characters, so far as they go, and the larger size of the species are favourable to the inference that †*Paratylopus* was an ancestor of †*Oxydactylus*, but much more complete fossils will be needed before the connection can be established. Another intermediate genus, †*Miolabis*, is found in the middle Miocene, but almost certainly originated in the John Day; it differs from †*Paratylopus* in the much reduced second premolar.

Dr. Matthew concluded that at least three tribes of the family were differentiated as early as the Oligocene, which were:

1. †*Paratylopus* — †*Miolabis* — †*Oxydactylus* — †*Alticamelus*
2. †*Poëbrotherium* — †*Protomeryx* — †*Protolabis* — †*Procamelus*
3.   ?   †*Pseudolabis*

Another short-lived side-branch of the family is that of the "†gazelle-like camels," of which only the Pliocene †*Rakomylus* and the

FIG. 211. — Small †gazelle-like camel, †*Stenomylus hitchcocki*, lower Miocene of Neb., Harrison stage. (Restored from a skeleton in Carnegie Mus.)

lower Miocene †*Stenomylus* have yet been recovered. In all probability, the latter was derived from †*Eotylopus*, or †*Poëbrotherium*, but the connecting links have yet to be found. †*Stenomylus* is very much smaller than its contemporary †*Oxydactylus*, of the †giraffe-like series and about as tall as a sheep. A very exceptional feature of this genus is the apparent presence of ten incisors in the lower jaw, the canine and first premolar of each side having taken on the form and functions of incisors. The molar teeth are low-crowned and fitted only for browsing; the head is small and rounded, the neck long and light, the limbs and feet are very elongate and excessively slender, whence comes the name "†gazelle-like." The feet are two-toed and the metapodials are free, not forming cannon-bones; the slender and pointed ungual phalanges show that the hoofs were like those of deer.

As yet the genealogy of the camels cannot be followed farther back than the Uinta. Whether some of the imperfectly known artiodactyls of the middle and lower Eocene will eventually prove to be ancestors of the family cannot, as yet, be determined, but it seems more probable that the seemingly sudden influx of the many selenodont genera which characterize the upper Eocene was caused by immigration from some region which has not yet been identified, but which may have been either northeastern Asia, or eastern North America.

Family 7. †Leptomerycidæ

In all probability this family was ultimately of Old World origin, but no member of it has ever been discovered outside of North America, in which continent it continued from the upper Eocene into the lower Pliocene. This family (often improperly called the †Hypertragulidæ) includes two very distinct series which have not hitherto been formally separated into subfamilies, yet that separation is so plainly advisable that it is here made. The following are the principal genera of the family:

†LEPTOMERYCIDÆ

SUBFAMILY a. †PROTOCERATINÆ

†Synthetoceras, †Prosynthetoceras, low. Plio. †Syndyoceras, low. Mio. †Protoceras, up. White R. †Calops, do. †Heteromeryx, †Pseudoprotoceras, low. White R.

SUBFAMILY b. †LEPTOMERYCINÆ

†Nanotragulus, low. Mio. †Hypertragulus, up. and mid. Olig. †Hypisodus, †Leptomeryx, mid. Olig.

One of these subfamilies, the †Leptomerycinæ, includes many small and some minute species of animals that have a strong, though superficial resemblance to the chevrotains, or "mouse-deer," of the East Indies. The other subfamily, the †Protoceratinæ, is made up of some of the strangest-looking, most grotesque animals that ever dwelt in North America. These peculiarities, however, are mostly confined to the head of the male animal, the body and limbs being normal and graceful enough. The species of this subfamily are much larger than those of the other group and the latest ones, those of the Pliocene, equalled a Virginia Deer in size.

Subfamily †Protoceratinæ. — This division came to an end, so far as is known, in the lower Pliocene of Texas in the fantastic creature which has been named †*Synthetoceras.* The skull is long, narrow and vertically shallow, and carries two pairs of horn-like bony protuber-

Fig. 212. — Skull of †*Synthetoceras,* lower Pliocene of Tex.   (Mus. Univ. Cal.)

ances which probably were not sheathed in horn. The posterior pair of "horns," to call them so, are much like those of a cow in shape, curving upward, outward and backward, and tapering to blunt tips; they spring from the hinder borders of the orbits. The anterior "horns," which arise from the maxillaries on each side of the nasal opening, are fused together into a single beam which bifurcates into two prongs that rise much higher than the posterior "horns." The nasals are much shortened, but the canal is partly roofed over by the conjoined pair of "horns," and there can hardly have been a proboscis.

†*Synthetoceras* was the latest and largest of these grotesque animals,

which must have been very rarely fossilized. The line could not have persisted as long as it did, from the middle Oligocene to the lower Pliocene, had its successive members been as rare individually as the fossils would seem to indicate. Indeed the whole subfamily was unknown as late as 1890, and therefore the failure to find it in the middle and upper Miocene is not significant, for that gap may be filled at

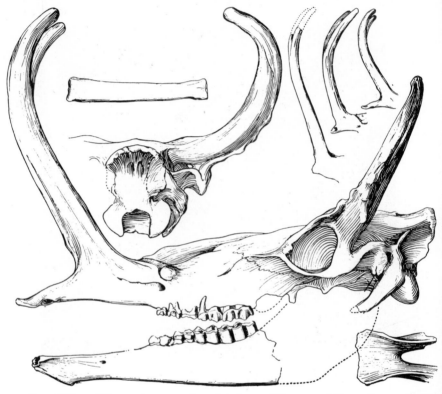

Fig. 213. — †*Prosynthetoceras francisi*, lower Pliocene of Tex. Large figure, skull and jaws. Lower right-hand corner, symphysis of mandible. Upper left, third metacarpal, occiput and right rear horn. Upper right corner, three rostral horns. (From Frick.)

any time. †*Synthetoceras* had hypsodont grinding teeth, but †*Prosynthetoceras*, which probably preceded it, had low-crowned molars.

The lower Miocene †*Syndyoceras* is only less fantastic than †*Synthetoceras*. This animal is distinctly smaller than the Pliocene, larger than the Oligocene genera and intermediate, not only in size, but in the structure of the skull. The posterior "horns" are cow-like in shape, as in †*Synthetoceras*, but the anterior ones are different, being united only at the base and curving away from each other, with the concavity outward. The very short nasals may indicate an inflated, Saiga-like muzzle, but such a division of the nasal passage has not been found in any mammal outside of this series and its interpretation is therefore difficult.

The upper incisors have all been lost and the canine is a small, recurved tusk; the lower canine has become one of the incisor series

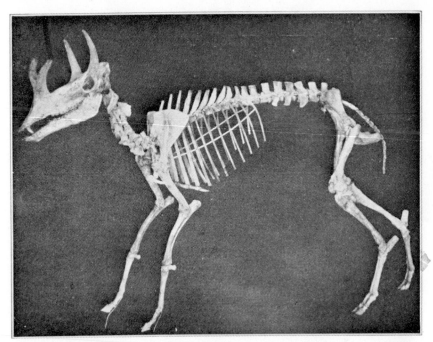

Fig. 214. — Skeleton of †*Syndyoceras cooki*, lower Miocene of Neb. (Neb. State Mus.)

functionally, while the first lower premolar has taken over the shape and function of the canine; this is an important point of resemblance to the †oreodonts (*q.v.*); the molar teeth are very low-crowned. The fore-limb is slender and of nearly the same length as the hind-leg, which is stout and not very long relatively to the head. The fibula has lost the shaft and retains only the ends; in the two-toed pes the metatarsals are united into a cannon-bone, and the ungual phalanges are narrow and pointed like those of antelope and deer.

The channel-sandstones of the upper White River beds have preserved the remains of what was probably an upland forest fauna, and have yielded numerous examples of †*Protoceras*, the first member of this series to be discovered and named. Entire skeletons have been collected and a sufficient number of skulls to demonstrate the remark-

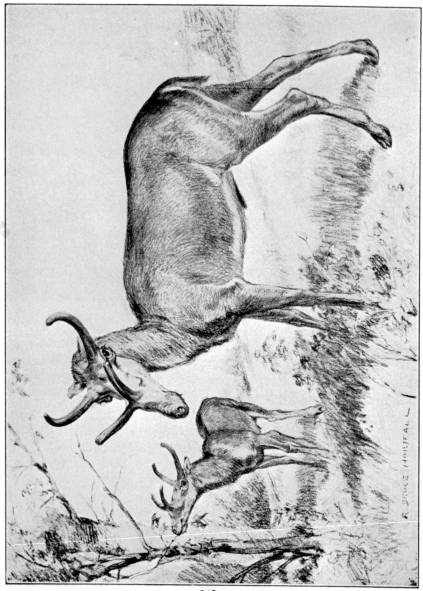

Fig. 215. — †*Synthyoceras cooki*, lower Miocene. (Restored from skeleton shown in Fig. 214.)

able differences between the sexes. The male has the two pairs of bony horn-like protuberances which are so conspicuous in the Miocene and Pliocene genera, but they are much smaller and of a different shape, and they differ also in form in the different species, but the number of skulls as yet collected is insufficient to show how extensive was the individual variation in the shape of these protuberances. In the species first named, †*P. celer*, the anterior, maxillary protuberances have little about them to suggest horns, as they are broad, heavy, recurved plates, thickened and rugose on the margins, and the two, of opposite sides, are not in contact with each other at the base, while the posterior "horns" are short and club-shaped. The nasal bones are much reduced, making the anterior nasal opening very long. In another species, †*P. nasutus*, which should, perhaps, be recognized as a separate genus, the anterior "horns" are much longer, narrower and more rod-like and articulate with each other at the base by a suture. The Miocene †*Syndyoceras* may very well prove to be an actual and direct descendant of this species.

In the female of †*Protoceras* the anterior protuberances from the maxillaries are wanting, and the posterior pair, while more horn-like in shape, are mere vestiges. The reader may wonder how it is possible to determine the sex of extinct animals from the skeleton alone. The determination is, of course, made from the analogy of living animals, in which the sexes differ as to such structures; tusks and horns are always smaller and frequently absent in the females. In †*Protoceras*, for example, the teeth, other than the canines, and the skeleton are identical in the two sexes, the difference is only in the "horns" and the tusks, which, in those individuals which are regarded as females, are so reduced as to be mere functionless vestiges.

A nearly allied and contemporaneous genus, †*Calops*, includes decidedly smaller animals, with somewhat differently shaped skulls; the male of this genus has not yet come to light, but the female differs from that of †*Protoceras*, in being entirely hornless.

All of these animals, males and females alike, have closely similar dentitions. The upper incisors have been completely suppressed; the upper canine in the male is a recurved tusk, of no great length, but short and strong; in the female it is reduced to vestigial proportions. The lower canines are like the incisors, and in the male their place is taken by the caniniform first premolars. The molars are very low-crowned and resemble those of deer, while the premolars are

Fig. 216. — †*Protoceras celer*, upper White River. Males on the right and left, female in the middle. (Restored from skeletons in Amer. Mus. Nat. Hist. and Princeton Univ. Mus.)

much extended antero-posteriorly, narrow, trenchant and sharp-pointed, very much as in the early camels, such as †*Poëbrotherium* and †*Protylopus.*

In the fore-arm the ulna and radius are beginning to coalesce, and in the lower leg the shaft of the fibula is lost, leaving only the ends. The manus has four functional digits, the laterals not very much shorter or more slender than the median pair. The pes is functionally two-toed, but the median metatarsals are separate, not uniting in a cannon-bone; the lateral metatarsals (II and V) are long and slender splints without phalanges.

In the lower White River beds (Chadron substage) have been found two genera of this subfamily, †*Heteromeryx* and †*Pseudoprotoceras,* neither of which would seem to have been directly ancestral to †*Protoceras,* though if a larger suite of specimens were available, enabling us to eliminate individual differences, one or other of them might prove to be the sought-for ancestor. At all events, they give a very good conception of what that ancestor must have been. In †*Heteromeryx* the skull, as a whole, is rather short, but the muzzle is elongate; the nasals are very short, though not so much reduced as in †*Protoceras;* horn-like protuberances are not present, but the only known skull may be that of a female. The molars are very low-crowned and there are four premolars, the first of which is isolated by gaps in front of and behind it; the others are pointed and trenchant, much like those of †*Leptomeryx* (*q.v.*). The ulna is more completely co-ossified with the radius than in †*Protoceras* and the shaft of the fibula is a vestigial spine. The feet are like those of the genus last-named, with four functional digits in the manus and two in the pes and with no cannon-bones.

The other Chadron genus, †*Pseudoprotoceras,* is represented by the skull of a male which has large upper canine tusks, relatively larger than in the succeeding genera of the subfamily. The upper incisors are already lost; the grinding teeth are essentially as in †*Protoceras.* The nasal bones are very short, leaving the nasal canal uncovered for most of its length. There is no indication of the maxillary protuberances, but there are small, horn-like outgrowths in front of the orbits. In most respects this genus is just what might have been expected of the ancestor of †*Protoceras,* but the dentition is slightly more advanced.

The †Protoceratinæ cannot, as yet, be traced farther back than the Chadron substage; they have not been detected in the Duchesne River beds, and while an ancestry common to both subfamilies will, no doubt, be found among the many selenodont genera of the upper Uinta, it is not yet feasible to determine it.

Subfamily †Leptomerycinæ. — All the mammals included in this group are very small and some are minute. In the size and proportions of the skeleton and relative length of the limbs and feet, there is much resemblance to the Tragulina, chevrotains, or "mouse-deer," of the Malay Archipelago, to which suborder these genera have sometimes been referred. On the other hand, their relation to the other subfamily is clear, and this makes a connection with the camels the more likely. So far as is at present known, the subfamily was relatively short-lived, extending only from the upper Eocene into the lower Miocene. The middle and upper Oligocene (White River and John Day stages) was the time when these small creatures were most flourishing and abundant.

Within the limits of the subfamily there are three well-defined tribes, but connecting links between these subdivisions have not been found, for these delicate little animals are mostly represented by fragmentary remains, and well-preserved skulls and skeletons are rare.

The first of these series, or tribes, terminated in the lower Miocene (Gering stage) in the genus †*Nanotragulus,* which differs but little from the much better known †*Hypertragulus* of the John Day. These lower Miocene species, which were no larger than a Jack Rabbit, must have been dainty, graceful little creatures, resembling the chevrotains in general appearance, but with different-looking heads, because of the elongate, narrow muzzles, which are more llama-like. The dental formula is: $i\frac{0}{3}$, $c\frac{1}{1}$, $p\frac{4}{4}$, $m\frac{3}{3}$; the very slender upper canine has evidently lost all functional significance, and the tiny, two-rooted first upper premolar is a miniature copy of the same tooth in †*Hypertragulus;* it is isolated by a long gap before and a shorter one behind it. The molars are much higher-crowned than in the John Day genus and may fairly be called hypsodont. The lower incisors are long, slender and styliform, and the canines form part of the same series. The first lower premolar is caniniform but so small and slender that it must have been useless. These teeth, the upper canine and first lower premolar, were functional in †*Hypertragulus,* but had become mere vestiges in the succeeding genus, †*Nanotragulus.* The skull is very much as in the John Day animal and has a similar llama-like appearance.

As in the Tragulina, the hind-legs are much longer than the fore, causing the line of the back to slope downward from the rump to the withers. The ulna and radius are co-ossified and in the manus there are four digits without cannon-bone. The lateral digits are complete, with phalanges, but are so small that they must have been mere dewclaws, not touching the ground. The pes is also tetradactyl, with no cannon-bone, and the lateral metatarsals are reduced to threads of bone, but all the phalanges are preserved.

So far as can now be judged, the Oligocene †*Hypertragulus* was directly ancestral to †*Nanotragulus* and was especially characteristic

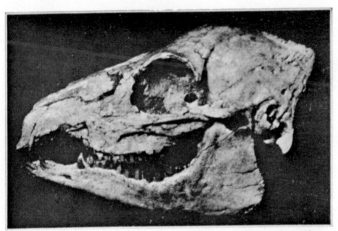

Fig. 217. — Skull of †*Nanotragulus* sp., nearly natural size, lower Miocene of Wyo., Harrison stage. (Mus. Comp. Zoöl. Harvard Univ.)

of the John Day stage, though beginning in the White River. In this genus the grinding teeth are very low-crowned and the upper canines and lower caniniform premolars are large enough to have been functionally important. The first upper premolar is very characteristic; it has a narrow, conical crown set upon two widely divergent roots, and the skull has a very llama-like appearance. The feet were apparently the same as those of †*Nanotragulus*, but the excessively delicate and fragile lateral digits of the pes have not yet been found.

The second of the tribes of this subfamily is that typified by †*Leptomeryx*, which has not been found except in the White River stage and is much the most completely known of any of the genera of the subfamily. Several species have been named, all of them very small and none so large as a Jack Rabbit. Except for the longer muzzle and more cameline head, these delicate little animals must have looked much like the Javan Mouse-deer (*Tragulus kanchil*), or the tiny "Dik-dik" antelopes of Tropical Africa (*Cephalophus*). In †*Leptomeryx* all the upper incisors have been lost and the canines reduced to functionless vestiges; the lower canines, as in all members of the family, are functional incisors, but the caniniform first premolars are useless remnants. It is plain, however, that this genus, like all the others, was derived from ancestry in which the lower canine had become functionally an incisor and its place was taken

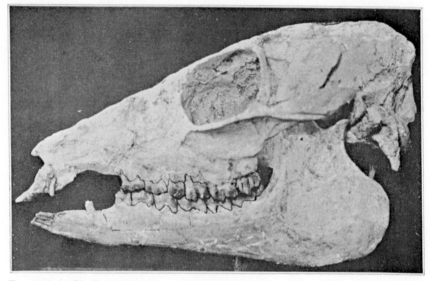

Fig. 218. — Skull of †*Leptomeryx evansi*, nearly natural size, White River. (Mus. State Sch. of Mines, S. D.)

by the first lower premolar, which, with the large upper canine, made an efficient pair of tusks.   †*Hypertragulus* is the only Oligocene member of the subfamily in which this primary condition is retained, though †*Protoceras* in the other subfamily has the same characteristics.

The premolars of †*Leptomeryx* are narrow, sharp-pointed and trenchant, and the molars, of which the crescents are imperfect, are very low-crowned. The skull has a very long slender muzzle, but is not quite so llama-like as in †*Hypertragulus*. The hind-legs and feet are much longer and more specialized than the fore; indeed, the difference between them is greater than in any other known artiodactyl. Thus, in the fore-arm the ulna is complete and separate from the radius, while the fibula is reduced to a minimum; the manus has four digits all separate, functional and complete, while the pes has but two digits, the metatarsals of which are fused into a cannon-bone.

Such a contrast between fore- and hind-feet is very remarkable and is unequalled among known ungulates. (See Fig. 385, p. 634.)

The third tribe of this subfamily is that of †*Hypisodus*, a tiny creature and smallest of American artiodactyls, which, like †*Leptomeryx*, is not known outside the White River formation; the species, †*H. minimus*, about equals an ordinary rabbit in size. The anterior upper teeth have not been found and, so far as is known, the dental

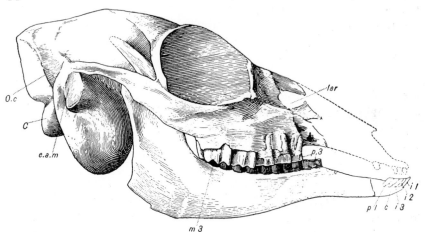

Fig. 219. — Skull, right side, of †*Hypisodus minimus*, much enlarged, × ³⁄₂. *i 1, i 2, i 3*, lower incisors. *c*, lower canine. *p 1*, first lower premolar. *m 3*, last upper molar. *e.a.m.*, entrance to the ear. *C*, occipital condyle. *O.c*, occipital crest. *lar*, facial vacuity. (From Matthew.)

formula is: $i\frac{?}{3}$, $c\frac{?}{1}$, $p\frac{3}{3}$, $m\frac{3}{3}$; the lower incisors are seemingly ten in number, because, as in †*Stenomylus*, the †gazelle-like camel, the canine and first premolar have become incisiform. These two are almost the only mammals in which this remarkable transformation has taken place. The second premolar, above and below, is present in young animals, but is shed in the adult. The third and fourth premolars are, like the molars, completely hypsodont, a very rare feature among White River artiodactyls, but, differing from the hypsodont teeth of later times, those of †*Hypisodus* are not covered with cement. It is interesting to note that the last upper milk-premolar $(dp\frac{4}{})$ is almost exactly the same as the corresponding permanent tooth $(p\frac{4}{})$ of †*Hypertragulus*.

The skull is relatively shorter than in any other member of the family; the orbits are unusually large, as are also the hollow tympanic bullæ, which actually meet anteriorly. Both of these structures point to nocturnal habits, which would seem to have been necessary for such utterly defenceless and tiny creatures. The angle of the lower jaw extends but little behind the condyle and the coronoid process is shorter and much more slender than in †*Leptomeryx*.

The ulna and radius are co-ossified and the lower end of the fibula is united with that of the tibia, which is a rare structure among artiodactyls. The fore-foot is not known; the hind-foot has no cannon-bone and the lateral metatarsals are threadlike.

There is a long hiatus in time, represented by the 1500 feet of the Duchesne River sediments, in which we have no information regarding this family other than the assurance that it persisted through that gap, which will in all probability be filled by discovery, as it has been for other families. It is therefore what might be expected, to find the Uinta, or upper Eocene, members of the †Leptomerycidæ very different from those of the White River and much more primitive. The Uinta genera, †*Leptoreodon*, †*Leptotragulus* and †*Camelomeryx*, are very much alike and constitute a group which may well have been ancestral to the White River genera of both subfamilies.

In the genera named there is a manifest likeness to the contemporary representative of the camel family, †*Protylopus*, from which they differ especially in the character of the anterior teeth. The lower canine has become incisiform and its place is taken by the first lower premolar, and there is a long gap behind the first premolar above and below; the other premolars and the molars are very much like those of †*Protylopus*. The skull is elongate and its llama-like character is plainly exhibited. Both fore- and hind-feet are four-toed, without cannon-bones, and the pes is considerably longer than the manus and has more slender and reduced lateral digits, but is not relatively so long as in †*Protylopus*.

Though the genealogy of the †Leptomerycidæ is incompletely known, its main outlines are clear, and the stages of development may be reconstructed with much confidence.

Relationships of the †*Leptomerycidæ.* — While I feel no doubt that this family is referable to the suborder Tylopoda, it is only fair to say that very different views on this subject have been and are still held by various palæontologists, who have assigned these strange and long-vanished creatures to the Pecora, the Tragulina or to both. For example, the late Professor Matthew always maintained that †*Leptomeryx* was the most ancient of American deer, and at one time I referred this genus to the Tragulina, to which it bears so strong a superficial resemblance. As this is not the place for technical discussions, it will suffice to quote the opinion of the eminent Swiss palæontologist, the late Professor L. Rütimeyer, of Basle. He wrote:

"The characteristics of the skull, especially those of the lower jaw, seem to point much more decidedly to a clear relationship of *Leptomeryx* to the forerunners of the camels (*Oreodon, Procamelus, Leptauchenia,* etc.) which are so strongly represented in North America. The almost completely preserved dentition seems to me to lead to the same conclusion. This is immediately notable in the irregularity of formation of the crescents in the upper and lower molars, which is so peculiar to the camels. . . . In every respect, therefore, *Leptomeryx* seems to me to be very far removed from the hornless ruminants of the European Miocene."

CHAPTER XIV

HISTORY OF THE ARTIODACTYLA

II. NON-RUMINANTIA

FAMILIÆ INCERTÆ SEDIS

There remain to be considered two artiodactyl families which have never been found outside of North America, the †Merycoidodontidæ and the †Agriochœridæ, the systematic position and relationships of which have been the subject of much debate and still remain open to question. More will be said concerning this problem after the history of these two families has been outlined; that they are closely related to each other, no one doubts.

Family 8. †Merycoidodontidæ, †Oreodonts

The inflexible law of priority in nomenclature demands that the genus of this family first described and named should be called by the cumbrous name of †*Merycoidodon*, instead of the familiar term †*Oreodon*, by which it has been known for nearly eighty years. The change of the generic name requires that the family name be altered to correspond, but the vernacular form "†oreodonts" may still be used. This was one of the most characteristic groups of American artiodactyls, though its origin must probably be sought elsewhere. The family was abundantly represented in the upper Eocene, the entire Oligocene and Miocene, coming to an end in the Pliocene.

In the course of this long history, exceptionally prolonged for one of the extinct groups, the †oreodonts passed through many changes and developed many modifications, forming several distinct tribes, though, at the same time, they remained curiously conservative. The many transformations affected chiefly the skull and teeth, while the remainder of the skeleton changed relatively little, such changes being mostly in size and proportions, greater or less slenderness, longer or shorter legs, etc. All of the genera are of small or moderate size, the largest not exceeding the Wild Boar, nor was there any decided increase in stature from one geological stage to another. Such increase is the rule in the long-lived series, such as horses, rhinoceroses, elephants and the like, but there are many exceptions. The most important genera are as follows:

†MERYCOIDODONTIDÆ

†*Merychyus*, †*Merycochœrus*, low. Mio. to low. Plio.   †*Metoreodon*, low. Plio. †*Pronomotherium*, mid. and up. Mio. †*Promerycochœrus*, up. Olig. to up. Mio. †*Hypselochœrus*, low. Mio. †*Cyclopidius*, mid. Mio. †*Pithecistes*, do. †*Leptauchenia*, mid. Olig. to low Mio. †*Limnenetes*, mid. Olig. †*Mesoreodon*, low. Mio. †*Ticholeptus*, mid. Mio. †*Eporeodon*, mid. and up. Olig. †*Merycoidodon*, mid. Olig. †*Protoreodon*, up. Eoc.

From the modern point of view, all the †oreodonts were strange beasts, some of them extremely grotesque, and they were probably

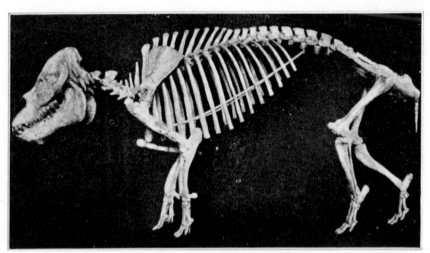

Fig. 220. — Skeleton of †*Merycochœrus magnus*, lower Miocene of Neb. (Col. Mus. Nat. Hist.)

gregarious, plains-dwelling types. Some would seem to have had amphibious ways of life and to have been largely aquatic, as much so, perhaps, as the modern Hippopotamus, though of incomparably smaller size. Dr. Leidy, who described and named most of the genera of the family, spoke of them as combining characteristics of deer, camels and pigs, and called them "ruminating hogs." This conception is expressed in some of the names which he gave, such as †*Merychyus* and †*Merycochœrus*, both of which mean "ruminant swine."

The proportions of most †oreodonts are very much as in the modern peccaries, or "Wild Texan Swine." For the most part, they had short head and neck, elongate trunk, short legs and feet, and tails which in the more ancient genera were long and heavy, becoming much shorter in some, at least, of the later ones. In the lower Miocene †*Mesoreodon*, there is a rudimentary clavicle and probably this bone was generally present in the family, but only by a rare and fortunate accident could such a small and loosely attached bone be recognized.

The teeth are in continuous series, without diastemata (or gaps), and there is one dental peculiarity which characterizes all the genera, except a few late ones which have demonstrably lost it. This con-

Fig. 221. — †*Promerycochœrus carrikeri*, lower Miocene. (Restored from a skeleton in Carnegie Mus.)

sists of the transformation of the lower canines into functional incisors, of which there appear to be eight in the lower jaw, while the first lower premolars have become caniniform, and bite *behind* the upper tusks. The change of the lower canines into incisor-like teeth takes place in all the Pecora, in †*Stenomylus*, the †Gazelle-like Camel, and in the †Leptomerycidæ, and the latter agree further with the †oreodonts in the assumption of the canine-like shape and function by the first premolar. The †Agriochœridæ, nearly related to the †oreodonts, have the same peculiar development of the teeth as the latter.

Only three genera of the †oreodonts, †*Merychyus*, †*Merycochœrus* and †*Metoreodon*, survived in the lower Pliocene, when this remarkably varied and long-lived family came to an end. Each of these three genera is the terminal member of a very distinct tribe and several others were thriving in the Miocene. Of some of these tribes, the origin and development may be satisfactorily traced, while for others, this remains to be accomplished, for they made their appearance unheralded and with seeming suddenness. The abruptness of these appearances is deceptive and owing to lack of information, a lack, which will, almost certainly, be supplied by future discoveries.

The tribe exemplified by †*Merycochœrus* was itself subdivided into two or three branches, all of which arose from a common Oligocene

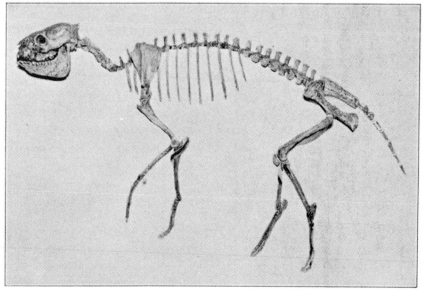

Fig. 222. — †*Merychyus* skeleton, upper Miocene. (Amherst Coll. Mus.)

ancestry. †*Merycochœrus* comprises the larger species of the tribe, which resemble a domestic boar in size and proportions, but with a very different-looking head, for the presence of a short proboscis is indicated by the much reduced nasal bones, and the facial part of the skull is shortened. The eye-sockets present obliquely forward and upward, instead of having the lateral presentation which is usual among mammals. Both eyes and ears were placed high in the head, which suggests more or less amphibious habits. The trunk is relatively long and the tail rather short, the legs and feet short and sturdy, the feet four-toed, with unreduced and functional lateral digits. The teeth are low-crowned, indicative of a diet of soft vegetation, but the upper canines and caniniform lower premolars were strong, effective tusks, which, no doubt, were formidable weapons.

In appearance and proportions, †*Merychyus* formed a strong contrast to †*Merycochœrus*, especially in the short, deep bullet-head, and

FIG. 223. — Head of †*Pronomotherium laticeps,* upper Miocene. (Restored from a skull in Carnegie Mus.)

in the very slender limbs and feet, with their much reduced lateral digits. Very few †oreodonts were of such light, almost gazelle-like proportions as was †*Merychyus,* and its high-crowned, persistently growing, grinding teeth point to habits of grazing and to a life on the open plains. Though unquestionably members of the same family, †*Merychyus* and †*Merycochœrus* were superficially very unlike, the latter a short-legged, heavy, proboscis-bearing, amphibious creature, subsisting on soft vegetable substances; the former a round-headed, very slender and lightly built grazer, probably dwelling in herds, and no doubt a very swift runner, on the treeless grasslands. Both of these types were survivors, with little change, from the upper Miocene, in which epoch were several other †oreodonts which did not continue into the Pliocene. Apparently a side-branch of the †*Merychyus* stem is the grotesque †*Hypselochœrus*, of the lower Miocene, which has a similar relatively long-legged skeleton, but a disproportionately large and elongate head.

Beside †*Merycochœrus*, was the second tribe of the same section, typified by the extraordinary †*Pronomotherium*, in which the skull

Fig. 224. — Head of †*Promerycochœrus superbus*, John Day stage. (Princeton Univ. Mus.)

has a remarkable resemblance to that of an anthropoid ape, so short and deep are the face and lower jaw, with the eye-sockets presenting almost forward. In the living animal there can have been no such resemblance, for the shortness of the face was masked by the proboscis, which was evidently much longer than in †*Merycochœrus*. †*Pronomotherium*, which was characteristic of the middle and upper Miocene, was the extreme of specialization in this group, though the less modified †*Merycochœrus* survived longer. The latter genus may be traced back to the upper Harrison formation; in the lower Harrison it was represented by the ancestral genus †*Promerycochœrus*, of which there were two tribes, the longer- and shorter-faced, that should perhaps, be separated generically. One of these, which goes back to the Gering, or lowest Miocene, has a shorter face and deeper jaw and was, to all appearances, the direct forerunner of †*Merycochœrus*, while the other has a very elongate face. In both of these tribes the zygomatic arch is extraordinarily short, massive and rugose. The long-faced type is especially common in the John Day and appears to have been derived from †*Eporeodon*, of the upper White River, which also gave rise to at least one other †oreodont line and perhaps to additional ones also.

The third of the Pliocene genera, †*Metoreodon*, represents the central line of the family, which underwent comparatively little

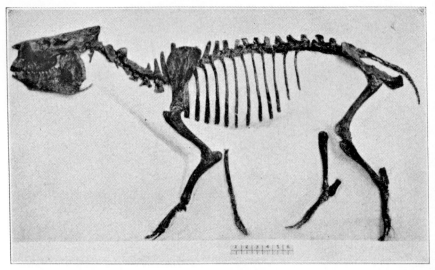

FIG. 225. — Skeleton of †*Ticholeptus*, middle Miocene. (Amherst Coll. Mus.)

change from its Oligocene ancestors. It retained the medium proportions of body, limbs and feet, but had a shortened tail and developed hypsodont, grazing teeth. The Miocene members of this series, in the Deep River and Harrison stages, are several species of †*Mesoreodon*, which differs but little from its Oligocene predecessors, †*Eporeodon* and †*Merycoidodon*, except that it is somewhat larger, has higher-crowned teeth and a much shorter tail. One species, at least, of †*Mesoreodon* of the lower Miocene had the remarkable peculiarity of an ossified thyroid cartilage in the larynx, which would seem to indicate unusual vocal powers, though the larynx is not inflated as it is in the Howling Monkey.

A short-lived side-branch, seemingly, of this central stem is the middle Miocene †*Ticholeptus*, which had acquired high-crowned grinding teeth and also a small vacuity in front of the orbit, where there was a failure of ossification, a feature which recurs in the later members of several †oreodont lines, but in none of the earlier ones.

The common genus of the John Day and upper White River is †*Eporeodon*, which differs from the characteristic middle and lower White River †*Merycoidodon* in being somewhat larger, in possessing inflated auditory bullæ and in having lost the pollex, or first digit of the fore-foot. †*Eporeodon*, and all subsequent genera of the family had four functional toes in each foot, though in the †*Merychyus* line the lateral digits became very slender.

The middle Miocene †*Cyclopidius* and †*Pithecistes* were the terminal members of a fourth tribe of the †oreodonts, comprising a

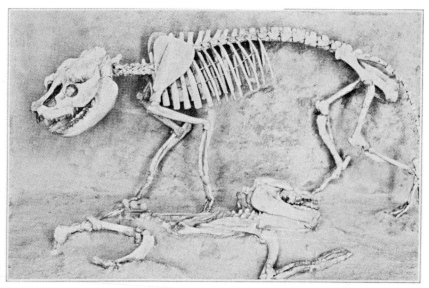

Fig. 226.— Skeleton of supposedly amphibious †oreodont, †*Cyclopidius*, lower Miocene of Neb., Gering stage. (Neb. State Mus.)

succession of small and very small species, which, so far as is yet certain, began in the upper White River beds with the genus †*Leptauchenia*. In these animals the face is much shortened and a relatively immense vacuity on each side reduces the nasal bones to narrow splints. The raised eye-sockets, which project above the level of the forehead, and the very high position of the tubular entrance to the ear, are evidence of an amphibious mode of life; probably also, the nostrils opened upward and were provided with valves, but there is nothing in the skull to demonstrate such a structure of the vanished soft parts. A Hippopotamus, in which the orbits and auditory entrances have the same relative position as in †*Leptauchenia*, can float submerged and almost invisible at a little distance, only the eyes, ears and nostrils showing above the water; probably the same was true of †*Leptauchenia*. In the latter the auditory bullæ are relatively enormous. The molars are high-crowned, while the premolars, incisors and canines are reduced in size, but none is lost. The skeleton is like that of the medium-weight genera of the family, except for a shortened tail.

The genus †*Cyclopidius*, of the lower and middle Miocene, is like †*Leptauchenia* except in having fewer incisors and the canines and

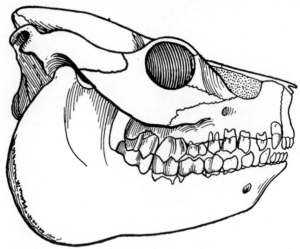

Fig. 227. — Skull of †*Leptauchenia nitida*, upper White River. (Princeton Univ. Mus.)

caniniform premolars are so much reduced that they are but little larger than the incisors. The facial vacuities are even larger. In the middle Miocene †*Pithecistes* the reduction is carried still further.

The animals of this series are common in the upper White River and in the lower and middle Miocene of the Plains, but never have been found in the John Day of Oregon. However, †*Leptauchenia* has been discovered in that part of the Sespé formation of California which corresponds to the lower, unfossiliferous part of the John Day. Below the uppermost White River, not only is †*Leptauchenia* completely unknown, but no immediate ancestors of it have been found.

In the Chadron of Montana, however, occurs the little †*Limnenetes* which, at least, gives a hint as to what the sought-for ancestor must have been. In fact, it may itself have been that ancestor, as has lately (April 1937) been suggested by Thorpe, though the time-interval, from the Chadron to the upper Brulé, may have been too short for so great a change to have taken place. In †*Limnenetes* the teeth are

ow-crowned and, so far as they are preserved, resemble those of a
small species of †*Merycoidodon,* such as †*M. gracilis,* but the skull is
different in several significant respects. The occiput is low, the sagittal crest descending back from the vertex; the orbit is completely
closed behind and is placed as high as it can be without arching up
the frontal. The auditory bullæ are remarkably large and longitudinally elliptical; in size and proportions these bullæ are intermediate

Fig. 228. — †*Leptauchenia nitida,* upper White River. (Restored from a skeleton
in Princeton Univ. Mus.)

between †*Leptauchenia* and †*Merycoidodon.* If not actually an ancestral form, †*Limnenetes* points to the way which was followed in the
evolution of the †*Leptauchenia* tribe.

   The time and place of origin of the †*Merychyus* series are unknown,
though that tribe does not hold quite so isolated a position. Inasmuch
as no member of the †oreodont family has ever been found outside
of North America, the place of origin of these problematical tribes
was almost certainly in some part of this continent, whence they
spread to the Great Plains and the Pacific Coast. As has been repeatedly emphasized, by far the greater part of the continent is *terra
incognita,* so far as Tertiary mammals are concerned; the United
States east of the Missouri River, except Florida, nearly all of Canada,
Newfoundland, Labrador and Greenland, very probably harboured a

considerable number of genera and even families that were never represented in the Great Plains fauna, and, no doubt, many elements of that fauna originated in distant parts of the continent. The unheralded appearance of new groups is almost always to be explained by migration, sometimes from another continent, Asia or South America, but, in all probability, sometimes from parts of North America which are palæontologically unknown.

In the middle and lower White River (lower Brulé and Chadron substages) the chief †oreodont genus is †*Merycoidodon*, the bones of

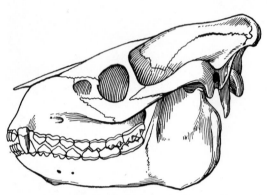

which so far outnumber those of all other mammals, that the collector comes to regard them as a nuisance. This is the main stem of the family and is, happily, as completely known as any Tertiary mammal can be. It is probable that, with the exception of the †*Leptauchenia* tribe, all of the upper Oligocene, Miocene and Pliocene genera

Fig. 229. — Skull of †*Merycoidodon culbertsoni*, middle White River. (From Leidy.)

of the †oreodont family were more or less directly derived from †*Merycoidodon*. The common White River species is †*M. culbertsoni*, an animal somewhat smaller than the Collared Peccary and with a much shorter head; the teeth are set close together, without gaps, and the family peculiarity of the canine-like first lower premolar is already well established; the other premolars are simple and trenchant, except $p \underline{4}$, which is like half a molar. The molars are typically selenodont and composed of four crescents in two transverse pairs, and are very low-crowned, much resembling those of deer. The skull is short-faced, the orbit completely encircled in bone, and in front of each eye-socket is a pit, which probably lodged a facial gland, also as in the modern deer; the auditory bullæ are conspicuously small. The neck, limbs and feet are short, body and tail long; the tail, in particular, is proportionally much longer than in any of the Miocene genera of the family. An especially significant feature is the five-toed manus, the first digit of which, or pollex, is very small, though complete, with metacarpal and two phalanges; it can have been only a dew-claw, without functional importance. This was the first five-toed artiodactyl to be discovered (1882), but several others were subsequently found, none of later geological date than the Oligocene. In the White River beds there is another species of †*Merycoidodon*, †*M. gracilis*, which is hardly half the size of †*M. culbertsoni*, but

FIG. 230. — †*Merycoidodon culbertsoni*, the most abundant of White River †oreodonts. (Restored from a skeleton in Amer. Mus. Nat. Hist.)

otherwise very like it. Several gradations of size between these two extremes are known, but they seem to be, at most, subspecies or varieties.

†Oreodonts have not yet been found in the Duchesne River beds, but it is assuredly only a question of time till they are discovered in that formation, for they existed in the region both before and after the Duchesne stage. Fossils are comparatively rare in those beds and the work of many years will be required before a fairly complete representation of the fauna has been obtained.

The Uinta genus, †*Protoreodon*, is of exceptional interest, for it is so exactly what might have been anticipated as the direct ancestor of †*Merycoidodon*. The functional transference of the lower canines to the incisor series and the replacement, in function, of the canines by the first premolars, had already taken place, but the molars are much more primitive than those of the White River and succeeding genera;

the crescentic cusps are thicker and less complete, plainly indicating their derivation from cone-shaped cusps, and in the upper molars there is a small intermediate conule between the crescents of the anterior pair. This feature recurs in the most ancient and primitive artiodactyl families and it is of particular interest to note that, before the discovery of †*Protoreodon*, the character of its molar teeth was predicted by the late Dr. Max Schlosser, of Munich, one of the ablest students of mammals.

The skull of †*Protoreodon* is much smaller than that of its White River successors, but. is similar in type, though retaining some

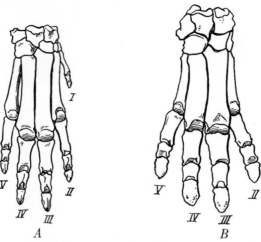

Fig. 231. — Left manus of †oreodonts. *A*, †*Merycoidodon culbertsoni*, White River. *B*, †*Merycochœrus proprius*, upper Miocene.

primitive characteristics. The orbits, for instance, are not entirely closed and there is no glandular pit on the face. The skeleton is incompletely known, but it has been learned that there are five digits in the manus and probably also in the pes.

Nothing has been discovered in the Bridger, or middle Eocene, which can be regarded as assuredly ancestral to this family, though among the imperfectly known artiodactyls of that stage the ancestor sought may be concealed. On the whole, it seems more likely that †*Protoreodon* was derived from an immigrant stock, though it is not yet possible to say whence that migrant stock came. According to Schlosser's opinion, the Old World family of the †bothriodonts was the nearest to the †oreodonts and their allies, the †agriochœrids, but certain structural characters seem to point to a closer relationship with the earliest camels, as was believed by Rütimeyer, and, seemingly, by Leidy.

The course of development followed by the †oreodonts in their long recorded history differed in several respects from that taken by other mammalian families. (1) There was a general increase of bodily size, but no member of the family ever attained more than moderate stature and some of the tribes, notably the †*Leptauchenia* series, were all very small. (2) The upper molars early lost the fifth cusp and there was small subsequent change in the teeth; the †*Merychyus*, †*Metoreodon* and †*Leptauchenia* series independently acquired the high-crowned, persistently grow- ing cheek-teeth and in the last- named tribe the incisors were di- minished in number and the canines reduced to the level of the other teeth. (3) There were more numer- ous and more divergent ramifica- tions of this family than of those previously considered, as four prin- cipal branches may be distin- guished, and in these the main differences concern the skull. The orbit, which is open behind in the

Fig. 232. — †*Protoreodon parvus*, much reduced, upper Eocene of Utah. (Princeton Univ. Mus.)

Uinta †*Protoreodon* is closed in the White River and all succeeding genera. In the †*Merycochœrus* tribe, which includes the largest members of the family, there are two sections, one with very long face (†*Promerycochœrus*), the other with shortened face, and nasal bones so reduced as to indicate a proboscis (†*Merycochœrus*) and culminating in the grotesque †*Pronomotherium*, with its ape-like skull.

In the central line, or main stem, which ended in the Pliocene †*Metoreodon*, there was very little change in the skull, but in the †*Merychyus* branch the head became short and deep and almost bullet-like, and in the †*Leptauchenia* series the skull was much modi- fied in adaptation to an amphibious mode of life and, at the same time, great vacuities appeared in the facial bones. †*Pronomotherium* and †*Cyclopidius* represent the extremes of skull modification within the family.

(4) The †oreodonts of the Uinta Eocene have five digits in the manus and presumably also in the pes; in the genera of the lower White River (Chadron and lower Brulé) there are five digits in the manus, four in the pes and thereafter four in both manus and pes. From that time on, digital reduction ceased and all subsequent species are tetradactyl before and behind. In the †*Merychyus* series,

however, the lateral digits became very slender and, had this tribe persisted through the Pliocene, it would probably have resulted in didactyl genera. (5) Throughout the history of the family the bones of the fore-arm and lower leg are complete and separate.

Family 9. †Agriochœridæ

This family, though one of the strangest and most anomalous groups of hoofed animals, is yet so obviously and closely allied to the †oreodonts, that many palæontologists unite them in one family, giving to each group only subfamily rank. This arrangement has the advantage of expressing the unquestioned fact that †oreodonts and †agriochœrids are much more nearly related to each other than either one is to any other family.

The successive steps of discovery by which these extraordinary animals were brought to light are curiously parallel to those by which the even more grotesque †chalicotheres (see Chap. XV) were made known. First, the disassociated skulls, limbs and feet were found at various times and in different places and were referred to *three different orders* of mammals, for, just as in the case of the †chalicotheres, it seemed impossible that such discordant parts could belong to one and the same animal. In both instances, the enigma was solved by the discovery of skeletons with the bones in their natural connections.

†AGRIOCHŒRIDÆ

†*Agriochœrus*, mid. and up. Olig. †*Mesagriochœrus*, low. Olig. †*Protagriochœrus*, †*Dichobunops*, up. Eoc.

The †agriochœrids had a much shorter known career than the †oreodonts, extending only through the upper Eocene and the whole Oligocene (Uinta to John Day, inclusive) and, consequently, there was no such diversification within the family as there was among the †oreodonts. The genus found in both the John Day and White River stages is †*Agriochœrus*, which, in size, is intermediate between †*Merycoidodon* and †*Eporeodon*. The dental formula is: $i \frac{0}{3}, c \frac{1}{1}, p \frac{4}{4}, m \frac{3}{3}$. The dentition has the same exceptional feature as in the †oreodonts, namely, that the lower canine is incisiform and the first lower premolar caniniform, biting *behind* the upper canine. Behind these tusk-like teeth, above and below, there is a considerable diastema (or toothless gap) which is a conspicuous difference from the †oreodonts, with their teeth in unbroken rows. The upper incisors are very small and are shed in the adult, as in the Pecora, or true ruminants. The molars are made up of four crescents, but these have very much the same peculiar shape as in the †bothriodonts, not at all as in the †oreodonts, which have deer-like molars. This is a very puzzling feature and adds much to the difficulty of fixing the systematic position of these two families. A very uncommon character among artiodactyls and another difference from the †oreodonts, is found in the fourth premolar, which, in the lower jaw, is completely molariform and, in the upper jaw, very nearly so.

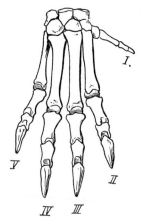

The skull resembles that of †*Merycoidodon*, but is relatively longer, especially the cranial portion, and more slender; the orbit is open behind and there is no preorbital, glandular pit. The neck is short and the trunk long and, in the loins, the backbone becomes very heavy, the lumbar vertebræ strongly suggesting those of the large cats, as though these animals had been powerful leapers. Another likeness to the cats is the very long and heavy tail, which is much

FIG. 233. — Right manus of †*Agriochœrus latifrons*, White River. (From Wortman.)

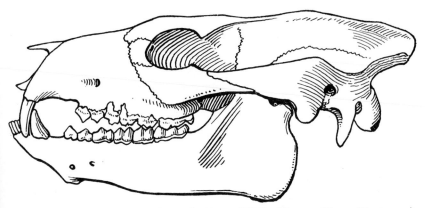

FIG. 234. — Skull of †*Agriochœrus latifrons*, White River. (From Wortman.)

longer and thicker than that of †*Merycoidodon*, and the caudal vertebræ are almost indistinguishable from those of the Leopard.

The limbs are longer than in the †oreodonts and the various bones have a decided likeness to the corresponding ones of carnivores, more especially to those of the cats. Except for the phalanges and particularly the unguals, the feet are not only typically artiodactyl, but also characteristically †oreodont in structure and, as in †*Merycoi-dodon*, there are five digits in the manus, four in the pes. But, on the other hand, the ungual phalanges have been converted into claws, which are sharp but not very large.

This skeleton is a paradoxical assemblage of incongruous characters. Found without the skull, the trunk, tail, limbs and feet

FIG. 235. — †*Agriochœrus antiquus*, White River. (Restored from a skeleton in Amer. Mus. Nat. Hist.)

might easily be, and actually were, mistaken for those of a predaceous animal, though the artiodactyl tarsus should "give us pause." On the contrary, the teeth negative any inference that †*Agriochœrus* could have been carnivorous and show, beyond peradventure, that the diet cannot have consisted of anything but soft vegetable matter. No satisfactory suggestion as to the probable habits of this strange creature has ever been made, the chief difficulty being due to the fact that nothing in the least like it is living to-day.

The Duchesne River beds have yielded a very interesting genus, †*Mesagriochœrus*, the skeleton of which is for the most part unknown. The dentition is intermediate in character between the White River genus and that of the Uinta. The upper incisors are present in full number (i $\frac{3}{3}$) and none of the premolars is molariform, though the fourth one, above and below, has taken the first steps, so to speak, toward the assumption of the molar pattern. The small, unpaired conule, between the anterior pair of crescents, is present in the first and second upper molars, but has been lost from the third.

The Uinta genus, †*Protagriochœrus*, which carries the line one stage farther back, has molars of the unmistakable †agriochœrid type, but these teeth are not so different from those of the Uinta †*Protorcodon* as are the molars of †*Agriochœrus* from those of †*Mery-coidodon;* manifestly, the two types were converging back to a common ancestry in the middle Eocene. In †*Protagriochœrus* all of the upper molars have the unpaired conule and none of the premolars has begun to assume the molar pattern. On the other hand, the substitution of the first lower premolar for the canine has already taken place, and the transformation of hoofs into claws has begun.

A branch of the †agriochœrid stock in the Uinta and perhaps also in the Duchesne is †*Dichobunops*, of which complete skeletons are in the Carnegie Museum of Pittsburgh. This was a long-bodied and long-tailed animal, somewhat smaller than †*Agriochœrus*, of which the five-toed feet were already armed with claws, but the teeth are much more primitive, and the molar cusps are even less †bothriodont than those in †*Protagriochœrus*, in which there is an approximation to †*Protoreodon*.

With the Uinta the backward extension of this line ceases, though the common ancestor of this family and of the †oreodonts may yet be found in the middle Eocene. The problems concerning the origin and relationships of these two families are still unsolved and the failure to find any trace of either family in Mongolia adds to the difficulty of those problems. Another perplexing fact in this connection is the undeniable resemblance of the molars of the †Agriochœridæ to those of the Old World †bothriodonts, and it was this resemblance which led Schlosser to his conclusion that †oreodonts, †agriochœrids, †bothriodonts and †anthracotheres were all closely interrelated, a conclusion which was accepted by Matthew, as against the older opinion of Rütimeyer and apparently of Leidy, that the †oreodonts were connected with the primitive Tylopoda. To the present writer this opinion seems the better founded.

That the likeness in molar-pattern between †*Agriochœrus* and †*Bothriodon* is due rather to convergence than to relationship, is made probable by several considerations. It is not to be doubted that †*Agriochœrus* and the true †oreodonts are nearly related, whether the two groups are treated as subfamilies, or as distinct families, yet the

†oreodont molars have no similarity to the †anthracothere type. In the second place, the Uinta genera †*Protagriochœrus* and †*Protoreodon* have molar teeth which are much more nearly alike than are those of their White River descendants, †*Agriochœrus* and †*Merycoidodon*. Unless, therefore, the apparent connection of †*Protagriochœrus* and †*Agriochœrus* is illusory, the molar-pattern of the latter was independently acquired in North America and not derived from an ancestry common to the †anthracotheres and the †agriochœrids.

If the supposed affinity between †*Agriochœrus* and †*Bothriodon* is actually more apparent than real, one formidable objection to the inclusion of †oreodonts and †agriochœrids in the suborder Tylopoda will be removed.

Schlosser's views as to the relationships of mammalian groups were determined almost entirely by the teeth, ignoring the fact that similar molar patterns have, in some instances, been independently acquired by unrelated groups. That this happened comparatively rarely, we have every reason to believe, but there is very strong evidence that it did occasionally happen. That the likeness in molar form between the †agriochœrids and †bothriodonts is an example of such convergent development, is made probable by the fact that the more ancient members of the two groups are less alike than the later ones. In the Uinta stage †*Protoreodon* and †*Protagriochœrus* have molars which are more nearly similar than those of their White River descendants, and †*Protagriochœrus* is less like †*Bothriodon* than is †*Agriochœrus*. In other words, as the †agriochœrids are traced back in time they become less like the †bothriodonts and more like the †oreodonts, which would not be true were they more nearly related to the former. In a paper published in 1899, the writer included †oreodonts and †agriochœrids in the Tylopoda and it is only out of deference to the general opinion of palæontologists that that classification is not here repeated.

Section A. Non-ruminantia

It may very well turn out to be true that Rütimeyer's division of the artiodactyls into the two primary groups of the Selenodonta, those with crescentic molar-cusps, and the Bunodonta, those with conical cusps, best expresses the natural relationships of the families. The division here adopted, of ruminant and non-ruminant sections, is nearly, but not quite, the same thing. The doubt is concerned with the three extinct families of the †oreodonts, †agriochœrids and †bothriodonts, which have more or less selenodont molars and yet may be most nearly related to the non-ruminants. Were there any living artiodactyls remotely like those three families, the problem would be much simpler.

Most of the non-ruminant section is composed of extinct families, only the hippopotamuses and the swine (i.e. Flower's suborder Suina) are represented in the modern world.

Suborder II. Hyodonta. Swine-like Animals

Not at all improbably this is an artificial rather than a natural group, for the two families which compose it have little in common except the character of the molar teeth. The only existing American members of the suborder are the peccaries.

Family 4. Tagassuidæ. Peccaries

The peccaries of to-day, or "Wild Texas Swine," range from New Mexico and Texas to Patagonia, but in the Pleistocene they extended all over North America from the Atlantic to the Pacific. They are but distantly related to the true swine of the Old World, which, so far as is known, never entered the Western Hemisphere. In many respects the peccaries are more advanced and specialized than the true swine, though far less diversified than the latter. In the extreme complexity of the molar teeth, on the other hand, the African Wart-hog (*Phacochœrus æthiopicus*) greatly surpasses all other artiodactyls and rivals the true elephants in this respect. In size also, the peccaries are inferior to the swine.

TAGASSUIDÆ

Tagassu. Pleist. to Rec. N. and S. A. †*Platygonus*, †*Mylohyus*, Pleist. †*Prosthennops*, up. Mio. †*Pediohyus*, †*Desmathyus*, low. Mio. †*Thinohyus*. up. Olig. †*Perchœrus*, mid. Olig.

There are, at present, two well-defined species of the peccaries, which are, by some naturalists, included in one genus, *Tagassu*, while others recognize a second, *Pecari*. The Collared Peccary (*T. tajacu*) is rather smaller, has a shorter snout, and ranges from Texas to Argentina, while the White-lipped Peccary (*T. labiatus*), which has a white lower jaw, is somewhat larger, much longer-snouted and more pugnacious and has a less extensive range, seldom occurring north of Guatemala, or south of Paraguay. Different as they are in habits and appearance, the two species interbreed freely in captivity; both are much smaller than the Wild Boar of Europe and Asia.

In *Tagassu* the dental formula is: $i \frac{2}{3}$, $c \frac{1}{1}$, $p \frac{3}{3}$, $m \frac{3}{3} \times 2 = 38$;

the median upper incisor (i $\underline{1}$) is much enlarged and the lateral (i $\underline{3}$) has been suppressed, as has also the first premolar (1) above and below. The molar teeth are quadritubercular, with four principal, conical cusps in two transverse pairs; numerous, very small cuspules are around and between the main cusps. The last lower premolar (p $\overline{4}$) has acquired the form of a molar and the last upper one (p $\underline{4}$) is partially molariform, as is also true of †*Agriochœrus* (p. 373), but such a premolar is otherwise very rare among artiodactyls. In the true swine of the Old World (family Suidæ) the molars are much larger than in the peccaries and bear many wart-like cusps, larger and smaller, which are seldom arranged in any definite pattern and the premolars are all smaller and simpler than the molars.

The canines of the peccaries display a very characteristic difference from those of the Suidæ, in which the large upper tusk, which is but partially covered with enamel, is strongly curved outward and upward and finally inward; the lower tusk, likewise incompletely covered with enamel, is directed outward and upward, curved in almost a semi-circle. Together the tusks make terrible weapons. In the peccaries, as far back as their history can be traced, the tusks are much smaller, vertical and straight, without any curvature; they are completely sheathed in enamel, except as that has been removed by mutual abrasion, which makes them almost needle-sharp. Small as they are, these tusks are nearly as formidable weapons as the much larger ones of the Boar; and even the great cats, the Jaguar and the Puma, shun an encounter with peccaries.

The bones of the limbs and feet, though remaining short, show a much higher degree of specialization than do those of the Old World swine. The fore-arm bones (ulna and radius) are co-ossified and the fibula is very slender, though separate from the tibia. In the fore-foot the two median metacarpals (III and IV) are stout and the two laterals (II and V) are very slender, much more so than in the true swine, but retain all the phalanges. In the hind-foot there are but two functional digits, the third and fourth, the metatarsals of which fuse into a cannon-bone; the second digit is greatly reduced and the fifth has been lost. Except in other genera of this family, no member of the Hyodonta has a cannon-bone.

Peccaries have the peculiar snout of the true pigs, a hairless, cartilaginous disc, pierced by two conspicuous circular and terminal nostrils, a structure which is well adapted for rooting up the soil. The stomach is complex, approximating that of a ruminant and very different from the simple stomach of the Old World pigs.

Though gregarious, peccaries are rare fossils as far back in time as they can be traced, except for a comparatively brief period in the Pleistocene. Not improbably, this rarity was occasioned by forest-living habits, for, as was previously pointed out, forest-dwellers generally escape fossilization.

In the Pleistocene, peccaries were ranging all over the Americas, and in North America there were three distinct, but not very different

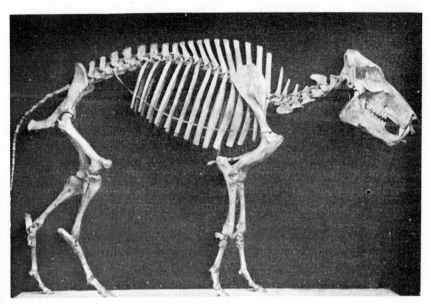

Fig. 236. — Skeleton of North American peccary, †*Platygonus leptorhynchus*, Pleistocene of U. S. (Amer. Mus. Nat. Hist.)

types. The commonest of these (†*Platygonus*) inhabited the Great Plains as well as the forested regions, and their skeletons have been found together in bands. The genus †*Platygonus* comprised larger animals than either of the existing species of peccary and had much longer legs, standing nearly twice as high as *Tagassu*. The molar teeth are of particular interest, for they reproduce a type that has been independently acquired many times and in groups as widely separated as tapirs and kangaroos. These teeth have each two high, transverse crests, formed by the coalescence of the inner and outer conical tubercles. Though having, thus, a more advanced and specialized type of molar than *Tagassu*, †*Platygonus* retained the simple premolars. The same type of grinding teeth occurred among the true swine in the genus †*Listriodon*, of the French Miocene, which has the upturned tusks so characteristic of the Suidæ. In †*Platy-*

gonus there are cannon-bones in the fore-feet as well as in the hind, and the lateral digits have been suppressed. Though †*Platygonus* was more advanced and modernized than are the Recent peccaries and might have been expected to outlive them, it failed to do so notwithstanding.

A second tribe of peccaries culminated and came to an end in the Pleistocene genus †*Mylohyus*, which is very much less common as a

FIG. 237. — Restoration of †*Platygonus leptorhynchus*, drawn from skeleton in Fig. 236.

fossil than †*Platygonus*. In this genus the upper incisors are greatly reduced and may be altogether wanting; the molars are tubercular and the premolars are more molar-like than in *Tagassu*.

The third series is that of *Tagassu* itself, which is found in the upper Miocene and Pliocene of North America and the Pleistocene of South America. Whether it withdrew altogether from the northern continent because of unfavourable climatic conditions and afterward returned as far north as Texas, or whether it has not yet been found in the Pleistocene of the United States, are doubtful questions.

Each of the three series may be traced back to the seemingly common ancestor, †*Desmathyus*, of the Gering (base of the lower

Miocene). The forerunner of *Tagassu* is †*Pediohyus*, of the upper Harrison (top of the lower Miocene), which has a full complement of incisors, though $i^{\underline{1}}$ is enlarged and $i^{\underline{3}}$ reduced. The first premolar, above and below, has been lost and the other premolars are simple, though the fourth one ($p\ 4$) is beginning to take on the molar pattern. This genus is intermediate in character between *Tagassu* and †*Desmathyus*.

The Pleistocene †*Mylohyus* is preceded by †*Prosthennops*, of the upper Miocene, in which the upper incisors have been reduced and $i^{\underline{3}}$

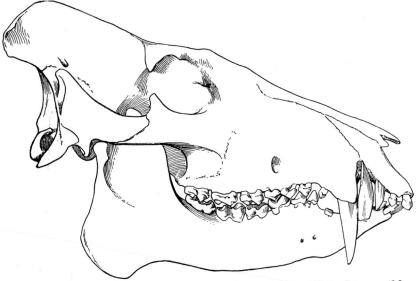

Fig. 238. — Skull of ancestral peccary, †*Perchœrus probus*, White River. (Mus. State Sch. Mines, S. D.)

lost, as has also the first premolar in each jaw, and the third and fourth premolars are molariform. †*Prosthennops*, in turn, would seem to have been derived from †*Desmathyus*, in which all three lines converge. In this genus there has been no loss of teeth, except for the first lower premolar ($p_{\overline{1}}$) but the first upper incisor ($i^{\underline{1}}$) is enlarged and the third ($i^{\underline{3}}$) reduced, a first step toward the conditions found in the three Pleistocene genera, all of which have lost $i^{\underline{3}}$, and †*Mylohyus* has lost all the upper incisors.

The John Day peccary is †*Thinohyus;* it has lost no teeth, and all the premolars are simple. Back to and including †*Thinohyus*, all the genera have a flat-topped cranium, without sagittal crest, and a notch in the maxillary, into which the lower canine fits, and behind it the alveolus of the upper canine forms a prominent projection. In the White River genus, †*Perchœrus*, there is no notch though the tusks are large and have the bayonet-like shape characteristic of the family. †*Perchœrus* is an unmistakable, though a primitive peccary, and its skull differs in many details from those of the genera which followed it in time. Most important of these differences is the less capacious brain-cavity, the consequent presence of a sagittal crest and the elevation of the cranium high above the level of the teeth. Fragmentary skeletons indicate that †*Perchœrus* had four functional digits in each foot, without cannon-bones. Two well-defined species of this rare animal have been found in the White River beds, one of which, †*P. probus*, though smaller than a modern Collared Peccary, is much larger than the other.

As yet, the line of peccary development cannot be carried beyond the White River, though the genus †*Helohyus* from the middle and lower Eocene may represent an ancestor of the family, and perhaps was descended from an immigrant genus allied to the European †*Palæochœrus*, which, in that case, would be the common ancestor of the peccaries and the true swine. That the two families are related is hardly open to question.

SUBORDER III. †**Ancodonta**

As proposed by Matthew, this suborder contained the †oreodonts and †agriochœrids, which have been removed. The suborder is pre-eminently Old World and, more particularly, European, only one of the families extending its range into North America and that for a comparatively brief period, Oligocene and lower Miocene. It has not yet been found in the Duchesne River, or in the John Day, being one of several groups which might be expected to occur in the latter formation but have not yet been found there. In many ways the John Day fauna is a puzzling one and it is very difficult to fit it into the Oligocene-Miocene succession. Conditions of living were, almost certainly, very different from those of the Great Plains region, perhaps because Oregon was then a heavy forest.

Family 5. †*Anthracotheriidæ*

The latest known American occurrence of this family is a fragment of an upper jaw, containing two molars, found in the upper Harrison beds. So far as it goes, this specimen cannot be separated from the Indian genus †*Merycopotamus*, but it almost certainly belongs to the American †*Arretotherium*. The characteristic feature of these teeth is that they have the structure and appearance of the upper molars of †*Bothriodon*, but have only four crescents, the unpaired, antero-intermediate cusps being absent. The earliest and most primitive artiodactyls had upper molars with four main cusps and two intermediate conules. In all the series of artiodactyls which persisted into the upper Miocene, or later, the intermediate conules have been lost, and †*Merycopotamus* and †*Arretotherium* are the four-cusped †bothriodonts.

†ANTHRACOTHERIIDÆ

†*Arretotherium*, low. Mio.   †*Bothriodon*, †*Octacodon*, †*Heptacodon*, mid. Olig.

This typically Old World family spread to North America in the Oligocene epoch, making its first recorded appearance in the Chadron. It continued through the whole White River stage, but has not yet been found in the John Day. It reappears in the lower Miocene of the Gering stage and continued through the Harrison, in the upper division of which is the last known occurrence of the family in America. Except in the latest genera, the Indian †*Merycopotamus* and the North American †*Arretotherium*, the upper molars have five cusps, the unpaired one being the small conule between the antero-external and antero-internal crescents. In the two genera named the conule has been lost, so that the upper molar crown carries four crescents. There can be no reasonable doubt that this reduction took place independently in Asia and America.

Determinable remains of †*Arretotherium* occur in the upper Harrison, but much the best-preserved material has been found in the lowest Miocene (Gering stage); this genus represents the final step in the evolution of the American forms, for there was considerable diversification of the group after it had established itself in the Western Hemisphere. The principal American genus, which runs through the whole White River Stage, has the European name of †*Bothriodon*, different species of which characterize the three substages of the White River.

The differences between the several genera and species of the family, which existed in North America during the White River age, are in the molar teeth and, more especially, in the shape of the skull; the skeleton, so far as is known, is very uniform throughout the family. The most complete remains that have as yet been found are those of †*B. brachyrhynchus*, which were collected in the channel-sandstones of the upper Brulé. This and other species of the genus found in the same sandstones probably belonged to the upland, or forest fauna, which characterizes the "†*Protoceras* Channels." Even in this relatively short-snouted species, the skull is elongate, with slender, tapering muzzle, and the head must have had something of an equine look, though, of course, there is no relationship between †bothriodonts and horses. The neck is short and the body very long

Fig. 239. — †*Bothriodon brachyrhynchus*, upper White River stage. (Restored from a skeleton in Princeton Univ. Mus.)

proportionally; the tail is not known and its length can only be conjectured; limbs and feet are short and, aside from the head, the size and proportions are very much like those of †*Merycochœrus* (see p. 360). Such a likeness might be considered evidence of affinity and as justifying referring the †oreodonts to the †Ancodonta, as Matthew and Schlosser did. As already pointed out (p. 376) that reference may possibly be confirmed by fuller information, but similarity of proportions and general appearance is no evidence of relationship. The early and primitive members of nearly all the families, both artiodactyl and perissodactyl, had very similar proportions, presumably a heritage from their common ancestors, the extinct order of the †Condylarthra. Another very primitive character is the five-toed manus, in which the pollex is much shorter than the other digits and may have been only a dew-claw.

Another species, †*B. rostratus*, is remarkable for the great elongation of the muzzle and there may have been several species of the
long-snouted kind, some of which attained altogether grotesque
proportions, but there is a great deal of individual variation and a
much larger suite of skulls must be obtained before these supposed
species can be delimited.

Another series of differences is to be observed in the pattern of
the upper molars, especially in the size of the valley between the
two external crescents, and in the number and prominence of the
buttresses, or styles, on the outer side of the crown. The genera
†*Heptacodon* and †*Octacodon* are predicated on these differences.

The †bothriodonts are unquestionably an Old World group that
gained but a brief residence in this continent; their distribution in
the Eastern Hemisphere was chiefly Oligocene.

Suborder I. †Palæodonta

These ancient and primitive artiodactyls, none of which persisted beyond the Oligocene and most of which were Eocene, or
even Paleocene in date, could not be included in any of Flower's
suborders, which were devised for the reception of Recent artiodactyls only, and ignored the extinct groups. The fossil remains of
this suborder are mostly very fragmentary and incomplete, yet
there is enough to show how very primitive they are and how far
removed from all existing families. Not at all improbably, the suborder is an artificial group of unrelated genera and may, on the finding of better material, require a rearrangement of the families.
Eocene artiodactyls are extremely rare as fossils in America, which
is in decided contrast to conditions in the Eocene of Europe, in which
they are far more abundant and varied and in a much better state
of preservation. In his revision of the Eocene Bunodonta Sinclair
recognized, in addition to the †achænodonts (†*Parahyus*) and possible ancestral peccaries (†*Helohyus*), eight genera and twelve species
in the middle and lower Eocene of Wyoming, but some of these,
because of their very fragmentary state, are but doubtfully referable
to the Artiodactyla. All of the genera except †*Parahyus* are included
in the European family †Dichobunidæ.

Family 1. †*Leptochœridæ*

This family, which contains but two genera, †*Leptochœrus* and
†*Stibarus*, both from the White River, has long been an enigma.
First named by Leidy in 1853, †*Leptochœrus* (or "small pig")

was known only from a few enigmatical teeth until 1894, when Marsh figured the dentition and, on account of its peculiarity, proposed the formation of a new family for the genus.

The dental formula is: $i \frac{?}{?}$, $c \frac{1}{1}$, $p \frac{4}{4}$, $m \frac{3}{3}$. The upper molars are exceedingly primitive in character and are but little removed from those of †*Diacodexis*, of the Eocene, one of the most ancient of American artiodactyls. These teeth are tritubercular and trigonodont, consisting of two external and one internal cusps in triangular arrangement, with two minute, intermediate conules. The premolars are thick and of conical form. In the allied †*Stibarus* the premolars have high, acute points and trenchant edges; the crowns are very much extended in the antero-posterior direction in a manner that is reminiscent of several other Eocene and Oligocene families, such as the European †Xiphodontidæ and, in America, such primitive camels as †*Protylopus* and †*Poëbrotherium*, and the strange †*Leptomeryx—* †*Protoceras* series.

The relationships of †*Leptochœrus* seem to be closest with the European family of the †Dichobunidæ, to which Sinclair refers almost all the genera of the American middle and lower Eocene and, eventually, it may be desirable to include †*Leptochœrus* in the same family, but, for the present at least, it seems more prudent to keep the two groups separate. Possibly †*Leptochœrus* is a descendant of the lower Eocene †*Diacodexis*, but the long hiatus between the Wasatch and the White River makes it seem more probable that the genus is of immigrant origin, derived from some Asiatic member of the †Dichobunidæ.

Family 2. †Dichobunidæ

To this European family appear to belong most of the artiodactyl genera of the American middle and lower Eocene, though some of these are of most uncertain position and relationships, because of the very fragmentary state of the fossils upon which the genera are founded; indeed, certain ones may not be artiodactyls at all.

†DICHOBUNIDÆ

†*Wasatchia*, †*Bunophorus*, low. Eoc. †*Lophiohyus*, †*Homacodon*, †*Nanomeryx*, ?†*Sarcolemur*, ?†*Microsus*, mid. Eoc. †*Diacodexis*, low. Eoc.

†*Sarcolemur* and †*Microsus* are of doubtful position and have been referred to the Primates. Except †*Diacodexis*, the genera listed

in this family have quadritubercular molars, with four conical cusps and intermediate conules; the premolars are of compressed-conical shape, trenchant and sharp-pointed, except that $p^{\underline{4}}$ usually has a relatively large internal cusp. †*Lophiohyus*, which is better known than most of the genera, is the largest of the definitely known Eocene artiodactyls, having a skull of nine or ten inches in length; skull and teeth have a suggestively peccary-like appearance, though the genus can hardly have been ancestral to the White River †*Perchœrus* because of the greatly reduced incisors.

A very interesting genus is the Bridger †*Homacodon*, of which the material is more complete than that of any other Bridger artiodactyl. This was a little creature, somewhat larger than a rabbit, with quadritubercular teeth that appear to have the beginnings of the selenodont pattern. In the upper molars the cusps are not conical, but rather pyramidal and in the lower molars the external cusps already have a crescentic shape, as has also the inner cusp of the upper fourth premolar. A selenodont type of dentition might easily have been derived from that of †*Homacodon*. The brain-case is more capacious than in most middle Eocene mammals and the cerebral hemispheres have longitudinal convolutions; the postorbital constriction is very far forward, almost immediately behind the orbits, which are widely open and without postorbital processes. The auditory bullæ were either not ossified, or not fixed to the skull. The feet have four functional digits each, probably five in the manus. It is entirely possible that †*Homacodon* may have been the earliest of the camel series. On the other hand, the outburst of at least four different selenodont families in the Uinta seems too sudden to be accounted for save by immigration.

The most ancient known artiodactyl, †*Diacodexis*, of the lower Eocene, should not, perhaps, be included in the †Dichobunidæ, because it has the more primitive trigonodont and tritubercular upper molars. The feet probably have five toes each, but this is not certain, and the femur has the third trochanter, the only instance known among artiodactyls.

Family 3. †Entelodontidæ. †Giant Pigs

The systematic position of these most curious and long extinct animals is a matter of doubt. Though it is customary to include them in the same suborder as the peccaries and swine, the relationship is not close and may be very remote.

†ENTELODONTIDÆ

†*Dinohyus*, low. Mio. †*Boöchœrus*, up. Olig. †*Archæotherium*, †*Pelonax*, †*Megachœrus*, †*Scaptohyus*, mid. Olig. †*Achænodon*, up. and mid. Eoc. †*Brachyhyops*, up. Eoc. †*Parahyus*, low. Eoc.

The latest American representative of the family, †*Dinohyus*, occurs in the Harrison (lower Miocene). Except the Hippopotamus,

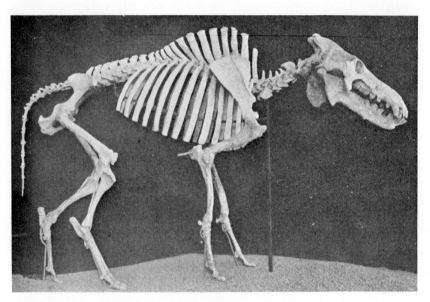

FIG. 240. — Skeleton of †*Archæotherium mortoni*, female, lower White River of Weld Co., Col. (Col. Mus. Nat. Hist.)

this was the largest of known suillines and, though less massive, was much taller, standing six feet or more in height at the shoulder. In the dentition and all parts of the skeleton, these great beasts are peculiar and aberrant and differ widely from other mammalian families. The bluntly pointed incisors and the very heavy, though not very long, canines form together a terrible lacerating apparatus and there is evidence that these animals were savage fighters. Seen from the front, these simply conical teeth have a reptilian rather than a mammalian appearance. The premolars are of a simple, compressed-conical form, much extended antero-posteriorly and in shape more carnivorous than herbivorous, though they are too thick to be effectively trenchant. These teeth are well-spaced apart in the very long jaws. The molar teeth are almost the only pig-like features in the whole structure of the animal; they are relatively small and essentially quadritubercular and the crowns are covered with thick, coarsely wrinkled enamel. The skull is immensely elongate, especially the facial region in front of the eyes, while the brain-case is so ridiculously small as to give the skull a crocodile-like aspect, when seen from above. Evidently these great creatures were inordinately stupid, in this respect rivalling the large quadrupeds of the Oligocene and Eocene, which had astonishingly small brains. Beneath each orbit

Fig. 241. — †"Giant Pig," †*Archæotherium ingens*, lower White River, Chadron substage. (Restored from a skeleton in Princeton Univ. Mus.)

is a long, plate-like descending process from the jugal, or malar bone, which is longer and heavier in the male. On the under side of the lower jaw are two pairs of bony knobs, one on each side of the chin, the others beneath the third and fourth premolars; these knobs also are larger and more prominent in the male. The function of the knobs and the jugal flanges is entirely unknown; no one has succeeded even in making a plausible guess as to what the uses of these very exceptional structures can have been. The orbits are completely encircled in bone, a rarity in the suborder.

The neck is short and thick, the trunk is moderately elongate and the tail short. The spines of the anterior dorsal vertebræ are exceedingly long and must have produced a conspicuous hump at

the shoulders in the living animal, and in the lumbar and posterior
dorsal regions the articulations between successive vertebræ are
exceedingly complex, even more so than in other artiodactyls, in all
of which these articulations are more complicated than in other
mammals, the American Edentata excepted.

The limbs are long and give a rather stilted look to the skeleton
with its shallow thorax. The fore-arm bones (ulna and radius) are co-

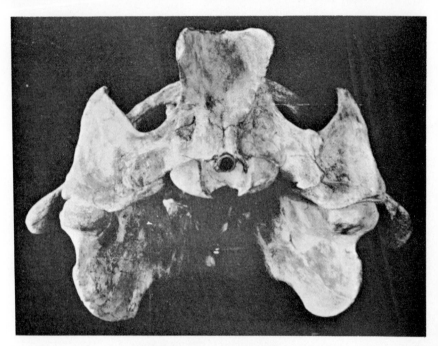

Fig. 242. — Skull of †*Archæotherium mortoni;* old male, from behind, lower
White River of Weld Co., Col., Chadron substage. (Col. Mus. Nat. Hist.)

ossified, but the tibia and fibula remain separate; the feet have but
two toes each, the third and fourth of the original five, though nodular
vestiges of the second and fifth remain to show the derivation of
these animals from a four- or five-toed ancestry. Cannon-bones are
not present in either manus or pes. In proportion to the size of the
skeleton, as a whole, the hoof-bones (ungual phalanges) are surprisingly small, which suggests that the weight was borne, partially at
least, upon elastic pads.

The line of the †entelodonts extended back to the lower White
River with very little change, except in size. In the John Day and
uppermost White River the species are very large, though somewhat
inferior to †*Dinohyus* in stature. In the middle and lower White River

the genus †*Archæotherium* is one of the commoner fossils and includes rather small and fairly large animals in such bewildering variety that it has not yet been feasible to arrange them in well-defined species.   In the uppermost White River beds are found some very large †entelodonts, which have been named †*Pelonax,* †*Megachœrus* and †*Scaptohyus.*

The European genus †*Entelodon,* from which the family is named, is so like the American †*Archæotherium* that they are frequently

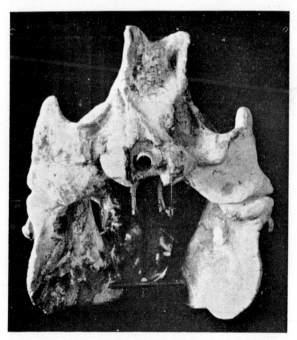

Fig. 243. — Skull of †*Archæotherium mortoni,* young female, from behind. (Col. Mus. Nat. Hist.)

merged. Both in Europe and in North America the line can be followed only into the lower Oligocene and nothing has yet been found in older formations which can be taken as ancestral to the Oligocene and Miocene genera. In all probability the ancestors sought lived in central or northeastern Asia and, at the beginning of Oligocene time, spread westward into Europe, eastward into North America. It is an interesting fact that †entelodont remains have been found in the marine Miocene of New Jersey, one of the rare occurrences of Tertiary mammals on the Atlantic seaboard, north of Florida.

Several restorations of different genera of the family have been made by various artists and some of them, including that figured in the former edition of this work (Fig. 137, p. 260), give the characteristic discoidal snout of the pigs and the peccaries, and no one can say that this procedure is not justified. On the other hand, the †entelodonts are so far removed from the pigs in their general structure, that reasoning from one to the other is of questionable validity. The restoration of †*Dinohyus* published by the late Messrs. Holland and Peterson has an entirely different type of muzzle, with lateral

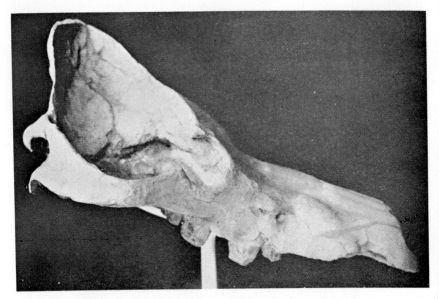

Fig. 244. — Skull, side view, of †*Achænnedon uintensis*, upper Eocene, Uinta. (Field Mus. Nat. Hist.)

nostrils and no terminal disc, and this may be nearer to the truth, but who shall decide?

It is not probable that the White River †entelodonts had much reason to fear the Carnivora of that age, but they must have fought savagely among themselves, especially the males in the breeding season. In a skeleton mounted in the Princeton Museum one of the ribs is broken and that the injury was inflicted on the living animal is proved by the large callus growths on the broken ends, but the pieces did not knit. It must have required a terrific blow to fracture so stout a bone, attached so as to yield elastically before reaching the breaking point. Many skulls show marks of teeth.

The whole Eocene of North America from the Wasatch to the Uinta, inclusive, had a series of pig-like genera, called the †achæno-donts, or "†short-faced pigs," which, though related to the †entelodonts, cannot well have been ancestral to them. The genus †*Achæ-nodon* of the Uinta and Bridger stages has teeth very much like those of †*Archæotherium*, but has one less premolar in the lower jaw, and the teeth are closely crowded, without interspaces, the jaws being short. The cranium is long and rises steeply above the face at the forehead, and the face is short; the orbit is open behind and this, together with the absence of the long infraorbital processes and the knobs of the lower jaw, give to the skull an appearance which is very different from that of †*Archæ-otherium* and far less grotesque. Very little is known of the skeleton of †*Achænodon*.

The newly discovered †*Brachy-hyops* (Fig. 245) was obtained by the Carnegie Museum, Pittsburgh, in the Uinta of Wyoming and described by Dr. E. H. Colbert, of the American Museum, to whom I am indebted for the fig-ures. The skull, without lower jaw, is in very perfect preserva-tion, but unfortunately the teeth are so worn that no pattern is discernible, and therefore the sys-tematic position of the genus is

FIG. 245. — Skull of †*Brachyhyops*, side and top views, upper Eocene, of Beaver Divide, Wyo., Uinta. (From Colbert.)

somewhat doubtful. It appears, however, to resemble †*Achænodon* and is provisionally included in the †entelodont family. It is the skull of a small animal, measuring but six inches in length, and its peculiar shape shows that it cannot be referred to any known genus. The orbit is closed behind, an unusual feature in the Uinta and the cranium, which is relatively more capacious than in other members of the family, has a very strange appearance, owing to the broad sagittal area with raised and thickened borders. Along the median line of the sagittal area runs the remnant of the sagittal crest, which is so low that it is no more than a *linea aspera*, yet is very conspicuous. In all the other genera of this group, the sagittal crest is very high because of the small brain-case and the powerful jaws, which require large areas for muscular attachment.

The lower Eocene member of the series is †*Parahyus*, which is smaller than †*Achænodon*, but otherwise like it, so far as the lower jaw is concerned, the only part of the former yet known. It would be necessary to merge the two genera, were it not for the great improbability of the same artiodactyl genus' occurring in the Wasatch and the Uinta. This †short-faced series must also have been of immigrant origin, but reaching North America at a very much earlier date than the †long-faced group. No doubt the two series are branches of the same ancestral stem; another wave of migration, or, more accurately, of spreading, brought in the true and typical †entelodonts early in the Oligocene, perhaps even in the Duchesne River stage, though they have not yet been found in that formation.

CHAPTER XV

HISTORY OF THE PERISSODACTYLA

I. HIPPOMORPHA

Existing perissodactyls are but a declining remnant of a once dominant order, which was abundantly represented throughout Tertiary Arctogæa (see Chapter VIII) but entered South America at a late period. The combined area of North America and eastern Asia was the scene of the principal perissodactyl development, but Europe also was well supplied and had certain families not known, or but scantily represented elsewhere.

At the present time, only three families of perissodactyls are in existence, horses, rhinoceroses and tapirs, only the last one of which occurs in the Western Hemisphere and that is restricted to Central and South America. In proportions and general appearance, the three families have little in common; that tapirs and rhinoceroses should belong to the same order is not surprising: Cuvier included them both in his Pachydermata, but horses seem to be as different as possible from both of the other families. A study of the anatomy, however, reveals such a fundamental likeness among them all and such radical differences from all other hoofed animals, that their reference to the same ordinal group is obviously the only course to take. In all existing perissodactyls the premolars, except the first one above and below ($p \frac{1}{1}$), have assumed the pattern of molars.

As so much importance is attached to the molar teeth in the subdivision of the Perissodactyla, something should be said concerning the different types of tooth-construction within the order. All the types were ultimately derived from the pattern seen in the earliest horses (†*Hyracotherium*) in which an upper molar-crown consists of four conical cusps, two external and two internal, the outer ones forming a partial wall. Between each transverse pair is a minute conule, very much smaller than the principal cusps, but important nevertheless. From this primitive plan several different types were formed by modification, in all of which the two outer cusps extended anteroposteriorly until they coalesced into a more continuous wall. In the rhinoceroses this outer wall is formed almost entirely by the extension of the postero-external cusp, the antero-external one lengthening but little. In all the other perissodactyl groups, families and superfamilies, the two external cusps are of nearly or quite equal size. In the post-Eocene horses, and in the †palæotheres, †brontotheres, and †chalicotheres, the external cusps are concave and give to the lower free and trenchant edge of the wall, a characteristically W-shaped outline. In the tapirs the two external cusps are of equal size and convex form, and in the †Hyrachyidæ the antero-external cusp is convex and the postero-external one is concave, a type from which both tapir and rhinoceros molars may have been derived.

Except in one group, the †brontotheres, transverse crests are developed through the extension of the intermediate conules and their junction with the internal cusps and, eventually, with the outer wall. Throughout the history of the †brontothere family these inner cusps retain their original conical shape and the intermediate conules are suppressed, no transverse crests forming.

In the tapirs, †hyrachyids and †lophiodonts the lower molars have two simple, straight, transverse crests and in all the other families the lower molars have the bicrescentic pattern, one crescent behind the other. The rhinoceroses have the crescents incomplete and their lower molars are, in a sense, intermediate between those of tapirs, on one side, and those of horses and †brontotheres, on the other.

The foramina of the skull, or perforations of the bones, by which the nerves and blood-vessels leave and enter the cranium, have a characteristic arrangement, different from that found in other orders of hoofed animals. The femur, with rare exceptions, has the third trochanter; the number of digits in each foot is usually odd, 1 or 3, but may be 4, as in the front foot of the tapirs. The significant character is that the median plane of the foot bisects the third digit, which is symmetrical in itself, while the second and fourth digits, each asymmetrical, together form a symmetrical pair. The additional digit, when present, is always the fifth, never the first, for no five-toed perissodactyl has yet been found. A foot of the perissodactyl type, in which the plane of symmetry passes through and bisects the third, or median digit, is said to be *mesaxonic*, and the term Mesaxonia is sometimes used for the order instead of Perissodactyla. In certain very heavy perissodactyls, such as the later †brontotheres and †metamynodonts, the toes of the fore-foot approach the artiodactyl, or paraxonic symmetry.

Especially characteristic of this order is the form of the astragalus and calcaneum, or ankle- and heel-bone. The astragalus has a single, deeply grooved trochlea, into which the lower end of the tibia fits, and it extends over the whole width of the calcaneum, so as to exclude that bone from any contact with the fibula. Distally, the astragalus rests almost entirely upon the navicular, having but a limited bearing upon the cuboid, though there are some exceptions to this statement, especially among the heavy and massive animals, in which the astragalus extends over more of the cuboid. The calcaneum does not articulate with the fibula and its distal end covers most of the cuboid.

This brief description includes the more important characteristics which are common to all perissodactyls and which differentiate them from other ungulate mammals. There are many other such features which it would be superfluous to mention.

The subjoined table gives the suborders, superfamilies and families of the Perissodactyla and it is advisable to include certain European families which are indicated by brackets.

The classification adopted will depend upon the relative importance given to the teeth, on the one hand, and the skeleton, on the other. As already pointed out, too exclusive a dependence upon the dentition has more than once led to unfortunate errors. In the scheme of classification here adopted, the Perissodactyla are first divided into two suborders: (1) the Chelopoda, or normal perissodactyls with hoofs and (2) the †Ancylopoda, or aberrant perissodactyls with claws. Judging from the dentition alone, such a primary division would be inadmissible, for the †Ancylopoda, despite their altogether exceptional feet, have teeth not unlike those of certain families with feet of normal type. Just what this likeness signifies, will remain uncertain until the course of evolutionary development of the †ancylopodan teeth shall have been made out.

Aside from the extraordinary and aberrant †Ancylopoda, the normal hoofed families group themselves naturally into two series, (1) the horse-†palæothere-†brontothere lines, and (2) the rhinoceros-tapir-†lophiodont lines, as was first suggested by Dr. H. E. Wood.

Order **PERISSODACTYLA.**
   Suborder I. **Chelopoda,** Hoofed Perissodactyls.
      Section A. HIPPOMORPHA.
         Superfamily a. HIPPOIDEA.
            Family 1. Equidæ, Horses.
            Family 2. [†Palæotheriidæ].
         Superfamily b. †BRONTOTHERIOIDEA.
            Family 3. †Brontotheriidæ.

SECTION B. CERATOMORPHA.
SUPERFAMILY c. TAPIROIDEA.
FAMILY 4. TAPIRIDÆ, Tapirs.
FAMILY 5. [†LOPHIODONTIDÆ].
SUPERFAMILY d. RHINOCEROIDEA.
FAMILY 6. RHINOCEROTIDÆ, Rhinoceroses.
FAMILY 7. †HYRACODONTIDÆ, †Cursorial Rhinoceroses.
FAMILY 8. †AMYNODONTIDÆ, †Amphibious Rhinoceroses.
FAMILY 9. †HYRACHYIDÆ.
SUBORDER II. †Ancylopoda, †Clawed Perissodactyls.
FAMILY 10. †CHALICOTHERIIDÆ.

Of no other mammalian family has so much been learned concerning its origin and development as of the horses. Indeed so oft-repeated and so familiar has this story become that both evolutionists and anti-evolutionists are weary of it and flout it.

SUBORDER I. **Chelopoda**, HOOFED PERISSODACTYLS.
SECTION A. HIPPOMORPHA.
Superfamily a. HIPPOIDEA
Family 1. Equidæ, Horses

Equus, Pleist. to Rec. N. and S. A. †*Hippidion*, †*Onohippidium*, †*Hyperhippidium*, Pleist. S. A. †*Hipparion*, Plio. †*Hypohippus*, Mio. to Plio. †*Pliohippus*, †*Protohippus*, †*Neohipparion*, up. Mio. and low. Plio. †*Merychippus*, mid. Mio. to low. Plio. †*Desmatippus*, mid. Mio. †*Parahippus*, low. and mid. Mio. †*Miohippus*, up. Olig. †*Mesohippus*, mid. Olig. †*Epihippus*, up. Eoc. †*Orohippus*, mid. Eoc. †*Hyracotherium*, low. Eoc.

In the existing members of this family the dental and skeletal characteristics are more uniform than might be inferred from external appearances. Colour-pattern, character of mane and tail, length of ears make horses, asses, zebras and quaggas look very different, but such characters are not registered in the skeleton. At the present time, true horses (*Equus przewalskii*) exist in the wild state only in central Asia; other so-called "wild horses," such as those of North and South America, are *feral*, i.e. descendants of domestic animals which escaped from captivity. Wild asses occur in Asia and Africa and the striped equines, zebras and quaggas, are exclusively African. No native members of the family are now found anywhere in the Western Hemisphere, but they were abundant in both northern and southern continents until the end of the Pleistocene.

Many naturalists admit but the single genus, *Equus*, for all existing representatives of the family and consider horses, asses, zebras, etc., as species of the one genus, while others recognize several additional genera, such as *Asinus, Hemionus,* etc. For the purposes of this book, it will suffice to consider all the Pleistocene and Recent species of the family found in the Northern Hemisphere as pertaining to one genus.

Teeth and skeleton of the modern horses are extremely characteristic and unlike those of any other family, except for one group

Fig. 246. — Asiatic Wild Horse, *Equus przewalskii.* (By permission of N. Y. Zoöl. Soc.)

of the South American †Litopterna. This has been true from the beginning of their recorded history in the lower Eocene, though not to the same extent. Those earliest horses were much nearer to the ancestral tapirs and rhinoceroses than are their descendants of to-day. The three families have developed along diverging lines from their first distinct appearance.

In *Equus* all the teeth, except the canines and first premolars $(p\frac{1}{1})$, are extremely hypsodont and continue to grow until advanced old age. Each incisor has on the masticating surface a deep, enamel-lined pit, "the mark," which is gradually removed by abrasion. As the permanent incisors come into use successively and "the mark" is worn away at different times in the various teeth, it is an excellent indication of a horse's age. The canines are reduced, never fang-like, and, though larger in the male, they are of little use, for a stallion bites an enemy, or a rival, with his incisors, not with his canines. Between the canines and the grinding teeth there are long, toothless gaps, or diastemata. Though *Equus* has the full dental formula: $i\frac{3}{3}$, $c\frac{1}{1}$, $p\frac{4}{4}$, $m\frac{3}{3} \times 2 = 44$, the number of functionally useful teeth is less by 8, for the canines and first premolars, above and below, are hardly more than vestiges. The other premolars have the shape and pattern of the molars and are even larger than they, $p\frac{2}{}$ being the largest of all the teeth, and of a shape somewhat different from the other grinding teeth, all of which have a masticating surface of extraordinary complexity. Each grinder is thickly covered with a layer of cement (see p. 45) which fills up all the valleys and thus the masticating surface, after a short period of wear, is a cross-section of the crown, exposing enamel, dentine and cement, which are each of a different degree of hardness. Differential wear keeps the grinding surface rough and efficient as a mill.

The masticating surfaces of the cheek-teeth are soon so much modified by abrasion that they seem to have nothing in common with the low-crowned grinders of the Oligocene and Eocene members of the family. If, however, the cement is entirely removed from the unworn molar of a colt, its community of plan with that of †*Parahippus*, or †*Mesohippus*, is made clear, although in these genera the teeth are very low-crowned, ceasing to grow as soon as they are erupted and in use.

The skull of *Equus* has a short, but relatively capacious cranium and a very long face, the orbit being shifted behind the last upper molar socket, so that the very high-crowned teeth may find space in the jaw without pressing upon the eyeball. The orbit is completely encircled in bone, the post-orbital process of the frontal extending down to a junction with the jugal, which has no process of its own. A long and prominent bony ridge extends forward from the orbit along the very high maxillary bone; this is the masseteric ridge and serves for the attachment of the muscle of that name. In marked contrast to many of the ancient genera, none of the modern equines has upon the maxillary a pit for the lodgment of a gland, or a fossa for a nasal diverticulum. In accordance with the great height of the teeth, the condyle of the lower jaw is raised above the masticating surfaces of the teeth. The notable beauty of a horse's head is determined by the proportions and contours of its bony foundation and no part of this frame-work is more important than the long graceful curve of the angle of the lower jaw.

The neck is long and, in consequence, the individual vertebræ are elongate and combine flexibility and strength by the character of the joints between them. Except for the articulation between atlas and axis, each intervertebral joint is made by a ball and socket, the anterior face of the centrum being a convex hemisphere and the posterior face a cup of corresponding shape. All the processes of the cervical vertebræ are characteristically equine and unlike those of other mammals. The odontoid process of the axis is spout-like, with deeply concave upper surface for the reception of the spinal cord, a shape which recurs in almost, but not quite, all long-necked mammals, and the development of this form from the usual peg-like process may be followed in the successive genera of the family.

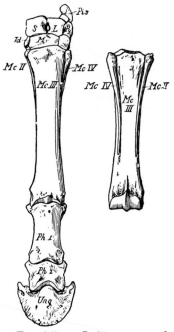

In the trunk the backbone is remarkably straight, though the upper contour is made slightly sinuous by the differing lengths of the neural spines. At the withers there is a low hump caused by the elongated spines of the anterior dorsal vertebræ. In the lumbar and posterior dorsal region the zygapophyses are cylindrical and interlocking, like those of artiodactyls. The caudals make a short bony part of the tail, most of which consists of long hairs, differing much in quantity in the various species.

There are no clavicles in any existing species of the family; the spine of the scapula dies away upon the neck without forming an acromion.

The limbs are proportionately long and the bones are as stout and heavy as is compatible with graceful lines.

FIG. 247. — Left manus of Horse, front side and rear of metacarpus. *S*, scaphoid. *L*, lunar. *Py*, pyramidal. *Pis*, pisiform. *Td*, trapezoid. *M*, magnum. *Mc II*, *Mc IV*, vestigial second and fourth metacarpals. *Mc III*, median metacarpal. *Ph 1*, *Ph 2*, first and second phalanges. *Ung*, ungual.

Before the middle Pliocene all equines had remarkably slender, deer-like legs. The humerus is stout and short (Fig. 20, p. 30) and its upper end has a peculiarity which is shared by camels and giraffes, but not by other ungulates, namely, that the groove for the tendons of the *biceps* muscle is double, being divided into two parts by a bony prominence, the *bicipital tubercle*. The external tuberosity is relatively small and the internal one large, the three prominences being almost equally conspicuous; this is a very unusual feature.

The fore-arm bones are co-ossified (Fig. 24, p. 32); the ulna is greatly reduced and the middle part of the shaft is lost; only the olecranon is of full size and that appears to be a process of the radius. The latter, which is considerably longer than the humerus, is stout and carries all the weight imposed on one fore-limb.

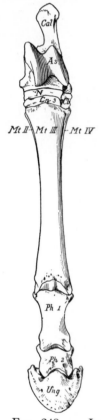

The pelvis has a very characteristic shape, owing to the manner in which the ilia of the two sides are everted.

The femur, or thigh-bone (Fig 29, p. 34), is very stout and has an unusually prominent great trochanter and a conspicuous third trochanter. From the most ancient known member of the family, †*Hyracotherium* of the lower Eocene, through all the successive stages of development, this bone has been characteristically equine in a manner easy to recognize yet difficult to describe.

The tibia is longer than the femur and carries all the weight of its limb (Fig. 32, p. 36), for the fibula would seem to have been entirely lost, but, as a matter of fact, only the shaft has been suppressed and the two ends, as may be seen in a young colt, remain and are ankylosed with the tibia.

The feet of a horse are very elongate, the so-called "knee" of the fore-leg being the wrist and the "hock-joint" the ankle and heel. Wrist and heel are thus raised far off the ground and the animal walks on the very tips of its toes and hence is said to be unguligrade, as are also nearly all existing artiodactyls, though hippopotamuses and camels are not unguligrade and the peccaries and swine are short-footed. The very long foot and unguligrade gait are cursorial features and are common not only to all equines, but to antelopes and deer, as well.

Fig. 248. — Left pes of Horse. *Cal*, calcaneum. *As*, astragalus. *N*, navicular. *Cn 3*, third cuneiform. *Mt III*, functional (third) metatarsal. *Mt II* and *Mt IV*, splints. Other letters as in Fig. 247.

The feet of *Equus* are unique among those of Recent mammals in that they are functionally monodactyl, or one-toed. Of the original five digits, only the third, or median one, is complete and supports the entire weight of the limb and its load. The hoof-bone, or ungual phalanx, is also unique in shape, which is like that of the hoof which encloses it, but necessarily smaller. Of the lateral digits, the second and fourth, the phalanges have entirely disappeared and only the "splint-bones" remain; these are the metapodials which articulate above with carpus and tarsus respectively and end in blunt points below. On the functional third, or median metapodial, the keel on the lower end, which fits into a groove of the first phalanx, is extended around to the anterior side so as to be visible from the front. Except in the †Litopterna, the encircling keel occurs only in one-toed and two-toed ungulates and not in all of them, for the camels and chevrotains have the keel only on the posterior face of the metapodials. This extension of the carina took place late in the history of the family and the first phalanx was modified accordingly, the groove running across the whole antero-posterior thickness of the bone and notching the anterior as well as the posterior edge. The keel of the metapodial and the grooved and notched phalanx make a very strong interlocking joint, which is necessitated by the narrowness of the feet. In sum, the skeletal and muscular structure of the Horse make him pre-eminently a "cursorial machine," as Huxley called him, and the successive steps by which this high degree of perfection was attained may be followed in the stages of the Quaternary and Tertiary periods.

The Pleistocene horses of North America all belonged to the genus *Equus*, but the True Horse, in the restricted sense, that is *Equus caballus*, has not been found anywhere in the Western Hemisphere. These Pleistocene species were numerous and varied, ranging in size from a Shetland pony (*E.* †*tau*) to animals exceeding the largest modern draught-horses (*E.* †*giganteus*), but most of the species were of moderate height, 14 to 15 hands, and some examples of *E.* †*occidentalis*, of California, retained the slender, deer-like legs of the ancestral three-toed genera.

The horses of the Pleistocene present many questions for which no answers can yet be found. It seems unlikely that they can all have been derived from the few species known in the later Pliocene. It must be left to future discovery, especially in eastern Asia, to determine how far the Quaternary species were indigenous and how far immigrant.

Though it can hardly be doubted that the horse family passed through the greater part of its development in North America, yet the immediate ancestry of all existing species is to be sought in the

Old World, as the Pleistocene species of North and South America, all became extinct, leaving no descendants behind them. In the Pleistocene, every continent except Australia had its horses and it was only in the Western Hemisphere that they disappeared altogether.

The upper Pliocene horse is †*Plesippus*, a name which signifies an "almost horse." First discovered in Texas, †*Plesippus* has been found most abundantly in the lake-deposits at Hagerman, Idaho, from which the U. S. National Museum has obtained a great number of skeletons. While the differences from the modern genus are almost entirely in skull and teeth, the skeleton is completely modernized and this is the most ancient of the horses which has the sturdy proportions of *Equus*. All the previous ones, as above noted, have the light, slender build of most existing deer and antelopes. Evidently, another link in the chain remains to be discovered, for the transition from the lower to the upper Pliocene, in equine development, is too sudden and abrupt and, no doubt, a transitional form will some day be discovered in the middle Pliocene.

The lower Pliocene genus is †*Pliohippus*, the first monodactyl form so far, at least, as external appearance went, for the phalanges had been lost from both fore- and hind-feet and each foot had but a single hoof. The lateral metapodials, however, were almost as long as the functional median one and had not yet begun to dwindle. Limbs and feet are very slender and deer-like and the stature is that of a pony, much smaller than the upper Pliocene †*Plesippus*. The teeth, though unmistakably of equine type, have a less complex system of enamel ridges and the crowns of the grinding teeth are only about half as high as in †*Plesippus*, but they are truly hypsodont and continued to grow until the animal was old. The external appearance was equine, though it may have been more zebra-like than horse-like.

A step farther back, in still lower Pliocene and upper Miocene stages, brings us to †*Protohippus*, which differs from †*Pliohippus* chiefly in being three-toed; the median digit is much enlarged, carrying most of the weight, while the lateral digits, though complete and having small hoofs, were little more than dew-claws. These diminished hoofs may, however, have been serviceable in soft ground, as the laterals of Moose and Caribou are useful in snow. The ungual phalanx, or hoof-core, of the median functional digit is already equine in shape, but is much thinner and flatter than in *Equus*. In †*Protohippus* the molar-crowns are almost twice as high as in †*Merychippus:*

FIG. 249. — †Western Horse, *Equus †occidentalis*, Pleistocene of Rancho La Brea. (From a skeleton in Los Angeles Mus.)

the orbit is completely enclosed in bone and is shifted behind the teeth to make room for the high-crowned molars.

Contemporary with †*Protohippus* was †*Hipparion*, different only in certain details of molar structure. †*Hipparion* made its way into Asia and spread westward into France and everywhere in the Old World was characteristic of the lower Pliocene. It is an unexplained fact that between †*Hyracotherium*, of the lower Eocene, and †*Hipparion*, of the lower Pliocene, no horses have been found any-

Fig. 250. — †Three-toed grazing horse, †*Neohipparion whitneyi*, upper Miocene. (Restored from skeletons in Amer. Mus. Nat. Hist.)

where in the Eastern Hemisphere, except the Miocene †*Anchitherium*. This genus, also of American origin, was off the main line of descent and left no successors in the Old World, and is thus no real exception to the general statement. In the Eocene and Oligocene epochs, eastern Asia and western North America were parts of the same zoölogical province and their mammals largely belonged to the same genera. The faunas of these two areas, Mongolia and the western United States, were much more nearly alike than either was like that of Europe, or north Africa. Yet Mongolia had no horses, so far as the great collections made in the Gobi Desert by the American Museum can testify and, with the exception noted, the same is true of all other parts of the Old World. Since so many genera and families of mammals made their way from one continent to the other and in both directions, the failure of the horses to gain a permanent footing in Asia and Europe before the early Pliocene is difficult to understand.

It has been held, especially by certain European palæontologists, that all existing members of the Equidæ are descended from the †hipparions which spread through Asia in the lower Pliocene and no one can positively assert that this opinion is untenable. It must be noted, however, that such a view postulates a dual origin for the genus *Equus*, which certainly arose in North America through the series †*Protohippus* — †*Pliohippus* — †*Plesippus* — *Equus*. That the same genus could have arisen twice independently in separate regions of the Earth has never been proved and seems very unlikely. From what little we know concerning the modes of evolutionary development, it seems much more probable that the Old World equines were derived from later emigrants such as †*Plesippus*.

The immediate ancestry of the lower Pliocene †*Hipparion* is somewhat uncertain because of the *embarras de richesse* of possible selections. The genus is very closely connected with †*Protohippus* and there are species in which the molar teeth belong first to one genus and then to the other, *according to definition*, dependent on the degree of abrasion. On the other hand, the upper Miocene genus, †*Neohipparion*, discovered and named by the late Dr. J. W. Gidley, who collected several skeletons for the American Museum, may be the ancestor desired.

Before attempting to trace back the main line of equine descent through the middle and lower Tertiary stages, something should be said concerning the side-branches from this main stem, all of which are now extinct. One such branch is that of the very peculiar South American horses, and these require a section to themselves. Another branch is typified by the genus †*Hypohippus*, which is very close to the French †*Anchitherium* and has more than once been identified with it. †*Hypohippus* may be considered an example of arrested development, for it retained the low-crowned, rooted teeth of the lower Miocene and Oligocene equines. These apparently were what Osborn has called them, "browsing horses," for their teeth were fitted only for grinding soft vegetable material, such as leaves, and their low-crowned incisors would speedily have been worn away by grazing, for grass, on account of its high silica content, is extremely abrasive and animals that feed upon it require hypsodont teeth, the growth of which compensates for wear. †*Hypohippus* was further unprogressive in the relatively large size of the lateral digits, the hoofs of which must have reached the ground. The upper incisors, though very short-crowned, had the enamel pit, or "mark," and the grinding teeth had no deposit of cement on their crowns.

The latest representative of †*Hypohippus* so far described is the relatively very large †*H. matthewi* from the lower Pliocene of Nebraska. The Miocene species of the genus are much smaller, especially †*H. equinus*, of the middle Miocene, which is the best known. †*Hypohippus* was apparently derived from the still smaller †*Parahippus* of the lower Miocene, which, if not itself the actual ancestor common to the main stem and the side-branch, is very close to that ancestor and, for all practical purposes, will serve as well.

Returning to the principal line of equine descent, which was left at the upper Miocene †*Protohippus*, the next backward step is to the exceptionally interesting †*Merychippus*, which, beginning in the middle Miocene, persisted into the lower Pliocene alongside of its own presumptive descendants, †*Protohippus* and †*Pliohippus*. †*Merychippus*, of which several species, from various parts of the Great Plains, have been described, comprises smaller animals than the species of †*Protohippus* and has permanent grinding teeth which are hypsodont and cement-covered with open bases, but are not so high-crowned, nor have such complex masticating surfaces, as those of †*Protohippus*. The milk-premolars, on the contrary, are brachyodont and have no cement on them. The milk-dentition is often more conservative than the permanent one and retains ancestral features which are lost in the second set, but there are only a few instances known in which there is such a perfect transition from brachyodont to hypsodont teeth as in †*Merychippus*. As the late Dr. W. D. Matthew clearly showed, there is great difficulty in connecting †*Merychippus* with *Equus*, through †*Proto-* and †*Pliohippus*. Considerations of space forbid discussion of the question here, but it is probable that the immediate ancestry of the modern horses has not yet been discovered.

Another middle Miocene genus, †*Desmatippus*, is contemporary with †*Merychippus*, just as the latter is with †*Protohippus* in the upper Miocene, ancestor and descendant coexisting, of which there are many instances. No doubt †*Desmatippus* arose in the unrecorded interval between the lower and middle Miocene and continued into the latter stage, by which time †*Merychippus* had come into existence. Like the genus last named, †*Desmatippus* is an especially interesting link in the chain of equine descent. The grinding teeth are still very low-crowned, but, for the first time in the history of the family, cement is deposited in a thin layer upon the enamel of the crown and the enamel crests are crenulate instead of simple and straight. These are both changes of great significance which became more and more marked in the subsequent genera, from †*Merychippus* to *Equus*.

The genus which runs through the whole lower Miocene is †*Parahippus*, the material of which is mostly fragmentary, but, happily,

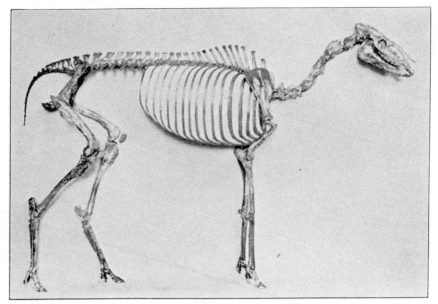

FIG. 251. — Skeleton of lower Miocene horse, †*Parahippus*. (Mus. Comp. Zoöl. Harvard Univ.)

there is a fine skeleton in the Harvard Museum which differs but little from those of the Oligocene horses, †*Miohippus* and †*Mesohippus*, but is somewhat larger and is intermediate between the genera of the middle and upper Miocene and those of the Oligocene. From †*Protohippus* to *Equus* the scapular spine has no acromion, but †*Parahippus* agrees with the Oligocene genera in having a prominent acromion, which is curved outward in peculiar fashion, quite as in the White River †*Mesohippus*. As previously noted, †*Parahippus* fulfils the conditions of being ancestral both to the grazing and to the later browsing horses, and may very well have been the actual ancestor.

In the John Day and upper White River the predominant genus is †*Miohippus*, an animal about equal to an ordinary sheep in size. It is closely similar to †*Mesohippus*, which passes through the whole

White River from bottom to top. †*Miohippus* is larger than all but the latest and largest species of †*Mesohippus*, and differs from them in small details in the structure of teeth and feet. Though small, these details mark the beginning of important structures.

†*Mesohippus* had many species, though very probably not nearly so many as have been named. The species of the upper Brulé, espe-

FIG. 252. — The small, browsing, three-toed, short-necked horse, †*Mesohippus bairdi*, Oligocene, White River.

cially those found in the channel-sandstones, are very much larger than those of the lower Brulé and still smaller are those which occur in the Chadron. Most marked and apparently sudden is the change from the lower Brulé species to those of the upper Brulé. Another difference between these species is that of proportions. In the smaller and more ancient ones the hind legs are longer than the fore and the rump is correspondingly higher than the shoulder, an inequality which recurs in many primitive hoofed animals. In these older species also, the feet are relatively shorter.

Aside from the later and larger species, †*Mesohippus* is of about the size of a large dog, such as a pointer or a greyhound, and has the more slender proportions of the latter, but these animals were already very equine in appearance and looked like miniature horses, as is so well shown in the beautifully restored group in the Field Museum of Natural History, Chicago (see Fig. 52, p. 69). Horse-like as they seem, almost every detail of structure, from the incisor teeth to the hinder hoofs, is notably different from the corresponding part of *Equus*, but the differences are like those between the embryo and the adult; one is clearly derivable from the other.

In †*Mesohippus* all the teeth are very low-crowned and fitted only for a diet of soft vegetation. This was the rule among White River herbivores, only two of which, both artiodactyls (†*Poëbrotherium* and †*Hypisodus*) had hypsodont molars. Indeed, there is reason to believe that the spread of grassy plains did not take place until much later. Though the upper incisors are very short-crowned, the beginnings of the "mark" are already obvious in the form of an enamel ridge which projects downward from the back of each tooth, but is not quite so long as the cutting edge. The lower incisors are still simple and chisel-like. All the premolars, except the first $(p \frac{1}{1})$ which is very small, have acquired the molar-pattern.

The skull is like that of a very small modern horse, but with a great many differences of detail, the most obvious of which is the slenderness of the muzzle and shallowness of the jaws, for the very low-crowned teeth require no depth of jaw for their reception; this, in turn, produces a short ascending ramus of the mandible. The face is relatively short and the eye-socket is far forward, directly over the molar teeth; the postorbital process of the frontal bone does not reach the jugal, leaving the socket partially open behind. The braincase is remarkably capacious for a White River mammal and the cerebral hemispheres are already well convoluted. In brain development this tiny horse was far ahead of its time. The neck is relatively shorter than in the Miocene genera and the ball-and-socket joints between successive vertebræ are in hardly more than an incipient stage. The odontoid process of the axis is intermediate in form between the peg-like and the spout-like shape; it is broadened and flattened on the upper side, remaining convex on the lower. The trunk is long, but the tail is of moderate length.

The limbs are elongate and very slender, the relative lengths of the feet vary considerably in the different species. The scapula has the same prominent and peculiarly shaped acromion as in the lower Miocene †*Parahippus*. The humerus has an undivided bicipital groove. The fore-arm bones are only partially co-ossified and the ulna, though greatly attenuated, has a shaft of full length. The lower leg-bones, likewise, are but partially ankylosed and the full length of the fibula is retained, though the shaft is little more than a bony thread. The manus has three functional digits, the median one of which is enlarged and bore most of the weight, but the laterals reached the ground and were not entirely without function. In addition there is the vestigial fifth metacarpal in the form of a short splint. The median hoof, viewed from the front, is very horse-like, but from the side is seen to be much thinner and flatter than in the Miocene and subsequent genera. The pes is three-toed, like the manus, but has no splint as a vestige of the fifth metatarsal.

The little upper Eocene horse, the Uinta genus, †*Epihippus*, is still very incompletely known, but enough of it has been found to demonstrate clearly its intermediate position between the much better known Oligocene †*Mesohippus* and †*Orohippus* of the middle Eocene. A horse of some kind has been found in the Duchesne beds, but the material is still too incomplete for description. †*Epihippus* is decidedly smaller than the Oligocene species and has but two molariform premolars, the third and fourth, the first and second still remaining smaller and simpler; the orbit is more widely open.

The Bridger (middle Eocene) genus is †*Orohippus*, of which several species that form a connected series have been named. The incisors are simple and chisel-like, with no trace of the "mark." Only one premolar in each jaw, the hindmost one ($p\frac{4}{4}$), has assumed the molar pattern, the others are all simpler and smaller than molars. The upper molars have the external cusps incipiently crescentic and uniting to form a wall; the conules are transversely extended and beginning the formation of transverse crests, though still separate from outer and inner cusps. The orbit is farther forward in the skull and less enclosed behind, making a shorter face than in †*Mesohippus*. The cranium is narrower and the brain-case is less capacious; the neck is proportionally shorter and the odontoid process of the axis still retains the primitive peg-like shape. The limbs and feet are conspicuously shorter than in the Oligocene genera; the ulna and fibula are stouter and less reduced and are entirely separate from the radius and tibia respectively. The manus has four functional toes, the fifth digit which, in †*Mesohippus* has been reduced to a splint, is fully developed in the Bridger horses, but the pes has only three digits.

†*Hyracotherium* is not only the most ancient, but also, as would be expected, by far the smallest and most primitive of the known equine series, yet is unmistakably a horse. Nevertheless, were the long chain of intermediate species and genera unknown, it would be a very bold speculation to look upon this little Wasatch animal as a horse-ancestor. In †*Hyracotherium* the premolars are all smaller

and of simpler pattern than the molars, which, in the upper jaw, are of particular interest, for they have no crests or ridges and incomplete wall; the crown is quadritubercular, with four principal conical cusps in two transverse pairs and between the cusps of each pair is a tiny conule no bigger than the head of a pin. These conules were the first step in the formation of the transverse crests, which were to be so important in the succeeding genera. The lower molars had already

Fig. 253. — The "Dawn Horse," †*Hyracotherium*, lower Eocene. (Restored from a skeleton in Amer. Mus. Nat. Hist.)

acquired the bicrescentic pattern which was kept throughout the history of the family, and persists even in the modern *Equus*.

†*Hyracotherium* was a little animal of about the size of a fox-terrier, but horse-like in all parts of its structure, though the equine likeness cannot always be expressed in a description. The skull has a long, slender, pointed face, with open orbits placed above the molar teeth, and a brain-case which is capacious for its geological date. There can be little doubt that the early development of the brain, as indicative of intelligence, was an important factor in determining the survival of the family through such an immense lapse of time.

The neck of the Wasatch genus is short and the cervical vertebræ have nearly plane faces, without ball-and-socket joints; the odontoid

Fig. 254. — A †Pampas Horse, †*Hippidion neogæum*. (Restored from a skeleton in Mus. of Buenos Aires.)

414

process of the axis is a conical peg. The back is strongly arched and rises to the rump, because of the greater length of the hind-legs. The limbs are relatively short, especially the anterior pair; the ulna and fibula are complete, separate and unreduced. The feet are very short in comparison with the horses of later geological date, though fully unguligrade; the manus has four digits and the pes three. Additional splint-bones have been reported, but there is some doubt about these.

South American Horses

The story of the horses in South America is a comparatively brief one, for they were among the immigrants from the north and

Fig. 255. — Skull of †*Hippidion*, Pleistocene of Tarija, Bolivia. Note the unsupported nasal bones. (Field Mus. Nat. Hist.)

cannot have arrived in the southern continent before the end of the Miocene. Even so, the early chapters of the history are still missing, for none of the three-toed genera has been found in South America, and the horses of the Pampean stage are all so specialized and so different from anything found in the north, that we must postulate a long antecedent period of equine development, somewhere within the Neotropical Region. Where that development took place, it is, as yet, impossible to say. Even the rich and varied middle Pliocene fauna of Catamarca, in northwestern Argentina, contains hardly any northern elements and no horses of any description have been found in it. The Pampean genera are mostly peculiar and we cannot yet determine which of the northern forms were ancestral to them. All the Pampean species were of medium, or small size, with short feet and large heads and, in general, ass-like rather than horse-like in appearance and proportions, though ears, mane and tail are, of course, unknown.

There are two distinct groups of the Pampean horses: (1) species of the genus *Equus*, which thus, at one time or another, inhabited every continent with the exception of Australia; (2) three genera peculiar to South America and developed there from northern ancestors, possibly †*Pliohippus*. Two of these genera, which differ from *Equus* especially in the pattern of the grinding teeth, †*Hippidion* and †*Onohippidium*, display curious modifications of the nasal bones, which are long, extremely slender and attached to the skull only at their hinder ends, instead of being, as in other horses, supported for nearly their whole length by lateral contact with the maxillaries and premaxillaries. One would expect to find many skulls in which these splint-like, fragile-looking bones had been broken in life, but no such fractures have been reported. The orbit is lower down and smaller than in *Equus*, a marked difference. The third genus, †*Hyperhippidium*, had remarkably short feet like those of the so-called "Mountain Goat," and was probably a climber.

SUMMARY OF EQUINE DEVELOPMENT

In chronological order the following sequence of changes may be noted:

(1) There was a continual increase in size from the tiny horses of the lower Eocene to the huge species of the Pleistocene.

(2) The molar teeth changed from a simple pattern of conical cusps to a highly complex one of ridges and crests and the premolars, beginning with the hindmost ($p \frac{4}{4}$) one by one became molariform; the low-crowned, rooted and cement-free teeth, fitted only for browsing, changed to very high-crowned, rootless and cement-covered teeth fitted for grazing. The "mark" of the incisors began as a low ridge and became an enamel-lined pit, deepening as the teeth grew in height.

(3) The face grew much longer, the orbits were completely closed and shifted back of the molar teeth. To accommodate the very high-crowned teeth, the jaws were much deepened vertically.

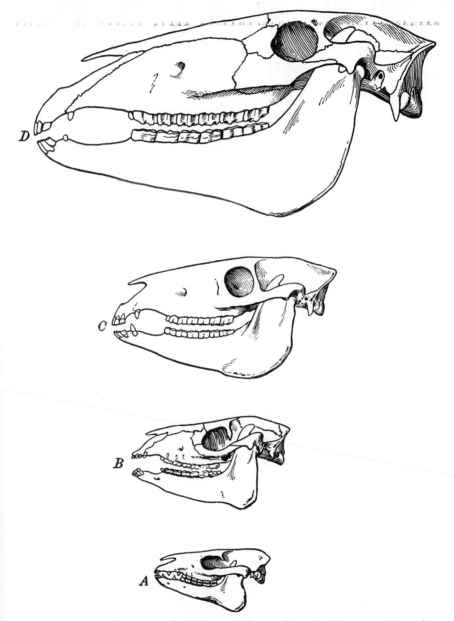

Fig. 256. — Series of horse skulls in ascending geological order. *A*, †*Hyracotherium*, lower Eocene (after Cope). *B*, †*Mesohippus*, lower and middle Oligocene. *C*, †*Protohippus*, upper Miocene (after Cope). *D*, *Equus*.

(4) The neck was greatly elongated and its vertebræ developed ball-and-socket joints; the odontoid process of the axis was converted from a peg-shape to a spout-shape.

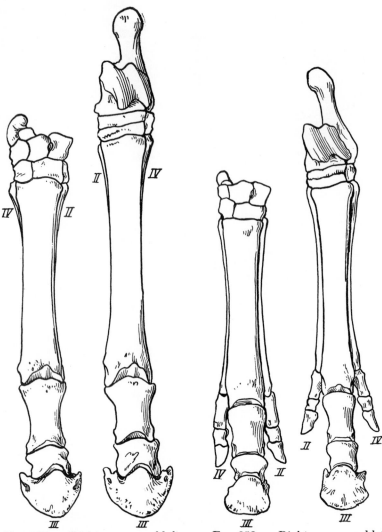

FIG. 257. — Right manus and left pes of *Equus*.

FIG. 258. — Right manus and left pes of †*Protohippus*.

(5) The arched back was straightened and the neural spines, especially those of the anterior dorsal vertebræ, elongated.

(6) The scapula lost the acromion.

(7) The limbs grew much longer; the ulna and fibula lost their

shafts and the ends were ankylosed with the enlarged radius and tibia respectively.

(8) The feet were greatly elongated; the median digit of each foot was gradually enlarged until it carried the whole weight and, *pari passu*, the hoof was enlarged and changed in shape, to fit it to be the sole support of the body. The lateral digits gradually dwindled into dew-claws, then lost their phalanges and became vestigial splints; the fifth digit was suppressed altogether.

(9) In addition to the main line of descent which ran, with such apparently unswerving directness, from †*Hyracotherium* to *Equus*, there were two side-branches given off, which flourished for a time and then died out. The first of these was the †*Hypohippus* — †*Anchitherium* series, of persistently conservative, browsing and presumably forest-dwelling species, in

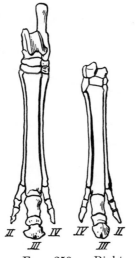

Fig. 259. — Right manus and left pes of †*Mesohippus*.

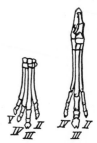

Fig. 260. — Right manus and pes of †*Hyracotherium*.

which the teeth remained low-crowned and the tridactyl feet underwent no further reduction. This line was probably given off from †*Parahippus*, which seems to have been the ancestor common to this branch and to the main line. The second branch is of the peculiar South American genera, but the place and time when this branch departed from the trunk remain to be determined.

The European family of the †Palæotheriidæ, which has not been found either in Asia or America, is manifestly related to the horses and must have had a common origin with them in the lower Eocene, or even the Paleocene and, after thriving abundantly in the upper Eocene, they became extinct without descendants.

This is the merest outline sketch of a marvellous story of progressive modification and adaptation to changing conditions. All parts of the structure must at every stage, throughout all the changes, have been co-ordinated into a harmonious whole, so that the animal could thrive and maintain itself against competition. †*Hyracotherium* must have been as perfectly fitted to its environment as are the modern species of *Equus*. Evolution was the response to changing needs.

Superfamily b.   †BRONTOTHERIOIDEA

Family 3.   †*Brontotheriidæ*

The †brontotheres were a comparatively short-lived group and nearly all of their development took place in the conjoined provinces of eastern Asia and western North America. There are, however, such marked differences between the †brontotheres of the two areas as to show that the spread of species from one region to the other was rather difficult, preventing a complete interchange of genera and species. The principal genera of the family, not including those of Mongolia, are as follows:

†BRONTOTHERIIDÆ

†*Menodus*, †*Megacerops*, †*Brontotherium*, †*Brontops*, mid. Olig.   †*Teleodus*, mid. and low. Olig.   †*Protitanotherium*, †*Sthenodectes*, up. Eoc.   †*Dolichorhinus*, †*Mesatirhinus*, †*Manteoceras*, †*Palæosyops*, †*Telmatherium*, mid. Eoc. †*Eotitanops*, †*Lambdotherium*, low. Eoc.

In the lowest of the three White River substages, the Chadron, occurs a bewildering variety of †brontotheres, for which no stratigraphical order of succession has yet been made out. There is also great individual and sexual variation and, despite long and arduous labours, the taxonomy and nomenclature of these huge and strange creatures are still in a chaotic state. Professor Osborn's magnificent monograph of the family admits a far greater number of genera and species than can be used for the purposes of this book, in which summarized and simplified treatment is requisite. In this confusing horde the principal and obvious differences are those of (1) bodily stature, (2) the shape and size of the horn-like protuberances of the skull, and (3) the length of the nasal bones. In cases where the distinction can be made, the females are found to be notably smaller than the males. The largest of these animals were almost elephantine in proportions, standing over six feet in height at the shoulders and exceeding the largest of living rhinoceroses in bulk.

The teeth are all extremely brachyodont, or low-crowned; the incisors are very small, reduced and variable in number, and with curious hemispherical, button-like crowns; they can have been of no use, for even in old animals they do not show any sign of wear. The

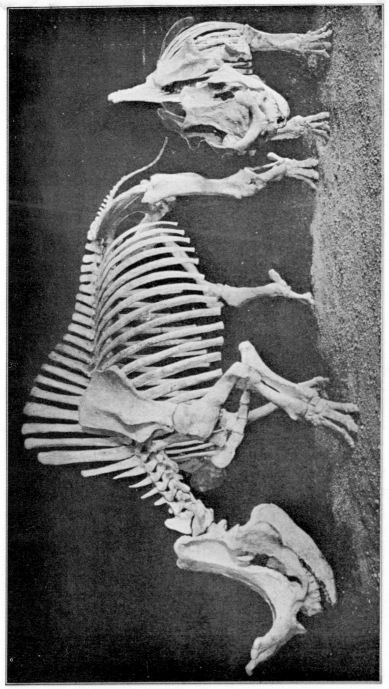

FIG. 261. — Skeletons of †*Brontotherium*, male and female, lower White River of Weld Co., Col., Chadron substage. (Col. Mus. Nat. Hist.)

canines are thick, but usually short, projecting but little above or below the level of the cheek-teeth; they cannot, therefore, have been serviceable as weapons. With such front teeth a prehensile lip and long tongue would seem to have been necessary in feeding.

The premolars never became molariform, though they probably would have done so, had the family not died out so early. The upper molars have an external wall formed by the meeting of the two outer cusps, which are deeply concave. The two internal cusps retain their primitive conical form, for there are no transverse crests, the intermediate conules having entirely disappeared. The lower molars have the bicrescentic pattern which is so widely spread among the early families of both artiodactyls and perissodactyls.

The skull has considerable resemblance to that of the larger modern rhinoceroses, a resemblance that is emphasized in almost all restorations of the living head. The so-called "horns" cannot be considered as anything more than permanent bony outgrowths of the skull; they cannot have been sheathed in horn, for they are often club-shaped and larger at the end than at the base, instead of tapering to a point, as a true horn-core always does. These "horns" (to call them so as a matter of convenience) are of an extraordinary variability of shape and size. Allowing for the fact that they are smaller in the female, they are sometimes short, of medium length and long, sometimes cylindrical, in other cases obscurely trihedral, in others again flattened, straight or recurved, of uniform diameter, or expanding at the tips. The permutations of all these variables give rise to an unnumbered variety which defies classification. The smaller and less specialized †*Teleodus*, which is especially characteristic of the Duchesne River beds, continued into the White River, and it is not yet possible to say whether it gave rise to all that horde of monsters, diversified as they are, or whether more or fewer of them may not have been immigrants from Asia, where the family flourished exceedingly in the Eocene and Oligocene. Westward it spread only as far as southeastern Europe.

As noted above, the chief differences in this welter of genera and species affect the size and shape of the "horns," otherwise, there is great uniformity of structure among them. That the "horns" were actually used as weapons, may be inferred from the shape of the skull and the occurrence of broken ribs in the skeletons, fractures which obviously were made in the lifetime of the animals, for the broken ends have deposits of bone around them (or "callus"). The fractured ribs never knit together, for the movements of the thorax in breathing

FIG. 262. — White River †brontothere, †*Brontops robustus*, males fighting. (Restored from a skeleton in Amer. Mus. Nat. Hist.)

prevented that, but formed a false joint, which, no doubt, became entirely comfortable in time. In the White River stage there were no Carnivora capable of inflicting such injury on one of these great beasts; that could have been done only by one of their own number.

The skull is, in many respects, highly remarkable; its upper profile is deeply concave, as in those rhinoceroses which have nasal horns, and as in them there is no sagittal crest, but a broad, flat surface, made concave by the curvature just alluded to. The brain-cavity is preposterously small and will hardly contain a man's fist. As in rhinoceroses and elephants, the cerebral cavity is surrounded by a mass of cancellous bone, which is a system of small communicating cavities, separated by many bony supports, which connect the inner and outer "tables," or denser surface layers, of the cranial bones. In this manner the great skull is much lightened without loss of strength. A characteristic of the White River genera is the immense massiveness and

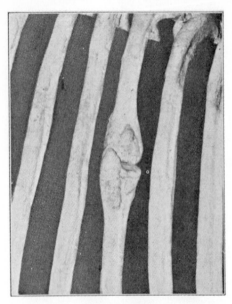

Fig. 263. — Rib of †*Brontops robustus* broken and partly healed in life, Oligocene, White River. (Amer. Mus. Nat. Hist.)

roughness of the zygomatic arch, particularly the squamosal portion of it and in the male; these arches give great breadth to the skull. No living mammal has arches at all comparable to those of the White River †brontotheres.

The disproportion in size between skull and brain is remarkable, for the enlargement of brain did not keep pace with the increase in stature and bulk of the animal. No doubt, the White River †brontotheres were even more dull and stupid than are modern rhinoceroses and that stupidity may have been a factor in their early extinction. There were several groups of Tertiary mammals with conspicuously small brains and it is a suggestive fact that none of them survived long and none are living to-day.

In †*Menodus* and its allies the proportions, other than those of the head, were much as in a small elephant. The neck is relatively shorter than in a rhinoceros, but longer than in an elephant, for there was no proboscis. The body is long and, as is indicated by the long, strongly arched ribs and by the greatly expanded hip-bones, it must have been of immense bulk. The spines of the anterior dorsal vertebræ are extremely long and form a great hump at the shoulders. The tail has about the same proportionate length as in an elephant.

The limbs are relatively somewhat longer than in an elephant and are of similar columnar shape. As is generally true of very large mammals, the femur has a flattened shaft, the third trochanter has nearly or quite disappeared and the marrow cavity is filled with spongy bone. The bones of the fore-arm and the lower leg are separate and the ulna is very heavy, the fibula much less so, but still stout. This is the strongest possible contrast to the horses and other cursorial ungulates, which have long, slender legs, with reduced ulna and fibula, which are co-ossified with the radius and tibia respectively. Heavy, slow-moving animals, such as rhinoceroses, tapirs and elephants, almost always have separate bones in the fore-arm and lower leg and, usually, a heavy ulna.

The manus has four digits and is considerably longer than the pes, which is tridactyl; fore- and hind-feet must have been supported on a great pad of elastic tissue, as in elephants and rhinoceroses, and the hoofs were mere nail-like, horny excrescences on the periphery of the feet, carrying very little of the weight. It is interesting to note how often this type of limb and foot has been repeated in unrelated groups of hoofed mammals, but only in those which have attained a certain degree of bulk and massiveness.

The extinction of the †brontotheres, which took place at the close of the Chadron substage, seems to have occurred with startling suddenness, but this seeming abruptness is, almost certainly, deceptive and owing to a hiatus in the deposition of the beds. In Mongolia the family survived to a later epoch and gave rise to some even more bizarre animals. One, in particular (*Embolotherium*) was of an altogether inexplicable oddity, having the whole anterior end of the snout bent up at right angles to the line of the face. What such a creature can have looked like in life, it is difficult to conceive.

In the Duchesne River formation the characteristic †brontothere genus is †*Teleodus*, which also survived into the Chadron substage of the White River. It was very probably ancestral to some of the Chadron species, but it seems hardly possible that it can have given rise to all of them. †*Teleodus* is much smaller than †*Menodus* and its contemporaries, and has much shorter horns and longer nasal bones. As its name implies, this genus has an unreduced dentition, 44 teeth in all, which is more like the Eocene genera.

In the upper Uinta the series is continued by †*Protitanotherium*, a smaller and more primitive animal than †*Teleodus*, but the horn-like protuberances of the nose are already prominent. The canines are large enough to have been serviceable as weapons and the incisors are well developed and must have been functional. Evidently, this animal had a different manner of feeding from that of †*Menodus*,

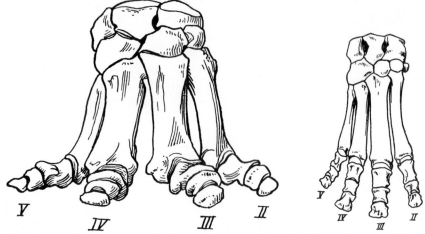

Fig. 264. — Right manus of †brontotheres. At left, †*Brontotherium*, White River (from Marsh). At right, †*Palæosyops*, Bridger (Princeton Univ. Mus.).

using the incisors in cropping and browsing, a function which, in the White River genera, seems to have been transferred to the lips and tongue. At the same time the growth of "horns" made the canines superfluous, as was noted in several of the artiodactyl families (Chapter XIII, p. 320) in which enlargement of horns and antlers was accompanied by the dwindling and disappearance of the canines. None of the Cavicornia has upper canines. True, the protuberances on the †brontothere skull were not horns in the strict sense of the word.

In the lower Uinta horizon occurs a very interesting transitional form, †*Sthenodectes*, in which there is a pair of fronto-nasal knobs, at least in the male; this is an early, though not the actually incipient stage of the "horns" which reached such great and often fantastic size and shape in the White River genera. †*Sthenodectes* resembled the preceding Eocene genera in having a long sagittal crest, which gave place to the flat-topped skull in the Oligocene. The canine teeth are relatively, not actually, reduced in size and the premolars had not yet begun to take on the molar pattern. This genus is smaller than †*Protitanotherium*.

So far as numbers, predominance and diversity are concerned, the middle Eocene, or Bridger stage, marked the culmination of the †brontothere family. They became larger, more specialized and differentiated, but they lost the dominating position in the fauna which they so conspicuously held in the middle Eocene. Through the middle and upper subdivisions of the Bridger (the lowest one is almost barren of fossils) there is a succession of changing species and genera, which can be arranged in several tribes and phyla, two of which were particularly important and are typified by the two genera

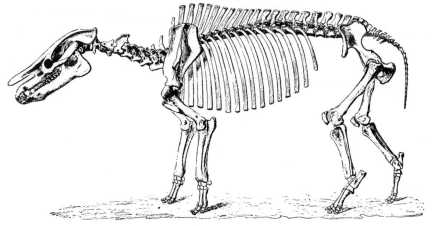

Fig. 265. — Skeleton of middle Eocene †brontothere, †*Dolichorhinus*. (Amer. Mus. Nat. Hist.)

†*Telmatherium* and †*Palæosyops*. The former seems to be the ancestor of the upper Eocene and Oligocene †brontotheres, the latter was one of a branch that ended in the lower Uinta. The principal difference between these two tribes is in the form of the upper molar teeth which, though of similar construction, have a decidedly different appearance. In †*Telmatherium* these molars are like those of †*Menodus* on a much smaller scale. The external cusps are but moderately concave and very nearly vertical, with high outer wall; in †*Palæosyops* the teeth are low on the outer side, the outer cusps very concave and pushed over, as it were, to the middle of the crown, very much as in the artiodactyl families of the †agriochœrids and †bothriodonts (*q.v.*); if the inner cusps were crescents instead of cones, the likeness would be close.

It is instructive to note that †*Telmatherium*, the ancestral form, is rare and but little diversified, with few species, while †*Palæosyops*, which was destined to a relatively early extinction, is the commonest of all Bridger fossils and was highly diversified, with many species and allied genera. †*Dolichorhinus*, with its extraordinarily long and narrow head, is one of the several upper Bridger and lower Uinta relatives of †*Palæosyops*.

The differences between the two tribes are principally in the skull and teeth; the skeleton, which is far better known in the †*Palæosyops* phylum, is quite uniform, except in size, among the Bridger †brontotheres, and that of †*Palæosyops* will serve very well to indicate the developmental changes in the Oligocene genera.

SUMMARY OF †BRONTOTHERE EVOLUTION

(1) There is, in the first place, the matter of size; the commonest species, †*Palæosyops paludosus*, was hardly half the size of †*Menodus* and many of the striking differences between the Bridger and the White River genera have been brought about by the great increase in the size of the latter, as mechanical adjustment to heavier weight.

(2) The skull, which varied considerably in the different species, has a straight upper profile, with long, high sagittal crest; the brain-case is small, but not to any such extraordinary degree as in †*Menodus*. The zygomatic arches, though stout, had no such massiveness as in the White River forms.

(3) The canines had much the appearance of a bear's fangs, which they equalled in size and in that of the swollen root; they must have been effective weapons, which they evidently were not in the White River animals; they were not actually reduced in size, but, like the brain, became very much smaller in proportion.

(4) The trunk is evidently much less bulky and the hip-bones are not so greatly expanded, indicating a smaller mass of viscera.

(5) The limbs are much lighter than those of †*Menodus;* the femur retains the cylindrical shaft found in all mammals, except the very large ones, and the marrow cavity is open; the third trochanter is large and prominent.

(6) The feet have the same number of digits, four in the manus, three in the pes, as in the Oligocene, the principal change being increment of size. One notable change there is: the ungual phalanges demonstrate that in †*Palæosyops* the hoofs were well developed, actually supporting the body-weight and not being mere nails on the circumference of the foot.

(7) Aside from the proboscis, the †brontotheres of the Bridger

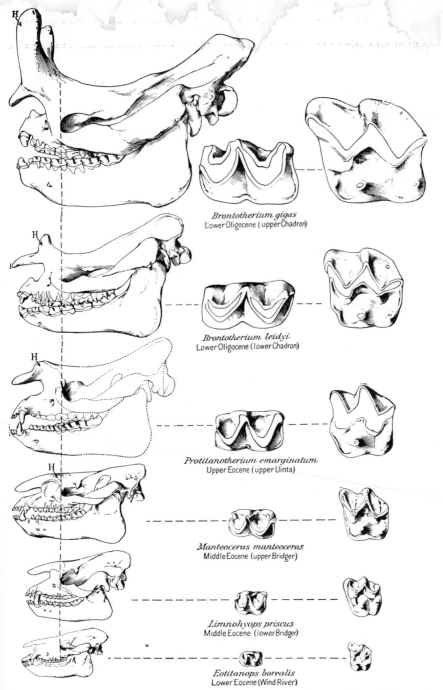

Brontotherium gigas
Lower Oligocene (upper Chadron)

Brontotherium leidyi
Lower Oligocene (lower Chadron)

Protitanotherium emarginatum
Upper Eocene (upper Uinta)

Manteoceras manteoceras
Middle Eocene (upper Bridger)

Limnohyops priscus
Middle Eocene (lower Bridger)

Eotitanops borealis
Lower Eocene (Wind River)

FIG. 266. — Evolution of skull and teeth in the †*Bronototheres*. (From Osborn.)

must have resembled tapirs in size and proportions and, in early days, when the mutual relationships of the perissodactyl families were little comprehended, these Bridger genera were said to be "tapiroid." If understood as a purely descriptive term, not implying relationship, the word serves a useful purpose.

The genera of the †brontotheres were much more numerous and varied in the later than in the earlier Bridger stage and in the upper Wind River stage of the lower Eocene, there was a single genus, †*Eotitanops*, which was apparently ancestral to both of the middle Eocene tribes. This lower Eocene animal is much smaller than the mid-Eocene species and more lightly built, but was otherwise like them. There was in the lower Wind River, a genus, †*Lambdotherium*, still very incompletely known, and for that reason enigmatical. This was the smallest known member of the family and had light slender limbs, while the molar teeth have a certain suggestive resemblance to those of the early horses. It is quite possible that †*Lambdotherium* is a surviving primitive member of the family, which was near to the point of divergence where the horses and the †brontotheres separated. That the two families are believed to be related, is shown by the inclusion of both in the Hippomorpha. Be that as it may, the earliest †brontotheres must have been immigrants, presumably from Asia, for there is nothing known in the lower Wasatch which could have been ancestral to them.

The evolutionary history of the †brontotheres is as different as possible from that of the horses; digital redaction ceased with the IV–III formula of †*Eotitanops* and the changes that went on through the Eocene and lower Oligocene are referable to two factors: (1) great increase in size and weight of the animals and (2) the development of functional horns on the skull. That the brain failed to develop proportionately may have been a cause of extinction. Nevertheless the law of change was much alike in the two families.

CHAPTER XVI

HISTORY OF THE PERISSODACTYLA

II. CERATOMORPHA

This section includes the tapirs and rhinoceroses in all their many ramifications and subdivisions; unlike as the twigs and tips of the branches became, there is everywhere evidence of a common origin.

Superfamily c. TAPIROIDEA

Family 4. Tapiridæ, Tapirs

The history of the tapir family continues to be in a very unsatisfactory state, because information is gathered so slowly. Tapirs

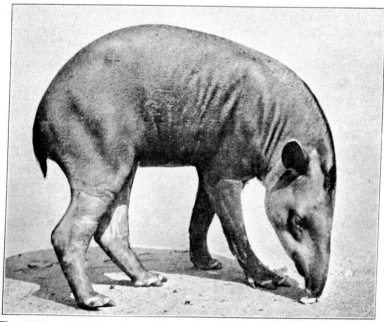

FIG. 267. — American Tapir, *Tapirus terrestris.* See also Fig. 133, p. 170.
(By permission of N. Y. Zoöl. Soc.)

are rare as fossils throughout the Tertiary epochs, presumably because they were always, like their Recent descendants, forest-dwellers and of solitary habits. In addition to this rarity and largely because

431

of it, the material yet collected is very fragmentary, not a half-way complete skeleton between Eocene and Pleistocene. Had these animals actually been present in Tertiary North America in such small numbers as the fossils would seem to indicate, they could not possibly have maintained themselves for so long a time; they would inevitably have died out at an early date.

The rarity and fragmentary nature of the fossils preclude any such comparatively full account of the tapirs as has been given for the

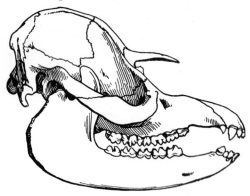

horses and †brontotheres, but this circumstance is less unfortunate than it would be for most other families, for the tapirs have been so unprogressive that they have undergone comparatively little change since their earliest appearance. Sir William Flower's term for them, "living fossils," is very apt, for they seem like belated survivors from a more ancient

FIG. 268. — Skull of American Tapir, right side.

world and out of place in this. The very curious present geographical distribution is, as has been mentioned (p. 124), limited to Central and South America and southern Asia. Existing tapirs are of moderate size, something like large-bodied, short-legged horses. The most striking peculiarity of existing tapirs is the proboscis, a long, flexible, dependent snout; were nothing known of these animals but the skull, the possession of the proboscis could have been confidently inferred from the great shortening of the nasal bones and the character of the nasal opening.

The dentition has undergone comparatively little modification. The formula is: $i \frac{3}{3}$, $c \frac{1}{1}$, $p \frac{4}{4}$, $m \frac{3}{3}$. Small tusks, hidden when the mouth is closed, are formed in an exceptional way by the lower canine and the third upper incisor, the upper canine being vestigial. The premolars, except the first, are molariform, as in all other modern perissodactyls. The upper molars have an outer wall which is made up of two conjoined cusps of equal size and convex externally and, in addition, two straight and simple transverse crests. The lower cheek-teeth have the two transverse crests, but the valley between them is open at both ends. This type of molar has persisted in the family with practically no change since the upper Eocene, at least.

Except for the modifications of the skull, which have been occasioned chiefly by the development of the proboscis, the skeleton might belong to any one of several Eocene or Oligocene families and

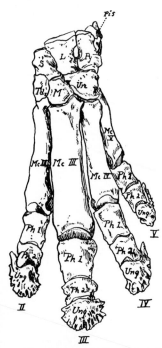

FIG. 269. — Left manus of Tapir, *Tapirus terrestris*. *S*, scaphoid. *L*, lunar. *Py*, pyramidal. *Pis*, pisiform. *Td*, trapezoid. *M*, magnum. *Un*, unciform. *Mc II, III, IV, V*, second, third, fourth and fifth metacarpal. *Ph 1, 2*, first and second phalanx. *Ung*, ungual phalanx.

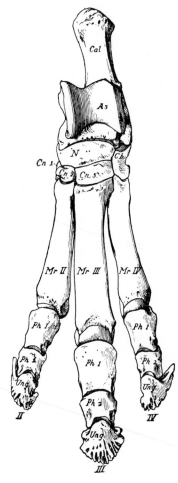

FIG. 270. — Left pes of Tapir. *Cal*, calcaneum. *As*, astragalus. *N*, navicular. *Cn 1, Cn 2, Cn 3*, first, second and third cuneiforms. *Mr II, III, IV*, second, third and fourth metatarsals. Other letters as in Fig. 269.

it is this generalized character, together with the proportions of body and limbs, which led to the frequent use of "tapiroid" for those families. In the Recent *Tapirus* the upper profile of the cranium rises steeply from the forehead and describes a convex curve to the occiput; the sagittal crest is short and broad, an area rather than a crest. The base of the cranium and occipital condyles are raised high above the level of the grinding teeth. The ascending ramus of the mandible has a characteristic forward inclination, and very convex posterior border. Neck and tail are short, body long; the odontoid process of the axis is partially spout-like, a very unusual feature in a

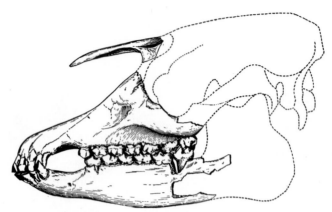

FIG. 271. — Skull of †*Miotapirus*, lower Miocene. (From Schlaikjer.)

short-necked ungulate. The limb-bones are short and stout, though by no means so heavy as in the rhinoceroses; ulna and fibula are separate and unreduced. There are four toes in the manus, three in

FIG. 272. — Lower and upper teeth of †*Miotapirus*. (From Schlaikjer.)

the pes, and they terminate in separate, well-developed hoofs, but behind these is a pad which carries most of the weight.

The body is covered with smooth, short hair, which, in the American species, is uniform brown or grey, but in the Asiatic species the head, neck and limbs are black and the body is white. In the young animal there is a colour-pattern of longitudinal light-coloured stripes and spots on a dark ground, thus probably reproducing the ancestral colouring. Tapirs are browsing, not grazing, animals and feed upon soft vegetable tissues. Shy and solitary they live usually in forests near water, which they frequently enter. At present, tapirs are the only perissodactyls in the Western Hemisphere.

In the Pleistocene, tapirs were apparently far more abundant than in any of the Tertiary stages, but the life of the forested regions was much more fully recorded in the Pleistocene and the difference may be illusory. One species, probably the same as the existing Central American form, was common in the forested area east of the Mississippi and in California. A second species, extinct, is larger and heavier than any now in existence (*T. †haysii*). Except in Texas, none have been found in the Great Plains, as that region was probably as treeless as it is now. These Pleistocene animals were adapted to a colder climate and a different vegetation from the existing ones, for these are tropical, except the Pinchaque Tapir (*T. roulini*) of the high Andes.

Little has been learned concerning the tapirs of the Pliocene, or of the upper and middle Miocene. A recent discovery of a fine specimen in the lower Miocene by Dr. E. Schlaikjer, collecting for the Harvard Museum, is therefore particularly welcome. He has named it *†Miotapirus*. In dentition and skull structure this animal is intermediate between the Pleistocene

Fig. 273. — Right pes of *†Miotapirus*. (From Schlaikjer.)

species and that of the Oligocene *†Protapirus validus*, a genus which was first discovered and named in the middle Eocene of France, and which is probably an immigrant here.

The White River genus, *†Protapirus*, is very rare in the Badlands and, in addition to jaw-fragments and scattered teeth, only two skulls have been reported, one in the State School of Mines (Rapid City, So. Dak.), the other in the museum of Princeton University; these supplement each other in a very gratifying way. The American species of †*Protapirus* is hardly more than half the size of the modern *T. americanus* and is, so far as it is known, more primitive and less specialized in every respect. The substitution of the third upper incisor for the canine had not yet taken place, the upper canine being larger than any of the incisors. None of the premolars is molariform, a very rare feature in a White River perissodactyl, for only in the †brontotheres is that primitive condition also found. In both families, however, the transformation had begun. In †*Protapirus* the upper premolars are tritubercular and triangular, with two external cusps,

FIG. 274. — Head of the White River tapir, †*Protapirus validus*. (Restored from a skull in Princeton Univ. Mus.)

connected by transverse crests with the single internal one; the separation of the crests and addition of a postero-internal cusp would produce the molar pattern, as actually took place in the succeeding genera.

The skull has an appearance very different from that of *Tapirus*, for it is evident that the proboscis was in a merely incipient stage of development and its modifying effects upon the skull had not yet been produced. The shortening of the nasal bones had begun, but they were still very much longer than in *Tapirus* and the proboscis can hardly have been more than a prehensile upper lip. The base of the cranium and occipital condyles are elevated but little above the level of the teeth, a long sagittal crest takes the place of the short area in *Tapirus* and the cranium rises so little at the forehead that the upper profile of the skull is not far from straight. The ascending ramus of the lower jaw has no forward inclination and the angle is more distinct than in the modern genus. Little is known of the skeleton, but such bones as have been found are proportionally more slender than in *Tapirus*.

Very little is known of Eocene tapirs in North America; the upper and middle Eocene †*Isectolophus* has tapir-like upper molars and

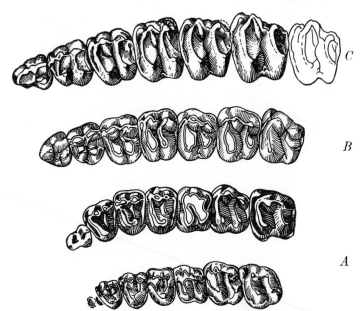

Fig. 275. — Evolution of upper cheek-teeth in the tapirs. *A*, two specimens of †*Protapirus*. *B*, †*Miotapirus*. *C*, Recent tapir. (From Schlaikjer.)

very probably belongs to this family, but in the lower Eocene nothing is known which can assuredly be called a tapir-ancestor. Inasmuch as †*Protapirus* occurs in the Eocene of France and the Oligocene of North America, its presence here must be regarded as due to immigration. How and where the later genera arose, it is impossible to say; tapirs ranged all around the northern hemisphere during the Tertiary, to all appearances, passing freely from one continent to another, until the events, probably climatic changes, of the Pleistocene exterminated them everywhere except in southern Asia, Central and South America.

The †Lophiodontidæ flourished greatly and had many representatives, large and small, in the Eocene and Oligocene of Europe, and many fossils, from the Bridger and White River stages in this country, have been referred to it, but from fragmentary material. There is, in fact, no clear evidence that the family ever reached America. It seems to have been a branch of the stock that gave rise to the tapirs, but to have been relatively short-lived, not extending beyond the Miocene.

Superfamily d. RHINOCEROIDEA

It may, perhaps, be better to erect another superfamily for a horde of small, primitive and generalized forms which abounded in the lower and especially in the middle Eocene, diminishing greatly in the upper Eocene, almost dying out at the end of that stage, but at all events, one of them is known to have survived into the White River.

Family 6. Rhinocerotidæ. True Rhinoceroses

Modern rhinoceroses, now confined to Africa and southern Asia, are but a small remnant of a vast and diversified group, which in the Tertiary was spread all over Arctogæa, but never entered South America or Australia. There have been three families of rhinoceroses, so clearly related that in the former edition of this book they were treated as subfamilies, a scheme of classification which has its advantages. Of the three families, two are extinct, and the third greatly reduced in numbers, variety and geographical range from what it was in Tertiary and even Quaternary times. The Old World and especially the great land-mass of Eurasia, was the principal area of development of the group.

The history of this family is long and complicated, and is recorded in the rocks with a completeness which is inferior only to the story of the horses. Yet the record is made extremely complex and difficult to interpret by the number of tribes which developed along converging or parallel lines, and by the migrations which spread species far from their places of origin, mingling them with indigenous forms.

The facts of rhinoceros history in North America cannot be made intelligible without some knowledge of the existing species, though the family disappeared from this continent early in the Pliocene. At the present time rhinoceroses are found only in tropical Asia and the Malay islands, Borneo, Sumatra and Java, and in Africa south of the Sahara, and these modern species are the terminal members of at least three, if not four, separate tribes. The Sumatran and Indian genera (*Rhinoceros* and *Dicerorhinus*) belong to two of these tribes, and it is usual to include the African species in one tribe and genus, *Opsiceros*. The Black Rhinoceros and the Broad-lipped Rhinoceros (mistakenly called "White") are so different in important structural features that it will be better to separate them generically. All the existing species are large and ponderous animals, ranging in shoulder-height from four to six feet, six inches and, except in females of the

Fig. 276. — African Black Rhinoceros, *Ceratotherium bicornis*. (By permission of N. Y. Zoöl. Soc.)

Javan species (*R. sondaicus*), they all have solid dermal horns, without bony horn-core, which are made up of agglutinated fibres. The Indian and Javan species have a single horn attached to the nasal bones and the Sumatran and African rhinoceroses have an additional horn, also in the median line, which is attached to the frontals. Though there are no horn-cores, the places of the attachment of the horns to the skull are unmistakably indicated by very rough areas and by the great thickening and upward arching of the nasal bones. Almost always nasal horns are present, unless the species is hornless, but in certain fossils only the frontal horns were developed.

The true rhinoceroses are especially characterized by the anterior teeth, if these are present at all, for in the African species incisors and canines have all been lost, but, when present, as they are in the modern Asiatic genera and in a host of extinct ones, they are very characteristic. Of the original three upper incisors, only the first one (i^1) remains and this has a low, sharp-edged crown, elongate antero-posteriorly and shaped like the sectorial of a carnivore. In the lower jaw, the first incisor ($i_{\overline{1}}$) is very small and without function; the second ($i_{\overline{2}}$) is a short, heavy, sharp-pointed and procumbent tusk, against the outer side of which the upper incisor bites, while the third ($i_{\overline{3}}$) has been lost. In the Indian species (*Rhinoceros unicornis*) the tusks are an effective defence against carnivores.

The genera of the lower and middle Oligocene have more numerous anterior teeth, which were successively lost, but for the post-Oligocene genera the usual dental formula is : $i \frac{0-1}{0-2}$, $c \frac{0}{0}$, $p \frac{4}{4}$, $m \frac{3}{3}$; the canines were lost early in the Oligocene and since then no member of the family has had them.

Except in a few Recent and Pleistocene species of the Old World, the grinding teeth are brachyodont and rooted and have no cement on the crowns. The premolars, except the first, are like the molars, though somewhat smaller, and all the cheek-teeth, throughout the family, have an exceedingly characteristic form. The outer side of an upper molar is a broad, smooth wall, formed by the extension of the postero-external cusp, the antero-external one being reduced to a mere pillar, and the two transverse crests are very oblique in their course. The third upper molar ($m^{\underline{3}}$) has a triangular crown because the outer wall and the posterior transverse crest are confluent. In all existing species and in many extinct ones, the upper cheek-teeth are further complicated by short spurs growing inward from the outer wall, or from the transverse crests, or from both. The lower grinding teeth have two crescents, one behind the other, but the horns, or arms, of the crescents are angulate, not curved, as they are in other bicrescentic teeth. In one existing species, the African Broad-lipped (or "White") Rhinoceros (*Opsiceros simus*) the teeth are so high-crowned as fairly to be called hypsodont, and this animal is a grazer.

The skull has thick nasal bones, which are strongly convex upward for the support of the dermal horn, and behind these, the upper contour of the skull is deeply concave, rising to the high occiput. There is no sagittal crest, but a broad, transversely flattened cranial roof; the brain-cavity is surrounded, as in elephants and †brontotheres, with cancellated bones, the thick cranial walls and roof being filled with large, membrane-lined and communicating chambers. This structure of the cranial bones is common to all large, tusk-bearing or horn-bearing ungulates, and combines strength with relative lightness. Except in the Sumatran genus (*Dicerorhinus*) the post-glenoid and post-tympanic processes of the squamosal are co-ossified below, forming a cylindrical passage-way to the auditory entrance; in the

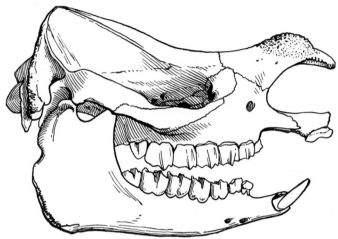

FIG. 277. — Skull of the Javan Rhinoceros, *R. sondaicus*. Note the single upper incisor, and the rough surface on the nasal bones for the attachment of the single horn.

Sumatran genus, as in the Tertiary forms generally, the two processes are not in contact. The premaxillaries are very small and articulate only with long projections from the maxillaries.

The mode of articulation between skull and lower jaw is, in some respects, unique among mammals. The post-glenoid process is a long spike, instead of the usual transverse ridge, which fits inside a bony hump, the post-cotyloid process, of the mandible, just behind the condyle. The spike-like processes of the two sides together hold the jaw in place and prevent dislocation, while permitting a hinge-like movement. The angle of the mandible is thick and has roughened borders, a feature which occurs in no other perissodactyls.

The neck is short and thick and the odontoid process of the axis is a short, heavy cylinder. The trunk is very long, broad and deep; the long, strongly arched ribs and widely expanded pelvis provide space for the great mass of viscera. The tail is rather short.

The limbs are short and very heavy, though there is considerable difference in proportionate length of leg among the various species.

The humerus has an unusually prominent deltoid ridge and the femur has a very large third trochanter. The ungual phalanges are less reduced than in the elephant and the hoofs are larger, but the feet are of the same columnar shape and the weight is supported by an elastic pad, which rests upon a sole of very thick skin, a type of foot which, so far as can be judged from the bones, has been common to all very large and heavy ungulates.

Each of the existing species of rhinoceros has its own dental and skeletal characteristics, but in a general survey it is not necessary to enumerate them.

Living rhinoceroses differ considerably in their external appearance and in the character of the skin, which is always very thick

FIG. 278. — Left manus of Indian Rhinoceros, *R. unicornis.*

and coarse, typically "pachydermatous," in short. Most of the species are hairless, except for the tuft at the end of the tail, but the Sumatran genus has a sparse covering of hair, which is a thick coat in the young animal. In the Indian *Rhinoceros unicornis* the enormously thick skin has conspicuous and regularly arranged folds which make the creature seem to be encased in armour, as he is in Dürer's famous print; the ears and tail are tufted with hair. The African and Sumatran species have a smoother appearance, for the skin-folds are obscure and irregular. In all but two of the living species the upper lip is prehensile and characteristically pointed and can pick up very small objects, like the "finger" on the end of an elephant's trunk. In the Sumatran Rhinoceros the lip, though pointed, is horny and inflexible, while in the African *Opsiceros simus* it is broad and straight-edged.

Rhinoceroses disappeared from North America after the early Pliocene, though a few stragglers may have survived till the middle, or even the later Pliocene, in Florida and California. In the lower Pliocene they were abundant and varied, the genera and species being more numerous than those now living in Africa and Asia combined, and were a curiously mixed assemblage of conservative and progressive types. As far as can be judged at present, the Pliocene and upper Miocene rhinoceroses of North America were not generally the descendants of middle Miocene native stocks. These species were mostly hornless (†*Aphelops*) or had a very small horn on the tip of the nose (†*Teleoceras*). In one genus (†*Peraceras*) the incisor teeth had been lost, as in the modern African species, and in all these American species the cheek-teeth are larger and higher-crowned than in the more ancient ones. Among these Pliocene rhinoceroses there were great differences in the proportions of the trunk, limbs and feet. One species, †*Teleoceras fossiger*, has the immense body and extremely short legs of a hippopotamus; other species, such as †*Aphe-*

FIG. 279. — †*Teleoceras fossiger*, a short-legged rhinoceros, with small nasal horn, lower Pliocene and upper Miocene of Neb. (Restored from a skeleton in Amer. Mus. of Nat. Hist.)

lops malacorhinus, have relatively much longer limbs and feet, and smaller trunk.

The rhinoceroses of the upper Miocene are much the same as those of the lower Pliocene, but those of the middle Miocene are fewer and less diversified. The middle Miocene species of †*Teleoceras*, †*T. medicornutus*, not only had the usual horn on the tip of the nose, but also an additional and still smaller one in the middle of the forehead.

Aside from the differences in the skull, which are obviously to be correlated with the very small size, or entire absence, of the horns, the Pliocene, upper and middle Miocene rhinoceroses of North America had skeletons which differed little from the type common to the modern genera of the family, and all had tridactyl feet. That is to say that the modern stage of skeletal development, other than that of the skull, had been attained in the middle Miocene. None of the American genera had large, fully developed horns and none of the Old World forms with large horns ever migrated to this continent.

In the lower Miocene the abundance of the small †diceratheres so overshadowed the larger rhinoceroses that the latter were long

Fig. 280. — The small, †pair-horned rhinoceros, *Diceratherium cooki*, lower Miocene.   (Restored from a skeleton in Carnegie Mus.)

believed to have died out in America, which involved the further belief that the middle and upper Miocene genera were all immigrants. The line was, however, continued in the Great Plains. The especially abundant genus of the lower Miocene is †*Diceratherium*, which, in the male, had a pair of horns *transversely* placed, instead of one behind the other in the median line, as in all other genera of the family. The horns are indicated by the pair of prominent and roughened knobs on the nasal bones; the female skulls are hornless. The common lower Miocene species is †*D. cooki*, no larger than a Wild Boar, the bones of which occur in incredible numbers at Agate, Neb. (Fig. 45, p. 53). The genus seems to have died out in the lower Harrison; at least no trace of it has been found in the upper division of that stage. In the John Day the only rhinoceroses so far certainly identified are larger and smaller species of †*Diceratherium;* the hornless kinds, which existed before and after John Day time, have not been found in Oregon. This is only one of several *lacunæ* in the John Day fauna, that is, the absence of mammals that might be expected to occur there. Several explanations of these lacks have been suggested, of which the most widely accepted is that Oregon was then forested, but the absence of silicified wood in the beds of volcanic ash in which the fossil bones are embedded, is an objection to the hypothesis. The very small area of the John Day exposures may explain many of the absences.

In the channel-sandstones of the upper White River occur skulls that seem to mark the beginning of †*Diceratherium,* in transition from the typical White River rhinoceros, the hornless †*Subhyracodon.* As compared with that of the latter, the channel-sandstone skull has greatly thickened nasal bones and on the outer side of each nasal a small roughened area which marks the place of attachment of a dermal horn. Hatcher, who discovered and described this transitional species, named it †*Diceratherium proavitum,* while other authorities have preferred to keep it in the characteristic White River genus †*Subhyracodon.*

†Pair-horned rhinoceroses were first discovered many years ago in France by Duvernoy, who named his species *Rhinoceros* †*pleuroceros,* and the presence of this species in the Old World offers a number of problems which can be solved only by a careful comparative study of the French and American species. The American origin of †*Diceratherium* seems to be demonstrated by the series of modifications, in proper stratigraphical order, which may be traced through the lower, middle and upper White River into the John Day and Harrison, but how is the European species to be accounted for? It may have been an immigrant from America, or the pair-horned modification may have arisen independently more than once. To choose between these alternatives it will be necessary to know whether "*R.*" †*pleuroceros* belongs in the European or the American series and the studies required for this have not been made.

In the middle White River (lower Brulé substage) the predominant genus is †*Subhyracodon,* the extremely ill-chosen name given by the Russian naturalist, J. F. Brandt. The best-known species is †*S. occidentalis.* This animal is an unmistakable rhinoceros, every tooth and bone being typical of the family, yet in innumerable details it differs from all the existing species of the group. In size and proportions this Oligocene genus is more like a tapir than a modern rhinoceros, being of much lighter and more slender build and longer-legged than the latter. The dental formula is: $i \frac{2}{2}, c \frac{0}{0}, p \frac{4}{4}, m \frac{3}{3} \times 2 = 36$; the canines and the third incisor, above and below, have been lost, though the upper canine occurs in immature animals; the small second upper incisor persists, as a remnant of a more primitive condition. The premolars, especially the upper ones, have not yet fully acquired the molar pattern, but in this respect there is great individual variation, hardly any two skulls agreeing; if a sufficiently

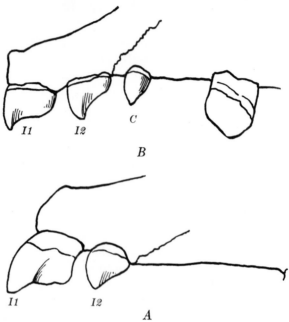

Fig. 281. — Anterior end of left upper jaw of †*Subhyracodon*, *A*, adult. *B*, immature animal (from Osborn). *I 1*, first incisor. *I 2*, second incisor. *C*, canine.

large number of skulls could be obtained, it might be practicable to group these variations specifically. The molars have all the essentials of the rhinoceros plan, but the upper ones seem to be much less complicated than in Recent genera, because they lack the accessory spurs from the outer wall and the transverse crests, which are so conspicuous in the latter. They are much lower-crowned and smaller than in the Miocene and Pliocene genera.

The skull of †*Subhyracodon* is hornless and, in consequence, differs much more from that of the modern genera than does any other part of the skeleton. The cranium is not flattened on top, but has a short sagittal crest and the cranial bones are thin and without cancelli. The upper contour of the cranium rises to the occiput in varying degrees of steepness, and sometimes the whole upper line of the skull is nearly horizontal. These may be specific, or only individual differences; more extensive series of skulls will be needed for the decision of this question. The nasal bones, having no horn to support, are thin and more or less flat, sometimes moderately convex. The premaxillaries are much less reduced than in the modern species and have ascending rami which almost reach the nasals, and the anterior end of the maxillaries is more normal, not having the lath-like projection, to the end of which the premaxilla is attached. The post-glenoid process

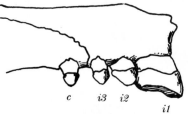

FIG. 282. — Right premaxillary of †*Trigonias osborni.* c, canine. *i1, i2, i3,* incisors. (From Lucas.)

is of the usual kind and only beginning to take on the peculiar rhinocerotic shape; this process is usually well separated from the post-tympanic process, but sometimes approximates it, though it is never co-ossified with it. The mandible lacks the post-cotyloid process which is present in all the existing genera, and the angle is not thickened as in them, but is thin and tapir-like. Thus, many of the characteristic features of the skull which are found in all the Recent and Pleistocene and most of the upper and middle Miocene rhinoceroses had not made their appearance in †*Subhyracodon.*

The neck is short, but not very heavy, the trunk long and relatively slender, for the ribs are not extremely long or very strongly arched and the hip-bones are so little expanded that they are tapir-like. Evidently, the White River genus can have had no such immense mass of viscera, even proportionately, as have existing rhinoceroses. The limb-bones, both actually and relatively, are much lighter and more slender than in the latter, and the femur has a more cylindrical, less flattened shaft. The feet, which are moderately elongate and slender, are tridactyl.

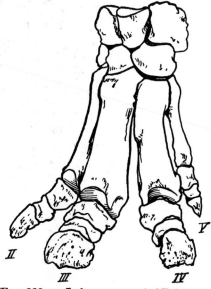

FIG. 283. — Left manus of †*Trigonias osborni.* (From Hatcher.)

Aside from jaw-fragments and more or less questionable material, the most ancient and primitive representative of the true rhinoceros family is †*Trigonias*, which is characteristic of the lower White River, or Chadron substage.

This genus had a more nearly complete dentition than any other known member of the family, the formula being: $i\frac{3}{3}, c\frac{1}{6}, p\frac{4}{4}, m\frac{3}{3}$ × 2 = 42, or 14 more than in the existing African *Opsiceros*. In the upper jaw the first incisor had already assumed the characteristic chisel-like shape, but was relatively smaller than in the succeeding genera; the other incisors, especially the third, are much smaller than the first and of simple conical shape; the canine is greatly reduced and so small that it can have had no function. The lower jaw also has three incisors on each side; the first and third very small, the second enlarged and tusk-like. The premolars are smaller and less complex than the molars, but there is great individual variation in this respect, hardly any two skulls having the premolars exactly alike, and several species may, perhaps, be involved.

The skeleton is essentially like that of †*Subhyracodon*, with the important exception that in the manus there are four digits instead of three; the fifth is very small and cannot have been of any use, but it is complete with metacarpal and three phalanges. In the pes there are only three digits, as in all Eocene perissodactyls, almost all of which have four in the manus.

In the middle Miocene of France is found a rhinoceros, †*Aceratherium aurelianense*, which also has four digits in the manus, but there is probably no close relation with †*Trigonias*. The four-toed manus was common to the ancestry of all the rhinoceros families and tribes and that it should have persisted in two or more unrelated series is not surprising.

With †*Trigonias* the definitely known history of the true rhinoceroses begins, and cannot yet be carried farther back. †*Eotrigonias* of the upper Eocene, known only from the teeth, is probably an ancestor of the White River genus, but no positive statements can be made until better-preserved skulls have been found, and the same considerations apply to the upper jaw (†*Prohyracodon*) which Dr. H. E. Wood has reported from the middle Eocene of Roumania, and which he regards as the ancestral true rhinoceros. It may well prove to be so, but more complete material is required for a decision of the question.

It was stated at the outset that by far the most numerous and the most extraordinary tribes of rhinoceroses arose and ran their course in the Old World. A brief statement concerning three of the

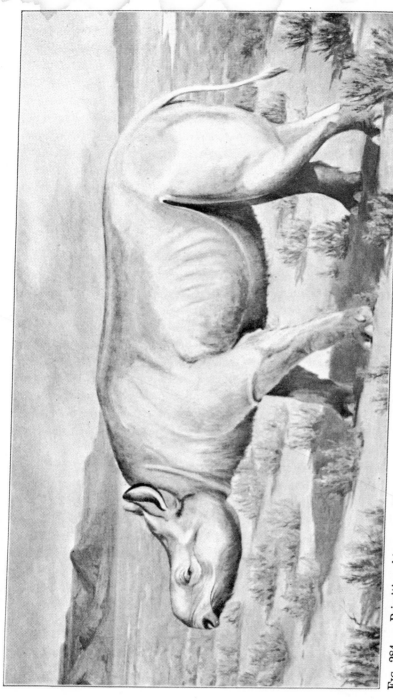

Fig. 284. — Primitive rhinoceros, †*Trigonias osborni*, lower White River, Chadron substage. The figure seems to err in showing four toes in the pes. (Restored by Irving Biehn under direction of E. R. Nelson Jr.; courtesy of Milwaukee Pub. Mus.)

449

most astonishing genera of Eurasia may not be out of place here. The first of these is †*Baluchitherium*, of the Asiatic Oligocene and Miocene, the most colossal land mammal that is known. First discovered by C. Foster-Cooper in Baluchistan, the American Museum parties obtained enough material in the Gobi Desert to make a restoration of this incredible monster. There were several species of different sizes, the largest of which stood 17 feet high at the shoulder, far overtopping the most tremendous of the fossil elephants. In †*Baluchitherium* the enormous skull is hornless and the nasal bones are weak, the frontals form a high convexity. The neck is colossal and the vertebræ look like those of †dinosaurs. This unmistakable rhinoceros, the descriptions of which have exhausted the stock of adjectives, is of limited Asiatic distribution, from Mongolia to Baluchistan, and has not been found in any other continent.

The second of these amazing monsters is †*Elasmotherium*, a Pleistocene genus, which ranged from France to Siberia, and was a very large animal of elephantine stature. There was no nasal horn, but an immense bony dome on the frontals must have supported a huge frontal horn. The most remarkable feature of this genus is in its grinding teeth, which, at first sight, look like those of a colossal horse; they are completely hypsodont and rootless and are covered with cement; the enamel crests are not simple, as in other rhinoceroses, but crimped and crenellated, as in horses. The plan of the teeth is, however, not equine. The only other known rhinoceros, fossil or Recent, with high-crowned, cement-covered teeth is the African Broad-lipped species, *Opsiceros simus*.

Finally, there is the †Woolly Rhinoceros (*Opsiceros* †*tichorhinus*) which in the Pleistocene extended from the south of France to northeastern Siberia. In the latter region complete carcasses have been found in the frozen gravels. It has thus been made known that these creatures, like the †Mammoth, were covered with a dense coat of hair and wool. In the Eastern Hemisphere the †Woolly Rhinoceros everywhere accompanied the †Mammoth and it is one of the mysteries of geographical distribution that he did not spread into Alaska and thence across North America, as the †Hairy Elephant did.

Family 7. †*Hyracodontidæ.* †*Cursorial Rhinoceroses*

This was a short-lived group, the upper Eocene (somewhat doubtfully) and the White River Oligocene are its present limits and it has never been found outside North America. The three rhinoceros families are each characterized by striking peculiarities of the anterior teeth. In the Rhinocerotidæ a few genera have lost all the canines and incisors, but in the great majority the first upper incisor is chisel-like and shears against the outside of the second lower, which is a large, pointed and procumbent tusk. The first lower incisor is retained, though it is a useless vestige; upper and lower canines are lost; functionally, therefore, the formula is: $i\frac{1-0}{1-0}$, $c\frac{0}{0}$. In the †Amy-

Fig. 285. — †Cursorial rhinoceros, †*Hyracodon nebrascensis*, White River. (Restored from a skeleton in Princeton Univ. Mus.)

nodontidæ the canines are large, hippopotamus-like tusks and in the †Hyracodontidæ all the front teeth are preserved, $i\frac{3}{3}$, $c\frac{1}{1}$, and they all have the same shape and nearly the same size. The final genus of the series and the only one yet found in the White River, is †*Hyracodon*, in which the anterior teeth are simple, pointed and slightly recurved hooks, utterly different from the incisors and canines of the other two families, as they differ completely from each other. The premolars, except the first, are mostly molariform, but there is great individual difference in the degree of completeness in assumption of the molar pattern. The molars are much like those of the contemporary †*Subhyracodon*, though considerably smaller; they are low-crowned, typically rhinoceros teeth of the simplest kind, having no accessory spurs from the transverse crests, or outer wall. One slight, though significant, difference there is. The last upper molar (m $\underline{3}$) has not yet perfectly acquired the triangular shape characteristic of all the true rhinoceroses, for the outer wall is not completely fused with the posterior crest, but projects a little behind it, as in perissodactyls generally; this is a remnant of a more primitive type of dentition.

The small anterior teeth were too weak to be of any importance as weapons and, as †*Hyracodon* had no horns, the sole means of escape from the attacks of Carnivora lay in speed, and the skeleton clearly testifies that these animals were swift runners. Possibly it was their complete defencelessness that led to their early extinction.

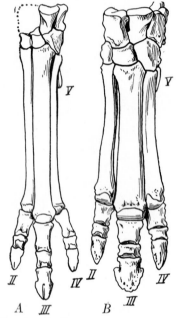

FIG. 286. — Left manus of †cursorial rhinoceroses. *A*, †*Triplopus cubitalis*, upper Bridger (after Cope). *B*, †*Hyracodon nebrascensis*, White River.

The skull is short, deep and thick, indicative of a clumsy, ungraceful head, and seems to be quite out of keeping with the rest of the skeleton. One might be misled into thinking that there had been some error in associating skull and skeleton. There is, however, no room for doubt of the correctness of this association. The neck is remarkably long, more elongate proportionately than in the contemporary genus of horses, †*Mesohippus*, but the cervical vertebræ are relatively heavy and strong, as was needed for the attachment of muscles to support the clumsy head. The trunk is elongate, but not massive, and the limbs are proportionately much longer and lighter than those of any other known rhinoceros. The limb-bones, despite their length and slenderness, are yet unmistakably rhinocerotic in form, and this same is true of the feet, which are narrow and elongate, approximating, though not attaining, the proportions of †*Mesohippus*. There are three digits in each foot and the median one is so enlarged and the laterals so reduced as strongly to suggest that, had the family continued to develop through the Miocene epoch, monodactyl forms would have been the result, as they actually were in their competitors, the horses. White River horses (†*Mesohippus* and †*Miohippus*) were quite as defenceless as the

†hyracodonts, and probably owed their survival to greater speed and higher intelligence.

No †hyracodonts have been found in the Duchesne River beds, but no doubt they existed in the region. The upper Eocene genus, †*Prothyracodon*, is still very incompletely known, but seems to have been an ancestor of the White River †*Hyracodon*, from which it differs in its smaller size and less complicated premolar teeth.

In the middle Eocene †*Triplopus* has frequently been regarded as the forerunner of †*Hyracodon*, as it is the only Bridger perissodactyl known to have a tridactyl manus. The only known species of †*Triplopus*, †*T. cubitalis*, could not have been the ancestor required, as it is already too far specialized in the great elongation and slenderness of its limbs. If †*Hyracodon* did actually descend from some genus of the American middle Eocene, a descent which is not very probable, the ancestor must be sought in the horde of small perissodactyls included in the †Hyrachyidæ, but it seems more likely that the ancestral genus is to be found in Mongolia, if anywhere.

Family 8. †*Amynodontidæ.* †*Amphibious Rhinoceroses*

The †amynodont family also was short-lived and was present in North America only from the upper middle Eocene to the middle Oligocene, but continued somewhat longer in the Old World. This is a very distinct, clearly defined group of hornless rhinoceroses, which, presumably, were adapted to a more or less aquatic life. The terminal member of the American series is the genus †*Metamynodon*, the bones of which occur chiefly in the consolidated sands and gravels which fill the ancient stream-channels of the middle White River (lower Brulé stage). The best-known American species yet discovered, †*M. planifrons*, was a large and massive, rather short-legged animal, the largest mammal of its time. After the disappearance of the great †brontotheres, the White River fauna consisted almost entirely of small mammals, the †amynodonts and the giant †entelodonts being the only exceptions.

As pointed out above, the †amynodonts are most conspicuously distinguished from the two other rhinoceros families by the character of the anterior teeth. The large and functional incisors are present in little reduced number and size, and are all similar in form; the canines, which are lost in the true rhinoceroses and greatly reduced in size in the †hyracodonts, are much enlarged in the †amynodonts into formidable hippopotamus-like tusks. The upper tusk is thick and heavy, but short and is obliquely truncated by the wear of the lower

FIG. 287. — Supposedly †aquatic rhinoceros, †*Metamynodon planifrons*, White River. (Restored from a skeleton in Amer. Mus. Nat. Hist.)

ROBERT BRUCE HORSFALL

one, likewise a very large tusk, curved in almost a semi-circle and resembling the corresponding tooth of a hippopotamus. Upper and lower canines would seem to have grown throughout the lifetime of the animal and not to have formed roots at all. Characteristic of this family is the reduction of the premolars, both in numbers and in size, giving the dental formula: $i\frac{3}{3}$, $c\frac{1}{1}$, $p\frac{3}{2}$, $m\frac{3}{3} \times 2 = 38$. The premolars are smaller than the molars, but $p\frac{3}{}$ and $\frac{4}{}$ have acquired the molar plan. The molars have the characteristic rhinocerotic pattern but are narrow and laterally compressed; the lower molars are prolonged antero-posteriorly but very narrow transversely and their crowns are incompletely encased in enamel, which is lacking along vertical bands, where the dentine is exposed. There is a remarkable resemblance between the cheek-teeth, especially the lower ones, to those of the Patagonian †Astrapotheria, a resemblance which is of particular interest, because it can be demonstrated that these teeth were independently developed in the two groups.

The skull of †Metamynodon is very peculiar and not only altogether different from that of all the other rhinoceros families, but also from that found in any other hoofed animal; the long and prominent sagittal crest and heavy, immensely expanded zygomatic arches give a surprising likeness to the skull of a great carnivore. The face is greatly shortened, the eye-sockets very far forward and the whole skull depressed, so that, in life, the head must have been low, broad and flat. The neck is short, the body elongate and massive, as is shown by the long and strongly arched ribs, which obviously enclosed a great bulk of viscera. The limbs are short and heavy and the feet archaic, for the manus retains four fully developed and functional digits. Except the tapirs, no other perissodactyl of the middle White River has a tetradactyl manus.

The whole structure of these animals is suggestive of amphibious habits, an inference which is strengthened by the general occurrence of their bones in the channel sands.

Another species of †Metamynodon has been found in the Oligocene of Mongolia, which differs only in details from the American one. In Mongolia also occurs another genus of the same family, †Cadurcotherium, which spread westward into France, where it was first discovered, but did not range eastward into North America.

The Duchesne River genus, †Mesamynodon, has not yet been fully made known; it may be said, however, to be intermediate in structure, as it is in time, between the genera of the White River and the Uinta Eocene.

†*Amynodon*, of the upper Eocene, was the first member of the family to be discovered and named, and entire skeletons of this genus have been found both in Utah and in Mongolia. It is clearly more primitive and less specialized than its White River successor, being a smaller and lighter animal with face less shortened and zygomatic arches not nearly so heavy, or so widely expanded. The canine tusks are much smaller, both actually and relatively, and had a limited period of growth. The premolars are present in unreduced number and are much smaller than the molars, though p $\underline{3}$ and $\underline{4}$ are molariform in pattern. The lower molars are not so narrow as in †*Metamynodon* and the crowns are completely covered with enamel. The skeleton is, in general, like that of the White River genus, but the bones are more slender.

In the upper part of the middle Eocene is found another species of †*Amynodon* which is still smaller than the Uinta animal, and which had less developed tusks, of which the lower one was quite erect, not so procumbent as is that of the Uinta species. The molars already have the typically rhinocerotic pattern, and this is the only Bridger mammal of which that can be said.

So far, it has not been possible to trace this family to more ancient formations than the upper Bridger, and Mongolia seems to be the most promising region to yield the ancestor common to the three rhinoceros families. When found, that ancestor will probably prove to be a member of the middle and lower Eocene family of the †Hyrachyidæ, but no American representative of the group is likely to be that ancestor, for the hiatus between these American ceratomorphs and the earliest rhinoceroses is too great to be filled in the time involved. Of course new discoveries may, at any time, entirely change this point of view, and show that the whole group arose in America. From present knowledge, however, it is most probable that the three families are of Asiatic origin. In Eocene and Oligocene times intermigration between eastern Asia and North America was, for many mammals, so easy that the difficulty of determining their places of origin is greatly increased and the problem loses much of its significance.

Family 9. †*Hyrachyidæ*

The latest member of this family is the White River †*Colodon*, as yet very incompletely known. Included in the family is a horde of small and medium-sized animals, which were once abundant in the Wind River and much more so in the Bridger, in which stage members of the family are, next after the †brontotheres, the commonest fossils.

†HYRACHYIDÆ

†*Colodon*, mid. Oligo. (White River) †*Hyrachyus*, †*Triplopus*, †*Colonoceras*, †*Desmatotherium*, †*Dilophodon*, †*Helaletes*, mid. Eoc. (Bridger). †*Homogalax*, †*Heptodon*, low. Eoc. (Wind River).

The typical, most abundant and most diversified genus is †*Hyrachyus*, from which the family is named. It is a generalized, undifferentiated

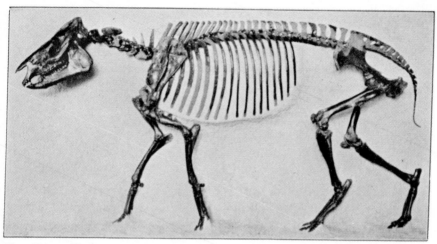

FIG. 288. — Skeleton of †*Hyrachyus eximius*, middle Eocene, Bridger stage. (U. S. Nat. Mus.; courtesy of C. W. Gilmore.)

perissodactyl which, aside from the teeth, might have given rise to almost any family of the order, the horses excepted. Many species of this genus have been named, many more than could have co-existed in the same area and the same time. Probably, however, these species, so called, were largely successive rather than contemporary. In size, they range from a tapir to a fox. Several skeletons of the common, medium-sized †*H. eximius* have been obtained and are exhibited in the American and National Museums and in Peabody Museum of Yale University. In †*Hyrachyus*, the dentition is unreduced and the total number of teeth is 44. The incisors, though not large, were all functional and the canines are of moderate size, forming small tusks. The premolars, as in most other Eocene perissodactyls, are all smaller and less complex than the molars. The upper molars are, in a sense, intermediate between those of tapirs and of rhinoceroses; the antero-external cusp is convex and the postero-external one is larger and flat, or slightly concave; the transverse crests are straight, not oblique; the lower molars are entirely tapir-like, with two simple transverse crests.

The skull is long, narrow and low, with moderately elongate cranium and very long face. The brain-case is not capacious and the sagittal crest is high. The neck is short, the trunk very long, with 25 dorso-lumbar vertebræ, and rather short tail. The limbs are of

Fig. 289. — Primitive rhinoceros, †*Hyrachyus eximius*, lower Bridger. (Restored from a skeleton in the Amer. Mus. Nat. Hist.)

medium length and thickness and the feet relatively short and narrow, with four digits in the manus, three in the pes, as in all other Bridger perissodactyls except †*Triplopus*. Aside from the head, which is different, the general proportions of this species are those of a more lightly built tapir.

An interesting modification of the †thyrachyid type is furnished by the Bridger genus †*Colonoceras*, which evidently had a small dermal horn on each nasal bone, as appears from the small, circular, roughened area on the bone. No other horned member of the family is known and no other perissodactyl with horns has been found in the Bridger formation. A possible exception is the †brontothere †*Manteoceras* ("prophet of horns"), of the uppermost Bridger, which may have had dermal horns as a first step in the development of the bony protuberances characteristic of the †Brontotheriidæ.

A tribe within the †Hyrachyidæ and sometimes separated as a distinct family, is that exemplified by the genus †*Helaletes*, which has hitherto been very incompletely known, but the U. S. National Museum has recently acquired an entire skeleton in a beautifully complete state of preservation. With rather more tapir-like teeth, †*Helaletes* may be described as a conspicuously more slender and lightly built †*Hyrachyus*. Several other Bridger genera, such as †*Desmatotherium* and the very small †*Dilophodon*, are included in this tribe, but these are known only from teeth.

In the lower Eocene, especially the Wind River stage of it, this family is common, but much less diversified than in the Bridger; the

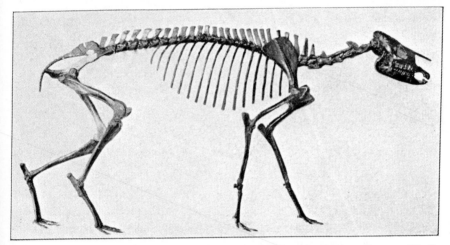

Fig. 290. — Skeleton of †*Helaletes nanus*, middle Eocene, Bridger stage. (U. S. Nat. Mus.; courtesy of C. W. Gilmore.)

two characteristic genera are †*Homogalax* and †*Heptodon* and, of the latter, there is a fine skeleton in the Harvard Museum, collected in the Wind River beds. These genera are very much like the smaller species of the Bridger †*Hyrachyus* and are somewhat more tapir-like than the latter. It is possible, though not very probable, that the veritable tapir-ancestors are concealed within this group. †*Heptodon* has proportions similar to those of †*Hyrachyus* and †*Helaletes*, though with longer and heavier tail; all of these have the level back and fore- and hind-limbs of nearly equal length. Of the Eocene perissodactyls which belong to the normal group (suborder Chelopoda) there are two types of bodily shape and appearance. In one, that of the horses, the hind-legs are so much longer than the fore that the rump is raised well above the shoulders and this is a feature which is found among

FIG. 291. — Primitive †tapiroid, †*Helaletes nanus*, middle Eocene, Bridger stage. (Restored from the skeleton in Fig. 290.)

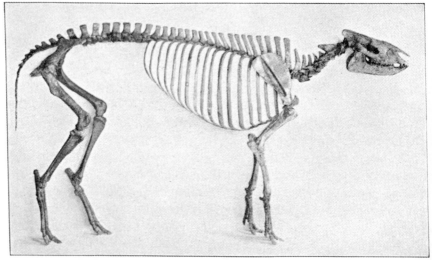

FIG. 292. — †*Heptodon brownorum*, Wind River stage. (Skeleton in Mus. Comp. Zoöl. Harvard Univ.)

many primitive artiodactyl groups, such as the living chevrotains, the †Leptomerycidæ, the early camels, etc. On the other hand, the Eocene †brontotheres and †thyrachyids and †amynodonts are "tapiroid" and have fore and hind legs of approximately equal length and horizontal vertebral column.

SUBORDER II. †Ancylopoda. PERISSODACTYLS WITH CLAWS

Family 10. †Chalicotheriidæ

This group of strange and grotesque ungulates is altogether extinct and, for lack of any living animals with which they can be compared, there is much concerning their habits and mode of life that is not understood.

The history of the discovery of the †Ancylopoda is both interesting and instructive, especially as two other groups, the artiodactyl family of the †Agriochœridæ (p. 372) and the South American †toxodont suborder, †Entelonychia (Chap. XVIII), afford almost exact parallels. The tale of these discoveries ought to put an end to the foolish notion that the palæontologist can reconstruct a lost animal from a single bone or tooth, but it will not. The idea has been exposed and confuted many times, but it is immortal and invulnerable and no doubt will long continue to flourish.

In 1823 Cuvier assigned certain foot-bones, found in the Miocene of Sansan, to the scaly anteaters, or pangolins, not giving a technical name, but calling the creature "le pangolin gigantesque," and in 1838 Lartet named it †*Macrotherium*. In 1833 Kaup described a skull, from the Pliocene of Eppelsheim in the Mainz basin, naming it †*Chalicotherium* and assigning it to the group which was subsequently called Perissodactyla. In 1863 Gaudry discovered in the lower Pliocene of Pikermi, near Athens, quite complete fore- and hind-feet of the †*Macrotherium* type, but of a much larger animal and this he named †*Ancylotherium*.

There the matter rested until 1887, when Forsyth Major, collecting in the Greek island of Samos, became convinced that †*Chalicotherium* and †*Ancylotherium* were the same animal, a conclusion which, to most people, seemed preposterous. It was, however, speedily confirmed by Filhol, who found at Sansan an entire skeleton with all the bones in their natural connections; this skeleton unites the feet of †*Macrotherium* with a skull and teeth which are of the †*Chalicotherium* type.

In this country the course of discovery was very similar to that in Europe. In 1877 Professor O. C. Marsh named certain foot-bones from the Miocene of Nebraska †*Moropus* and referred the genus to the Edentata, on the supposition that it was one of the great †ground-sloths (Chap. XXIII). Many years later, the Carnegie Museum of Pittsburgh obtained complete skeletons of †*Moropus* in the famous "bone quarry" of Agate, Neb., and Messrs. Holland and Peterson published an elaborate monograph in description of it and showed

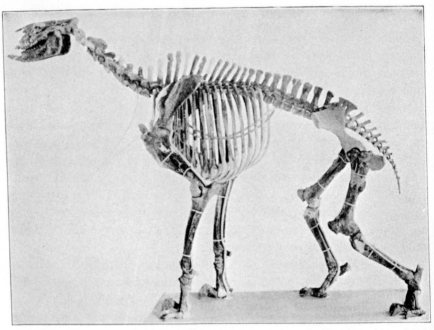

Fig. 293.— Skeleton of †*Moropus elatus*, with front end of skull broken away, lower Miocene of Agate, Neb., lower Harrison. (Mus. Comp. Zoöl. Harvard Univ.)

that the supposed †ground-sloth was an American representative of the †Ancylopoda.

In China and India the suborder survived into the Pleistocene, but, elsewhere, has not been found in beds later than the Pliocene. The time of greatest abundance of these extraordinary creatures in North America was in the lower Miocene (Harrison stage). That the †chalicothere family was represented in the upper Miocene and lower Pliocene of the Great Plains is demonstrated by remains so fragmentary, that it is impossible to determine the genus, or genera, to which they should be referred. The European genus †*Macrotherium* invaded North America for a time and has been found in the middle Miocene of Colorado.

The only well-known American genus of the †chalicotheres is †*Moropus*, of the lower Miocene, of which the common species is †*M. elatus* and this considerably exceeded the largest modern horses in bulk and stature. †*Moropus* is in most respects decidedly less specialized than †*Macrotherium* from the middle Miocene of Europe. The dental formula is: $i \frac{0}{3}$, $c \frac{0}{0}$, $p \frac{3}{3}$, $m \frac{3}{3} \times 2 = 30$; all the upper incisors and canines have been suppressed as has also the first premolar above and below. The cheek-teeth are low-crowned and the premolars are all smaller and simpler than the molars, which are formed as in the Old World genera, and have some resemblance to those of the †brontotheres. The upper molars have an outer wall made up of two very concave cusps and one transverse crest, or ridge. The lower molars are bicrescentic, one crescent behind the other; but there is a difference in the median internal pillar, where the two crescents unite; the pillar is single in †*Macrotherium*, double in †*Moropus*. While the likeness to the grinding teeth of the †brontotheres is suggestive, there is reason to think that the likeness is due to convergent development rather than to relationship.

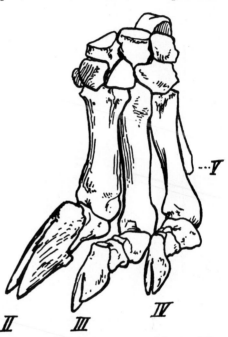

Fig. 294. — Left manus of lower Miocene †chalicothere, †*Moropus*. (After Peterson.)

In the living animal there was a proportionally rather small head, which was slender and pointed and not unlike that of a horse in appearance; the neck is moderately long, much longer than that of †*Macrotherium*, the trunk is very long and the tail short. The limbs are long, especially the fore-legs, which are decidedly longer than the hind-legs and thus the back slopes down from the withers to the rump, as in a giraffe, though not so steeply. The fore-arm, the bones of which are co-ossified, and the thigh are the longest limb-segments and the fore-foot is longer than the hind. As will be shown in Chapter XVIII, the South American †Entelonychia, which are not perissodactyls at all and are but remotely related to the †Ancylopoda, are also clawed ungulates and it is of great interest to observe how the proportions of the limbs and of the feet in the fully developed †Entelonychia, such as the Miocene genus †*Homalodotherium,* closely correspond to those of †*Moropus.*

The feet of †*Moropus* depart less from those of the normal perissodactyls than do those of the European †chalicotheres, but have similar great claws. A considerable remnant of the fifth digit persisted in the manus; the metacarpal is a long, slender splint, without

FIG. 295. — †Chalicothere, †*Moropus elatus.* (Restored from a skeleton in Carnegie Mus.)

phalanges. In the Miocene and Pliocene genera of Europe, no trace of this digit remains. The longest digit is the second, which has also the largest claw, but the greater length is entirely due to the phalanges, which are much larger than those of the other toes, and the second metacarpal is much stouter than the third or fourth. So far as the metacarpals are concerned, the original perissodactyl symmetry is retained; metacarpal III is longer than II or IV, which are of about equal length, but metacarpal II is much the stoutest of the series. The ungual phalanges, or claw-cores, are deeply cleft at the tip.

In the hind-foot the digits are much shorter and of more nearly equal length than in the manus, but the fourth is the longest and has the largest claw. A noteworthy feature in the tarsus of †*Moropus* is the exclusion of the astragalus from any contact with the cuboid. In the normal perissodactyls (Chelopoda) except the earlier genera of horses, the astragalus rests more or less upon the cuboid. Whether this separation of astragalus and cuboid occurs also in the Old World †*Macrotherium*, is uncertain, for the published figures and descriptions are not clear on this point. In the earliest known American member of the family, †*Eomoropus* of the Bridger Eocene, this structure of the tarsus is already conspicuous.

There has been much speculation as to the manner in which the clawed feet of the †Ancylopoda were used, and no satisfactory answer has been found, perhaps never can be found, for there are no animals, now existing, which are remotely like the †chalicotheres, and the habits of these extraordinary creatures can only be conjectured. The only assured fact in the problem is that the †chalicotheres were herbivorous, as is demonstrated by the teeth. Two other groups of hoofed mammals, the South American †Entelonychia and the artio-dactyl family of the †Agriochœridæ, have had their hoofs more or less completely transformed into claws. The large size of all these animals precludes the idea that they could have been burrowers, though, not improbably, they may have used their great claws for digging up roots, tubers and the like. To the existing Ant-bears (*Myrmecophaga*) the great claws which they use for opening the hard termite nests are effective as defensive weapons and inflict ghastly wounds upon any attacker. The clawed ungulates may have made a similar use of their feet, but that can have been only secondary; the principal use must have been connected with feeding habits. The great †ground-sloths (†Gravigrada, see Chap. XXIII) which reached such immense size in the Pleistocene, present an analogous problem, the teeth of herbivores and the claws of colossal anteaters in combination. For reasons that will be explained in Chapter XXIII, Owen's suggestion that the fore-feet were used to draw down branches of trees, so as to bring the foliage within reach of the prehensile tongue and lips, is a plausible and not unlikely one, but the elbow joint of †*Moropus*, which had only a hinge-like movement, precludes such an explanation for the †chalicotheres. Be that as it may, this paradoxical structure lasted through such æons of time and was independently repeated so often, that it must have been useful to its possessors.

In the John Day stage remains of †chalicotheres, indistinguishable from †*Moropus*, have been found; very probably, less fragmentary fossils would prove to belong to a different genus, as hardly any genera of mammals are common to the John Day and the Harrison. Nothing referable to this family has been obtained from the White River, Duchesne or Uinta stages of the United States, though in the Chadron substage of the Canadian province of Saskatchewan, fragmentary fossils occur, which have been referred to the Old World genus †*Schizotherium*, but the reference is so doubtful that little importance can be attached to it.

Of †*Schizotherium*, a considerable part of the structure is known, and it is probably an important link in the chain of descent of the Old World †chalicotheres. In this genus the premolar formula is $p\,\frac{3}{3}$, the first premolar of each jaw having been lost, and the molars are of the †chalicothere type; the manus has four functional digits, II–V, and a vestige of the pollex. The symmetry of the metacarpals is neither typically chelopodan nor †ancylopodan; the third and fourth metacarpals are of nearly the same length and thickness; the articular surfaces for the phalanges have the characteristically hemispherical, cat-like shape and it is probable that the transformation of hoofs into claws had already taken place; the ungual phalanges are still unknown.

In the Eocene of France has been found a genus, †*Pernatherium*, which, though very imperfectly known, is, almost certainly, referable to this family, but which can hardly have been in the direct line of descent. Much more complete is the fossil from the American middle Eocene, which is named †*Eomoropus amarorum*. The upper teeth in this genus have been lost, except for broken molars, and the only formula that can yet be written is: $i\,\frac{?}{3},\ c\,\frac{?}{1},\ p\,\frac{?}{3},\ m\,\frac{3}{3}$. In the single known skull attributable to this species, the inner half of $m\,\underline{3}$ is preserved and this shows the two transverse crests, the anterior one interrupted.

The lower molars are more primitive than in any other known member of the group, in that the crescents of the bicrescentic crown are incomplete, but the median internal cusp is double, as it is in †*Moropus*. The manus has four functional digits, the symmetry of which is normal perissodactyl, rather than †ancylopodan in character; the third metacarpal is the longest and stoutest of the series, while the fifth is reduced and slender, but is complete; the second and fourth form a symmetrical pair, as in all the Chelopoda. In the pes there are three digits, also of normal perissodactyl symmetry. No phalanges have been found in the American species.

The data are still insufficient for working out the phylogeny, or evolutionary stages of the †Ancylopoda in any but the most general way. The genera of the Old World form a parallel series with those of the New and must have had a common ancestry with them. †*Eomoropus* is probably a member of that common ancestry, but the separation of the two lines must have begun at a later date than the middle Eocene, unless we are prepared to admit a degree of independent parallelism which seems very unlikely. †*Eomoropus* was probably a migrant from Asia, where it occurs in the Eocene of Mongolia and China, for nothing is known in the lower or lowest Eocene of this country which can be regarded as a probable ancestor to it. An allied Mongolian genus, †*Grangeria*, also Eocene, shows that the phalanges of the first and second row are like those of the Chelopoda, but the unguals are not known.

†*Pernatherium*, in the Eocene of France, from the little that is known of it, seems to be already too specialized to be ancestral to any of the later genera. The Oligocene †*Schizotherium*, so far as its structure has been ascertained, might well have given rise to the later European genera, the Miocene †*Macrotherium* and the Pliocene †*Chalicotherium*. It may also have been ancestral, or near to the ancestor of †*Moropus*, especially if the supposed examples of it in the Canadian White River be really such. If not the actual common ancestor of the Old and New World tribes of the family, it is very close to that ancestor. Later than the Oligocene, there can have been no common progenitor.

†*Eomoropus* is but little removed from the Chelopoda, or normal perissodactyls, and shows that the †Chalicotheriidæ were derived from them. Indeed, Dr. Simpson does not admit the subordinal separation, and gives the †chalicotheres only family rank. The †brontotheres have usually been regarded as the chelopodan family which is most nearly allied to the †chalicotheres, but there is no good reason for this view, which rests entirely upon a superficial resemblance in the molar teeth; †*Eomoropus* is nearer to the primitive horses than to the early †brontotheres, though the latter also belong to the Hippomorpha, and it seems probable that the †chalicotheres arose as a branch of the hippomorphous stock in early Eocene, or perhaps in Paleocene time.

CHAPTER XVII

HISTORY OF THE †AMBLYPODA AND †CONDYLARTHRA

These are two groups which long ago became extinct, the †Amblypoda in the upper Eocene, the †Condylarthra in the lower, unless the very doubtful †Hyopsodontidæ be an exception; the former died out without descendants, while the latter are regarded as the probable ancestors of most, if not all, of the other ungulate orders.

ORDER †**AMBLYPODA,** †SHORT-FOOTED UNGULATES
SUBORDER I. †**Dinocerata.**
FAMILY 1. †UINTATHERIIDÆ.
SUBORDER II. †**Pantodonta.**
FAMILY 2. †CORYPHODONTIDÆ.
SUBORDER III. †**Taligrada.**
FAMILY 3. †TITANOIDEIDÆ.
FAMILY 4. †PANTOLAMBDIDÆ.
FAMILY 5. †PERIPTYCHIDÆ.

The region in which the principal development of the †Amblypoda took place and in which it is almost exclusively recorded, is western North America and Central Asia. We have evidence that "central Asia" must be taken to include all of the eastern part of that continent and that the early Tertiary faunas of western North America extended with little change to the Atlantic Coast. Even so, however, the fossils are found only in the region west of the Rocky Mountains and in the Gobi Desert, with the exception of one genus of the †Pantodonta, †*Coryphodon*, the type specimen of which was dredged out of the North Sea. The Gobi Desert has yielded a variety of representatives of the †Amblypoda, which, to our eyes, seem utterly fantastic and incredible, even more so than the extraordinary beasts previously known from the American Northwest.

SUBORDER I. †Dinocerata

Family 1. †Uintatheriidæ
†*Eobasileus*, up. and up. mid. Eoc. †*Uintatherium*, †*Elachoceras*, mid. Eoc. †*Bathyopsis*, low. Eoc. †*Probathyopsis*, Paleoc.

This group came to an end in the upper Eocene, where it is but sparsely represented and though going back into the Paleocene, is yet pre-eminently characteristic of the Bridger stage. The †uinta-theres were much the largest mammals of their time, especially the last-surviving genus, †*Eobasileus*, though hardly deserving the term "gigantic," which has been applied to them. They were of about the size of the larger African rhinoceroses, six or seven feet high at the shoulder. †*Uintatherium* is somewhat smaller, †*Elachoceras* and †*Bathyopsis* very much smaller and †*Probathyopsis* smallest of all.

In †*Eobasileus* and †*Uintatherium* the skull carries three pairs of bony protuberances, or horn-like processes, the anterior pair of

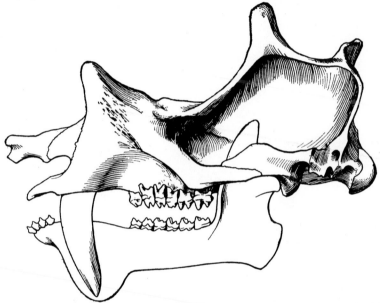

Fig. 296. — Skull of †uintathere, †*Uintatherium alticeps*, lower jaw supplied from another species. (Princeton Univ. Mus.)

which, on the tip of the nose, may, in †*Uintatherium* at least, have supported dermal horns like those of the †pair-horned rhinoceroses. The second pair, which are rather long and more or less cylindrical, are chiefly formed by outgrowths from the maxillaries, or upper jaw-bones. These protuberances were probably not sheathed in horn, but merely covered with skin, as were also those of the third pair, the shape of which makes it well-nigh impossible that they should have been covered with horn. If they did possess horny sheaths, these sheaths must have been periodically shed and renewed. The protuberances of the third pair, which grew from the parietal bones, are massive and club-shaped, eight to ten inches long, broadening to the free end. The occipital crest is developed into a

FIG. 297. — One of the elephantine †amblypods, †*Uintatherium alticeps*, Bridger stage. Male in foreground, female behind. (Restored from specimens in Yale Univ. and Princeton Univ. Mus.)

high ridge, which extends forward on each side to the parietal "horn" and slopes down from the "horn" forward to the orbit. The top of the cranium is thus a deep basin, open in front, such as is found in no other mammals, and is one of the most peculiar features of this extraordinary skull.

Proportionally, the brain-cavity is remarkably small, and is, as it were, hidden away in the postero-inferior part of the great skull. The cranial walls and roof are exceedingly thick, lightened by a spongy structure of the bones and by a system of sinuses, but these are much less extensive than in other large mammals, such as elephants, rhinoceroses and †brontotheres, which wield heavy tusks or horns. Nearly all Tertiary mammals have relatively small brains, with smaller and more simply convoluted cerebral hemispheres than in modern forms, but there are several groups of large animals that had exceptionally small brains, which did not keep pace with the growth of head and body and thus seem to be almost reptilian in relative size. Two such small-brained groups, the artiodactyl †entelodonts (p. 389) and the perissodactyl †brontotheres (p. 422) have already been mentioned and a third group of similar sort is that of the †Dinocerata. It is significant that each of these families became extinct after a comparatively short career, leaving no descendants. It seems likely that a low grade of intelligence was one of the factors which led to the extinction of these exceptionally small-brained mammals.

The premaxillaries are slender, rod-like bones, which do not meet in front and carry no teeth. The long and massive nasal bones, overhanging the premaxillæ in front, and the size and position of the anterior nasal opening show that there can have been no proboscis. The lower jaw is a single piece, the two rami being co-ossified at the symphysis; in the male there is, on each side, near the anterior end, a large flange given off from the lower border and serving to protect the great canine tusks of the upper jaw. In the female the upper canine is not a tusk, but a small tooth which can have had little or no function and, correspondingly, the mandible has no flange for its protection. The condyles of the lower jaw are on peduncles and present backward, instead of upward; such a joint must have permitted an uncommonly wide opening of the mouth, so as to clear the tusks, which otherwise would have been of no use.

Here may be noted certain indisputable examples of the independent acquisition of similar structure in two or more unrelated groups of mammals. The conversion of the upper canines into long, thin, sharp-pointed and recurved sabres has taken place in the chevrotains, in the hornless and small-antlered deer (p. 320) and in other artiodactyl groups (p. 349), in the †sabre-tooth cats (Chap. XXI), in the extraordinary predaceous marsupial, †*Thylacosmilus* (p. 706) from the Pliocene of Argentina and in the †Dinocerata. In three of these, the †uintatheres, the marsupial and in many of the †sabre-tooths, but not in the artiodactyls, great protective bony flanges have appeared on the lower jaw. Unless all our conceptions of mammalian evolution are entirely erroneous, it is impossible that these similarities should have been derived from a common ancestry.

In later †Dinocerata the dental formula is: $i\frac{0}{3}$, $c\frac{1}{1}$, $p\frac{3}{3}$, $m\frac{3}{3} \times 2 =$ 34; the upper incisors are all lacking and the upper canine, as already noted, is a very large, thin, compressed, sharp-edged and sharp-pointed tusk, which is usually curved, but sometimes straight and with the end shaped like a spear-head, or hastate. The lower incisors seem to be eight in number, as in the true ruminants (Pecora) and certain other artiodactyl groups, for the lower canines have acquired the shape and function of incisors. These teeth are of a peculiar shape, extended antero-posteriorly, with a conical cusp in front and a long heel behind, which sometimes bears a smaller cusp, and in †*Eobasileus*, they are bilobate. As in the ruminants, the toothless premaxillaries must have supported an elastic cushion, against which the lower incisors could bite, when cropping leaves and other soft vegetation. The cheek-teeth are low-crowned and rooted and surprisingly small in proportion to the size of the skull; premolars and molars are very much alike and have transverse enamel crests which, in the upper teeth, converge in V-like shape and, in the lower teeth, when unworn, have beaded edges. These teeth are unlike those of any other mammals and the homologies cf their parts have been much debated.

Aside from the remarkable and exceptional skull, the skeleton is elephantine in character, so much so, indeed, that the †uintatheres have often been classed with the Proboscidea. This classification, however, is almost certainly a mistake and is now universally abandoned. As there was no proboscis, the neck is considerably longer than in the elephants; the body is very long and, as is shown by the length and curvature of the ribs and the great width of the pelvis, it must have had great bulk. The pelvis and the bones of the hindleg are much as in the Proboscidea and, if found isolated, might well be referred to some unknown elephant. The femur, in particular, is very elephant-like, with its small knee-condyles, flattened shaft and missing third trochanter. The fore-leg bones, on the contrary, are much less elephantine in form and the fore-leg was not so straight, being much more bent at the elbow than in any of the Proboscidea. As in the large and massive mammals generally, the long bones have no marrow cavities, but are filled with spongy bone. The unrelated groups of the †uintatheres, †brontotheres and elephants agree in this structure, which gives strength without increase of diameter.

Though there are important and significant differences in the bony structure of the feet between †uintatheres and proboscideans, the feet must have been very much alike in appearance in the two groups. There are five digits in each foot, fore and hind, with short, heavy bones, which are block-like in the carpus; the ungual phalanges are nodular in shape. No doubt, the feet had the same columnar form and a similar development of elastic pads as in the elephants.

Aside from the fantastic head, the living animal must have had much the appearance of a small elephant, not exceeding six or seven feet in height. Whether or not there was a coat of hair, it is impossible to say, but it seems improbable that any Eocene mammals should have lost all hairy covering even in the mild, subtropical climate of that age.

The history of the †Dinocerata, which ran from the later Paleocene to the end of the Eocene, is, so far, recorded in terms of skulls and teeth, for no skeletal remains have yet been found in stages earlier than the Bridger. The last surviving genus, †Eobasileus of the Uinta and upper Bridger (Washakie substage) differed in several important respects from its predecessor, †Uintatherium; the skull is remarkably long and narrow, more so in some species than in others. The anterior, or nasal pair of bony protuberances differ entirely in shape from those of the genus last named and are so broad and overhang so much forward, that it is difficult to see how they could have supported dermal horns, or how such horns could have been shaped. The canine tusk is long and strongly recurved and the lower incisors are very peculiar in being bilobate, having two cusps of nearly equal size, one behind the other. The animal, as a whole, must have been larger than its predecessors.

†Uintatherium, of the earlier Bridger, is represented in the collections by several entire skeletons and was described and illustrated with extraordinary fulness of detail by the late Professor O. C. Marsh in his great monograph on the †Dinocerata. This genus has a relatively shorter and wider skull, especially in the cranial region. The anterior pair of protuberances are much smaller than in †Eobasileus

and of a different shape, which is compressed-hemispherical; they look very much like the horn-supports of the †pair-horned rhinoceroses of the genus †*Diceratherium* (p. 444). The tusks are somewhat shorter and less curved than in †*Eobasileus* and they may even be straight with hastate ends. In the lower incisors the posterior cusp is much smaller than the anterior one and is often lacking, so that these teeth differ greatly from the bilobate incisors of †*Eobasileus*. Little is known of the skeleton of the latter, but it appears not to differ in any important way from that of †*Uintatherium*.

Occurring in the same strata as †*Uintatherium* is the very much smaller and less specialized †*Elachoceras*, which is, almost certainly,

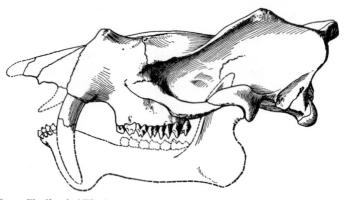

Fig. 298. — Skull of †*Elachoceras parvum*, lower jaw restored; upper tusk, as restored, probably too long. (Princeton Univ. Mus.)

a survival from the lower Bridger, the beds of which have, as yet, yielded no fossils. This genus is, so far as the skull is concerned, precisely what the immediate ancestor of †*Uintatherium* might be expected to be. The only known species, †*E. parvum*, is hardly half as large as the commoner species of †*Uintatherium* and the nasal "horns" are either very small, or entirely lacking, the broken tips of the nasal bones not permitting a definite decision on this point. The middle pair of protuberances are mere low knobs and the posterior pair are inconspicuous thickenings of the crest which encloses the roof of the cranium on three sides. This crest is much lower than in †*Uintatherium* or †*Eobasileus* and the basin-like top of the skull is therefore much shallower. The upper canine is already a sabre-like tusk, though relatively smaller than in the subsequent genera. A fragment of the lower jaw indicates the presence of definite flanges for the protection of the sabres.

In the Wind River stage of the lower Eocene the genus †*Bathy-*

opsis carries the line a step farther back and is manifestly the ancestor of †*Elachoceras*, as the latter is of †*Uintatherium*. †*Bathyopsis* is no larger than a tapir and decidedly smaller than †*Elachoceras*. It is not yet known whether, in the former, the upper incisors had already been suppressed, but it is almost certain that the upper canine is a tusk and the lower canine is also a tusk, not at all incisiform, but much larger than the incisors. The first premolar is retained and all the premolars are somewhat smaller and simpler than the molars. The skull has a broad and rather concave cranial roof, with slightly raised, enclosing crest and the middle and posterior pair of horn-like protuberances are in an incipient stage, even smaller than in †*Elachoceras*, and the nasal pair were probably lacking, but this has not been proved.

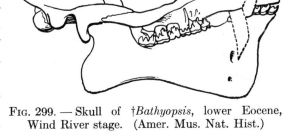

The lower jaw has a peculiar shape; the anterior part is very Fig. 299. — Skull of †*Bathyopsis*, lower Eocene, Wind River stage. (Amer. Mus. Nat. Hist.) deep vertically, affording protection for the upper tusks, but there is no distinct flange, as there is in the succeeding genera, the lower border of the jaw rising uninterruptedly to the angle.

No representative of the suborder has yet been found in the Gray Bull stage of the lower Eocene and a more ancient member of it is †*Probathyopsis* of the later Paleocene (Clark Fork stage), which is known only from teeth, but these are of great interest. They indicate an animal still smaller than †*Bathyopsis*, with upper and lower canine tusks of nearly the same size; the upper tusk is obliquely truncated by the abrasion of the lower. The molars are unquestionably of the †uintathere type. Very recently the discovery of a larger, specialized †uintathere-like tooth has been reported from the †*Barylambda* level in Colorado (Patterson).

The only region of the world, outside of North America, in which †Dinocerata have been discovered, is Mongolia, where genera clearly referable to this suborder and yet very different from any that occur in this country, have been collected by the American Museum parties. From the data now available, it would seem that the group originated in North America and early sent off migrants to Asia, where they underwent peculiar modifications.

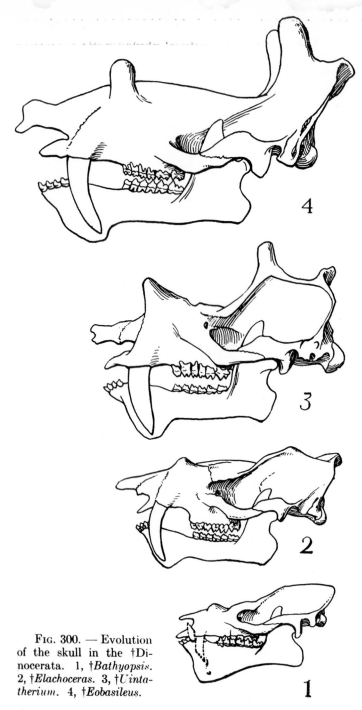

Fig. 300. — Evolution of the skull in the †Dinocerata. 1, †*Bathyopsis*. 2, †*Elachoceras*. 3, †*Uintatherium*. 4, †*Eobasileus*.

The series of genera which, in descending order, is †*Eobasileus* — †*Uintatherium* — †*Elachoceras* — †*Bathyopsis* — †*Probathyopsis*, gives a strong impression of being a natural phylogenetic succession of ancestors and descendants. True, in only one of these genera, †*Uintatherium*, has the skeleton (other than the skull) been brought to light, but there is no reason to suppose that more complete knowledge would require a change in the succession.

The succeeding steps of evolutionary development, so far as they can be recognized, are like those which have been formulated for other mammalian orders. There was (1) a generally continuous increase in size and weight, each genus being larger and more massive than its predecessor, smaller and lighter than its successor.

(2) The upper canines, already tusks at the beginning of the series, grew relatively larger and more curved, until they became the great laniary sabres of †*Eobasileus*.

(3) The lower canines, at first effective tusks, were reduced in size at each stage, *pari passu* with the enlargement of the upper tusks, until they became, in appearance, part of the incisor series.

(4) Small knobs appeared on the top of the skull, which were continually enlarged until they became three pairs of prominent bony protuberances, which resemble horns.

(5) At the same time, the slightly concave roof of the cranium was converted into a deep basin by the upgrowth and extension of the occipital crest.

(6) The lower jaw, at first very deep vertically in front, growing shallower backward and with lower border inclined steeply upward, had the anterior part distinctly set off on each side as a flange for the protection of the upper tusk. In the female, however, there is no flange.

(7) When the animals had attained a certain degree of size and weight, the marrow-cavities were filled with spongy bone, as in all other very large and massive ungulates.

SUBORDER II. †Pantodonta

There is, at present, among palæontologists a tendency to create separate orders for the †coryphodonts and †uintatheres and to restrict the term †Amblypoda to the former and its allies. This may eventually prove to be the best course, but it must, at the same time, be recognized that the families now included in the †Amblypoda are more nearly related to one another than they, or any of them, are to other groups. This relationship should find expression in the scheme of classification.

Family 2. †Coryphodontidæ

As the †Dinocerata, though beginning in the Paleocene and ending in the upper Eocene, are especially characteristic of the Bridger, or middle Eocene, so the †coryphodonts, beginning in the Paleocene and ending in the Wind River, are particularly characteristic of the

Fig. 301. — The commonest of Wasatch ungulates, the †amblypod, †*Coryphodon testis*. (Restored from a skeleton in Amer. Mus. Nat. Hist.)

Gray Bull or lower Wasatch. Throughout the lower Eocene, the †coryphodonts were the largest mammals of their time, though they were greatly inferior to the Bridger †uintatheres in size. The typical Wasatch genus is †*Coryphodon*, which, though first named in England, is yet far more abundant and varied in eastern Asia and western North America than anywhere else in the world. The Wasatch species vary in size from a tapir to an ox, but were of incomparably heavier build. In †*Coryphodon* the number of teeth is complete and unreduced from the primitive placental formula, $i\frac{3}{3}, c\frac{1}{1}, p\frac{4}{4}, m\frac{3}{3} \times 2 = 44$. The upper incisors are relatively small, but were evidently functional; the canines, above and below, are heavy, formidable tusks and are shorter and thicker than the great sabres of the †uintatheres. The premolars are of a simpler pattern than the molars, which resemble those of the †uintatheres in a general way, but not closely, which is the reason for the proposed ordinal separation of the †Dinocerata from the †Amblypoda.

The skull has a broad, flat top, without sagittal crest, or basin-like concavity, or bony protuberances, features which give the head a totally different appearance from that of the †uintatheres. The neck is proportionately longer than in the latter, the body elongate and the tail of medium length. The trunk-vertebrae have surprisingly short and weak neural spines, which is, perhaps, an indication of amphibious habits. Indeed, the whole skeleton is suggestively like that of a hippopotamus in its proportions. Two of the extinct and extremely peculiar South American orders of hoofed mammals, the †Pyrotheria and the †Astrapotheria, have similar surprisingly short and weak neural spines on the dorso-lumbar vertebræ; the explanation may be the same.

The limbs of †Coryphodon are rather short and very heavy and the bones, in comparison with those of the †uintatheres, are less proboscidean and more perissodactyl in character. For example, the femur has a third trochanter and the long bones are hollow, with marrow-cavities. The five-toed feet, on the contrary, are closely similar to those of the †uintatheres and have the same elephant-like appearance; indeed one species of †Coryphodon is named †C. elephantopus.

The family is extensively represented in the lower Eocene of Mongolia, where several peculiar and aberrant forms arose; one of these had a remarkably inflated and domed forehead.

SUBORDER III. †Taligrada

The propriety of making a subordinal separation between this group and the Pantodonta is doubtful and until more is known of the problematical †Periptychus (p. 484), will remain undecided.

Family 3. †Titanoideidæ

In the later Paleocene †Barylambda represents the monstrous type of which almost every one of the Tertiary stages had its peculiar example. Not all of these astonishing beasts were very large, though generally they were the giants of their own day, but, to our eyes, they appear monstrous in the sense of "outrageously absurd." Even the modern world is not without its fantastic and monstrous quadrupeds; elephants, rhinoceroses, hippopotamuses, wart-hogs and giraffes are all familiar sights and familiarity blunts our sense of the ludicrous, but they can hold their own against the extraordinary beasts of ancient times.

This family contains, as yet, but two genera, †*Titanoides* and †*Barylambda*. The first named genus was found in Montana and is known only from teeth, but of late years Mr. Bryan Patterson of the Field Museum, has been finding entire skeletons of a new genus, †*Barylambda*, in western Colorado and astonishing creatures they turn out to be. Like the †Ancylopoda of the Northern Hemisphere,

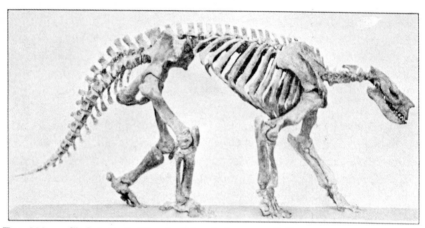

Fig. 302. — Skeleton of †*Barylambda*, Paleocene, Tiffany stage. (Field Mus. Nat. Hist.)

and the †Pyrotheria and †Astrapotheria of South America, they defy interpretation of their mode of life, because they are all so totally unlike anything now living and so completely without relatives in the modern world, that little help can be found in analogies. In one respect all those strange creatures agree and it is the only thing that can be confidently asserted concerning their habits, and that is that they were all plant-feeders and subsisted upon soft vegetation. Beyond that, everything is uncertain and often conjecture seems utterly futile.

Though much the largest mammal of its time, †*Barylambda* is considerably smaller than †*Coryphodon*, but of grotesquely disproportionate massiveness. The trunk is long and the extraordinarily heavy tail is provided with chevron-bones, a very rare feature in hoofed animals. This great tail must have served as a fifth leg, as it did in the gigantic †ground-sloths of the Pleistocene and in modern kangaroos. The skull is relatively small and, in shape, resembles that of the larger †Condylarthra, such as †*Phenacodus;* the face is extremely short, which is in keeping with the reduction of the premolars. Except for the upper incisors, which may number two or three on each side and were evidently on the way to disappearance, and the lower incisors, the dental formula is the same as in *Coryphodon*. The canines are too small to be called tusks; the grinding teeth resemble those of †*Pantolambda* (*q.v.*).

Collar bones, or clavicles, are present and of such size that they must have been functionally important. This is an extremely prim-

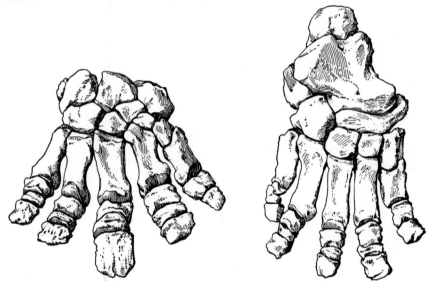

Fig. 303. — Right fore- and hind-foot of †*Barylambda;* same skeleton as Fig. 302. (Field Mus. Nat. Hist.)

itive character in any ungulate and has been verified in only a few families, sometimes with these bones in a reduced, or even vestigial condition. In hoofed animals, which use the limbs only for locomotion and have lost all power of rotating the fore-foot, clavicles are superfluous and no existing large ungulates have them. In †*Barylambda* the limb-bones are very massive in proportion to their length and retain many features which, like the clavicles, are a heritage from a claw-bearing ancestry.

The humerus is like that of a burrower, which, as the broad, flat hoofs demonstrate, †*Barylambda* cannot have been; the ridges for the attachment of the deltoid and supinator muscles are extremely prominent. Another strikingly primitive structure, which is not found in any hoofed animal of later than early Eocene date is the retention of the internal epicondylar foramen for the passage of the ulnar nerve. This foramen occurs in many Carnivora and Insectivora, but not in post-Eocene ungulates. The small, round head of the radius indicates the retention of a certain power of rotating the manus, which is in harmony with the presence of clavicles.

The feet are short and extremely broad, with five equally developed digits, with remarkably broad and spade-like ungual phalanges. In the carpus is a large, separate central, a surprisingly

Fig. 304. — †*Barylambda*, restored from skeleton shown in Fig. 302. (Field Mus. Nat. Hist.)

primitive feature, such as is found in few mammals to-day and, except the Hyracoidea, in no post-Paleocene ungulate. A feature which is unique among mammals is in the sacro-iliac joint. The sacrum not only articulates with the ilium laterally, but also extends over the top of that bone, making a joint of exceptional strength. The tarsus resembles that of †*Coryphodon*, but the metatarsals are much weaker than in that genus and decidedly more slender than the metacarpals.

†*Barylambda* is evidently a curiously specialized and aberrant form, which could not have given rise to †*Coryphodon* and which did not survive in the lower Eocene. As yet, this exceedingly strange mammal has been found only in North America.

Family 4. †Pantolambdidæ

The middle Paleocene, Torrejon stage, furnishes the interesting genus †Pantolambda, which, though not directly ancestral to either †Barylambda, or †Coryphodon, is collaterally so and permits an estimate of the actual common ancestor and a reconstruction of its principal characteristics. The best-known species, †P. bathmodon, of which an almost entire skeleton has been found, was an animal with head and body somewhat smaller than those of a sheep, with

Fig. 305. — The Torrejon forerunner, †Pantolambda bathmodon, of †Coryphodon. (Restored from a skeleton in Amer. Mus. Nat. Hist.)

shorter legs and far longer tail. The dentition is unreduced, the teeth numbering 44 in all; the canines are tusk-like, but have no such development as in †Coryphodon; the premolars are smaller and simpler than the molars, which closely represent the common starting-point of the molar-patterns of all the different members of the sub-order. The skull is long and narrow and has a prominent sagittal crest, such as is retained in †Barylambda, but lost in the flat-topped cranium of †Coryphodon. The neck is of moderate length, about equal to that of the head; the body is elongate and the tail, in length and thickness, rivals that of the great modern cats. The hip-bones are narrow and slender; they are not everted and have no such breadth as in †Barylambda, or †Coryphodon.

The limbs are short and stout and the various bones are of such primitive character that, if found isolated, they would hardly be considered as ungulate at all. As in †*Barylambda*, the humerus has the prominent deltoid ridge and epicondylar foramen and the femur has the third trochanter. The feet are five-toed and the slender digits are arranged in radiating fashion, like the sticks of a fan and terminate in flat, pointed, well-developed hoofs; the gait was probably semi-plantigrade, the weight resting chiefly on the hoofs.

Though †*Pantolambda* is undoubtedly ungulate, its skeleton has many points of resemblance to the primitive carnivores. Evidently this genus is not far removed from the ancestry common to the clawed and the hoofed mammalian orders.

Family 5. †Periptychidæ

The only known genus of this family, †*Periptychus*, is found in the lowest Paleocene, the Puerco stage, and seems to be the most ancient representative of the order, but it is very imperfectly known. Mr. Patterson refers the family to "Amblypoda *Incertæ Sedis.*" The position of the genus and family as ancestral forms, direct, or collateral, remains to be determined.

ORDER †**CONDYLARTHRA**

This order is looked upon as the connecting link between clawed and hoofed mammals and, therefore, ancestral to most, or perhaps all, of the ungulate orders. The known North American representatives of the †Condylarthra, from the Paleocene and lower Eocene, cannot have stood in this ancestral position, for they are too late in time and too specialized in structure. They are rather to be regarded as the more or less modified survivors of the ancient and primitive group which, in the early Paleocene, or late Cretaceous, of some Old World region, gave rise to the various ungulate orders, save those which originated in South America.

So little are these animals distinctively ungulate in character, that unusually complete specimens are required, to make sure of their presence in any particular region. As to North America there can be no question, for it was here that they were first identified and named and here they ranged through the Paleocene and lower Eocene, but are not certainly known in later stages. Almost certainly, they were represented in Europe and probably also in South America, where the †Didolodontidæ are included in the order, but the reference is uncertain, until feet in undeniable association with teeth, shall have been found.

ORDER **CONDYLARTHRA**

FAMILY 1. ?†HYOPSODONTIDÆ
FAMILY 2. †MENISCOTHERIIDÆ
FAMILY 3. †PHENACODONTIDÆ
FAMILY 4. ?†DIDOLODONTIDÆ (S. A.)

Family 1. ?†Hyopsodontidæ

The genus †*Hyopsodus,* from which the family is named, was described by Dr. Leidy in 1870 and, as the name, which means "pig-like teeth," indicates, he regarded it as an artiodactyl. Several years later it was believed to be a primitive monkey and transferred to the Primates, but was subsequently shifted to the Insectivora and, finally, to the †Condyarthra, where it has an uneasy seat and may not remain long. There are difficulties in the way of classing it either with the Insectivora, or the †Condylarthra, but the discovery of the foot-structure shows that it cannot be referred to the Primates or the Artiodactyla.

All of the numerous species of †*Hyopsodus* are small, none of them much larger than the Grey Squirrel. They ranged through the whole Eocene, but are most numerous in the Bridger, where fossils of them are very common.

Though it is not worth while to devote much space to a genus of such uncertain position, it is nevertheless instructive to note how very much alike the ancient, small and primitive members of various mammalian orders are, and that fact, in itself, is strong evidence of a common origin.

The complete skull of †*Hyopsodus* is much like that of many Eocene primates, but the teeth forbid inclusion in that order and the feet, which have claws, not hoofs, seem to negative its reference to the †Condylarthra, but do not conclusively fix its position. The †Condylarthra are believed to bridge the gap between clawed and hoofed animals and, if so, it is conceivable that some members of the order should have retained claws. Conceivable, perhaps, but not very likely.

Family 2. †Meniscotheriidæ

So far as is yet known, this family is confined to the lower Eocene of North America, where it is represented by †*Meniscotherium,* a genus in which the dentition is decidedly more advanced than that of its contemporary condylarth †*Phenacodus* and even than that of the Wasatch horse, †*Hyracotherium*. This genus obviously presents a case of premature specialization, which led to no lasting results. The species are all of small animals, hardly so large as a fox-terrier.

The molars have acquired a crescentic pattern, which resembles that of the Hippomorpha among perissodactyls, the †palæotheres, †brontotheres and post-Wasatch horses. In the upper molars the two outer cusps, which are concave externally, unite in a wall, a prominent ridge, or "style," marking their junction. The lower molars have the bicrescentic pattern, one crescent behind the other, which

Fig. 306. — Lower Eocene †condylarth, †*Meniscotherium terræ-rubræ*. (Restored from a skeleton in Amer. Mus. Nat. Hist.)

is so widely spread among the early families of both artiodactyls and perissodactyls, in which it must have several times been independently developed.

The body and tail of †*Meniscotherium* are long and the limb-bones are lighter than in †*Phenacodus;* the limbs themselves are short and the feet were presumably plantigrade. The five-toed feet are so like those of the klipdasses of Asia Minor and Africa, that some palæontologists have referred this family to the same order, the Hyracoidea. The fact that no other hyracoids have ever been found in the Western Hemisphere is not a fatal objection to this reference; they might have invaded North America for a brief period and failed to establish themselves. It is on structural grounds that the †meniscotheres are included in the †Condylarthra, from Old World forms of which the Hyracoidea were, most probably, derived and the retention of certain †condylarthrous features by the hyracoids is not to be wondered at.

It is altogether likely that the †meniscotheres died out, not leaving any descendants. At all events, no later American genera can be derived from them.

Family 3. †Phenacodontidæ

†*Phenacodus*, low. Eoc. †*Euprotogonia*, mid. Paleoc. †*Protogonodon*, low. Paleoc.

Much the best-known genus of this family is †*Phenacodus*, of which several beautifully complete skeletons have been found in the

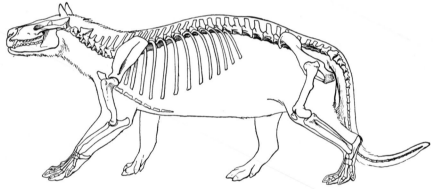

FIG. 307. — Skeleton of the Wasatch †condylarth, †*Phenacodus primævus*. (Amer. Mus. Nat. Hist.)

Big Horn basin of Wyoming. The species range in size from a fox to a small sheep. The dentition is unreduced and has the typical formula of all the more ancient and primitive placental mammals, with a total of 44. The incisors are small and simple and the canines are fang-like, but not large, and the premolars are smaller and less complex than the molars. The molar pattern is quadritubercular, that is, the very low crown has four simple, conical cusps, arranged in two transverse pairs, and this seems to be the fundamental plan from which the molars of almost all hoofed animals were ultimately derived. Even the astonishingly complex grinders of the modern elephants may be traced back to teeth of this type, as may the only less complicated molars of the modern horse *Equus*. The upper molars of the most ancient known horse, †*Hyracotherium*, are like those of †*Phenacodus*, with the addition of the two minute conules between the pairs of primary cusps and the formation of an outer wall.

The skull is elongate, narrow and low, with long, high sagittal crest; as in primitive skulls generally, the face is relatively short, the eye-sockets being very far forward, though the brain capacity is conspicuously small. The jaws are short and shallow, in accordance with the small and very brachyodont teeth.

The neck is of moderate length, the body elongate, the tail very long and thick. The limbs are short and stout and the various bones retain many primitive characteristics inherited from clawed ancestors. Thus, the humerus has a very prominent deltoid crest and an epicondylar foramen, which only the earlier ungulates have. The forearm bones are not co-ossified and the ulna is almost as stout as the radius. The femur has the third trochanter and the bones of the lower leg are separate, though the fibula is slender.

The feet are of great interest; both manus and pes are short and are pentadactyl, the five digits arranged with mesaxonic symmetry. That is to say, the median plane of the foot bisects the third digit, which is enlarged, while the first and fifth are reduced as though about to disappear, thus giving rise to a three-toed perissodactyl foot. The ungual phalanges unmistakably supported hoofs and the transition from claws to hoofs had been definitely made, whatever may be true as to the propriety of including the unguiculate †*Hyopsodus* among the †Condylarthra. If found by itself, the astragalus of †*Phenacodus* would hardly be assigned to a hoofed animal and might easily be mistaken for that of a carnivore, for its lower end is a rounded, convex head, which fits into a concave navicular without touching the cuboid. Except the Hyracoidea, no existing hoofed animal has such an astragalus.

The †Condylarthra were common in the Paleocene, in the middle stage of which, or Torrejon, †*Euprotogonia* represented the †phenacodonts, displaying an even more primitive type of dentition than that of †*Phenacodus*. The upper molars are not quadritubercular, but tritubercular; the three cusps are arranged in a triangle, the two outer cones forming the base and the single internal cone the apex. The tritubercular molar pattern is common to the primitive, unspecialized members of many mammalian orders, marsupials, rodents, insectivores, carnivores, lemurs, artiodactyls, etc. For most hoofed animals the quadritubercular stage succeeded the tritubercular, before the various ordinal types of dentition were differentiated.

Fig. 308. — †*Phenacodus primævus*, the best known Wasatch representative of the †Condylarthra. (Restored from the skeleton shown in Fig. 307.)

†*Euprotogonia*, even more than †*Phenacodus*, is of interest as connecting the hoofed and clawed orders (Ungulata and Unguiculata). While essentially an ungulate, it yet retains in the dentition, limbs and feet so many unguiculate characteristics as to point to an unguiculate ancestry.

†Condylarthra were probably present in the Puerco stage of the lower Paleocene, the genus †*Protogonodon* of that stage being referred to the †Phenacodontidæ. The reference is, however, doubtful, for the known material is so fragmentary, that no certain assignment of the genus can be made.

Family 4. ?Didolodontidæ

†*Didolodus*, †*Lambdaconus*, †*Notoprogonia*, †*Proectocion*, Casa Mayor (Low. Eoc.)

In the lower Eocene of Patagonia (Casa Mayor stage), have been found certain fossils which Ameghino believed to be referable

FIG. 309. — Left upper teeth of †*Didolodus*, supposed South American †condylarth, Casa Mayor stage. (Ameghino collection.)

to the †Condylarthra and several students of South American fossil mammals have accepted this determination, which must remain tentative until the discovery of more complete material. The existence of †Condylarthra in Eocene South America is not surprising, for the Americas were connected in the late Cretaceous and, presumably, in the Paleocene also, as is indicated by the presence of several supposedly identical orders in the Eocene of both continents.

Of the Casa Mayor genera which are provisionally referred to the †Condylarthra the best-known is †*Didolodus*, which has quadritubercular molars, with conules between the principal cusps, which are so very similar to those of the †phenacodonts, that the genus is sometimes included in the North American family, an assignment that may eventually be confirmed. At present, however, with knowledge so incomplete, it is advisable to keep the Patagonian genera apart.

A very considerable number of Casa Mayor and Musters genera have been referred to the †Condylarthra and it is probable that more or fewer of them are properly so classed, though several may eventually prove to be †Litopterna (Chap. XX). As yet, these supposed †Condylarthra are known only from jaws and teeth and discovery of the feet may require a change of classification.

CHAPTER XVIII

HISTORY OF THE †NOTOUNGULATA

The term †Notoungulata, proposed in 1903 by Dr. Santiago Roth, of the La Plata Museum, was quite unnecessary, for Owen's term, †Toxodontia, covers the same ground. Nevertheless, Roth's name caught the fancy of palæontologists everywhere and has been well-nigh universally adopted. The strict law of priority does not apply to groups above the rank of families and I am the less reluctant to adopt the newer term, for it serves to commemorate the fine paper in which Roth first proposed it.

The South American hoofed mammals are an extremely peculiar assemblage and have but few connections with those of any other region, yet there are so many resemblances to the ungulates of other continents, that some palæontologists (Ameghino conspicuously among them) have included the northern and southern families in the same orders. This procedure is now generally abandoned, but such abandonment involves the acceptance of the independent development of similar structural characters on a very surprising scale. Parallel and convergent evolution must, then, be regarded as normal, though it is not necessary to suppose that they are the commonest and most important modes of development.

The classification of the fossil mammals of the Neotropical region, has been a bone of contention for many years. The advance of knowledge, of late years, due chiefly to the great collections made in South America by the Field Museum of Chicago, and the American Museum of New York, has set the problem in a very different light and a general agreement may be expected in the near future. The subjoined scheme is that recently proposed by Dr. G. G. Simpson, merely changing the order of the groups.

NEOTROPICAL UNGULATA
> ORDER   I. †NOTOUNGULATA, Roth, 1903.
> ORDER   II. †ASTRAPOTHERIA, Lydekker, 1894.
> ORDER III. †LITOPTERNA, Ameghino, 1889.
> ORDER IV. †PYROTHERIA, Ameghino, 1895.
> ORDER   V. ? †CONDYLARTHRA, Cope, 1881.

Much the most diversified, numerically abundant and long-lived of these orders is that of the †Notoungulata, which persisted from the earliest Eocene of the Rio Chico to the Pleistocene of the Argentine Pampas and the Brazilian caverns. The very diverse suborders and families of this group are united by the remarkable structure of the auditory region, unique among hoofed animals, which is common to all †notoungulates. The order is very varied and in size ranges from the tiny †*Notopithecus*, of the Eocene, to the great Pleistocene †*Toxodon*, which is as large as an African rhinoceros. Most of the Tertiary genera are of small, or moderate size.

Notwithstanding their great diversity of size, manner of life and external appearance, the †Notoungulata form unquestionably a natural group of closely interrelated genera and families. The most obvious characteristic and the one upon which Roth principally relied in delimiting the order, or superorder, as he regarded it, is the unique structure of the auditory apparatus, which has already been mentioned. In addition to the hollow and inflated tympanic bulla, there is a second chamber, a large cavity in the squamosal, which communicates with the bulla by a canal. The squamosal chamber produces a convexity on the surface of the skull, which is sometimes very prominent and resembles the inflated protuberances in the skull of certain rodents, but in the latter the protruding element is the mastoid, not the squamosal.

Another feature which is common to all †notoungulates is the very high level at which the zygomatic process of the squamosal arises, so that the upper border of the process is nearly as high as the sagittal crest. This upper border of the zygomatic process passes imperceptibly into the occipital crest. Less exceptional, but not common, is the elevated position of the auditory *meatus*, or entrance to the ear, which is as high above the base of the cranium as in the pigs.

Certain features of the dentition are found in all members of the order; the molar pattern is the same throughout; the upper molars have an outer wall from which two transverse crests run inward and backward and after considerable abrasion, the valley between the crests is converted into an oblique and isolated enamel "lake." Most †notoungulates have no tusks; when present, the tusks are the second upper and third lower incisors. Only the suborder †*Entelonychia* has canine tusks and these are small. Though with certain superficial resemblances to the teeth of rhinoceroses, the dentition of the †Notoungulata is unique among hoofed mammals.

The best-known families are listed in the table below.

ORDER I. †NOTOUNGULATA
  SUBORDER A. †Toxodonta
    FAMILY 1. †TOXODONTIDÆ
    FAMILY 2. †NOTOHIPPIDÆ
    FAMILY 3. †LEONTINIIDÆ
  SUBORDER B. †Typotheria
    FAMILY 4. †TYPOTHERIIDÆ
    FAMILY 5. †INTERATHERIIDÆ
    FAMILY 6. †HEGETOTHERIIDÆ
    FAMILY 7. †NOTOPITHECIDÆ
    FAMILY 8. ?†ARCHÆOHYRACIDÆ
    FAMILY 9. ?†ACŒLODIDÆ
  SUBORDER C. †Entelonychia
    FAMILY 10. HOMALODOTHERIIDÆ
  SUBORDER D. †Notioprogonia
    FAMILY 11. †NOTOSTYLOPIDÆ
    FAMILY 12. †HENRICOSBORNIIDÆ
    FAMILY 13. †ARCTOSTYLOPIDÆ

It is manifestly impossible to deal with this portentous list of families and the still longer one of genera within the space available in this book; a selection of the more characteristic and significant groups must be made. This and the subsequent lists are compiled, in order to give some conception of the incredible richness and variety of the early Patagonian faunas, but, at best, any conception so gained is extremely inadequate. The countless names of genera and species which have been applied to these faunas are in a terrible confusion of synonomy and no one can tell how many of the terms are valid and how many new names are yet to be given to undescribed fossils. Notwithstanding these drawbacks, it is already possible to give a general account of the successive faunas, thanks principally to the recent work of Dr. Simpson.

SUBORDER A. †Toxodonta

Family 1. †Toxodontidæ

†*Toxodon*, up. Plio. and Pamp. †*Xotodon*, do. †*Trigodon*, Mt. Herm. †*Nesodon*, †*Adinotherium*, Santa Cruz. †*Pronesodon*, †*Proadinotherium*, Colhué-huapi and Deseado. †*Coresodon*, Deseado.

The first representative of this family to be discovered and named was a skull found by Charles Darwin in the Pampean loess and called

†*Toxodon,* or "Bow-tooth," by Sir Richard Owen. The name refers to the strongly curved upper grinding teeth, those of the opposite sides almost meeting in the median line above the hard palate. For many years, this animal, of which only the skull and teeth were known, was a zoölogical puzzle, for it obviously was not referable to any of the established ungulate orders. Owen's proposal to erect

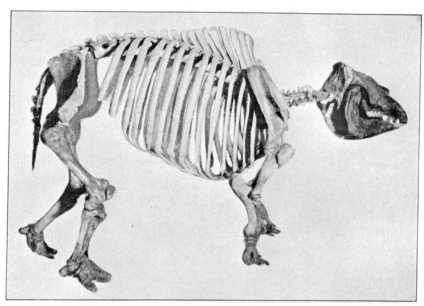

Fig. 310. — Skeleton of †*Toxodon platense,* Pampean of Argentina. (Mus. Comp. Zoöl. Harvard Univ.)

a new order for its reception was fully justified by the discovery of entire skeletons. Newer explorations have carried the history of the group far back into the Tertiary period and have demonstrated its autochthonous origin. No member of the suborder has ever been found outside of the Neotropical Region, Nicaragua being the northernmost known limit.

The Pampean loess contains several nearly allied genera of the family, which differ in size and in the complexity of the teeth, but only of †*Toxodon* is the entire skeleton known. The Pampean species of this genus were massive creatures which rivalled the largest rhinoceroses in bulk, but not in height, because of the disproportionately short legs.

The teeth are all completely hypsodont and apparently continued to grow, without forming roots, throughout the lifetime of the animal. The dental formula is: $i \frac{2}{3}$, $c \frac{0}{0}$, $p \frac{3}{3}$, $m \frac{3}{3}$, $\times 2 = 34$. The first upper incisor is broad and chisel-shaped, the second narrow and more like a tusk, but in some of the species these proportions are reversed. The lower incisors are procumbent and point directly forward and, of these, the third is the largest. There are no canines and between the incisors and premolars are long, toothless gaps, or diastemata. The three premolars are smaller and less complex than the mo-

FIG. 311. — A Pampean †toxodont, †*Toxodon burmeisteri*.   (Restored from a skeleton in La Plata Mus.)

lars; the anterior ones are very small and were frequently shed, so that the number of these teeth is variable.

The upper molars have a very simple pattern; the broad, smooth outer wall is not divided into cusps and from it arise two obliquely transverse crests. The deep cleft, or valley, between these crests is made Y-shaped on the masticating surface by a prominent spur on the inner side of the external wall. The lower molars are composed of two very narrow crescents, of which the posterior one is much the larger.

In side view, the general aspect of the skull is not unlike that of some of the hornless rhinoceroses, except for its unusual vertical height. The nasal bones are so shortened as to suggest the former presence of a short proboscis, or a prehensile lip. The auditory apparatus, as in all of the †Notoungulata, is extraordinary, though such rodents as the Kangaroo Rat have an analogous structure. In addition to the outer ear-chamber, formed by the inflated tympanic bulla, there is a second chamber, communicating with the first by a canal and formed in the squamosal, in the hinder wall of the skull. Unless this structure is indicative of unusually keen hearing, it is difficult to imagine what its significance can have been. The external entrance to the ear, or *meatus auditorius externus*, is placed very high up on the side of the skull, as in the hippopotamuses and other aquatic mammals, suggesting that †*Toxodon* may have been more or less amphibious in habits. The anterior, or symphyseal region of the lower jaw is broad, flat and shovel-like and hardly projects below the level of the incisor teeth.

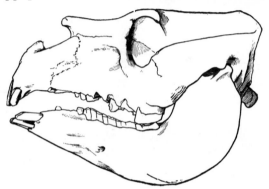

The neck is short and thick, the trunk long and very bulky, with an immense, almost hippopot-

FIG. 312. — Skull, left side, of †*Toxodon*. (La Plata Mus.)

amus-like girth, and the spines of the anterior dorsal vertebræ are exceedingly long, significant of a prominent hump at the shoulders.

The limbs are proportionally short and massive; the separate bones are heavy and have prominent projections for muscular and ligamentous attachments. The fore-leg is much shorter than the hind, lowering the head and neck in characteristic fashion. The shoulder-blade is rather narrow and has neither acromion, nor distinct metacromion. The hip-bones are greatly expanded and everted in an elephant-like manner, as is true of very bulky mammals generally. Like the pelvis, the femur resembles that of a small elephant in shape, in the flattening of the shaft and in the absence of the third trochanter. In the fore-arm the ulna and radius are separate and unreduced, but in the lower leg, which is very short in comparison with the thigh, tibia and fibula are co-ossified at their upper ends, not at the lower, a very exceptional feature.

The feet, which are three-toed, are surprisingly small in view of the bulk and weight of the animal. The calcaneum, or heel bone, is so articulated with the other bones of the tarsus as to project almost directly backward, nearly at right angles with its normal direction. The ungual phalanges are so small and nodular in shape that the hoofs must have been nail-like, as in the elephants, and the feet must have been columnar in shape, with the weight supported on an elastic pad.

†*Toxodon* may be followed back, without any noteworthy change, into the Pliocene, where it is associated with the curious genus

FIG. 313. — Head of horned †Toxodont, †*Trigodon gaudryi*, Pliocene of Monte Hermoso. (Restored from a skull in Ameghino Collection.)

†*Trigodon*, of which only the skull is known. The presence of a large, bony knob on the forehead, indicates the possession of a single, frontal and dermal horn, like that of a rhinoceros. Very few of the indigenous South American ungulates possessed horns and these were invariably small, with the sole exception of †*Trigodon*. All the known horned genera belonged to the suborder †Toxodonta.

†Toxodonta are very common in the Santa Cruz Miocene and the commonest fossils of that horizon are those of †*Nesodon imbricatus*, which was discovered by Darwin and named by Owen nearly a century ago. This was the first member of the marvellous Santa Cruz fauna to be made known. Between †*Toxodon* and †*Nesodon* there is so long a hiatus in time and so great is the difference between them, that there is much doubt whether the latter genus can have been directly ancestral to the former, especially as †*Nesodon* has the more complex grinding teeth. The Santa Cruz genus is, however, at all points so nearly what the actual ancestor must have been, that it will serve all purposes. All the species of †*Nesodon* are very much smaller than those of †*Toxodon;* the commonest one, †*N. imbricatus*, is in size about like a big-headed, short-legged tapir.

The dental formula of †*Nesodon* is unreduced: $i \frac{3}{3}, c \frac{1}{1}, p \frac{4}{4}, m \frac{3}{3}$ $\times 2 = 44$; several of the anterior teeth, including the canines, are so diminished in size as to have lost all function, and individual skulls are found which have lost one or more of these insignificant teeth. The first upper incisor is a broad, chisel-like tooth, which continued to grow for a time, then ceased growing and formed a root. The second upper incisor is a stout, pointed, trihedral tusk, which grew throughout life and developed no root. In the lower jaw the first and second incisors are rooted and chisel-shaped and, being

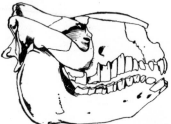

Fig. 314. — Skull of Santa Cruz †toxodont, †*Nesodon.* Same scale of reduction as Fig. 312.

rather narrow, they both occlude against the broad upper median incisor. The third incisor is a rootless, persistently growing tooth, which is broad and thin and inclines forward, impinges against the hinder face of the upper tusk, by abrasion with which it is obliquely truncated and its length limited. The upper tusk, on the contrary, continued to grow in length and was made narrower and sharper-pointed by wear. Few of the indigenous South American ungulates had canine tusks; for the most part, they either had no tusks at all, or the tusks were formed by the enlargement of the second upper and third lower incisors. All of the lower incisors are more or less erect, not procumbent as they are in †*Toxodon.*

The remarkable changes of appearance which took place within the lifetime of the individual and which have led to the bestowal of more than a score of generic and specific names upon this single

species, are chiefly due to the differential growth of the incisors, especially of the upper ones.   To make confusion worse confounded,
Owen's type-specimen had milk-teeth, which he described as the
second set and, thus, when the permanent dentition was found, it was
naturally supposed to represent a different genus.   It is to the late

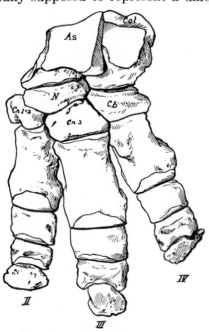

FIG. 315. — Left pes of †*Toxodon*.
Cal, calcaneum.   *As*, astragalus.
N, navicular. *Cn 1* and *2*, co-ossified
internal and middle cuneiforms. *Cn 3*,
external cuneiform. *Cb*, cuboid. (La
Plata Mus.)

FIG. 316. —
Left pes of †*Neso-
don*. Letters as in
Fig. 315 and scale
of reduction the
same. (Princeton
Univ. Mus.)

Dr. F. Ameghino, the famous Argentinian palæontologist, that is due
the bringing of order out of this chaotic condition.

The premolars of †*Nesodon*, which are smaller and less complicated
than the molars, have high crowns, but ceased to grow and formed
their roots at an early stage.   The molars are truly hypsodont, and
strongly curved, though the crowns are hardly half as high proportionally as those of †*Toxodon;* roots appear late in life.   The upper
molar-pattern is fundamentally the same as in †*Toxodon*, but is made
much more complex by several spurs and crests projecting inward
from the external wall; these produce a certain superficial likeness to
rhinoceros teeth.   The lower molars are simpler and more like those of
the Pampean genus.

The skull of †*Nesodon* is like that of †*Toxodon*, but is far smaller and displays certain minor differences; sagittal and occipital crests are decidedly more prominent and the former is relatively longer, for the brain-cavity is less capacious and the formation of cancellous tissue in the cranial bones was still in an incipient stage. The nasal bones are so long that †*Nesodon* could not have had a proboscis. The jaws are shallower than in †*Toxodon*, in correlation with the lower-crowned teeth, and the chin is rounded and erect, not procumbent. In life the head of this curious Santa Cruz ungulate must have had something rodent-like in its appearance, though there can have been no nearer relationship between rodents and †notoungulates than that which connects all placental mammals.

The skeleton of †*Nesodon* is far smaller and lighter than that of †*Toxodon* and otherwise differently proportioned, but, nevertheless, there is close agreement between the two genera. The neck is heavy and of medium length; the body is tapir-like with no such relative massiveness and the hump at the shoulders is already prominent, but less so than in the Pampean genus. The length of the tail has not been ascertained.

The shoulder-blade is relatively broader than in †*Toxodon* and its spine has an acromion and two very long metacromia, only one of which is feebly indicated in the Pleistocene animal. The narrower hip-bones are almost parallel with the spinal column and but little everted. Fore- and hind-legs are of nearly equal length and the backbone is almost level; there is no such shortening of the fore-arm, or elongation of the thigh as is seen in †*Toxodon*. The limb-bones are rather slender and, in size and proportions, are not unlike those of a tapir, but, in form, they resemble the much larger and more massive bones of †*Toxodon*. The femur is not flattened, but has the ordinary cylindrical shaft and a conspicuous third trochanter. Tibia and fibula are co-ossified at the upper end, separate at the lower, the same exceptional condition as obtains in †*Toxodon*. The long bones all have marrow cavities.

The feet, which have three digits each, are remarkably small in proportion to the size of the skeleton; in structure, they resemble those of †*Toxodon*, but are relatively narrower and more slender; the calcaneum has the normal mode of articulation with the other tarsal bones and the ungual phalanges, or hoof-cores, are large, showing that the hoofs were functional and supported most of the weight. In external appearance, the feet of †*Toxodon* differed from those of †*Nesodon* in much the same way as do those of modern rhinoceroses and tapirs.

Fig. 317.—†*Nesodon imbricatus*, Santa Cruz stage. (Restored by C. Knight from a skeleton in Princeton Univ. Mus.)

The species of †*Nesodon*, of which many have been proposed without sufficient reason, differ but little in size, but are so variable and fluctuating, that specific distinctions are difficult to draw. One species, †*N. cornutus*, from the upper Santa Cruz beds, would appear to have had a small median horn on the forehead and was thus a possible ancestor of the Pliocene †*Trigodon*.

A second Santa Cruz genus of the family is †*Adinotherium*, the species of which are very much smaller and lighter than those of

FIG. 318. — †*Adinotherium ovinum*, small, horned ††toxodont of Santa Cruz. Note the minute horn on the forehead. (Restored from a skeleton in Princeton Univ. Mus.)

†*Nesodon;* the commonest species, †*A. ovinum*, is, as its name implies, about like a short-legged sheep in stature. Many individuals, presumably males, show indications of a small, median horn on the forehead, while others, which are believed to be females, have smooth frontal bones. A similar, secondary sexual difference is exhibited by the Javan Rhinoceros (*R. sondaicus*) (p. 439).

In teeth, skull and skeleton, †*Adinotherium* differs but little from †*Nesodon*, save in smaller size and more slender proportions, but the living animals must have been quite unlike in appearance, for †*Adinotherium* had no hump at the shoulders and the hind-legs are much longer than the fore, but the rump was raised little above the level of the withers, because of the flexed hind-limb.

In the Colhué-huapi and Deseado stages the genera of the †*Toxo-dontidæ* are very like the Santa Cruz members of the family, which is not known to occur in formations more ancient than the Deseado, but in the Musters and Casa Mayor faunas are fossils which, when better known, may turn out to be primitive representatives of the †Toxo-dontidæ.

Family 2. †*Notohippidæ*

†*Notohippus*, Santa Cruz. †*Argyrohippus*, Colhué-huapi. †*Rhynchippus*, †*Morphippus*, Deseado. †*Eomorphippus*, †*Interhippus*, Musters.

The members of this family may well be called "the Fake Horses" and, in naming the genera of the group, Ameghino gave expression

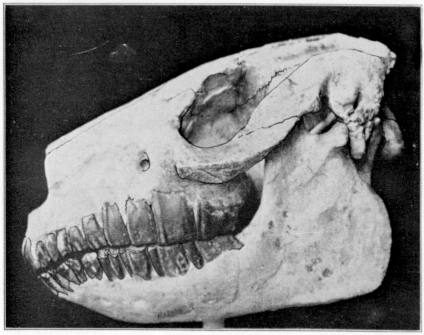

FIG. 319. — Skull, left side, of †*Rhynchippus*, Colhué-huapi stage. (Field Mus. Nat. Hist.)

to his belief that these actually were primitive and ancestral horses, an opinion which has nowhere found acceptance. It is true that the lower molars of the Santa Cruz genus †*Notohippus* ("Horse of the South") have a distinctly equine appearance, but the likeness is superficial.

One conspicuous feature, in which the present family differs from the †Toxodontidæ, is the absence of tusks; the incisors and canines, all of similar shape and nearly the same size, are in each jaw arranged in a semi-circle at the end of the muzzle; in the later genera (†*Notohippus*, †*Argyrohippus*) the grinding teeth are covered with cement, which is not found in any known member of the †*Toxodontidæ*.

Very little has yet been ascertained concerning the structure of limbs and feet in this family, but certain fragments, which may belong to the Deseado genus, suggest that functionally monodactyl feet had been acquired. The material is far too imperfect to justify

FIG. 320. — Lower teeth with thin layer of cement of †*Argyrohippus fraterculus*, Colhué-huapi stage. (Ameghino Collection.)

any positive statements, but the matter is of more than usual interest and importance, and further collections will be anxiously awaited.

Family 3. †*Leontiniidæ*

†*Colpodon*, Colhué-huapi. †*Leontinia*, †*Scarrittia*, Deseado.

The proper subordinal position of this family is somewhat questionable and it has been referred to both the †Toxodonta and the †Entelonychia and to each of these suborders it has certain resemblances. If Gaudry's statement that the pes is tridactyl and that the calcaneum and astragalus are like those of †*Nesodon*, is correct, there can be no doubt that the †Leontiniidæ belong to the suborder †Toxodonta.

The latest surviving genus of the family is †*Colpodon*, of the Colhué-huapi stage, in which there are no tusks, the lower incisors differing little from one another in shape, but with some increase in size from the first to the third, as in the †Notohippidæ. †*Leontinia*, a common and characteristic genus of the Deseado, has considerable tusks, the second upper and third lower incisors being larger than the others, as in the †Toxodontidae, though they are not nearly so large as in that family, and they did not grow persistently, but

formed roots at an early stage. The grinding teeth also are somewhat different from those of the †Toxodontidæ, having lower crowns
and a simpler molar pattern.

The skull has very characteristic peculiarities, especially in the
anterior region. Compared with the skull of †Nesodon, for instance,

Fig. 321. — Horned †toxodont, †*Leontinia gaudryi*, Deseado stage. (Restored
from a skull in Ameghino Collection.)

the premaxillaries are less extended upon the sides of the face and
the anterior nasal opening is carried much farther back. The nasal
bones, though actually shorter, have a longer free portion, which
is bent upward and thickened and the tips bear evidence of having
supported a small horn, or perhaps, a pair of horns. The facial region
is shorter proportionally, the cranial longer and the orbits have a
more anterior position.

The genus †*Scarrittia*, which is much the most completely known
of the Deseado ungulates, is, with some doubt, referred to the
†Leontiniidæ, a doubt that cannot be removed until the skeleton of
†*Leontinia*, or †*Colpodon*, has been discovered. Dr. Simpson obtained

in his latest Patagonian journey, several entire skeletons of †*Scarrittia* which are now in the American Museum.

The dental formula is: $i\frac{3}{3}$, $c\frac{1}{1}$, $p\frac{4}{4}$, $m\frac{3}{3} \times 2 = 44$, and the teeth are arranged in continuous series, without diastemata; though rooted, they are of moderate height, or *mesodont*. The first upper incisor is

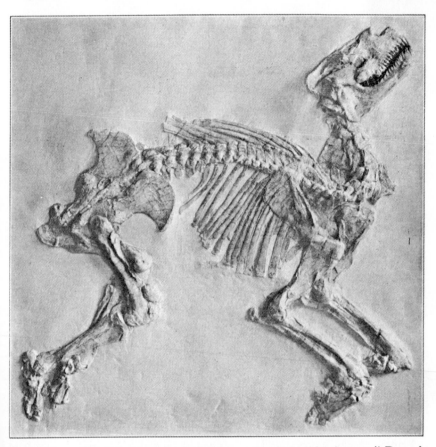

FIG. 322. — *Scarrittia canquelensis* skeleton as found in "death pose," Deseado stage. (Amer. Mus. Nat. Hist.)

a long, narrow tusk, with convex anterior face and sharp cutting edge; the second incisor is very much smaller and incisiform, with pointed tip; $i\frac{3}{}$ is almost exactly like $i\frac{2}{}$, except that it is somewhat larger, and the canine is similar, but slightly larger, and is set obliquely in the jaw. The second and third incisors and the canine form a series of three teeth, arranged in the same antero-posterior line and all alike, but differing a little in size.

The lower incisors are much smaller than the upper ones, especially the first and second; $i_{\overline{1}}$ is the smallest of the three and those of the opposite sides are deeply worn on the anterior face by the abrasion of the upper tusks, even in young adults.

The upper premolars are all smaller and simpler than the molars and have two external ribs; $p^{\underline{1}}$ is much the smallest and has a cingu-

FIG. 323. — Restoration from the skeleton of †*Scarrittia* in Fig. 322. (Amer. Mus. Nat. Hist.)

lum which extends down along the anterior margin; in the other premolars and the molars there is an anterior pillar, or "style"; $p^{\underline{2}}$ and $\underline{3}$ have a very distinct external cingulum, which is obscure in $p^{\underline{4}}$, absent in the molars. In these upper premolars the valley is a longitudinal cleft, opening anteriorly and becoming an enamel lake in old animals. The upper molars have a Y-shaped valley, except in $m^{\underline{3}}$, the stem of the Y opening internally; $m^{\underline{3}}$ is different in having a single, longitudinal valley, which opens backward. The upper molars are much like those of †*Nesodon*, but $m^{\underline{3}}$ recalls that of †*Astrapotherium*.

The lower cheek-teeth are not so plainly divisible into molars and premolars, as are the upper ones, but change gradually in form from $p_{\overline{2}}$ to $m_{\overline{1}}$. The second premolar exhibits the bicrescentic form in an incipient stage, in which the valleys are no more than indicated, while, in $p_{\overline{3}}$ and $_{\overline{4}}$, the crescents become successively more distinct and the valleys deeper. The lower molars are very long antero-posteriorly, especially the last one, and the hinder crescent is much more elongate than the forward one; the pillar in the posterior crescent is connected with a diagonal ridge, which is approximately parallel with the outer wall and, after some abrasion, encloses an enamel lake. While thoroughly †notoungulate in character, the teeth are not distinctively like those of any of the suborders.

The skull, the largest specimen of which measures 510 mm. in length, looks very much like that of †*Nesodon* and is considerably larger than in †*N. imbricatus*, but the proportions are nearly the same and the zygomatic arches have similarly elevated positions on the side of the cranium. The jaws are notably shallower, in correlation with the lower-crowned and rooted teeth; the lower jaw is especially shallow and the ascending ramus low. Neck and trunk are elongate and the tail very short, not extending behind the pelvis; in the living animal, the tail must have been almost imperceptible.

The limbs are more massive than those of †*Nesodon*, but the individual bones are very similar in form and, as in the Santa Cruz genus, tibia and fibula are co-ossified at the upper end. There are four functional digits in the fore-foot, three in the hind, and vestiges of the first metacarpal and fifth metatarsal are indicated by facets on the adjoining metapodials. The feet, especially the manus, are longer than in †*Nesodon* and the metacarpals are slender; the symmetry of the foot is mesaxonic. The phalanges are relatively shorter and wider than in the Santa Cruz genus, especially the second one of each digit, which is broader than it is long. The unguals are shaped more as in the perissodactyl †*Palæosyops*, of the North American Eocene, than as in †*Nesodon*, but the cleft is even longer and deeper.

No member of the †Leontiniidae has been found in any formation later than the Colhué-huapi, nor can any of the Santa Cruz or subsequent genera be regarded as having descended from that family.

The family is not known to be represented in any of the formations older than the Deseado.

SUBORDER B. †Typotheria

This suborder comprises much smaller animals than the †Toxodonta; none are large and many are very small, no bigger than rabbits. Of all the †notoungulate suborders, this is, by far, the most numerous and diversified, though, inasmuch as the limits of the group are uncertain, the number of genera and species already named and described cannot be definitely stated. This uncertainty is due to the lack of material in the more ancient formations; quantities of jaws and teeth have been collected and several finely preserved skulls, but skeletons and feet are almost unknown. In the Musters and Casa Mayor formations a bewildering variety of small mammals has been found, many of which are obviously †Typotheria, many more are doubtfully so, while others again, though having the appearance of †typotheres, are probably referable to other groups.

As before mentioned, the Musters and Casa Mayor stages were the time when the †typotheres flourished most abundantly, but their recorded history is longer than that of any other suborder of the †Notoungulata. Two of the families persisted into the Pleistocene, while others died out from time to time in the Tertiary.

Family 4. †Typotheriidæ

†*Typotherium*, Pampean.   †*Pseudotypotherium*, Araucanian.   †*Eutypotherium*, †*Typothericulus*, Frias.   †*Trachytherus*, Deseado.

The first genus of the family and suborder to be discovered was the Pampean †*Typotherium*, from which those groups received their names. The species of this genus are the largest animals of the suborder, most members of which are very small; the Pampean †*Typotherium cristatum* is as large as a Black Bear. At first sight, the skull of this animal might easily be mistaken for that of a rodent and was, at one time, actually referred to that order. Indeed, a superficial likeness to the Rodentia characterizes most of the †Typotheria, though some are so like the klipdasses, that Ameghino included them in the Hyracoidea, the relationship with which is very remote.

In †*Typotherium* the number of teeth has been considerably reduced, the formula being: $i \frac{1}{2}$, $c \frac{0}{0}$, $p \frac{2}{1}$, $m \frac{3}{3} \times 2 = 24$. The first incisor, above and below, is a broad, rodent-like tooth, which is rootless and continued to grow through life; it is not abraded to a sharp, chisel-edge, as in the rodents, but is abruptly truncated by wear. The second lower incisor is a similar, but much smaller tooth; the canines, two upper and three lower premolars have been lost. The molars are large, rootless, completely hypsodont, with a pattern of the grinding surface which is much like that of †*Toxodon*, but showing characteristic differences.

The skull, with the lower jaw in place, is very deep vertically, which, in the living animal, must have given it a bullet-headed appearance. The cranium, despite the prominent sagittal crest, is low and depressed, and the orbit is nearly closed behind by the very long postorbital process of the frontal. As in the †Notoungulata generally, the hinder part of the zygomatic arch is placed very high on the side of the skull, its upper border being almost on a level with the sagittal crest and the entrance to the ear is high up. In front of the eyes, the face is suddenly constricted, to form a narrow, tapering rostrum, which adds much to the rodent-like look of the skull. The lower jaw, or mandible, has a short, deep horizontal portion and a high ascending portion, to give the space needed for the hypsodont teeth.

The skeleton, so far as it is known, is decidedly more primitive than that of the contemporary †*Toxodon*, as is shown by the retention of the collar-bones and by the larger number of digits, of which there are five in the manus and four in the pes. The ungual phalanges are narrow and nail-like in the fore-foot, somewhat broader in the hind-foot.

In the Pliocene of Monte Hermoso is found the genus †*Pseudotypotherium*, which so closely resembles the Pampean genus, as to require no particular description, and in the Friassian stage of the upper Miocene there are two genera, still very incompletely known, †*Eutypotherium* and †*Typothericulus*, which have the same dental formula as †*Typotherium*, but the milk-dentition has two lower premolars, a step toward the Oligocene genus. One or other of these Miocene genera is probably in the direct line of descent, but not at all certainly so.

Between the Friassian and the Deseado is a long hiatus in time in which no member of this family has been found, though, no doubt, it continued to flourish in some more northerly region, where favourable climatic conditions prevailed. It must always be borne in mind that in South America those mammal-bearing formations which are more ancient than the Pliocene are almost all confined to the far south and that the absence of many groups, which might reasonably be expected to occur there, was probably occasioned by climatic factors.

In the Deseado (presumably Oligocene) the family recurs in the genus †*Trachytherus*, which, in view of the long time-interval between Oligocene and Pleistocene, differs surprisingly little from the Pampean †*Typotherium*. The Deseado genus already has rootless, hypsodont molars, which are covered with cement and the molar pattern is such as might well have given rise to that of †*Typotherium*.

On the other hand, the reduction in the number of teeth had not been carried nearly so far; the dental formula is: $i \frac{3}{2}, c \frac{1}{1}, p \frac{4}{4}, m \frac{3}{3} \times 2 = 42$. This implies the loss of only one tooth, a lower incisor, on each side, but the second and third incisors, the canines and the first two premolars in the upper jaw and the third incisor, canine and three premolars in the lower jaw, are all very small and on the point of disappearance.

The skull is similar to that of †*Typotherium*, but is less specialized and what little is known of the skeleton (humerus and astragalus) agrees perfectly with the corresponding parts of the Pampean animal.

On the basis of very scanty remains, the family is believed to have been already differentiated as such in the Casa Mayor stage.

Families 5 and 6. †*Hegetotheriidæ and* †*Interatheriidæ*

These two groups are very closely allied, differing chiefly in the anterior teeth; in the †thegetotheres the first incisor, in upper and lower jaw, is enlarged and scalpriform and grew persistently, while in the †interatheres these teeth are low-crowned and rooted. Both of these families are most abundant and diversified in the Santa Cruz Miocene and in these beds several complete skeletons have been obtained. The principal genera of these families are as follows:

†HEGETOTHERIIDÆ: †*Pachyrukhos*, Colhué-huapi to low. Plio. †*Propachyrucos*, Deseado. †*Hegetotherium*, Colhué-huapi and Santa Cruz. †*Prohegetotherium*, Deseado. †INTERATHERIIDÆ: †*Interatherium*, †*Protypotherium*, Santa Cruz. †*Cochilius*, Colhué-huapi. †*Archæophylus*, †*Argyrohyrax*, Deseado.

The latest survivor of the †Hegetotheriidæ is the little, rabbit-like †*Pachyrukhos* in the upper Pliocene and the genus went back without noteworthy change to the Santa Cruz, in which the best-preserved material has been found. The dental formula is like that of †*Typotherium* except for a greater number of premolars and reads: $i \frac{1}{2}, c \frac{0}{0}, p \frac{3}{3}, m \frac{3}{3} \times 2 = 30$; the enlarged, scalpriform, persistently growing incisors are as in †*Typotherium*, except for having sharp edges. The molar pattern is fundamentally the same as in †*Nesodon*, but is very shallow and can be seen only in unworn teeth, for abrasion rapidly removed it, leaving only a dentine surface surrounded by a wall of enamel; the crowns continued to grow while the animal lived.

The skull has a very rodent-like appearance, which is largely due to the flat top, narrow, tapering rostrum and gnawing teeth. The very large eye-sockets and enormously developed auditory apparatus are suggestive of nocturnal habits and the inflated, pro-

tuberant squamosals give the skull a decided resemblance to that
of the dainty little Kangaroo Rat (*Dipodomys*) and indicate somewhat similar modes of life.

The neck is short, the body relatively elongate and the tail very
short; collar-bones are present, as they probably were in all members
of the suborder. The limbs are relatively long, especially the posterior pair, and very slender; the bones of the fore-arm, ulna and
radius, are separate, but those of the lower leg, tibia and fibula, are
co-ossified at both ends. The feet, which have four digits each, are of
unequal size, the pes much exceeding the manus in length; the
ungual phalanges are long, slender, pointed and almost claw-like.
The entire skeleton (especially the feet) suggests a leaping gait and
is remarkably like that of a rabbit, though in an altogether superficial way. In the restoration (Fig. 416, p. 714) Mr. Knight has followed these indications and drawn an animal that might easily be
mistaken for a short-eared rabbit. The ears are, of course, entirely
conjectural and are, perhaps, too small, if the creature's habits were
really nocturnal.

A second genus of the family is †*Hegetotherium*, the latest known
appearance of which is in the Pliocene of Monte Hermoso, but is
most abundant in the Santa Cruz Miocene. This genus is much
larger than †*Pachyrukhos* and with far thicker, sturdier bones. It
cannot possibly have been ancestral to the latter, but, in many respects, serves to show what the desired ancestor must have been like.
One upper and two lower incisors are enlarged, scalpriform and rootless and none of the teeth has been lost, but those teeth which are
lacking in †*Pachyrukhos* are very small in †*Hegetotherium* and ready
to disappear. The molars and premolars are hypsodont and rootless.

The †hegetothere family is well represented in the Deseado, but
cannot be assuredly traced to an earlier formation than the Musters
stage; very probably it arose from one of the Eocene brachyodont
groups.

The †Interatheriidæ, which came to an end in the Pliocene, are
less specialized and more conservative than the †hegetotheres and
are numerously represented in the Santa Cruz beds by the species
of two genera. A persistently primitive form is the genus †*Protypotherium*, the latest known occurrence of which is in the Monte Hermoso
Pliocene; the Santa Cruz fossils are much the best preserved. The
skeleton is that of a small animal with the full complement of
44 teeth, arranged in continuous series in each jaw, without gaps.
Molars and premolars are hypsodont and rootless, but the incisors

Fig. 324. — Santa Cruz †typothere, †*Protypotherium australe*, and armadillo, †*Stegotherium tesselatum*. (Restored by

and canines are rooted and very low-crowned. A striking difference from the †hegetotheres is in the form of the incisors, none of which are enlarged and scalpriform and those of the lower jaw are deeply cleft and furcate and are not unlike those of the Hyracoidea. From the incisors to the molars there is a gradual transition in the size and complexity of the successive teeth and the molar pattern is that which is fundamentally common to all of the †notoungulates.

The skull is long, tapering anteriorly to the slender muzzle; the neck is short, the body elongate, the tail long and thick. This long and heavy tail is very exceptional among the Santa Cruz hoofed animals. The limbs are relatively long and slender, the forearm and lower leg bones are all slender and the digits number four in both manus and pes; the ungual phalanges are so narrow and pointed as to be more claw-like than hoof-like.

The restoration (Fig. 324, p. 514) shows the animal as being, as in most other †typothere genera, decidedly rodent-like in appearance, a likeness which, possibly, may be unduly increased by the shape given to the ears.

The family is named from †*Interatherium*, in which the head is short, broad, deep and bullet-like, resembling that of †*Typotherium* in miniature. The first incisor is enlarged, while the other incisors and the canines are diminished. The permanent grinding teeth are hypsodont and rootless, but the milk-premolars are low-crowned and rooted, just as in the North American horses, of which the middle Miocene genus †*Merychippus* has low-crowned and rooted milk-premolars, high-crowned and rootless permanent ones (p. 408). Both of these instances are remarkable cases of transition from the brachyodont to the hypsodont type of teeth.

The limbs of †*Interatherium* are shorter than those of †*Protypotherium* and, as in the latter, there is a long tail, except for which the skeleton suggests that the living animal had considerable resemblance to the existing Hyracoidea, a suggestion which Mr. Knight has followed in his drawing (Fig. 414, p. 712).

In the Colhué-huapi and Deseado stages is found †*Cochilius*, a genus which resembles †*Interatherium*, but seems not to have been one of its direct ancestors. Characteristic of the Deseado formation is the remarkable genus †*Argyrohyrax*, in which the grinding teeth are covered by a deposit of cement. Attention has already been called to the fact (p. 505) that, in the Colhué-huapi and Deseado stages, and even in the Casa Mayor there are several genera of †Typotheria and †Toxodonta which have cement-covered cheek-teeth, while in the succeeding stage, the Santa Cruz, there is only one such genus, †*Notohippus*, and that was short-lived. This is, to a certain extent, a reversal of the course of events followed in the northern hemisphere, where hypsodont, rootless, cement-covered teeth appeared late and were the culminating phase of tooth-development. In South America, on the contrary, it would seem to have been a premature and unsuccessful experiment.

Family 7. Notopithecidæ

†*Notopithecus*, Musters and Casa Mayor.   †*Gulielmoscottia*, Musters. †*Archæopithecus*, †*Transpithecus*, etc., Casa Mayor.

This family which came to an end in the Musters stage, and is chiefly confined to the Casa Mayor, includes some of the most primitive forms of the suborder. Especially primitive is †*Notopithecus* itself, which cannot be far removed from the common ancestry of all the †typotherian families. The teeth are present in the full number of 44 and are in continuous rows without gaps; they are all very low-crowned and have conspicuous roots. There is a gradation of pattern from the first incisor to the last molar.

Fig. 325. — Lower teeth, with cement, of †*Plagiarthrus clivus*, Casa Mayor stage. (Ameghino Collection.)

The skull is like that of the †Typotheria generally and the auditory apparatus, so characteristic of all the †Notoungulata, has already reached a high degree of specialization. In the Casa Mayor beds numerous genera of the family have been described, but the number of valid names is doubtful.

Families 8 ?†Acœlodidæ and 9 ?†Archæohyracidæ

There is no doubt that these families belong to the †Notoungulata, but their subordinal status is questionable, for they may be referable to the †Typotheria, or they may possibly be primitive members of the †Toxodonta; the general aspect of skull and teeth is more as in the †typotheres. The most important genera are as follows:

†Acœlodidæ: †*Acœlodus*, †*Oldfieldthomasia*, Casa Mayor. †Archæohyracidæ: †*Archæohyrax*, Deseado; †*Eohyrax*, Musters.

The best-known and by far the most interesting member of the †Accelodidæ is †*Oldfieldthomasia*, which looks very much like one of the Santa Cruz †Interatheriidæ. The teeth, 44 in number, are in

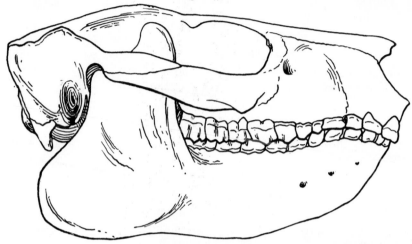

FIG. 326. — Skull, right side, of †*Notopithecus adapinus*, Musters and Casa Mayor stages. (From Simpson.)

uninterrupted rows and, in form, make a gradual transition from incisors to molars; the canines are small and like the incisors in shape, all the teeth are very low-crowned. The lower molars have the bicrescentic pattern and in the concavity of the hinder crescent stands the more or less independent pillar which is so nearly universal in South American ungulates.

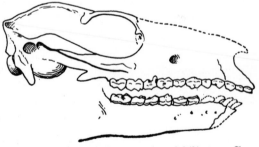

FIG. 327. — †*Oldfieldthomasia debilitata*, Casa Mayor stage. (From Simpson.)

The skull resembles that of †*Protypotherium*, but has a relatively longer face and shorter cranium and much more slender jaws in a more pointed muzzle.

The particular interest of this genus arises from the fact that it is nearly what the common ancestor of all the †Notoungulata must have been. It is not to be regarded as the actual ancestor, for it was contemporary with distinctive †Entelonychia, †Typotheria and, perhaps, even †Toxodonta; it is rather a persistent primitive form, surviving from an earlier period. "*Oldfieldthomasia* comes closer than either *Notostylops* or *Notopithecus* to being a really generalized notoungulate" (Simpson).

The family †Archæohyracidæ requires but brief notice here because of the uncertainty as to its systematic position; in general aspect, the likeness is nearest to the †Typotheria. The latest known appearance of the family is in the Deseado fauna, from which the single genus, †*Archæohyrax*, has been obtained. The group is much more abundantly represented in the Musters stage, which seems to have been the time of its culmination and from which half a dozen or more genera have been named (†*Archæohyrax*, †*Eohyrax*, etc.). The family has been reported, though doubtfully, from the Casa Mayor stage.

Suborder C. †Entelonychia

In the chapters on the hoofed animals of North America it was shown that almost every stage of the Tertiary and Quaternary periods had its own monstrous and bizarre animals which, to us, seem "outrageously absurd." This was still more conspicuously true of Tertiary and Pleistocene South America. Even there, few groups can have been of more peculiar character than the †Entelonychia, which may be designated as the "clawed †toxodonts," for the hoofs had been transformed into thick claws, deeply cleft at the end, very much like those of the †chalicotheres of the Northern Hemisphere. So great, indeed, is the likeness, that Ameghino eventually referred them to the northern suborder †Ancylopoda, abandoning his own term †Entelonychia.

Family 10. †Homalodotheriidæ

The principal genera of this family are given in the following table:

†*Homalodotherium*, Frias., Santa Cruz. †*Diorotherium*, †*Prochalicotherium*, Colhué-huapi. †*Asmodeus*, Deseado. †*Rhyphodon*, †*Periphragnis*, †*Distylophorus*, etc., Musters. †*Isotemnus*, †*Pleurostylodon*, †*Thomashuxleya*, etc., Casa Mayor.

This long-lived family extended from the early Pliocene to the Casa Mayor of the early Eocene; the Friassian fossils of the group are very fragmentary, but the Santa Cruz material, though rare, is fairly complete. The only well-known genus of the Santa Cruz is †*Homalodotherium*, of which the Field Museum has secured the unique specimen of a partial skeleton. The Santa Cruz species are of moderate size, about equalling a tapir in stature, but of very different proportions and general appearance.

The teeth, present in the unreduced number of 44, are in continuous series, without gaps and with a gradual transition in shape from incisors to molars. It is this feature which suggested the name of the genus, but, as was pointed out above, the term is even more strictly applicable to such primitive †typotheres as †*Notopithecus* and †*Oldfieldthomasia*. Though rather high-crowned, the teeth are all rooted and devoid of cement. The canines are small tusks, pro-

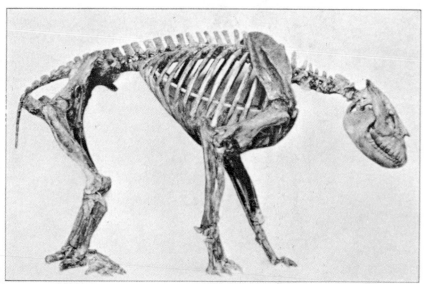

Fig. 328. — Skeleton of †*Homalodotherium cunninghami*. Feet, limbs and skull practically complete, backbone largely restored by T. H. Quinn, under the direction of E. S. Riggs. (Field Mus. Nat. Hist.)

jecting but little above and below the lower and upper tooth-rows respectively; in some individuals, presumably males, the tusks are considerably larger than in others.

The skull, with lower jaw in place, is short, broad and vertically deep and has a decided likeness to the type seen in many unrelated kinds of hoofed animals, such as †*Diadiaphorus*, a large member of the Santa Cruz †Litopterna, and †*Hyracodon*, North American †cursorial rhinoceros. The long cranium and short face are the skull proportions of many primitive ungulates. A notable difference from all of these, however, is the great abbreviation of the nasal bones, carrying the nasal opening almost back to the orbits. This structure is suggestive of a proboscis, or, perhaps, an inflated muzzle.

The neck-vertebræ are incompletely known, but it would seem
that the neck was short and the body elongate. The trunk-vertebræ
are remarkable for their short and weak neural spines, a character
which recurs in the †Astrapotheria and †Pyrotheria and is an inexplicable feature in these large hoofed animals.

Collar-bones seem to be present, as in the †Typotheria; the hip-
bones are broad and strongly everted. The limbs and feet are the
most remarkable parts of this peculiar animal; the fore-legs and feet

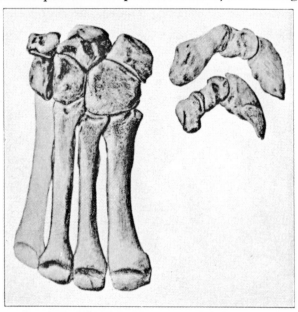

Fig. 329. — Left manus of †*Homalodotherium*, carpus
and metacarpus, vestigial mc I not shown. Lower right,
phalanges of digit V from the side. Upper right, †*Moropus elatus*, phalanges of digit III from the side. From
skeleton in Fig. 328.

are considerably longer than the hind, making the back slope downward from the shoulders to the rump, as in †*Moropus* (p. 462). The
proportions of the different limb-segments are, as in the latter, unusual; the upper-arm and thigh are elongate, fore-arm and foot very
long, lower leg and hind-foot very short; the metacarpals are more
than twice as long as the metatarsals.

The massive humerus has unusually large and prominent ridges
for the attachment of the deltoid and supinator muscles, recalling
the humerus of the Wombat (*Phascolomys*) a burrowing Australian
marsupial. The radius is very long and relatively slender and articulates with the humerus by a discoidal head, indicating that the fore-

foot had considerable power of rotation; the ulna is heavy and unreduced. The form of the humerus, radius and claw-bearing manus, together with the probable presence of clavicles, strongly suggests habits of digging for food; for burrowing, the animal was far too large, but he probably dug up roots, tubers and the like. This hypothesis, first suggested by the late Mr. R. Lydekker, best explains the peculiar fore-leg and foot.

The manus has four digits, the metacarpals of which are long and slender and the phalanges are so articulated with each other, and with the metacarpals that the heavy claws could be folded back upon the foot. The pollex is not fully known but was probably vestigial and without phalanges. In shape, the ungual phalanges are claw-like and deeply cleft at the tip, but they are so thick as to make the term "claw" hardly applicable.

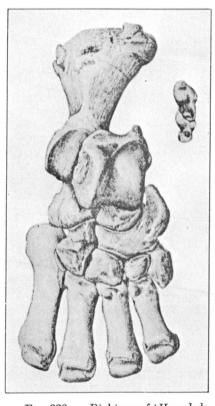

As in fossorial mammals generally, the pes, which has four digits and the vestige of a hallux, is much smaller than the manus. In walking, the hind-foot apparently rested upon its external border, as in the †ground-sloths. This was made possible by the long neck and unusually convex head of the astragalus, which allowed an exceptional degree of freedom in the rotation of the hind-foot upon the leg.

Fig. 330. — Right pes of †*Homalodotherium*, tarsus and metatarsus. First and second phalanges of digit V, from the side. From skeleton in Fig. 328.

Little has been learned of the Colhué-huapi genera of this family, †*Diorotherium* and †*Prochalicotherium*, and, so far as they are known, they do not differ in any important way from the Santa Cruz genus.

The Deseado member of the family is †*Asmodeus*, which may be described as a gigantic †*Homalodotherium*; it is not likely to have been ancestral to the latter. The actual ancestor is still to seek.

In the Musters stage the †Entelonychia are a highly diversified and abundant group, far more so than they were in the succeeding faunas. Many genera have been distinguished and named, but, for the most part, from such fragmentary and uncharacteristic materials, that little can be ascertained about them. Much the best known genus of this stage is †*Periphragnis*, the position of which in the line of descent is far from clear and is involved in a number of obscure problems, both anatomical and stratigraphical.

The skull and teeth of †*Periphragnis* are like those of a small †*Homalodotherium*, but the canines are decidedly larger and form

Fig. 331. — Restoration from the skeleton of †*Homalodotherium* shown in Fig. 328.

small tusks. A nearly perfect fore-foot in the La Plata Museum, belonging to this, or some closely allied genus, is far less specialized than that of the Santa Cruz genus and is rather the manus of a normal †notoungulate. The carpus is relatively much wider and shorter than that of †*Homalodotherium*, from which it differs in many details, as, for example, in the much smaller size of the magnum and trapezoid. There are five digits and the metacarpals are very much shorter and relatively heavier than in the Santa Cruz genus. The first metacarpal is strongly divergent from the others, which are almost parallel, with but slight divergence. The greatest differences from †*Homalodotherium* are to be seen in the phalanges, which are like those of the †toxodonts. The unguals are broad, thin and flattened and must have supported true hoofs; the only unusual feature about these unguals is the manner in which they are deeply and widely cleft at the free border.

In attempting to estimate the position of †*Periphragnis* within the family and suborder, several alternative possibilities present themselves. If this genus is really ancestral to the Santa Cruz animals, then, either the interval in time between the Musters and the Deseado formations was far longer than has been generally supposed, or the rate of evolutionary development was much more rapid than

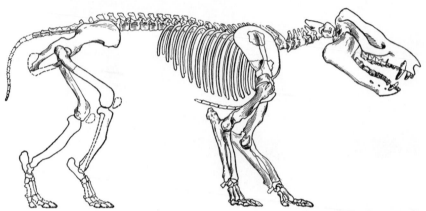

FIG. 332. — Skeleton of †*Thomashuxleya*, Casa Mayor stage. (From Simpson.)

has hitherto been believed. More probable is the remaining alternative, that †*Periphragnis* is not a direct ancestor of †*Homalodotherium*, but collaterally related, retaining the ancestral type of foot which was common to all early †notoungulates.

The Scarrit expeditions from the American Museum of Natural History obtained in the Casa Mayor beds a fine skeleton of †*Thomashuxleya* and extensive, though less complete, remains of †*Pleurostylodon*, which is nearly the same thing in miniature. For an opportunity to study these unique specimens, I am indebted to the kindness of Dr. G. G. Simpson, who made the collections.

In †*Thomashuxleya* the teeth are present in unreduced size and number; the upper incisors are relatively large and increase from the first ($i\,\underline{1}$) to the third ($i\,\underline{3}$) which is sharp-pointed and shaped like a canine; the lower incisors are similar, but considerably smaller. The canines are tusks, of no great length, but much more prominent than any of the other teeth and proportionally as thick and heavy as in a bear. The jaws, when seen from the outer side, resemble those of such an Eocene perissodactyl as †*Palæosyops*, though the molar-premolar pattern is altogether different and is like that of †*Homalodotherium*. The skull is incomplete, but the base and the posterior nasal opening are as in the latter, but, on the other hand, the nasals are so long as to preclude any possibility of a proboscis. In size the skull of the Casa Mayor genus is not much inferior to that of †*Periphragnis*, or may even be a little larger.

The vertebral column is nearly complete and has the formula: C.7, D.?13, L.7, S.4, Cd. ?, the vertebræ show that the neck was

Fig. 333. — Restoration of †*Thomashuxleya*, drawn from skeleton shown in Fig. 332.

short, the body long, the tail short and thick. All the dorso-lumbar vertebræ have singularly short and weak neural spines and all of them incline backward, as in the Proboscidea, an unusual feature among mammals. In view of the great geological antiquity of this genus, it is very surprising to find that the lumbar vertebræ have such a remarkably complex method of articulation. The zygapophyses are not only of the cylindrical, interlocking type found in all Artiodactyla, but they show the additional complication of the scroll-like cross-section, which elsewhere occurs only in the †Astrapotheria and in the †entelodonts, or †"giant-pigs" of the northern hemisphere (p. 390). There can be no question of relationship here.

The long sacrum consists of four coalesced vertebræ. The anterior caudal vertebræ are very broad, soon becoming short and narrow, but the hinder ones are nearly as wide as they are long. These vertebræ indicate a short, thick and "stumpy" tail.

There is no such difference in length between fore- and hind-legs as there is in †*Homalodotherium*. The scapula is peculiar in the position of the spine, which is far back, making the anterior part of the blade (*prescapular fossa*) much broader than the posterior part. The spine is broad and has a very large and bifid metacromion, which seems to have been lost in the Santa Cruz genus. Collar-bones are present. The pelvis resembles that of the latter, on a smaller scale.

The humerus is suggestively like that of †*Homalodotherium*, but is far less extreme in its development, the extraordinary characters displayed in the Santa Cruz animal being all present in incipient degree. The deltoid crest dies away gradually and the supinator ridge is prominent, but far less so than the deltoid; the epicondylar foramen is conspicuous. The fore-arm bones are relatively short and sturdy. The head of the radius is wider and less discoidal than in †*Homalodotherium* and so interlocks with the humerus as to prevent any rotation of the fore-foot. The shaft of the radius is irregularly trihedral, widening and thickening downward. The nearly straight ulna is much stouter than the radius, a primitive feature. The manus is short and wide and closely resembles that of the genus next succeeding in time, †*Periphragnis* of the Musters stage. There are five digits and the pollex diverges so strongly from the others, as in the Musters genus also, that it might have been opposable; the first metacarpal is much shorter and more slender than the others. Metacarpals II to V, are short and stout, II and III are of nearly the same length, IV is shorter and V still shorter. The remarkable shape which characterizes the lower ends of the metacarpals in †*Homalodotherium* is not indicated at all, but a curious feature is the very faint development of the keel. The fifth metacarpal has on the outer side of the upper end a rough projection, which seems to be the beginning of the process that is so prominent in the Santa Cruz genus. The phalanges are somewhat longer and narrower than in †*Periphragnis*, and those of the first row have but a shallow notch for the metacarpals. The mode of articulation of the phalanges with each other and with the metacarpals is such as to show that the foot was of the ordinary †notoungulate type, aside from the possibly prehensile first digit.

The hind-limb is much less completely represented in the collections than the fore, but, by combining the material of †*Pleurostylodon* and other small animals referable to the family, a fairly complete reconstruction of the hind-leg and foot may be made. The femur is much shorter in relation to the humerus than in †*Homalodotherium*, the shaft is more cylindrical, less flattened and all three trochanters are more prominent and the groove for the knee-cap is extended much farther up the shaft. The femur of †*Homalodotherium* has a distinct suggestion of a Proboscidean likeness, but there is nothing of the sort about †*Thomashuxleya*, in which the femur is of the usual †noto-ungulate kind.

The tibia is not at all like that of †*Homalodotherium;* it is very much longer in proportion to the femur, the relation being about 4:5; the upper end is not nearly so wide and has no such outward extension overhanging the head of the fibula and the lower end is much less broadened transversely and compressed antero-posteriorly; the articular surface for the astragalus is very primitive in its flatness. The fibula is not known.

The astragalus is moderately grooved and retains the very primitive feature of a vascular canal perforating it from above downward. The lower end is a strongly convex, almost hemispherical head for the navicular, which embraces the outer side of the head in such a manner as to indicate a freedom of rotation of the hind-foot on the leg, like that observed in †*Homalodotherium*. Of the three cuneiform bones, the internal one is much the largest and the median one the smallest. The first metatarsal seems to have been opposable, like the hallux of a monkey; the second has a very slender shaft and III, IV and V are much stouter.

The known material of †*Thomashuxleya* and †*Periphragnis* is sufficient to prove that these genera were normal notoungulates, with proportions very much as in †*Nesodon* and digits shod with ordinary hoofs. That those Eocene and ?Oligocene genera were nearly related to †*Homalodotherium* and were members of the same family, is not open to question. Furthermore, it may be confidently asserted that †*Thomashuxleya* very nearly represents what the unspecialized ancestor of the Santa Cruz genera must have been. When it comes, however, to maintaining that †*Thomashuxleya* itself was that ancestor, the question assumes a very different aspect and formidable difficulties arise. There is, first, the question of time, whether such radical changes of structure could have been effected in the time between the Casa Mayor and the Deseado. Other families do not exhibit such changes between those stages. Another difficulty involves Dollo's principle of the "irreversibility of evolution."

†*Homalodotherium* has retained the primitive power of rotation of the manus, which the more ancient †*Thomashuxleya* has already lost. Is it possible that the more primitive structure could have been lost and reacquired? Nothing that is known of concrete cases of development would justify such an assumption, but, of course, it may be true nevertheless. Definite conclusions are not yet attainable, but, in a tentative way, the most likely result seems to be that †*Thomashuxleya* is not the actual ancestor of †*Homalodotherium*, but is very near that ancestor and serves all practical purposes for reconstructing the course of development. †*Periphragnis*, which seems indubitably to be a descendant of †*Thomashuxleya*, is even farther removed from the ancestry of †*Asmodeus* and †*Homalodotherium*.

SUBORDER D. †Notioprogonia

This suborder has (1934) been proposed by Dr. G. G. Simpson, to receive the most ancient and primitive of the †Notoungulata, genera which do not fit naturally into any of the preceding suborders and families and almost all of which are Eocene, or Paleocene in date. One family is represented in the Musters stage, but none is known from any later formation. This group contains the only †notoungulates which have ever been found outside of South America, †*Arctostylops* in the lower Eocene of North America and †*Palæostylops* in the Paleocene of Mongolia.

Family 11. †*Notostylopidæ*

The only genus of this family which is sufficiently known to call for attention here is †*Notostylops*, type genus, which was used by Ameghino to designate the fauna of the Casa Mayor stage. Though very primitive, this genus is more specialized than others of the suborder; the specialization, which was premature and led to no lasting result, consisted in the reduction of the number of teeth and in the enlargement of the incisors. The teeth are very variable in number, but the usual formula is: $i\frac{3}{2}$, $c\frac{0}{0}$, $p\frac{3}{3}$, $m\frac{3}{3} \times 2 = 34$. The first upper and second lower incisors are enlarged and have a scalpriform appearance, but they are rooted and did not grow permanently. In both jaws there are long diastemata between the incisors and the grinding teeth, the absence of the canines and first premolars producing these gaps, which are so uncommon in the order except in the Pliocene and Pleistocene. All of the teeth are low-crowned.

The skull has a †typotherian aspect, as is true of all the early and primitive †notoungulates. The brain, as revealed by an internal cast of the cranium, is of a low order. The olfactory lobes are large and the pear-shaped cerebral hemispheres are small, leaving the

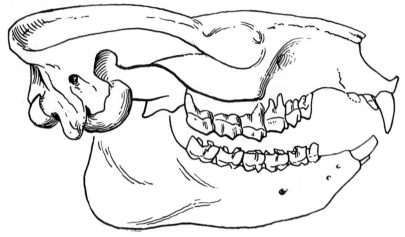

Fig. 334. — Skull of †*Notostylops brachycephalus*, Casa Mayor stage. (From Simpson.)

olfactory lobes and cerebellum uncovered and exposed. The hemispheres show but slight traces of convolutions.

Family 12. †Henricosborniidæ

The principal genus of this family, †*Henricosbornia*, is exceedingly primitive and might represent the ancestral types of any, or all of the †notoungulate suborders. The same statement has already been made as to †*Notopithecus* and †*Oldfieldthomasia* and is equally true of them. In fact, the three genera, though differing decidedly in certain points of detail, are all very primitive and very much alike and all of them are but little removed from the family, not yet fully identified, which gave rise to all the †Notoungulata.

Family 13. †Arctostylopidæ

The two known genera of this family are, as yet, represented by fragments of lower jaws, with some teeth. Their interest, which is unusually great, is principally geographical, for they are the only †notoungulates that have been found outside of the Neotropical Region. They are referred to this South American group on the strength of the pillar which stands in the concavity of the hinder crescent of the lower molars and which is so nearly universal among

South American hoofed animals, but has not been observed in other mammals. In the two northern genera the pillar is small and undeveloped, but is characteristic nevertheless.

†*Arctostylops*, a minute animal, was found in the lower Eocene of Wyoming, and †*Palæostylops* in the Paleocene of Mongolia.

The problem of the origin of the South American mammalian faunas has long been an extremely puzzling one. For a very long time, from the lower Eocene to the early Pliocene, the two Americas were severed by a sea across the site of the Isthmus of Panama and whatever connections with Africa and Australia there may have been, were transitory and difficult for spreading mammals to make use of. As a result of this long isolation Neotropical mammals became extremely peculiar and unlike those of other continents and the questions as to where they came from and when, have been much debated but never satisfactorily answered. North and South America were connected in the Cretaceous and probably also in the Paleocene. That the †Condylarthra and the earliest †Notoungulata entered South America from the north and there gave rise to an immense diversity of families and genera, is made not unlikely by the discovery of these northern †notoungulates.

CHAPTER XIX

HISTORY OF THE †ASTRAPOTHERIA AND †PYROTHERIA

Beside the †Notoungulata, which included the great body of Neotropical Tertiary hoofed mammals, there were three other orders of Tertiary ungulates in the region (†Astrapotheria, †Pyrotheria and †Litopterna), which are clearly distinguished from one another and from all †notoungulates. They agree in the negative characteristic of lacking the remarkable auditory apparatus which distinguishes the †notoungulates, but no common structural feature unites them, and while they may possibly have had a common origin, such origin cannot yet be demonstrated.

Tertiary South America abounded in curious and grotesque creatures, so completely unlike anything now living, that it is very difficult to understand their structure and interpret it in terms of habits and mode of life. Of all these unintelligible beasts, none are quite so strange as the †astrapotheres and †pyrotheres, the subjects of this chapter.

The order †Astrapotheria ran a parallel course with the †Entelonychia, with which it has frequently, though mistakenly, been united. Its latest appearance was in the lower Pliocene, and it went back to the Casa Mayor as a distinctly differentiated group. In geographical distribution, the order is exclusively South American. Of the two suborders into which Simpson has divided the group, one, the †Trigonostylopoidea, is doubtfully associated with the true †astrapotheres.

Suborder A. †Astrapotherioidea

Family 1. †Astrapotheriidæ

The most important genera of the family are as follows:

†*Astrapotherium*, Colhué-huapi to Frias. †*Astrapothericulus*, Colhué-huapi. †*Parastrapotherium*, Deseado and Colhué-huapi. †*Astraponotus*, Musters. †*Albertogaudrya*, Casa Mayor.

In formations subsequent to the Santa Cruz, the remains of this family are fragmentary, no more complete than is necessary for identification. In the Santa Cruz the fossils are in a far better state of preservation; fine skulls and jaws of †*Astrapotherium* are not rare and in the Field Museum is the unique treasure of an almost entire skeleton. So far as the dentition and bony framework are concerned, hardly anything remains to be learned and yet it is well-nigh impossible to understand this paradoxical and self-contradictory skeleton. Nothing now living is remotely like this extraordinary animal and that is the reason for the difficulty in comprehending the facts of structure.

For the opportunity to make a study of this magnificent fossil, I am indebted to the kindness of Director Simms and Mr. E. S. Riggs of the Field Museum of Natural History in Chicago.

The only Santa Cruz genus of the family, which is definitely known is †*Astrapotherium*, for which a less appropriate name could scarcely have been found than the one chosen by Dr. H. Burmeister (Gk. 'Αστραπή, lightning). Lightning-like speed and agility were far beyond the capacities of this dull brute, though one should not vilify or ridicule anything so profoundly interesting.

The first discovery of this animal was made by Captain Sullivant, of the British Navy, who found some fossil teeth in Patagonia and sent them to Owen (1853). That famous palæontologist identified them as belonging to †*Nesodon* and called them †*N. magnus*. The species name must be retained, even though the fossils should be referred to another genus. Thus it comes about that the commonest Santa Cruz species is †*Astrapotherium magnum* (Owen). Several species of the genus have been named, some of which were the largest mammals of their day and region. Species differed from one another chiefly in size. How many of these names will ultimately stand, is a doubtful question; in making them, little attention was paid to the differences due to age, sex and individual variability and no sufficient suite of skulls has yet been obtained to eliminate these sources of error.

The dentition of all the suborder differs in several important respects from that of any other South American group. In †*Astrapotherium* the formula is: $i \frac{0}{3}$, $c \frac{1}{1}$, $p \frac{2}{1}$, $m \frac{3}{3} \times 2 = 28$, a loss of 16 teeth from the primitive number of 44. The upper incisors are entirely wanting, but the lower ones are retained in full number and are procumbent. The crowns of these teeth are broad and leaf-like and display the unusual peculiarity of a partial division into two lobes; the cutting border is notched and a groove marks the superior (or posterior) face of each tooth. It is important to note that these lower incisors were functional and show abrasion.

The canines are large and formidable tusks which grew from permanent pulps and never formed roots; the upper tusk is relatively short and very thick, obliquely truncated by abrasion. The lower tusk is far larger and more strongly curved, the exposed portion describing a quarter of a circle and very much resembling the tusks of a hippopotamus and, as in that animal, the enamel of these teeth is ribbed and fluted. Even closer is the resemblance to the canines of the North American †*Metamynodon* (p. 453), an Oligocene rhinoceros of presumably aquatic habits. In most individuals the lower tusks show a number of transverse grooves of the anterior border in places where no other tooth can have reached, and yet evidently due to abrasion. No other South American ungulate, indigenous or immigrant, has tusks of this description. In the only other group with canine tusks, the †Entelonychia, these teeth are very much smaller and diminished in the course of evolutionary development, being decidedly larger in the early Eocene †*Thomashuxleya* than in the Miocene †*Homalodotherium*. In other South American tusked animals, such as the †Toxodonta and the †Pyrotheria, the tusks are incisors.

The premolars are greatly reduced in number and size, only two above and one below remaining; the pattern of the masticating surface is simpler than that of the molars. The milk-dentition, which so often preserves ancestral characteristics, has the formula: $dp \frac{4}{3}$. The pattern of the upper molars is essentially like that of the †Toxodonta, a fact to which eloquent testimony is borne by Owen's reference of the first jaw fragment, with upper molars, that was brought back from Patagonia, to †*Nesodon*, as was mentioned above. There is also a decided resemblance to the rhinoceroses, which has led several writers to postulate a relationship between †astrapotheres and rhinoceroses. It is well-nigh certain that, in both cases, these resemblances were independently acquired; they are, in fact, remarkable instances of convergent development, but what the starting point in the Casa Mayor genera was, has yet to be ascertained.

The lower molars have the bicrescentic crowns which are so nearly universal among South American ungulates, the only exceptions being the †Pyrotheria and the †Condylarthra. The characteristic pillar in the hinder crescent differs from that in other Neotropical orders in its connection with the external wall and, in †*Astrapotherium* itself, it was undergoing reduction as compared with the genera of the Colhué-huapi and Deseado formations. The lower molars are very elongate antero-posteriorly and very narrow in proportion to their length and have a strong resemblance to those of †*Metamynodon*, a resemblance

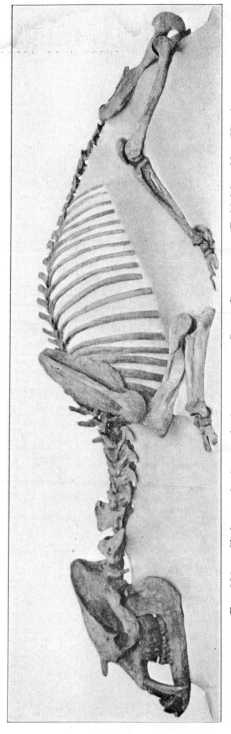

Fig. 335. — Skeleton of †*Astrapotherium magnum*, Santa Cruz stage. (Field Mus. Nat. Hist.)

already noted in the case of the canine tusks, but they differ in several respects, notably in the complete enamel covering of the teeth.

All parts of this skeleton are peculiar and exceptional, but the skull and feet are the most remarkable of all and, outside of the family, no known mammal has a skull in the least like it, save, of course, such features as are common to all hoofed mammals whatsoever. The toothless premaxillaries are short and thick, without ascending rami or palatine processes and articulate only with the maxillaries. They cannot have supported an elastic pad against which the lower incisors could bite, as in the true ruminants, for those teeth project far in front of the premaxillæ. The nasal bones are extremely short, proportionally as much reduced as in the elephants. This reduction of the nasals and the shape and position of the anterior nasal opening irresistibly suggest that the living animal had a proboscis, but this is apparently contradicted by the length of the neck. As an alternative, it might be assumed that instead of a proboscis there was a swollen, inflated snout, as in the Moose (*Alce americanus*) or the Saiga Antelope (*Saiga tatarica*), but in both of these modern ruminants the maxillaries and premaxillaries are so prolonged forward that they extend over the lower incisors and thus are in a position to support the cropping pad. Taking all the contradictory factors into consideration, the most likely conclusion seems to be that †*Astrapotherium* did have a proboscis, on the under side of which was a horny band against which the lower incisors occluded. That those incisors were actually used, is shown by their abraded state in old individuals and, to be used effectively, there must have been some firm opposing surface. The four-tusked †mastodonts of the Miocene and Pliocene (see Fig. 177, p. 289) present a somewhat analogous problem, except in the "shovel-tuskers," which seem to have used their lower incisors for digging rather than biting. In those †mastodonts in which the upper and lower tusks did not meet, the plainly marked abrasion of the lower tusks must have been done by the trunk.

The facial region is greatly shortened and the cranium relatively elongated; the orbits are very far forward and are incompletely closed behind. The brain-case is of small capacity and, in consequence, the sagittal and occipital crests are greatly developed, in order to afford the necessary surfaces of attachment for the temporal muscles. The forehead is raised in a great dome-like convexity, produced, no doubt, by an extraordinary development of the frontal sinuses; there is no roughening, or other indication that a dermal horn was attached to the dome, the surface of which is smooth. The immense Pleistocene

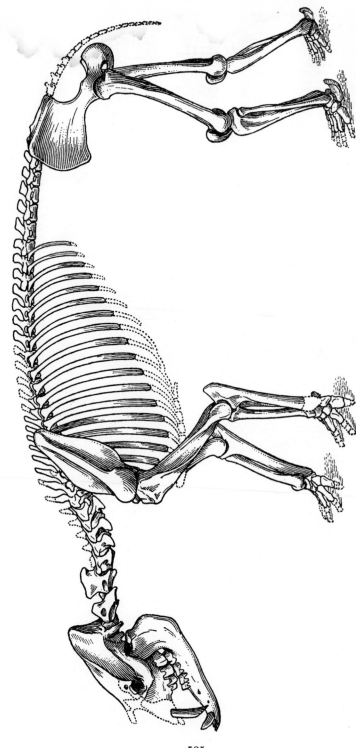

Fig. 336. — †*Astrapotherium magnum*, same skeleton as Fig. 335, drawn in standing position. (From Riggs.)

535

rhinoceros, †*Elasmotherium*, of the Old World, has an even higher frontal dome, but that was for the support of a horn. The two halves of the lower jaw are co-ossified at the symphysis into a mandible of one piece. The symphyseal region is broad, depressed and shallow, with the six incisors arranged in a semi-circle around the alveolar border. The horizontal ramus of the mandible is of unusual shape; vertically, it is shallow and, in side-view, looks remarkably weak in comparison

Fig. 337. — Restoration of †*Astrapotherium magnum*, made from the skeleton shown in Figs. 335 and 336.

with the size of the skull, but this shallowness is compensated by great relative thickness, the ramus being of almost cylindrical shape, so that the jaw does not lack strength.

The neck is of moderate length, not actually long, but longer than one would expect to find in a proboscis-bearing animal. Proportionately, the cervical vertebræ are extraordinarily heavy, especially when compared with the lumbars. So far as size and massiveness are concerned, one might say that this skeleton unites the neck of a large rhinoceros, with the loins of an ox. The neural spines of the trunk-vertebræ are disproportionately short and weak and the large muscles of the back, such as the *longissimus dorsi*, can have had no great strength. The massive cervical vertebræ imply corresponding development of the muscles of the neck, but in view of the large and heavy head, the short neural spines of the anterior dorsal region are very difficult to understand, unless the animal's habits were largely aquatic. The spines of all the trunk-vertebræ have a backward inclination, as in the Proboscidea, and, in the lumbar region, the transverse processes are strikingly short, thin and weak. The intervertebral articulations in the lumbar region are, as in the †Entelonychia, extremely complex, having a scroll-like cross-section, such as is seen in the †"giant-pigs," or †entelodonts, of the northern hemisphere.

The sacrum consists of five vertebræ, all of which are not only in contact with the pelvis, but actually ankylosed with it, forming an ilio-sacral joint of extraordinary strength and of most exceptional character. This is another of the many paradoxes which this skeleton exhibits; as will be seen, the limbs and feet are relatively weak and slender and how these are to be harmonized with an ilio-sacral joint of unprecedented strength, it is difficult to see. The posterior end of the sacrum is so small and its neural canal so contracted, as to indicate that the animal cannot have had a long tail.

The vertebral formula is: C 7, D 19, L 6, S 5, Cd? The body is long, as is also the thoracic part of it, but the thorax has no great breadth, or depth, as is shown by the length and curvature of the ribs. These bones show no very striking peculiarities; the anterior four are short, straight and broad; behind the fourth they become slender and rod-like, remarkably so for so large an ungulate.

Limb-girdles, like everything else in this strange skeleton, are peculiar; no trace of clavicles has been seen, but as the sternum has been completely lost from the sole and only skeleton, this failure to find them is inconclusive. On the other hand, their existence in the living animal is made unlikely by the character of the elbow joint.

The scapula has an unusual, mitral form, the upper part of the blade narrowing gradually and making the upper border very narrow and rounded, almost pointed. The spine is the most remarkable feature of this curious shoulder-blade; it increases in height downward and is very prominent at the lower end; the free border of the spine is broad and terminates in an immensely expanded, somewhat irregularly shaped acromion, unlike that of any other mammal.

The pelvis has considerable resemblance to that of †Nesodon; it is very large with almost equal length and width; the ilium has a contracted neck and expands suddenly into a broad plate, which is not everted at all; the visceral mass behind the ribs must have been supported by the abdominal muscles alone.

The limbs are remarkably short and weak, out of all proportion to the elongate trunk; the relative lengths of body and limbs being not unlike those of a hippopotamus, but in the latter the limb-bones are proportionately much heavier. These facts suggest an amphibious mode of life for †*Astrapotherium* and several other structural features suggest the same thing, but none of them is conclusive and there are difficulties in the way of the aquatic, or any other hypothesis.

The humerus is relatively elongate, much more so than the fore-arm bones and but little shorter than the femur. The shaft is slender, but is given an undue appearance of thickness by the deltoid ridge, which, though not prominent, runs nearly the whole length of the shaft, but there is no distinct supinator ridge, epicondyle or foramen. The fore-arm bones are not unlike those of †*Nesodon;* they are in contact only at the ends, making the narrow radio-cubital arcade continuous. The radius is short in proportion to the length of the body and shorter than the humerus in the ratio of 14:19. It is slender and its mode of articulation with the humerus is such as to prevent any rotation of the fore-foot. The ulna is considerably heavier than the radius, and has a trihedral shaft, tapering downwards; it appears to have a connection with the lunar, which, if true, is extremely exceptional.

The femur is the longest of the limb-bones, exceeding the humerus in length by nearly three inches. The great trochanter can hardly be said to exist, as it is merely a roughening and, in consequence, there is no sigmoid notch; the shaft is flattened and has some resemblance to that of a small elephant; there is no third trochanter. The patella is long, rather narrow and of nearly uniform width; its anterior surface is finely and irregularly ribbed. The bones of the lower leg are slender and straight and, in length, exceed those of the fore-arm but little. The tibia has an odd resemblance to the human shin-bone; the upper end is broad and thick and the lower end of the shaft is so twisted that, when the patellar ligament attachment is directly in front of the eye, the lower end is oblique and the internal malleolus is almost as much posterior as lateral. This is one of the many paradoxical features connected with the hind-foot, for which no explanation has been suggested. The surface for the astragalus is nearly flat, quite elephantine in appearance, and is continued down over the distal end of the malleolus, which fits into a deep fossa on the astragalus. The fibula is rather slender, though not reduced; the lower end is much more enlarged than the upper end and forms a massive and rugose external malleolus, which has no contact with the calcaneum.

The feet, notwithstanding a certain likeness to the Proboscidea and †Amblypoda, are different in significant ways from those of any other known ungulates.

The carpus is short and wide, the breadth being almost exactly double the length, and the various carpal elements have a massive, block-like appearance that is decidedly elephantine, but in the details of form and manner of interarticulation, these carpals are *sui generis*. A full description of the carpus would be out of place in such a work as this, but one or two peculiarities may be mentioned. Thus, the pyramidal extends down over the outer side of the unciform and articulates with the fifth metacarpal, a very unusual arrangement. The lunar is the largest bone in the carpus, surpassing even the unciform, which is normally the largest.

The metacarpus consists of five short, broad members, arranged in radiating fashion. In shape, these bones are most peculiar; though broad transversely, they are very thin and plate-like and thus altogether different from the metapodials of other ungulates. Their antero-posterior thickness is suddenly diminished at the half-way point of length. It is difficult to see how such plate-like metacarpals could have supported any considerable weight, which must have been borne almost entirely by the elastic pad, which, no doubt, cushioned the bones of the fore-foot. The phalanges, unfortunately, are not known.

Even more peculiar is the structure of the hind-foot, every part of which is exceptional, often unique and unexampled and most difficult of interpretation. The astragalus, in general appearance, bears some likeness to that of the †Amblypoda of the North American Eocene, as was long ago pointed out by Schlosser. The trochlea for the tibia is nearly flat and the convex head fits into the deeply concave navicular, without touching the cuboid. When examined in detail, it proves to be one of the most peculiar ankle-bones ever discovered.

The calcaneum is still more curious than the astragalus and is altogether unlike that of any other ungulate. The astragalus extends over the whole width of the calcaneum and shuts it off from contact with the fibula. In all the other indigenous groups of South American ungulates, in which the foot-structure is known, the fibula rests on the calcaneum. The bone is short and very massive and its articular surface for the cuboid is greatly reduced. No other known mammal has a calcaneum at all like this. The navicular is even more exceptional; it looks like a thin slab of clay that had been moulded around the head of the astragalus. The other tarsal bones are equally peculiar and exceptional, but space is lacking for a description of them.

Repetition of adjectives, such as peculiar, extraordinary, grotesque, etc., grows wearisome and so for the metatarsals it must suffice to say that they are the strangest and most inexplicable features of this unique skeleton and the relative sizes of its members are different from those in any other known mammal. Five metatarsals are present, of which Nos. I, IV and V are broad, but Nos. II and III are very much more slender and have a withered, pathological look, that suggests disease or injury, but as these bones are just alike in each hind-foot, they must be regarded as normal. All of these metatarsals have a relatively very thick upper half and a much thinner lower half. The appearance suggests that some sort of a pad supported the phalanges and the lower half of the metatarsals, which did not extend to the upper half. No. V is the strangest of all, and looks more like the calcaneum of a Santa Cruz †ground-sloth than the metatarsal of an ungulate, which it undoubtedly is. What the soft parts of this paradoxical foot can have been, it is most difficult, if not impossible, to imagine.

Two phalanges, the first and second of the same digit, are associated with this hind-foot, yet their incongruous character is such as to cause a doubt that they could have belonged to †*Astrapotherium*. If they did so belong, they are the most unexpected and surprising feature of the skeleton and must have been part of either digit II, or digit III, the slender ones. The lower ends of those metatarsals are so eroded that the phalanges cannot be fitted to them, but there is no impossibility, so far as size is concerned, in their association with these metatarsals. Instead of the broad, heavy, block-like bones that one would expect to find in such a foot, these phalanges are slender, elongate, very thin and flat and, in shape, resembling those of one of the †three-toed horses of the North American Miocene. Of course, the full-sized digits may have had phalanges of a very different type.

As is the rule in the larger Santa Cruz ungulates, the feet of †*Astrapotherium* are very small in comparison with the size of the body. How these extraordinary feet were used and what sort of a gait the animal had, are very puzzling questions, the difficulty of which is increased by the absence of phalanges, especially of the unguals. The relations of the carpus to the fore-arm bones seem to imply a digitigrade position. The hind-foot was apparently plantigrade for, when the tibia and astragalus are fitted together, no other gait seems possible. Such a difference between the action of fore- and hind-feet may appear to be questionable, but it is not so great as must be inferred for †Homalodotherium.

The puzzling shortness and weakness of the neural spines is repeated in several other South American groups of indigenous ungulates, notably in the †Entelonychia and †Pyrotheria. The meaning of such a structure is very obscure.

Limitations of space make it impracticable to enter into a discussion of the habits of the †Astrapotheria; in spite of all difficulties

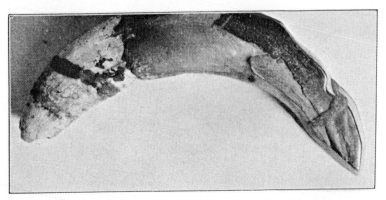

FIG. 338. — Upper canine tusk, with enamel bands and closed root, of †Astrapothericulus iheringi, Colhué-huapi stage. (Ameghino Collection.)

and contradictions, the hypothesis of an amphibious life seems to be the one most in harmony with the structure.

Such a full description of †Astrapotherium, far more detailed than for any other genus in the book, has been given because, hitherto, this wonderful skeleton has remained almost unknown, and it has seemed worth while to depart from the scale of other descriptions.

The family may be followed back to the Eocene, but the genera from formations more ancient than the Deseado are still very imperfectly known and it is not yet possible to trace the origin and development of the many strange characteristics with which the skeleton of †Astrapotherium abounds. In the Colhué-huapi formation three genera are reported; the earliest appearance of the Santa Cruz †Astrapotherium is assigned to this horizon and the typically Deseado genus, †Parastrapotherium, is said to come to an end in these beds. Not improbably these assignments are correct; at all events one or other of these genera occurs in the Colhué-huapi, but, with incomplete material, it is often impossible to decide between them. The Santa Cruz species ?†*A. giganteum*, may perfectly well be a survival of the Deseado genus.

The third Colhué-huapi type, †*Astrapothericulus*, is perfectly distinct and represents a tribe of which no other members are known and which may be presumed to be a migrant from the north. It is much smaller in stature than the other genera and it differs from

FIG. 339. — Lower jaw of †*Albertogaudrya unica*, Casa Mayor stage. (Ameghino Collection.)

them in the much more conspicuous development of the pillar in the concavity of the hinder crescent of the lower molars and in the limited growth of the canine tusks, which formed roots at a comparatively early period. Neither ancestors, nor descendants of this genus are known.

The genus †*Parastrapotherium*, though probably occurring in the Colhué-huapi beds also, is especially characteristic of the Deseado and, like so many genera of that stage, its species are, on the average, very much larger than those of the Santa Cruz †*Astrapotherium*, from which it further differs in a number of details; the grinding teeth are not so high-crowned and the premolars are more numerous, $\frac{3}{2}$. Fairly complete skulls and a considerable part of the skeleton have been found and these do not differ in any important way from the corresponding parts of †*Astrapotherium;* vertebræ and limb-bones from the Colhué-huapi formation are remarkable for their fine state of preservation and freedom from crushing or distortion.

The representative of the family in the Musters stage is †*Astraponotus*, which was insofar primitive, that it retained all the premolars, $\frac{4}{4}$, but little else is known of it.

The Eocene genus is †*Albertogaudrya*, a much smaller animal than the Oligocene and Miocene members of the family and yet the largest known mammal of its time. The genus is, as yet, known only from lower jaws, and a knowledge of the skull-structure would be most interesting. The lower teeth suffice to make certain the reference to this family.

In the long life of this suborder and family, one cannot but be struck by the comparative scarcity and lack of diversity of the group. In none of the stages is it at all common and in most of them there is but a single genus. In the Colhué-huapi, it is true, there seem to be three genera, but this is merely overlapping and but one genus, †*Astrapothericulus*, is characteristic of the stage. These facts make it difficult to resist the conclusion that the Patagonian representatives of the suborder were but outliers of the main body, which found more favourable conditions in the tropical and subtropical regions of the north. The great abundance and diversity of the †Toxodonta and especially of the †Typotheria in Tertiary Patagonia are in striking contrast to the rarity of the †Astrapotheria and †Entelonychia.

Suborder B. †Trigonostylopoidea

Family 2. †Trigonostylopidæ

As yet, this family contains but two genera, †*Trigonostylops* and †*Scabellia*, and is definitely known only from the Casa Mayor, though it may have been represented in the Musters stage also. The former genus is much the better known and shows that the group is a very isolated one, so far removed from all the others that its systematic position is very uncertain. Provisionally, it is placed in the †Astrapotheria, to which it shows some resemblances, but there is almost as much reason to refer it to the †Litopterna. Though very primitive, it already displays some specialization, chiefly in the reduction of teeth. The dental formula is: $i \frac{?}{2}$, $c \frac{1}{1}$, $p \frac{4}{4}$, $m \frac{3}{3}$; not only has one incisor been lost, but the first premolar, above and below, is a mere vestige.

The upper molars are very primitive and resemble the last two premolars in their simply triangular shape, having two external cusps and an internal crescent. The lower molars are like those of the †astrapotherian †*Albertogaudrya*, though somewhat simpler. The skull is peculiar and, in some respects, unique, but until the skulls of the early †astrapotherioids from the Musters and Casa Mayor stages shall have been recovered, it will be impossible to learn the significance of the structural peculiarities in the †*Trigonostylops* skull.

Concerning the relationships of this genus, Dr. Simpson concludes: "That it is a very aberrant branch from some ancient primitive stock," and "that it shows some evidence of collateral relationship to the astrapotheres on the one hand and litopterns on the other, and is perhaps slightly closer to the former.'

Order †PYROTHERIA

Family 1. †Pyrotheriidæ

This group had but a relatively brief career in geological time, from the Casa Mayor to the Deseado, inclusive. The principal genera are:

†*Pyrotherium*, Deseado; †*Propyrotherium*, Musters; †*Carolozittelia*, ?†*Paulogervaisia*, Casa Mayor.

The †pyrotheres are an unexplained mystery, so far as their origin and relationships are concerned. Only of the Deseado genus, †*Pyrotherium*, is any considerable part of the skeleton known and much of that still remains to be discovered. The material is widely scattered and the most important parts of it are in the Muséum de l'Histoire Naturelle, Paris, the Field Museum, Chicago, and the Amherst College Museum, which has the only skull. Much valuable material has not yet been described, though the writer has been privileged to see everything in the American collections. Assembling these remains, a fairly complete conception of this strangest of known mammals may be gained.

The †Pyrotheria have been assigned by different writers to many different groups; Ameghino, who first described and named them, believed that they were related to the elephants and, in his final classification, he included them in the Proboscidea, an opinion which was formerly shared by Professor Loomis, while, in the first edition of this book, the group was made a suborder of the †Notoungulata. At the opposite extreme is the view of the late Mr. Lydekker, who regarded †*Pyrotherium* as a marsupial, allied to the kangaroos. The distinguished French palæontologist, M. Albert Gaudry, was of the opinion that the †Pyrotheria were not nearly related to any other known ungulates and said of †*Pyrotherium* that it was one of the most astonishing creatures which Ameghino had discovered in Patagonia. Dr. Simpson has declared himself to be of Gaudry's opinion. He writes: "The group seems to be a very distinctive one of unknown sub- or proto-ungulate origin and can at present only be classified as an independent order," a classification which is here adopted. The material collected since 1913 strongly supports Gaudry's view.

The last and much the best-known member of the family is the Deseado genus †*Pyrotherium*, of which a fairly adequate conception may be formed. A reiteration of such terms as were exhausted in the descriptions of the †Astrapotheria and †Entelonychia, would be wearisome; Gaudry's phrase, that †*Pyrotherium* is the most astonishing of them all, will suffice without further insistence upon its grotesque character.

The number of teeth is greatly diminished, as appears from the formula: $i \frac{2}{1}$, $c \frac{0}{0}$, $p \frac{3}{2}$, $m \frac{3}{3} \times 2 = 28$. The upper incisors are short tusks, directed obliquely downward, the first one rather small, the second much larger. The single lower incisor of each side is a stout, horizontal and not very long tusk, the enamel of which is confined to a longitudinal band. All the tusks are faced with enamel, as in rodents, and, though growing throughout life, were kept short by abrasion with each other. The other incisors, the canines and the first premolar of each jaw have been lost. The premolars, except the foremost one, are like the molars in form, which is not true of any other of the post-Eocene indigenous South American ungulates. The anterior upper premolar (p $\underline{2}$) has three conical cusps, one in front and two behind. The other grinding teeth are alike in both upper and lower jaws; the crown is composed of two transverse crests, with no outer wall, like the lower cheek-teeth of the tapirs. When entirely unworn, these crests have on their summits a row of tubercles, as in certain †mastodonts (Fig. 178B, p. 290). This form of tooth has been repeated at least five times in as many mammalian groups, which acquired it independently and it is, therefore, no proof of relationship among the groups that possess it. The two rows of teeth in the upper jaw converge forward so that the anterior teeth of the opposite sides are in contact and, even posteriorly the tooth-rows are separated by a narrow space.

The skull of †*Pyrotherium* is very peculiar and has certain features which are not known in any other mammal. It is long and narrow, with short face, and cranium elevated much above the facial region; the occipital condyles are raised a foot or more above the level of the teeth. The anterior nasal opening is moved back between the orbits and, in front of this opening, there is a narrow, solid rostrum, which tapers anteriorly and is formed by the union of the premaxillaries and, for a short distance, of the maxillaries also, very much as in

†*Macrauchenia* (p. 553), and, as in that strange animal, the nasal canal passes vertically downward through the head. Such a position of the nasal opening implies the existence of a proboscis, an inference which is confirmed by the extreme shortness of the neck. If the rodent-like incisors seem rather incompatible with the presence of a trunk,

Fig. 340. — Head of †*Pyrotherium*, showing the two pairs of upper tusks. (Restored from a skull in Amherst Coll. Mus.)

the example of the four-tusked Miocene †mastodonts shows that there is no actual incongruity.

Usually, such a vertical nasal canal, opening so far back in the head, is accompanied by a great reduction of the nasal bones, as in †*Macrauchenia* and the elephants, but in †*Pyrotherium* the reduction of length is not nearly so great and the nasals are displaced backward to an altogether exceptional position between the frontals and *behind* the orbits.

The flat-topped cranium is narrow and the brain-case is of exceedingly small capacity; the thick walls and roof of the cranium are lightened by a system of sinuses and membrane-lined chambers, as in the very large ungulates generally, especially those in which the skull carries tusks or horns. The zygomatic arches are very broad vertically, but thin and plate-like. Not the least peculiar feature of this extraordinary skull is the bony palate, which is as extremely reduced as in certain rodents. In front of the tooth-rows, the palate occupies the whole breadth of the rostrum, but the second and third premolars of opposite sides are almost in contact, and between the two fourth premolars a very narrow strip of bone is visible. The bony strip widens to a maximum between the last molars of the two sides, yet, even here, the palate is not so wide as one of the teeth. It is difficult to imagine what kind of a tongue the creature could have had and how it could have been used.

In the Amherst collection there are the first four cervical vertebræ, associated with part of a skull, and these prove that the neck must have been thick and very short; in both atlas and axis the transverse width greatly exceeds the antero-posterior length. The 3rd and 4th cervicals are thick discs, nearly three times as wide as they are long. In all four vertebræ the neural arches are low and weak and there

FIG. 341. — Series of dorsal vertebræ, right side, of †*Pyrotherium romeri*. (Field Mus. Nat. Hist.)

are no spines. The Field Museum has a fine series of dorsal vertebræ, which are very large and massive and short in proportion to their breadth and thickness. The remarkable feature of these vertebræ is the extreme shortness of the neural spines, which terminate in heavy knobs and are an exceedingly puzzling characteristic, most difficult to understand. In the †Pyrotheria, †Astrapotheria and †Entelonychia, which were by far the largest and most massive animals of the Deseado age, the shortness of the neural spines indicates that the long muscles of the back must have been very thin. How the great head, with its formidable tusks, could have been supported by such slender muscles, it is impossible to see. In all of the Artiodactyla, Perissodactyla, Proboscidea and †Amblypoda of comparable height and bulk, the spines of the anterior dorsal vertebræ are far longer than in the South American groups named and, in many of them, are so long as to produce great humps at the shoulders, as is also true of many †*Toxodonta*, though not of all. It is an extraordinary fact that in none of these South American Tertiary orders of large ungulates, except in †*Scarrittia* and the Casa Mayor

†Entelonychia, is the tail known; in most of them it can only be inferred from the character of the sacrum.

The limb-bones are almost completely known and have been figured by Gaudry, but those of the feet are still but imperfectly represented in the collections. The posterior extremities are con-

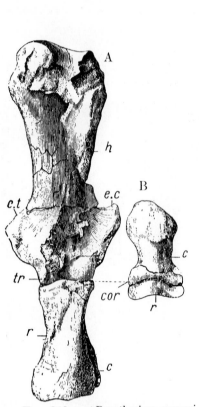

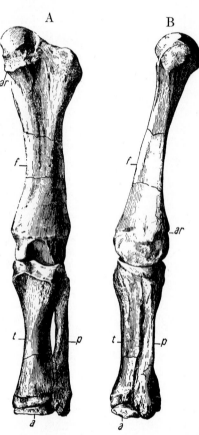

Fig. 342. — †*Pyrotherium romeri*, Deseado stage. A, left fore-leg. *h*, humerus. *c.t*, internal epicondyle. *e.c*, supinator ridge. *tr*, trochlea. *r*, radius. *c*, ulna. B, ulna and radius, upper end. *cor*, coronoid process. (From Gaudry.)

Fig. 343. — Left hind-leg of †*Pyrotherium romeri*. A, front view. *ar*, articular surface. *f*, femur. *t*, tibia. *p*, fibula. *a*, astragalus. B, left side. (From Gaudry.)

siderably longer than the anterior, in the proportion of 100:74. All of the limb-bones are astonishingly massive, so much so as to make it difficult to picture the creature as a living animal. The humerus, which is rather more than twice as long as the radius, is exceptionally heavy and thick and the lower end is made uncommonly broad by the great prominence of the internal epicondyle and the supinator ridge. In view of the impossibility of the slightest rotation of the fore-foot, this great development of the supinator ridge seems paradoxical. The fore-arm bones, which, in some cases at least, are co-ossified throughout, are grotesquely short and heavy, the length of the radius being less than the width of the lower part of the humerus. The radius is so broad as entirely to conceal the ulna in front-view, but is much flattened, making an elbow-joint unlike that of any other ungulate; the radius widens downward and its lower end is so wide as to indicate an extremely broad fore-foot. The ulna is chiefly remarkable for the tremendous size and massiveness of the olecranon.

The hind-leg is much more proboscidean in character than the fore-leg and has a decided similarity to that of †*Uintatherium* of the North American Eocene (p. 472). The femur is very elephantine in shape and relative length; the great trochanter is lower than the head and the third trochanter is lacking. As in the †Dinocerata and the elephants, the shaft is no longer cylindrical, but broad and flattened and the groove for the knee-cap is wide, shallow and short. Tibia and fibula are very much shorter than the femur and are very heavy; though in contact with each other for most of their length, they are not co-ossified.

The feet are incompletely known, but a general idea of their structure may be gained from the bones scattered through the various collections. The carpal bones are block-like and massive, with a superficial likeness to those of the elephants, but the phalanges are rather less heavy. The astragalus, or ankle-bone, according to Gaudry is extremely simple, "for it has neither a trochlea for the tibia, nor neck, nor head and its navicular facet is concealed below. The navicular has not, as in the Proboscideans, four facets; it has three for the cuneiforms and none for the cuboid." It may be confidently inferred that the feet, fore and hind, were five-toed and were short, broad and columnar, as in so many unrelated groups of large and massive ungulates.

Preceding †*Pyrotherium*, †*Propyrotherium*, a much smaller animal, occurs in the Musters fauna. The Casa Mayor genus, †*Carolozittelia*, is still smaller and does not exceed a tapir in size; both of these genera are known only from teeth. The Casa Mayor fossils, as pointed out by Simpson, give some welcome hints as to the mode of origin of the grinding teeth and thus help to connect the †Pyrotheria with other ungulate groups. The two transverse crests are already formed, but the internal and external cusps and intermediate conules are still recognizable, showing that these teeth were derived from others of a quadritubercular pattern. In addition, the beginning of oblique, transverse crests from the external cones may be detected. As previously pointed out, this same type of tooth arose independently in the two subdivisions of the pig group, appearing in †*Platygonus*, of the American peccaries, and in †*Listriodon*, of the Old World swine. In both cases the quadritubercular molar was the starting point from which the two-crested teeth were developed. The Casa Mayor genus †*Paulogervaisia* has teeth of the pattern desired and may have been a survivor of the ancestral group from which the typical †Pyrotheria were descended. The history of these teeth in the marsupials, such as the kangaroos and allied extinct genera, has not been brought to light, but for the proboscideans and tapirs a similar mode of origin is known.

In †*Carolozittelia* the incisor teeth were already enlarged to form incipient tusks.

The teeth of the Casa Mayor genera which have been referred to the †Pyrotheria are decidedly suggestive of origin from a condylarthrous ancestry, but the connection has yet to be made out. Fossils from the Rio Chico formation may yet solve the problem.

CHAPTER XX

HISTORY OF THE †LITOPTERNA

Two very different families, the †Macrauchenidæ and the †Proterotheriidæ, are included in this order, which has been the subject of much debate. The group has frequently been referred to the Perissodactyla and even Ameghino, who first distinguished and named the order, eventually reached the same conclusion. This problem is one of great significance for the philosophy of evolution and the position taken involves far-reaching consequences concerning the actual modes of development and how far convergence may account for similarities.

Family 1. †Macrauchenidæ

†*Macrauchenia*, Plio. and Pleisto. †*Scalibrinitherium*, Entrerian, †*Theosodon*, Santa Cruz, †*Cramauchenia*, Colhué-huapi, †*Protheosodon*, Deseado.

The Pampean genus †*Macrauchenia* was discovered by Charles Darwin, who wrote of it: "At Port St. Julian, in some red mud capping the gravel on the 90 foot plain, I found half the skeleton of the Macrauchenia Patachonica, a remarkable quadruped full as large as a camel. It belongs to the same division of the Pachydermata with the rhinoceros, tapir and palaeotherium [i.e. the group now called Perissodactyla]; but in the structure of the bones of the long neck, it shows a clear relation to the camel, or rather to the guanaco and the llama." [1] Owen's opinion would seem to be expressed in the name which he gave to this genus, signifying "Great Llama."

In †*Macrauchenia* the teeth are present in the unreduced number of 44 and those of each jaw are in continuous series, without gaps; they are decidedly hypsodont, but eventually form roots. The incisors, above and below, are arranged in straight transverse lines and each has a "mark," or enamel pit, as in the horses. The canines are but little larger than incisors and cannot be called tusks; the premolars are smaller and less complex than the molars.

The upper molars have two concave and crescentic external cusps united by a vertical ridge, as in several families of perissodactyls; two

[1] *Voyage of a Naturalist*, p. 172.

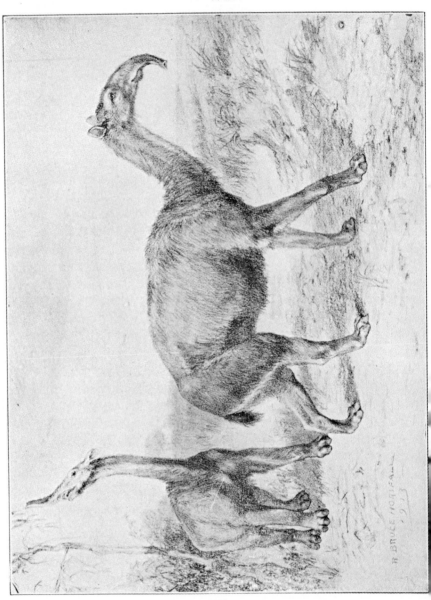

Fig. 344. — A Pampean †Litoptern, †*Macrauchenia patachonica*. (Restored from a skeleton in La Plata Mus.)

transverse crests and several accessory spurs and enamel pockets give to the grinding surface, when somewhat worn, the appearance of considerable complexity. The lower molars have the bicrescentic pattern which is so nearly universal in the South American ungulates, but the pillar in the concavity of the hinder crescent, which is so characteristic of those same ungulates, is lacking in the true molars, but is found in the milk-premolars. This is still another illustration of retention in the milk-teeth of ancestral features which the permanent teeth have lost.

The skull is small in proportion to the size of the animal and of unusual shape; it is long, narrow and low, sloping and tapering forward to the blunt muzzle, which is slightly broadened, to afford space for the transverse row of incisors. The sagittal crest is replaced by a short, narrow and flat area. The cranium is short, the face long; the orbits, which are entirely encircled with bone, have been shifted behind the teeth, as in the later and more advanced horses. In both the horses and the †macrauchenids the displacement is made necessary by the great elongation of the grinding teeth, which would press upon the eye-balls, if the orbits had remained in their original positions. The nasal bones are reduced to a minimum, retaining but a small fraction of their original length and bringing the anterior nasal opening so directly over the posterior, that the nasal canal passes directly down through the head. Such a structure is intelligible only if a proboscis was present in the living animal. Another very curious feature of this skull is the long, solid, bony rostrum, extending in front of the nasal opening and formed by the union, in the middle line, of the upper jaw-bones, maxillaries and premaxillaries. Outside of this family, no other known land mammal has such a rostrum, though †*Pyrotherium* has something like it.

The neck is very long, relatively almost as much so as in a camel and the cervical vertebræ agree with those of the camels and llamas in having the canal for the vertebral artery perforate the neural arch instead of the transverse process. In nearly all really long-necked ungulates the odontoid process of the axis is spout-shaped, to enclose the spinal cord. †*Macrauchenia* is an exception in having the odontoid short and peg-like, of transversely oval cross-section. The body is relatively short and the legs long, which gives a rather stilted appearance to the skeleton.

The proportional lengths of the different limb-segments are unusual; the upper arm is short, the fore-arm very long, the thigh long and the lower-leg short. Compared with such artiodactyls and perissodactyls as pigs and hippopotamuses, rhinoceroses and tapirs, the feet of †*Macrauchenia* would be called long, but in comparison with cursorial types, such as camels, antelopes, deer and horses, they are of moderate length. The short humerus is very heavy; the ulna and radius, which are co-ossified throughout, are disproportionally broad transversely, thin and compressed antero-posteriorly. The long femur has a broad, flattened shaft, with inconspicuous third trochanter. Tibia and fibula are united at both ends and the former is very heavy at the upper end, but contracts downward; the stout fibula articulates with the calcaneum, as in the Artiodactyla.

The feet are tridactyl and of mesaxonic symmetry, as in the perissodactyls; it was probably to this feature that Darwin referred, when he wrote that †*Macrauchenia* belonged "with the rhinoceros, tapir and palæotherium." On the other hand, the highly significant structure of the ankle and heel joints is radically different from that of the Perissodactyla; not only does the calcaneum have a conspicuous facet for the fibula, but the astragalus has a convex head which fits into the navicular and does not touch the cuboid, as in the †Condylarthra, †Notoungulata and Hyracoidea. Not even the most ancient and primitive of known perissodactyls display such a foot-structure as this, which excludes the †Litopterna, all of which are alike in this respect, from the Perissodactyla. The ungual phalanges of †*Macrauchenia* are so small as to suggest that the feet were columnar and supported on elastic pads, as in the "pachyderms" generally; if so, this must have been a singularly clumsy-looking beast.

Attention has already been called to the strange and bizarre character of the Pampean fauna, with its multitudinous †groundsloths and †glyptodonts, and †*Macrauchenia* must have been one of the most grotesque members of this assemblage of nightmares, as it would have seemed to our eyes. The small head, with its proboscis, the long neck and stilted, but heavy limbs and clumsy feet made up a creature that was utterly unlike any other ungulate outside of its own family. The proboscis and the long neck are indicative of browsing habits, while the hypsodont teeth suggest grazing; probably both methods of feeding were used.

The later Pliocene members of the family are not very well known and, hence, call for no particular description, but in the Entrerian are several less advanced genera, which possess much interest. For example, †*Scalibrinitherium* may well have been a direct ancestor of †*Macrauchenia;* it is considerably smaller than the Pampean genus, with brachyodont (or low-crowned) teeth, which early formed roots.

Fig. 345. — Santa Cruz †macrauchenid, †*Theosodon garrettorum*, and predaceous marsupial, †*Borhyæna tuberata*. (Restored by C. Knight from skeletons in Princeton Univ. Mus.)

555

The upper molars are rather less complex than those of †*Macrauchenia* and the lower molars have the pillar in the posterior crescent, which the latter had lost in the second dentition, but retained in the first. The skull is very similar to that of the Pleistocene descendant, but less extremely specialized; the orbits are somewhat farther forward, extending over the last molar, and are not closed behind. The nasal bones, though very short, are not so much reduced and the nasal opening has a more anterior position. The maxillary bones are united for a short distance only, but the premaxillaries are solidly co-ossified for their whole length.

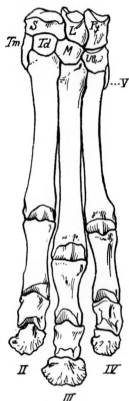

FIG. 346.—Left manus of †*Theosodon. S,* scaphoid. *L,* lunar. *Py,* pyramidal. *Tm,* trapezium. *Td,* trapezoid. *M,* magnum. *U,* unciform. *V,* vestigial fifth metacarpal.

Between the Entrerian and the Santa Cruz representatives of the family there is a long hiatus, in which no well-preserved fossils of the group have yet been found, but the Santa Cruz genus †*Theosodon* is very completely known from entire skeletons, thus making possible a detailed comparison with †*Macrauchenia,* to which it seems to have been directly ancestral. †*Theosodon* is, in the first place, considerably smaller, not much exceeding a Guanaco in stature. The teeth have lower crowns even than those of †*Scalibrinitherium* and the incisors are in line with the cheek-teeth, not in a transverse row, but curving slightly so that the foremost incisors (*i 1*) of the two sides almost meet in the median line. The incisors, canines and first premolars, of both upper and lower jaws, are all much alike, being simple, conical and sharp-pointed teeth, which give an almost crocodilian aspect to the anterior part of the skull.

The upper molars are of the same fundamental plan as those of †*Macrauchenia,* but in a less advanced state of development, the transverse crests being incomplete and the internal cusps have a certain degree of separateness from the crests and from each other. Evidently, these teeth were derived from a quadritubercular type. In the bicrescentic lower molars, the pillar in the posterior crescent is very conspicuous.

The resemblance of the skull to that of †*Macrauchenia* is immediately obvious, but it is less specialized and departs much less from that of other †Litopterna. The cranium is longer and has a distinct sagittal crest, the face is shorter and the orbits are farther forward even than in †*Scalibrinitherium*, extending over the second molar. The nasal bones are greatly shortened, though decidedly longer than in the genus last named; and the anterior nasal opening is extended forward as a long, narrow slit, because the maxillaries are not in contact; the premaxillaries touch each other but do not co-ossify. The nasal canal, though very short, is horizontal, not vertical; the lower jaw is remarkably slender.

The neck is proportionally longer than in †*Macrauchenia* and the shifting of the canal for the vertebral artery from the transverse process to the neural arch had already taken place except in the 6th vertebra; the odontoid process of the axis is relatively longer and more conical. The body is rather short and the spines of the trunk-vertebræ are relatively higher and more prominent than they are in the Pampean genus. No caudal vertebræ have been found but, from the sacrum, it may be inferred that the tail was short.

The limbs are long, but relatively more slender and less elongate than in †*Macrauchenia*. The scapula has two long and very conspicuous metacromia, as in the Santa Cruz †toxodonts, but of a different shape and more widely separated. The humerus is short and slender and the much longer fore-arm bones are not co-ossified. The femur has a slender shaft, cylindrical, not flattened, and a much more prominent third trochanter than in the Pampean genus. The tridactyl feet are smaller and lighter than those of †*Macrauchenia*, otherwise very much like them.

The appearance of the living animal, as shown in the restoration (Fig. 345) was, very probably, that of a smaller, lighter and less grotesque †*Macrauchenia*. The presence of a proboscis of some sort is made likely by the greatly abbreviated nasals, though, as shown in the drawing, it may have been no longer than in the Saiga Antelope (*Saiga tatarica*). The long neck, short body and tail and long limbs indicate an animal not unlike a Guanaco (*Lama huanacus*), but larger and heavier; the spreading, three-toed feet were altogether unlike those of any artiodactyl. The hair is given a woolly appearance, as in the Guanaco, but this, of course, is entirely conjectural.

The next genus, in ascending order is †*Cramauchenia*, of the Colhué-huapi formation, a decidedly smaller animal, the skull of which differs in many ways from that of its successor †*Theosodon*, yet

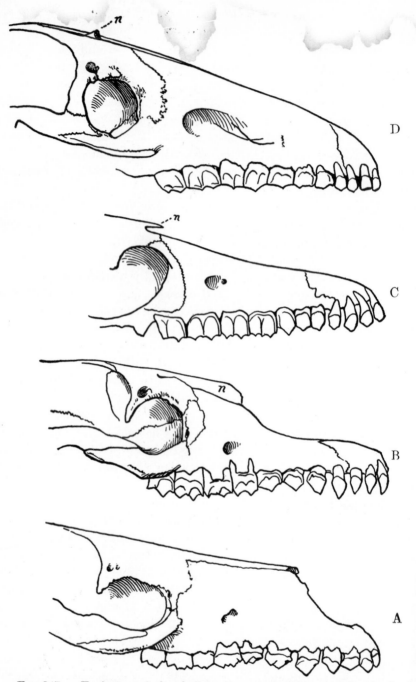

FIG. 347. — Evolution of the skull in †macrauchenids. A, †*Cramauchenia*, Colhué-huapi. B, †*Theosodon*, Santa Cruz. C, †*Scalibrinitherium*, Entrerian. D, †*Macrauchenia*, Pampean. *n*, nasal bones. Figures not drawn to scale.

has an unmistakable likeness to it. In available specimens the teeth are so worn, that the upper molar pattern is indistinguishable, but it may be seen that the upper canine is implanted by two roots, which is not true of any of the subsequent genera of the family. The principal differences from †*Theosodon* are to be seen in the forward part of the skull, where, in †*Cramauchenia*, the anterior nasal opening is nearly normal and but little farther back than in the †notoungulates. The nasal bones are of ordinary length, relatively four or five times as long as in †*Theosodon;* the contact between the premaxillaries is only partial and much shorter than in the Santa Cruz genus. There can have been no proboscis.

The skulls of the four successive genera of the family, †*Cramauchenia* — †*Theosodon* — †*Scalibrinitherium* — †*Macrauchenia*, form an excellent genetic series, which displays the encircling of the eye-sockets, through the growth of the post-orbital processes, the gradual backward shifting of the orbits, to make room for the increasingly high crowns of the teeth, the retreat of the anterior nasal opening accompanying the great abbreviation of the nasal bones, and the formation of a solid bony rostrum by the gradual approximation and fusion in the median line of the upper jaw-bones. In all of these respects, the change from †*Cramauchenia* to †*Theosodon* is so great, as to make it seem probable that there is a link in the chain missing at this point. If not, either the hiatus in time between the Colhué-huapi and the Santa Cruz formations is greater than has been believed, or the rate of development in this tribe was much more rapid than in other series.

In the more ancient geological stages antecedent to the Colhué-huapi, the †macrauchenids are known only from fragmentary fossils, but, imperfect as they are, they yield some important information. In the Deseado †*Protheosodon*, in which the feet are like those of its Santa Cruz successor, the upper molars are much more primitive, in that the internal cusps and intermediate conules are isolated and of conical shape, not forming transverse crests. Such a tooth-pattern is a distinct step (in reverse) toward the quadritubercular plan of the †Condylarthra.

In the still earlier formations, the Musters and the Casa Mayor, the two families of the †Litopterna can no longer be distinguished with certainty; it is not improbable that, in the Casa Mayor, it will be found that the two families merge into a third, which was ancestral to both of them. Until more complete material, including skulls and feet, shall have been obtained, such an inference must be speculative.

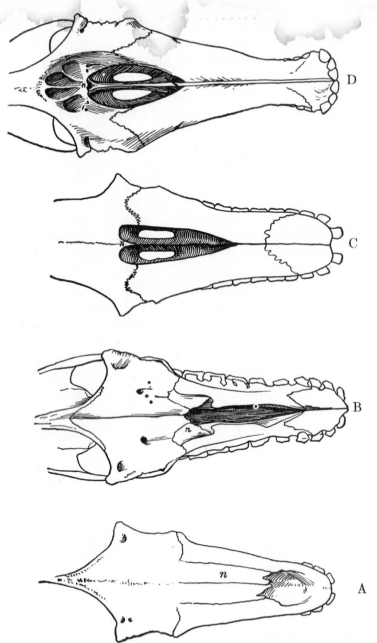

Fig. 348. — Evolution of the skull in †macrauchenids. A, †*Cramauchenia*, Colhué-huapi. B, †*Theosodon*, Santa Cruz. C, †*Scalibrinitherium*, Entrerian. D, †*Macrauchenia*, Pampean. *n*, nasal bones. Figures not drawn to scale.

Family 2. †Proterotheriidæ

The principal genera of this family are as follows: †*Epitherium*, Mte. Hermoso. †*Diadiaphorus*, †*Proterotherium*, Santa Cruz and Entrerian. †*Licaphrium*, †*Thoatherium*, Santa Cruz. †*Prolicaphrium*, †*Licaphrops*, Colhué-huapi. †*Deuterotherium*, †*Prothoatherium*, Deseado.

The members of this family are remarkable for the many and deceptive resemblances to the horses which they display, a most striking case of convergent development. No representative of the family has been found in the Pampean deposits, and though unmistakable fossils of the group are known from the Pliocene, they are so incomplete as to afford little information. As yet, it is only in the Santa Cruz that material has been found so well preserved, that all the essential facts of the structure of these extraordinary animals may be learned. They are not extraordinary in the sense that so many of their contemporaries are, as being grotesque or monstrous; on the contrary, they are well proportioned and, no doubt when alive, they were agile and graceful creatures and resembled in appearance their very distant relatives of the northern hemisphere. It is in just this likeness to relatives which are both structurally and geographically so distant, that the wonderful features consist.

In Santa Cruz times the family was represented by a large, but indeterminate number of species, grouped together in four or five genera, all of which are very much alike, though one (†*Thoatherium*) is more distinctly different. They all have the same dental formula, which is: $i \frac{1}{1}$, $c \frac{0}{1}$, $p \frac{4}{4}$, $m \frac{3}{3} \times 2 = 36$. Except in †*Thoatherium*, a pair of small tusks is formed by the enlargement of the second upper and third lower incisors, as in the †toxodonts, but the first lower incisor and the first and third upper ones and the canines, above and below, all of which are very small in the Santa Cruz †toxodonts, have been completely suppressed in the †proterotheres. The teeth are all very low-crowned and none of the family, so far as is known, displayed any tendency to the acquisition of hypsodont, rootless teeth, or to the deposition of cement upon the crowns. The premolars are always simpler than the molars, though the last one (*p* 4) approximates the molar pattern. The upper molars have two crescentic outer cusps, connected in a vertical ridge and together forming the external wall of the tooth; the transverse crests are incomplete, especially the posterior one. The lower molars have the almost universally prevalent bi-crescentic pattern, but the pillar in the posterior crescent is reduced, or absent. Except in †*Thoatherium*, there is a considerable gap between the upper tusk and the premolars, but in the lower jaw this gap is filled by the greatly reduced canine.

The skull has a long cranium and short face, with long, high sagittal crest; the orbit, which is far forward, with anterior rim above the first molar, is completely encircled in bone and the usually large and single infraorbital foramen is sometimes replaced by three small foramina, the branches of the trigeminal nerve emerging separately. The nasal bones are rather short, but not sufficiently so to suggest the presence of a proboscis, and the ascending rami of the premaxillaries are wide. The neck is short and the canal for the vertebral artery is in its normal position, perforating the transverse processes of the cervical vertebræ. The body is rather short, like that of a deer; the number of trunk-vertebræ is not definitely known for any of the genera, but was very probably 19 or 20, as in the Artiodactyla, and the tail must have been short.

The limbs are slender and of moderate length; the bones of the fore-arm (radius and ulna) and lower leg (tibia and fibula) are all separate, with no co-ossifications. Except in †*Thoatherium*, which is one-toed, the feet are structurally tridactyl, but the lateral digits are so reduced, that they must have been dew-claws, raised well above the ground and all the weight was supported by the median digit, or third of the original five; in these respects, fore- and hind-feet are alike. The shape of the hoofs and the whole appearance of the feet are most surprisingly like that of the †three-toed horses, such as †*Parahippus*, which characterized the Tertiary formations of North America, but there are many structural differences of great significance.

Taking up the separate genera, the last-known survivor of the family was †*Epitherium* of the Pliocene (Monte Hermoso), which, so far as it is known, differs so little from the Santa Cruz †*Diadiaphorus*, as to call for no description here. The Santa Cruz genus, the largest of the family, was rather taller and heavier than an ordinary sheep. The general aspect of the animal was probably not unlike that of a stocky, short-necked antelope, but with the feet of a †three-toed horse. But, as already suggested, the resemblances to horses are superficial, while the differences from them are fundamental. In the horses the reduction of the digits was accompanied by a readjustment of the carpal and tarsal articulations, so that, in proportion as the median toe was enlarged and the laterals diminished, the carpus and tarsus bore more completely upon the enlarged metapodial.

FIG. 349. — Three-toed †proterothere, †*Diadiaphorus majusculus*, Santa Cruz. (Restored by C. Knight, from skeletons in Amer. Mus. Nat. Hist. and Princeton Univ. Mus.)

This method of digital reduction was called by Kowalevsky "adaptive" and is exemplified by all existing artiodactyls and perissodactyls and in none more perfectly than in the monodactyl horses. In "inadaptive reduction," the method followed in †*Diadiaphorus* and other genera of the family, there was no readjustment, or a very imperfect one, of the articulations, the lateral metapodials, however small and vestigial, retaining the carpal and tarsal connections which they originally had, when functional and of full size. This distinction of "adaptive" and "inadaptive" methods of digital reduction may

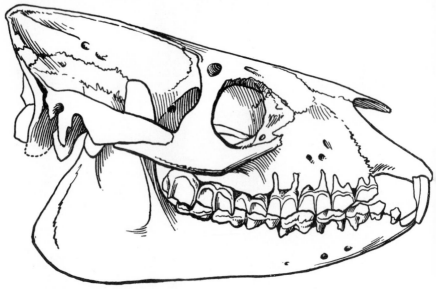

Fig. 350. — Skull of †*Diadiaphorus*, Santa Cruz.   (Amer. Mus. Nat. Hist.)

seem to be a trivial one, but its great importance is shown by the fact that not a single hoofed mammal with inadaptively reduced feet has survived into the Recent epoch. In still another respect the feet of †*Diadiaphorus* differ notably from those of the horses and that is in the relative lengths of metapodials and phalanges. In all of the ††tridactyl horses, the metapodials of the median digits are considerably longer than the combined lengths of the phalanges of the same digits. In the †proterotheres, on the contrary, the phalanges are together longer than the metapodials.

The skull of †*Diadiaphorus* is comparatively short and deep and narrows anteriorly; the brain-case is large for a Miocene mammal, but the sagittal crest is long nevertheless. The nasals are rather short, but not sufficiently so to suggest the former existence of a proboscis. Several ancient groups of hoofed animals, which are but distantly related to the †proterotheres, have very similar-looking skulls, such as the †entelonychian †Homalodotherium (p. 519), the artiodactyl †Merycoidodon and the †cursorial rhinoceros †Hyracodon, of the North American Oligocene.

The genus †Proterotherium, from which the family is named, was originally described as †Anoplotherium by the French naturalist Bravard, and it was long regarded as a most puzzling circumstance that a genus characteristic of the Oligocene of France should be found in South America and not in North America, but the discoveries of Ameghino proved that the supposed paradox was non-existent and the alleged †Anoplotherium turned out to be a very different animal and one not even referable to the Artiodactyla. In Santa Cruz times †Proterotherium was in a state of vigorous expansion and diversification and a long list of species has been named. These, however, are so extremely variable that no two specimens are alike and no satisfactory discrimination of species is feasible. These are all much smaller and more slender animals than the species of †Diadiaphorus, which, otherwise, they closely resemble, even to the smallest details of the three-toed feet. The very similar skull has relatively longer nasals and a broader occiput.

The genus †Licaphrium may be described as a somewhat larger and sturdier †Proterotherium, intermediate between the latter and †Diadiaphorus; it also differs from both of those genera in certain details of the dentition.

A more isolated position is held by the

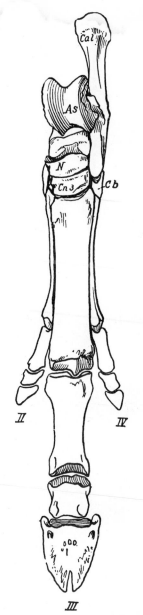

FIG. 351. — Left pes of †Diadiaphorus, from specimens in Princeton University and the American Museum of Natural History. Cal, calcaneum. As, astragalus. N, navicular. Cn 3, external cuneiform. Cb, cuboid.

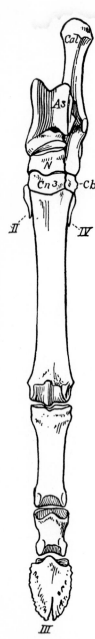

FIG. 352. —
Left pes of †*Thoa-
therium*. Letters
as in Fig. 351.
(Princeton Univ.
Mus.)

extraordinarily interesting genus †*Thoatherium*, which is very clearly separated from the other contemporary genera of the family by its completely monodactyl feet, to mention only the most obvious distinction. The species of this genus are much the smallest of the Santa Cruz †Litopterna and were evidently light and graceful animals and, no doubt, they were the swiftest runners of their time, for their whole structure is that of a cursorial type.

The dental formula is the same as in the preceding genera of the family, but there are no tusks; the single upper incisor is slightly enlarged, but the two lower ones are small and of nearly the same size. The upper molars have the same elements as in the other genera; the external wall is similar, but the two internal cusps and the anterior intermediate conule are united to form a longitudinal ridge, almost parallel with the outer wall.

The skull is light, tapering forward; the nasals are shortened, though less so than in †*Diadiaphorus;* the sagittal crest is much shorter and the occiput far narrower than in the latter. Neck, body and tail are all short, but the limbs and feet are proportionally longer than in any other member of the family, giving the skeleton a stilted appearance. Though the ulna and fibula are much reduced and very slender, they remain separate from the radius and tibia respectively. The limb-bones, especially the femur, have a decided resemblance to those of †*Mesohippus*, of the North American Oligocene, a †three-toed horse, and the best-known species, †*T. minusculum*, agrees well in size with †*Mesohippus bairdi*.

The most remarkable feature of the skeleton is the structure of the single-toed feet, *which are more completely monodactyl than in any other known mammal.* The single functional digit (No. III of the original five) has on each side of its upper end a very small, scale-like nodule of bone, which are the last vestiges of the lateral metapodials, Nos. II and

Fig. 353. — Single-toed †proterothere, †*Thoatherium minusculum*, Santa Cruz. (Restored by C. Knight from a skeleton in Princeton Univ. Mus.)

IV, which correspond to the immensely larger splint-bones of the Horse. Despite the extreme digital reduction in this genus, the mode of reduction is inadaptive and the vestigial metapodials retain the same carpal and tarsal connections that they originally had in the primitive five-toed foot, a radical difference from the horses and from the Perissodactyla generally. The ankle and heel joints also are of the same primitive type as in the other genera of the order; the fibula articulates with the calcaneum and the convex head of the astragalus fits into the concavity of the navicular and is far removed from the cuboid. The limb-bones are relatively longer and more slender than in the other †proterotheres and the single metapodial is longer in relation to the phalanges, approximating much more closely to the proportions seen in the horses. In all of the Santa Cruz †Litopterna the lower ends of the metapodials have the articular surface encircled by the keel which fits into a groove of the first phalanx; in †*Thoatherium* this keel is more prominent and better defined than in the other genera of the family.

Aside from the size and shape of the ears, nature of the hair, mane and tail, colour-pattern and other external characteristics, the appearance of the living animal may be inferred from the skeleton (Fig. 353). †*Thoatherium* was much smaller and more lightly built than †*Diadiaphorus*, or even than †*Proterotherium* and must have been as slender and graceful as a gazelle. The head would seem to have had some resemblance to that of a small horse, but the neck and trunk were shorter than in the horses and the proportions of body and limbs were more as in the smaller antelopes. It must again be emphasized, however, that such likenesses to horses and antelopes are superficial; the fundamental and significant characteristics are more primitive than in the most ancient of known artiodactyls and perissodactyls.

It is only from the Santa Cruz beds that satisfactory material of the †Proterotheriidæ has been obtained. In the preceding and succeeding formations very little has been collected, other than jaws and teeth and these are insufficient for tracing genetic connections in any but a preliminary and tentative fashion. Two of the Santa Cruz genera, †*Proterotherium* and †*Diadiaphorus*, continued into the lower Pliocene and two additional ones have been named, but little is known of them. It is a noteworthy fact that the less specialized genera outlasted the more advanced monodactyl †*Thoatherium*.

In the Colhué-huapi formation several genera of this family are found, the names of which indicate their relationships, †*Prolicaphrium*, †*Licaphrops* and †*Prothoatherium*, but they are very incompletely known. The two families of the order are still clearly distinguishable in the Deseado and, of the †proterotheres, much the best known is †*Deuterotherium*, which serves to bring the isolated †*Thoatherium* into closer connection with the other members of the family and, it is interesting to note, it retains the pillar in the posterior crescent of the lower molars which the Santa Cruz genera have lost.

In the still more ancient Musters fauna, the probable †Litopterna are many, but it is not yet practicable to assign them to families. The same statement applies to the Casa Mayor fauna, in which a long list of supposed †litopterns have been named, but from the available material, which is very fragmentary, it cannot be told how many of these genera and species should be assigned to the †Condylarthra and whether, as a matter of fact, any true †Condylarthra were present in these faunas. They probably were, but it cannot be positively stated.

In summing up the probable relationships between the †Litopterna and the †Astrapotheria, Dr. Simpson writes: "It may hence be very tentatively concluded that from a primitive and remote ungulate stock, probably in or very near the Condylarthra, arose the litopterns, retaining rather more of these ancestral characters, and astrapotheres, more strongly aberrant, and that †*Trigonostylops* also came from this remote ancestry, possibly nearer to, or even in the most ancient astrapothere line, but diverging strongly in a third direction." This conclusion, tentative though it is, expresses well the present state of knowledge, but it does not deal with the problem of the relationships of the †Notoungulata, on the one hand, and the †Astrapotheria and †Litopterna, on the other. Regarding this problem, something must be said.

The late Mr. Lydekker, one of the most distinguished of English palæontologists, expressed the opinion many years ago, that all of the indigenous South American hoofed mammals, the †Pyrotheria alone excepted, were more nearly related to one another than they were to any other ungulate group. The author of this book has always been inclined to accept that opinion, though it is evident that the †Astrapotheria and †Litopterna are closer together than either order is to the †Notoungulata. The latter seem to have been already distinct in the Paleocene, but were probably derived from †condylarthrous ancestors. The two orders appear to have entered South America together from the north before the Paleocene land-connection of the Americas had been severed. From the date of that immigration to the end of the Miocene, South America was an isolated continent, except for possible transitory connections with Australia and Africa, and in that sequestered land a great evolutionary experiment was carried on, affecting not only the hoofed animals, but the edentates, rodents, monkeys and marsupials as well. The successive steps of this wonderful story are recorded in the continental formations of Patagonia and that record, despite the usual gaps and failures, is yet one of exceptional completeness. Throughout the Tertiary period Patagonia was apparently an arid, treeless plain and hence forest-loving mammals are rare or absent as fossils. Had the deposits of Eocene, Oligocene and Miocene date been laid down in northern Argentina or southern Brazil, many of the gaps would have been filled and many puzzling paradoxes would have been resolved.

CHAPTER XXI

HISTORY OF THE CARNIVORA

I. FISSIPEDIA

The Carnivora, or beasts of prey, are a very natural and homogeneous group, though exhibiting a wide range of differences in accordance with varying habits of life. Almost all of them live by killing and devouring herbivorous animals, though some, like the hyenas, are carrion-feeders and others, such as the bears, pandas and raccoons have adopted a diet that is largely vegetable. The group comprises three suborders: (1) the Fissipedia, land animals, except for the otters, (2) the Pinnipedia, or marine carnivores, which are outside the scope of this book, and (3) the †Creodonta, extinct carnivores which form a side-branch of the same stock.

Under ordinary conditions, the carnivores are much less common as fossils than are the ungulates and rodents upon which they preyed, for at any given time or place the beasts of prey must have been far less numerous, just as to-day, there are innumerable antelopes and zebras for every lion in central Africa. For this reason, the history of the Carnivora is even more incomplete than that of the hoofed animals and leaves open many problems of relationship and classification.

The first suborder, that of the Fissipedia, is, almost entirely, composed of land animals, although it includes the aquatic and marine otters. Of the eight families into which the suborder is divided, one, the †Uintacyonidæ, is extinct and is commonly referred to the †Creodonta, to which it is transitional. Two other families, the Viverridæ, or civet-cats, and the Hyænidæ, or hyenas, are not known to have entered the Western Hemisphere at any time, and the Ursidæ, or bears, a family of Old World origin, did not reach North America till the Pliocene.

The classification of the suborder is as follows:

SUBORDER **Fissipedia**, LAND CARNIVORA
    SUPERFAMILY I. CYNOIDEA
        FAMILY 1. CANIDÆ, Dogs, Wolves, Foxes, etc.
        FAMILY 2. PROCYONIDÆ, Raccoons, etc.
        FAMILY 3. MUSTELIDÆ, Martens, Weasels, Badgers, Otters, etc.
        FAMILY 4. URSIDÆ, Bears

SUPERFAMILY II. ÆLUROIDEA
[FAMILY VIVERRIDÆ, Civets, Not American]
[FAMILY HYÆNIDÆ, Hyenas, Not American]
FAMILY 5. FELIDÆ, Cats
SUPERFAMILY III. †MIACOIDEA, Ancestral Carnivores
FAMILY 6. †UINTACYONIDÆ

The present geographical distribution of the various families is very unequal; the Canidæ, or dog family, are cosmopolitan, occurring in every continent, though the Australian Dingo, or Wild Dog, was probably introduced by human agency. Antarctica, which has no land mammals of any sort, need not be taken into consideration. The weasel and cat families, Mustelidæ and Felidæ, are found in all the continents except Australia. The Ursidæ, or bears, are characteristically northern, though one species occurs in northwestern Africa, one in the Peruvian Andes and one in the Malay Archipelago. The Procyonidæ, which include the coatis and kinkajous of Central and South America and the raccoons of all the Americas, are chiefly confined to the Western Hemisphere; some naturalists refer the Pandas (*Ailurus* and *Æluropus*) to this family, others exclude them. Though South America contains representatives of all the carnivorous families, except the civets and hyenas, none of these are indigenous in the geological sense of that word, the five families having entered in successive waves of migration from the north during the Pliocene and Pleistocene epochs. The North Polar region has members of three of the families, the Canidæ, Mustelidæ and Ursidæ, some of which, like the Polar Bear (*Thalassarctus maritimus*), are always white, while the others are white only in winter, such as the Ermine (*Mustela erminea*) and the Arctic Fox (*Vulpes lagopus*).

Though typically beasts of prey, the Fissipedia are adapted to a great variety of habits. The Canidæ are terrestrial and have neither arboreal, aquatic nor burrowing species, though foxes live in holes; many, like the foxes, are solitary, others, like the wolves and Indian dholes, hunt in packs and these have remarkable powers of sustained speed. The cats (Felidæ) which have extraordinary range of size, are either terrestrial, or arboreal; they take their prey by stalking and leaping upon it, not by running it down. There are no aquatic or burrowing species in the family. The bears (Ursidæ) seldom kill their prey, but subsist largely upon a vegetable diet and, in regions that have cold winters, they hibernate. They are chiefly ground-livers, though arboreal to a limited extent. The raccoon family (Procyonidæ) comprises animals of small size, which are chiefly arboreal. The

Asiatic pandas (*Ailurus* and *Æluropus*) are referred here and are much larger. The diet of the Procyonidæ is principally vegetable, but also includes insects, birds and their eggs and small mammals; they are typically omnivorous. The Mustelidæ, or weasels, are much the largest and most diversified of all the fissiped families and include animals of moderate, small and very small size and they vary much in mode of life, but they are nearly all fierce and bloodthirsty little animals that kill for the joy of it. The otters (*Lutra*) are aquatic and the Sea Otter (*Latax*) is marine, almost as much so as the seals; both marine and fresh-water otters are fish-eaters. Minks and fishers are semi-aquatic and weasels, sables and martens are arboreal, skunks terrestrial and badgers fossorial. The largest existing member of the family, after the Sea Otter, is the Wolverene, or Glutton (*Gulo*), which looks like a small bear and is distributed through the boreal zone of the northern hemisphere.

With all this diversity, there is an unmistakable unity in the structural plan throughout the Fissipedia. With few exceptions, the incisors are present in full number; the canines are formidable weapons, varying much in length, thickness, acuteness of point and the like, but, with rare exceptions, most effective in the seizing of prey. Indeed, the word *canine*, as applied to teeth, is taken from the fangs of a dog. An especially characteristic feature of the dentition is the pair of shearing teeth, "sectorials," or "carnassials," which are always the 4th upper premolar and 1st lower molar. These appear in the most ancient Carnivora of the Paleocene and when, as in the bears, pandas and raccoons, there are no shearing teeth, it is because the sectorials have lost the function and have become tuberculated grinders. In addition to the sectorials, most fissipeds have a number of tubercular teeth which are employed in the crushing of bones. In all the Carnivora the teeth are low-crowned and rooted, never hypsodont, or cement-covered.

There are a few members of the suborder, such as the Aard Wolf (*Proteles*) one of the South African hyenas, and the musteline *Eupleres*, of Madagascar, in which the jaws are weak and the teeth much reduced in size or number, in adaptation to insectivorous habits. Normally, the jaws are large and stout and the sagittal and occipital crests are prominent, to afford attachment to the powerful masticatory muscles, especially the temporal, which arises on the side of the brain-case. In some very small fissipeds, such as weasels and stoats and the small foxes, the crests are low, or absent, the relatively large brain-case having sufficient surface for muscular attachments. Very characteristic are the strong, boldly outcurved zygomatic arches, which give origin to the powerful masseter muscles and these are inserted in deep pits, the *masseteric fossæ*, one on each half of the lower jaw, near the posterior end.

The face and jaws may be elongate, as in the dogs, or very much shortened, as in the cats, or of intermediate length. The brain-case is relatively large and the orbits, except in the cats, are widely open behind. The neck is never very long, but the body usually is and the tail varies greatly in length and thickness, from the long, heavy tail of the Leopard, to the very short one of lynxes and bears, with the intermediate one of foxes and wolves, which have bushy tails, in contrast to those of the cats, which are covered with short hairs, in the Lion tufted at the end. The limbs likewise vary greatly in proportionate length, but are never very long as compared with those of most hoofed animals. Except in the cats and some viverrines, there is no power of rotation of the fore-paw on the arm, and the collar-bones, having become useless, are vestigial or lacking. The bones of the fore-arm and lower leg are always separate.

In the wrist, or *carpus* there is, in all existing Carnivora, a large compound bone, made up of the coalesced scaphoid, lunar and central and called the *scapho-lunar*. The feet nearly always have five toes and never less than four; in modern dogs and cats the manus has a very small, vestigial pollex and the pes is four-toed, but the hyenas are the only family in which both manus and pes are four-toed. The feet are armed with claws, which are usually sharp-pointed and, as in the bears and large cats, may be terrible weapons, but in the cursorial dogs and hyenas they are blunt. In the cats the claws are retractile and when not in use, they are folded back into the foot and protruded when required, a feature with which the Domestic Cat has made every one familiar. In the Viverridæ also several genera have claws that are more or less retractile, but in none so completely as in the cats.

Superfamily I. Cynoidea

In 1869 Flower proposed the division of the Fissipedia into three sections, or superfamilies, as they would be called now; these were, I, the Cynoidea, including only the Canidæ, II, the Arctoidea, with the Ursidæ, Mustelidæ and Procyonidæ, and III, the Ailuroidea, comprising cats, viverrines and hyenas. Winge (1895) united the first two groups, a manifest improvement, though he made unnecessary changes in Flower's names, which are here restored.

Family 1. Canidæ, Dogs, Wolves, Foxes, etc.

The most important American genera of this family are as follows:

Canis, true Wolves. *Vulpes*, Red Fox. *Urocyon*, Grey Fox, Rec. and Pleist. †*Ænocyon*, Pleist. *Cerdocyon*, *Chrysocyon*, Fox-like Wolves, S. A. *Icticyon*, Bush-dog, S. A. Rec. and Pleist. †*Palæocyon*, †*Speothos*, †*Dinocynops*, S. A. Pleist. †*Hyænognathus*, up. Plio. †*Borophagus*, mid. Plio. †*Ælurodon*, low. Plio. and up. Mio. †*Tomarctus*, low. Plio. to mid. Mio. †*Cynodesmus*, low. Mio. †*Mesocyon*, low. Mio., up. Olig. †*Daphænus*, mid. Olig. †*Amphicyon*, †*Dinocyon*, †*Pliocyon*, †*Hemicyon*, low. Plio., mid. Mio. †*Daphænodon*, low. Mio. †*Paradaphænus*, up. Olig. †*Prodaphænus*, up. Eoc. †*Pseudocynodictis*, up. and mid. Olig. †*Procynodictis*, up. Eoc. †*Parictis*, mid. and up. Olig.

(*Unless otherwise noted, the genera of the table are North American.*)

Throughout the chapter, for the sake of convenience, the term "dogs" is used to mean the family Canidæ. It is a singularly homogeneous family, in spite of its diffusion all over the world and in every sort of climate and environment. The differences that characterize the various modern genera and species of the family affect chiefly the number and size of the teeth and such external features as the size of the ears, nature and colouring of the hair, bushiness, or otherwise, of the tail.

The dogs are the only fissipeds which capture their prey by running it down and they are endowed with remarkable speed and endurance. The entire organism is adapted to cursorial habits, for not only the skeleton, but the muscles, heart and lungs must all be especially fitted to endure this long-sustained speed. It is this particular adaptation, both in the fox and in the hounds, that is taken advantage of in the sport of fox-hunting.

The teeth and skeleton of a modern Wolf were sufficiently described in Chapter II, but it will be useful to summarize briefly those characters in which the existing representatives of the family resemble and differ from their Tertiary forerunners. For most Recent genera the dental formula is: $i\frac{3}{3}$, $c\frac{1}{1}$, $p\frac{4}{4}$, $m\frac{2}{3} \times 2 = 42$; only the third upper molar has been lost, but the third lower is minute and apparently on the point of disappearance. A very puzzling creature is the Long-eared Fox (*Otocyon megalotis*) of South Africa, in which the molar formula is $\frac{4}{4}$ as usually given for the marsupials. The meaning of this striking departure from all other known carnivores and almost all other placental mammals will be discussed in the final chapter of the book. The upper sectorial has a blade of two external shearing cusps and a small internal cusp carried on a separate root; the upper molars are tribubercular and used for crushing. The lower sectorial, $m_{\overline{1}}$, has an anterior shearing blade of two cusps and the vestige of a third and, behind this, a low "heel," which is usually basin-shaped, but may be trenchant, a significant difference.

The skull is characterized by the long face and jaws and by the nature of the auditory region; the tympanic bone is inflated into a large, hollow, one-chambered bulla, and the external opening is an irregular hole, without tubular prolongation. The paroccipital process is in contact with the bulla behind, but does not embrace it. There is an alisphenoid canal for the transmission of the internal carotid artery. Neck, body and tail are of moderate length and the vertebræ of the loins are not especially large and heavy. The *os penis*, or *baculum* is straight, of irregular diameter, without perforation, or forking at the free end.

The limb-bones have a superficial resemblance to those of hoofed animals, especially of the artiodactyls; the humerus has no very prominent ridges or crests for muscular attachment and no epicondylar foramen and the femur has no trace of a third trochanter. The ulna and radius so interlock with the humerus as to prevent any rotation of the fore-foot. The manus has five digits, but the first of these, or *pollex*, is reduced to a functionless dew-claw. The four functional digits are arranged in two symmetrical pairs very much on the artiodactyl plan; the metacarpals are parallel, not spreading, and closely appressed. The median pair, the 3rd and 4th, are longer and quadrate, nearly square, in cross-section, a very unusual shape among the Carnivora, in most of which the cross-section of these bones is oval. The lateral pair, the 2nd and 5th, are somewhat shorter and more trihedral in shape. The pes, in all existing wild species of the family, has lost the hallux and the four remaining digits, like those of the manus, are arranged in artiodactyl fashion. The claws are blunt and non-retractile and are of little use as weapons, but very effective in digging. All modern dogs are digitigrade, the weight being carried upon five pads of each foot, one under the phalanges of each digit and a larger, central one, under the metapodials.

Within the family, there are several different tribes, or genetic series, as they may be considered, some of which can be traced back to early beginnings, but concerning others we have no information. Several of these tribes are still in existence, while others became extinct at various times in the Tertiary and Quaternary periods. The differences between these genetic series were principally in the teeth and, to a less degree, in the skull; the skeleton, on the contrary, is remarkably uniform throughout the modern members of the family. The dogs of Miocene to Recent times group themselves naturally into three series, or subfamilies. There is (1) the *Canine* series, which includes the wolves, jackals, foxes, etc., of the present, together with their immediate ancestry and certain short-lived side-branches, such as the †hyena-like dogs. In this series the first lower molar (m $_\overline{1}$) has a basin-heel, m $_\overline{2}$ and $_\overline{3}$ are oval and tuberculate.

(2) There is, secondly, the †*Simocyonine* series, represented at present by three widely scattered genera, *Cyon*, of India, *Lycaon*, of South Africa and *Icticyon*, the Bush-dog, of Brazil. In this series the heel of the lower sectorial is a single trenchant cusp, not a basin, and in the Indian and Brazilian forms the teeth are reduced in number. (3) The †*Amphicyonine* series has been extinct since the Pliocene and comprises the †"bear-like dogs," which are so different, not only from all other dogs, but also from all other fissipeds, that they might be assigned to a separate family. They were the predominating carnivores of the upper Miocene and most of the Pliocene, but died out before the end of that epoch. No doubt, *Otocyon* should be placed in a fourth series, but nothing has yet been learned of its history.

In some cases, extinct groups have a more or less striking resemblance to other carnivorous families and for these groups descriptive names have been devised, such as †"bear-like dogs" for the †Amphicyonine series, and †"hyena-like dogs" for †*Ælurodon*. More commonly used are the terms †"bear-dogs," and †"hyena-dogs," but these terms are open to the serious objection that they have generally been misunderstood to imply relationship, when only superficial likenesses are involved. As a matter of fact, "bear-like" was not a happily chosen name, for the likeness to bears is confined to certain teeth and, in other respects the †amphicyons were about as unlike bears as they could possibly be. The discovery of the skeleton has made the descriptive term rather inapplicable.

The statement made above as to the uniformity of the skeleton throughout the family applies only to the later genera. As the different series are traced back into more and more ancient formations, all parts of the skeleton, as well as the teeth and skull, are seen to be less and less like the modern type, until, in the Oligocene and upper Eocene, we find very striking differences, which affect all parts of the structure.

The Canidæ would seem to be the central line of the fissiped stock and to have undergone less change than the other carnivorous families. Development consisted in an enlargement of the brain, with concomitant increase in the convolutions of the cerebral cortex, and in adaptation of the whole organism to swift and long-sustained running.   Huxley once called the Horse "a cursorial machine"; with equal truth he might have said it of wolves and foxes.

The dogs cannot be arranged in any single genetic series, but rather in the ramifications of a family tree; it will, therefore, be neces-

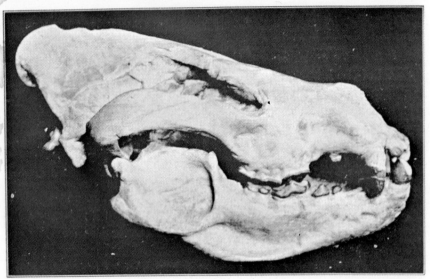

Fig. 354. — Large †bear-like dog, †*Hemicyon*, orbit distorted by crushing, lower Pliocene of Neb. (Courtesy of Mr. Childs Frick.)

sary to treat each series separately, returning several times to the starting point.   This is an awkward method of treatment, but it is far less confusing than attempting to deal with all contemporary genera together.

The Pleistocene had most of the modern forms in addition to some very large extinct ones.   The commonest fossil found in the tar of Rancho La Brea is the †Dire Wolf (*Canis* †*dirus*), sometimes made into a separate genus †*Ænocyon*, which differs from modern wolves not only in its very large size, but also in its proportionally heavy head, small brain and light limbs.   That it was not a very intelligent animal seems to be indicated by the multitude that were trapped in the viscid, semi-liquid asphalt.   Though seemingly most abundant in California, it was probably spread all over the continent, having been found in the Mississippi Valley, Florida and the Valley of Mexico.   Associated with this great creature were others almost identical with the existing Grey Wolf (*Canis occidentalis*), Coyote (*C. ochropus*) and Grey Fox (*Urocyon virginianus*).

Pliocene dogs are abundant fossils, though they belong mostly to extinct tribes, †bear-like and †hyena-like genera, while those which gave rise to the existing wolves and foxes have not been found. It may be that this series died out in North America and was subsequently re-established by renewed immigration. Space is lacking for a discussion of this problem, but, for several reasons, it is more probable that they continued here, but withdrew from the Great Plains before the competition of the huge †*Amphicyon*, †*Dinocyon*

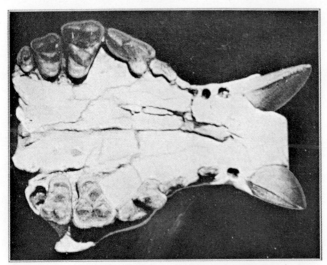

FIG. 355. — †*Amphicyon*, lower Miocene. (Peabody Mus. Yale Univ.)

and †*Hemicyon*, great wolves that were as large as Grizzly Bears and flourished to a surprising extent in the Miocene and Pliocene. In the lower Pliocene there continued a genus, †*Tomarctus*, which was very abundant in the middle Miocene. So far as skull and teeth are concerned, the only parts yet known, there is no obvious reason why this genus should not have been the actual ancestor of *Canis*. Naturally, the skull differs from that of the latter in many particulars, but these are all primitive features which point back to the earlier ancestral genera, such as †*Cynodesmus* and †*Mesocyon* of the lower Miocene. The long cranium and short face, the very prominent sagittal and occipital crests and the smaller brain-case are all primitive. No doubt, the skeleton, when eventually found, will prove to be of intermediate character.

The lower Miocene genera of this Canine series are †*Cynodesmus* and †*Mesocyon*, the latter dating back to the John Day. †*Mesocyon* is much the better known of the two, as complete skeletons have been obtained, and is a very satisfactory connecting link between †*Tomarctus* and the ancestral Oligocene types. The dental formula of †*Mesocyon* is the same as in *Canis*, with a total of 42 teeth and only $m \underline{3}$ lost; the lower sectorial, $m \overline{1}$, has the basin-like heel characteristic of all this tribe and the skull retains many ancestral features, which have been lost or radically modified in Recent dogs. Thus, the brain-case is relatively small, which occasions high crests, both sagittal and occipital; nevertheless, the cranium is long and

FIG. 356. — Giant Canid, †*Dinocyon gidleyi*, Miocene of Tex. (Restoration by Charles R. Knight, Amer. Mus. Nat. Hist.)

the face short, elongation of the jaws and enlargement of the teeth being modern characteristics. The postorbital constriction is more pronounced than in *Canis* and much farther behind the eye-sockets, and the postorbital processes of the frontals are decidedly less prominent. The base of the cranium is thoroughly canine, with large, inflated tympanic bullæ, which have irregular openings, without tubular prolongations.

In all parts of the skeleton there are a great many minor differences between †*Mesocyon* and *Canis*, but consideration of space makes it necessary to omit mention of all save a few of especial significance. The body is long and the tail as long and heavy proportionally as in the Leopard, much more so than in any existing dog. The limbs and, especially, the feet show plainly that this lower Miocene genus was a much less finished "cursorial machine" than are the Recent wolves, foxes and jackals. The shoulder-blade has not the narrow, nearly quadrate shape seen in *Canis*, but is broader and more oval and not unlike the scapula of the mustelines, and the acromion is much wider than in the modern genus. The humerus is very canine in shape, but retains the epicondylar foramen, which no existing member of the family has. The other limb-bones are very dog-like and modern-looking.

In a very interesting way the feet are intermediate between those of the Recent dogs, on the one hand, and those of the White River †*Daphœnus*, on the other. The manus has five functional digits, which still show the primitive, spreading arrangement, though a beginning

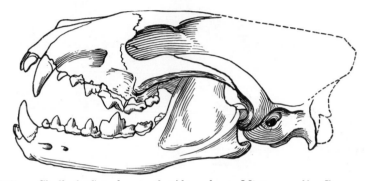

Fig. 357. — Skull of †*Cynodesmus thoöides*, a lower Miocene wolf. Compare with Fig. 1, p. 15. (Princeton Univ. Mus.)

of the closely appressed, parallel position of the metacarpals may be noted. These metacarpals are distinctly shorter and heavier than in *Canis* and have not the quadrate cross-section of the modern genera. The ungual phalanges are short and sharp-pointed, not like the blunt nails of modern dogs and there is even less of a bony hood around the base of the claw, merely a bony ring.

The pes of †*Mesocyon* differs even more from that of Recent dogs than does the manus, for there are five functional digits, though the hallux is much the shortest of them. The other metatarsals are decidedly shorter and stouter than in *Canis* and their relative lengths are different, for the symmetry is rather mesaxonic than paraxonic, the median metatarsal (mt. III) being the longest and thickest of the five.

There is no obvious reason why †*Mesocyon* should not be regarded as actually ancestral to †*Cynodesmus*, †*Tomarctus* and the later canines, as distinguished from the †simocyonine and †amphicyonine branches.

In the White River are two very distinct types of dogs; one a short-lived series of civet-like animals (†*Pseudocynodictis*) which is dealt with below, and the other, †*Daphœnus*, which, according to present opinions, is the ancestor common to the true canines and the †amphicyonines, or †bear-like dogs. Several species, some contemporaneous, others successive, are assigned to this genus, though some authorities would separate these generically as well as specifically. It is, however, a relatively unimportant question as to what name, or names, shall be given to these larger White River dogs, for,

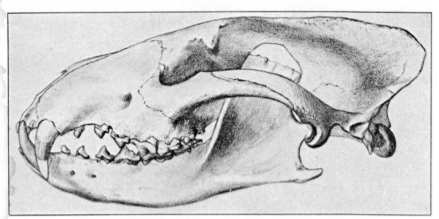

Fig. 358. — Skull of primitive †bear-like dog, †*Daphœnus vetus*, White River stage. (Field Mus. Nat. Hist.; from Scott and Jepsen.)

obviously, they form a natural group of closely interrelated species, which differ from one another only in minor details. In particular, a larger species, †*Daphœnus vetus*, is regarded as beginning the line of the †bear-like dogs, and a smaller one †*D. hartshornianus*, as ancestral to the true canine series, including the modern dogs.

†*Daphœnus* is a far more primitive animal than †*Mesocyon*, and if only the skeleton were known, without skull or teeth, it may be doubted whether it would be referred to the Canidæ at all, though it would be difficult to decide where else to put it. The dentition is typically canine with unreduced numbers: $i \frac{3}{3}$, $c \frac{1}{1}$, $p \frac{4}{4}$, $m \frac{3}{3} \times 2 = 44$. The sectorial teeth ($p \frac{4}{}$ and $m \frac{}{1}$) are comparatively small and ineffective, but they have all the elements of the later more advanced and efficient teeth. The skull is dog-like, but in a primitive fashion, with long cranium and short face, brain-case of small capacity, long and very prominent sagittal and occipital crests. The natural brain-cast has large olfactory lobes and small hemispheres which leave the olfactory lobes and cerebellum uncovered; the cerebral convolutions are extremely simple, less numerous and much less complex than

those of *Canis*. The tympanic forms a very small bulla, which is but little inflated and so loosely attached, that but few fossil skulls have it; the entotympanic apparently was not ossified at all. This is a striking difference from all the later dogs, Miocene to Recent, in which the bullæ are large and conspicuous and firmly attached to the skull.

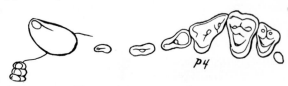

FIG. 359. — Upper teeth of †*Daphænus vetus.* *p4,* fourth premolar. (From Hatcher.)

The body is long and the lumbar vertebræ are remarkably large and heavy, more feline than canine in character, as is also the long, heavy tail. The *baculum* is likewise very different from that found in Recent members of the family and more as in the raccoons and weasels; it is long and fully developed, curved and forked at the end. The limbs are relatively short and stout; the humerus has the epicondylar foramen and the femur a remnant of the third trochanter. The radius has a discoidal head and evidently retained some power of rotation, which all the later genera of the family have entirely lost. The feet have five spreading digits, which are all of different lengths, another difference from *Canis*.

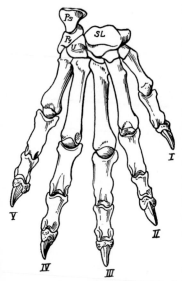

FIG. 360. — Right manus of †*Daphænus vetus. SL,* scapholunar. *Py,* pyramidal. *Ps,* pisiform. *U,* unciform. Compare with Fig. 26, p. 33. (From Hatcher.)

In reading a description of the skeleton of †*Daphænus,* such as that published by the late Mr. J. B. Hatcher, one cannot fail to be struck by the frequent reiteration of phrases like "more feline than canine in character." How these many resemblances to the cats are to be interpreted, is a question to be dealt with in another chapter.

In the Eocene no satisfactorily complete material of this series has been found, yet the line was plainly represented by †*Prodaphænus* of the Uinta, which, as its name implies, is a more ancient and primitive form of the White River genus. In the middle Eocene the family can no longer be recognized as such and appears to merge in the family †Uintacyonidæ, a group which is not far removed from the common ancestry of all the fissiped families.

There was mentioned above a short-lived series of small, civet-like dogs, which extended only from the Uinta to the John Day. The Oligocene genus, common to both John Day and White River stages, is †*Pseudocynodictis*. Despite their viverrine appearance and proportions, these animals are clearly canine in their affinities, but just how they are related to the other tribes and series of the family is far from clear. It has been held that this series, rather than †*Daphœnus* is the ancestral group of the modern Canidæ. According to another opinion, this tribe is the starting point of the foxes, con-

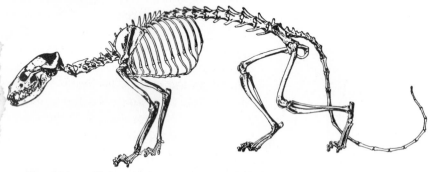

Fig. 361. — Skeleton of †*Pseudocynodictis gregarius*, White River stage. (From Matthew.)

cerning whose history so very little is known. Still a third view is that the group died out at the close of the Oligocene, leaving no descendants.

The genus †*Pseudocynodictis* is found in both the John Day and the White River and is much more abundant and varied in the former, but well-preserved skeletons have been obtained from both formations. In some respects this genus is more like *Canis* than is †*Daphœnus*, as, for instance, the large, inflated, thick-walled auditory bullæ, so firmly attached to the skull that they are seldom missing in the fossils. The dental formula also is that of *Canis*, the last upper molar having disappeared, but, aside from the skull and teeth, there is little in the skeleton to suggest canine relationships. Body and tail are relatively very long, limbs and feet short and weak. The humerus is more modernized than in †*Daphœnus*, lacking the epicondylar foramen, and the femur has lost the third trochanter. The five-toed feet have spreading digits, as in the less specialized fissipeds generally, and the claws are sharp. The *baculum* is very large, and has a sigmoid curvature as in the raccoons. As the restoration shows, †*Pseudocynodictis*, when alive, must have looked much more like one of the civets (Viverridæ) than like a canine, which it undoubtedly was.

Huxley divided the dog family into two sections, which he called the Thoöids, or Wolves, and the Alopecoids, or Foxes, a principal

FIG. 362. — Small, civet-like dog, †*Pseudocynodictis gregarius*, White River stage. (Restored from skeleton shown in Fig. 361.)

distinction between them being the presence or absence of frontal sinuses, which the wolves have and foxes have not. Though this division has not found favour with naturalists generally, it is tempting to apply it to the White River dogs, for †*Daphœnus* has the sinuses and †*Pseudocynodictis* is without them, and we might consider the latter as a very early alopecoid and the former as almost the beginning of the thoöids. However attractive such a hypothesis may seem, it is, at present, no more than a speculation, so far as the foxes are concerned, for there is such a long gap in the history of that group, that no positive statement can be made about them.

Nearly allied to †*Pseudocynodictis* in the John Day and White River genus is †*Parictis*, which resembles the European †*Cynodon* and may possibly be identical with it; †*Parictis* will be considered in connection with the raccoon family.

Another side-branch of the canine stem is that of the †hyena-like dogs, which ran a brief course (geologically speaking) through the upper Miocene, the Pliocene and, perhaps, persisting into the Pleistocene. The last surviving genus of this branch was †*Hyænognathus*,

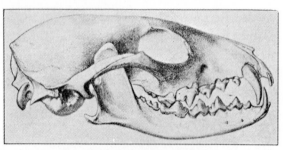

a large wolf with short and very massive jaws; the heel of $m_{\,\overline{1}}$ (the lower sectorial) is bicuspid and basin-shaped, but reduced in size, as the second and third lower molars also are. The sectorial blade of $m_{\,\overline{1}}$ and the crowns of $p_{\,\overline{4}}$ and $p_{\,\overline{3}}$ are very thick and heavy and resemble

FIG. 363. — Right side of skull of †*Pseudocynodictis gregarius*, small civet-like carnivore, White River stage. (Peabody Mus. Yale Univ.; from Scott and Jepsen.)

those of hyenas, which explains the term "†hyena-like dogs." $P_{\,\overline{2}}$ is implanted by a single root and $p_{\,\overline{1}}$ has been lost, yet there is no gap between the canine and the foremost premolar, $p_{\,\overline{2}}$. The canine is rather short, but stout. These strikingly heavy teeth and powerful jaws are very suggestive of carrion-feeding and bone-crushing habits.

The lower Pliocene and upper Miocene †*Ælurodon* is very much better known from entire skeletons and appears to have been

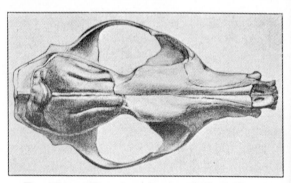

FIG. 364. — Top view of same skull of †*Pseudocynodictis gregarius* shown in Fig. 363, with brain-cast drawn from another individual. (Peabody Mus. Yale Univ.; from Scott and Jepsen.)

the ancestor of †*Hyænognathus*. There are several species of †*Ælurodon*, which differ much in size and of which the commonest, †*Æ. sævus*, equalled the Grey Wolf in stature. In the skeleton, the structure of the body, limbs and feet is very modern, but the skull is short and massive. The premolars are so thick and hyena-like, that this genus has mistakenly been regarded as actually ancestral to the hyena family, whereas the skull and skeleton are typically dog-like. The name of the genus, which means "Cat-tooth" is taken from the upper sectorial, which, as in the cats, has no internal cusp, but a third root indicates its former presence. The skull is short and massive and looks somewhat like that of a bear, because of the steep descent at the forehead from the cranium to the face.

Some genus like the middle Miocene †*Tomarctus* (if not †*Tomarctus* itself) was the common ancestor of the wolves and the †hyena-like dogs, for the latter are wolf-like in everything but the teeth and the teeth are only modifications of the wolf-type, but habits, no doubt, were different.

The †Simocyonine tribe is represented to-day by three genera, *Lycaon*, the Cape Hunting Dog, of South Africa, *Cyon*, the Dhole, or Wild Dog, of India, and *Icticyon*, the Bush-dog, of Brazil. In all of these the heel of the lower sectorial is a single trenchant ridge, not a bicuspid basin, as it is in all other existing dogs; the second lower molar is also trenchant, not tuberculate, and the third is usually lacking. The history of this group has many gaps, but is, nevertheless, fairly well known. *Lycaon*, now confined to South Africa, occurs in the Pleistocene of France and Italy; *Cyon*, living, at present only in southern Asia, had Pleistocene representatives in South America. In North America there is a hiatus throughout the Pliocene, which remains to be filled, but †*Euoplocyon*, of the middle Miocene, is one of this group, having the trenchant heel of the lower sectorial and trenchant second and third molars; it differs, thus, from the modern forms in having the full number of teeth.

Much better known is †*Temnocyon*, of the John Day, of which there are several species, ranging in size from a fox to a large wolf. The trenchant heel of the lower sectorial and the ridged crowns of $m_{\overline{2}}$ and $_{\overline{3}}$ plainly indicate that this genus belongs to the †Simocyonine tribe, but the skeleton is thoroughly canid, as are those of the modern *Cyon* and *Lycaon*. Indeed, this genus approximated the modern skeletal structure earlier than †*Mesocyon*, believed to be the direct ancestor of *Canis*.

The †Simocyonine series cannot yet be definitely traced to a stage earlier than the John Day, but there is much reason to believe that the White River †*Daphœnus* will eventually prove to be the starting point of this line also.

A peculiar side-branch of this stock is that of the †"short-faced dogs," of which the latest member is †*Simocyon*, of the European Pliocene, from which the tribal name is taken and in which the reduction in the number of teeth and the shortening of the jaws attain their maximum. The latest member of the series yet discovered in North America is the genus †*Enhydrocyon*, of the Gering and John Day stages; it has the dental formula: $i\frac{3}{3}$, $c\frac{1}{1}$, $p\frac{3}{3}$, $m\frac{2}{2} \times 2 = 40$; the trenchant heel of the lower sectorial puts this genus into the †Simocyonine series. The teeth are crowded together and the upper premolars are set obliquely in the jaw, to gain space; the last molar in each jaw, $m\frac{2}{2}$, especially the upper one, is reduced to a vestigial condition. The lateral upper incisor ($i^{\underline{3}}$) is large, the median ones ($i^{\underline{1}}$ and $^{\underline{2}}$) much smaller and the same relative sizes recur in the lower jaw, though they are all actually smaller than in the upper series.

The skull, though clearly canid, nevertheless has very much the appearance of that of a weasel, or otter, which Professor Cope suggested in the name which he gave to the genus, the "Water Dog," for the face is extremely short and the cranium very long. The neck is rather short and the fore-limb bones are considerably longer than those of the hind-leg. The groove for the knee-cap on the femur is very peculiar in being short, wide and shallow and facing downward rather than forward. The relative proportions of the limb-bones are like those of the hyenas, and, except for its short, cat-like bullet-head, †*Enhydrocyon*, no doubt resembled the hyenas in appearance and gait, but there was no closer relationship with the hyenas than other dogs have; there is merely a superficial resemblance. Speaking of this genus, Professor Matthew said: "It is an aberrant type of the Canidæ without marked relationship to any other family." The White River †*Brachyrhynchocyon* seems to be the ancestor of this branch.

The third tribe, or subfamily, the †Amphicyonines or †bear-like dogs, is much the strangest and most aberrant of them all. This was the dominant canid type in the Pliocene and upper Miocene, so much so that it completely overshadowed the true wolves and apparently drove them from the Great Plains region altogether, though they returned in the later Pliocene, when the †bear-like dogs dwindled and disappeared. The tribe is abundantly represented in both Europe and North America and such were the migrations, back and forth, that it is well-nigh impossible to determine the place of origin of the various genera.

One genus, †*Amphicyon*, which is common to North America and Europe, is typical of the whole subfamily and was especially abundant and diversified in the lower Pliocene, middle and upper Miocene. In these animals the unusually large size of all the tubercular molars is very characteristic of the group, while the sectorials and premolars are proportionally reduced. In †*Amphicyon* the third upper molar ($m \underline{3}$) is retained, while in the contemporary †*Pliocyon* and †*Hemicyon* it is lost.

The skull is very different from that of the other subfamilies, especially in the character of the significant auditory bullæ, which are more musteline or ursine than canine. The bullæ are small, not much inflated and have long tubular entrances, such as are found in no other dogs, and they fill only the anterior half of the periotic space. If, as seems likely, an ento-tympanic was present, it cannot have been ossified.

The skeleton is even more peculiar than the skull; the neck and spinal column are heavy and the tail remarkably long and thick, quite as much so as in the larger cats. The limbs are short and massive, the five-toed feet, with spreading digits and sharp claws, are somewhat between cat and bear in shape. The gait may have been plantigrade, but was, more probably, semi-digitigrade.

Matthew wrote of †*Amphicyon:* "This was a very extraordinary animal, as different from living dogs as a badger or an otter from a weasel and not much like any other carnivore." So many are the bear-like characters of these animals that they have frequently been regarded as the ancestors of the Ursidæ, but this opinion is no longer held, for the †amphicyonines are specialized in a manner that leads away from other carnivorous families.

The latest representative of this tribe was †*Borophagus*, of the middle Pliocene, though, perhaps, †*Hyænognathus* may, when better known, prove to belong to this series rather than to the †Simocyonine tribe, where it is now placed. †*Borophagus* is a very large, bear-like dog, the massive premolars of which are suggestive of hyena-like habits. A forerunner, possibly a direct ancestor of †*Borophagus* is †*Borocyon*, of the lower Pliocene. †*Amphicyon* and †*Dinocyon* are especially characteristic of the middle Miocene, and the latter is one of the largest of known American fissipeds, rivalling in size the great Brown Bear of Alaska.

In the lower Miocene †*Daphœnodon* carried the line back, but, with the available data, it is not yet possible to decide whether the giant wolves of the middle and upper Miocene were of native or of immigrant stock. At all events, †*Daphœnodon* is very nearly what the actual ancestor must have been and serves to make plain the steps of evolutionary change. It was the largest canid of its time, the contemporary wolves, †*Cynodesmus* and †*Mesocyon*, being hardly half so large. †*Daphœnodon* leads directly back to the White River

†*Daphœnus;* the species †*D. vetus* is the very probable ancestor of the lower Miocene genus.

Structurally, at least, †*Daphœnus* is very near the common term to which all the tribes, or subfamilies of Canidæ that have been described in this chapter, converge; that is to say, this genus in its various species closely represents the common ancestry of them all. No doubt, however, the actual story was not so simple as all that.

Fig. 365. — Lower Miocene †bear-like dog, *Daphœnodon superbus.* (Restored from a skeleton in Carnegie Mus.)

The confusing effects of intermigration obscured the course of events, but, notwithstanding this element of uncertainty, the succession of North American fossil dogs gives a good conception of the course of development and it is a highly significant fact that so plausible a narrative can be given.

Family 2. Procyonidæ, Raccoons, etc.

Leaving aside the Asiatic pandas (*Ailurus* and *Æluropus*) as doubtful members, all the genera of this family are confined to the Western Hemisphere, where they form a small group, of which the more important genera are as follows:

Procyon, Raccoon, Pleist. to Rec. N. and S. A. *Nasua,* Coati Mundi, Pleist. to Rec., S. A. to California. †*Amphinasua,* mid. and up. Plio. S. A. *Bas-*

sariscus, Cacomistle, Plio. to Rec. †*Probassariscus*, low. Plio. †*Cynarctus*, low. Mio. to low. Plio. *Potos*, Kinkajou, Neotropical, Recent. †*Phlaocyon*, low. Mio.

The raccoons (*Procyon*) and coatis (*Nasua*, curious animals with long, flexible, pig-like snouts) are especially familiar, the Central American genera less so. The family includes mammals of moderate and small size, none of the existing species are large; they are generally arboreal in habit and subsist upon a mixed diet of fruit, eggs, birds and insects. Consequently, the molars are tuberculate, adapted to crushing and grinding and the sectorials have mostly lost their shearing function, through the addition of conical cusps on the internal side of the crowns. The raccoons have bushy tails of moderate length and the other genera have long and frequently prehensile tails. The feet are five-toed, with naked soles and the gait is plantigrade; the print of a raccoon's hind-foot is very like that of a small child.

FIG. 366. — Dentition of Raccoon, *Procyon lotor*, left side. *i 3*, external incisor. *c*, canine. *p4*, fourth premolar. *m1*, first molar.

Very little is known regarding the history of this family, as fossils of it are rare and mostly fragmentary: *Bassariscus*, which now extends from the southern United States to Central America, ranged into Kansas in the Pleistocene and †*Probassariscus*, of the lower Pliocene, appears to be the direct ancestor of the Recent genus, but gives little information regarding the course of development. †*Leptarctus*, of the middle Miocene, was long referred to the Procyonidæ, but the discovery of more complete skulls has led to its transfer to the Mustelidæ; it serves to approximate the two families and hints at a close relation between them.

Much the most primitive member of the family so far discovered is †*Phlaocyon*, of the lower Miocene, which points to a connection of the raccoons with the primitive dogs, a connection which is not incompatible with that above suggested between raccoons and mustelines. The genus to which †*Phlaocyon* most directly points is †*Parictis* of the John Day and White River stages. The dentition resembles that of †*Parictis*, but with several changes, all of which are in the direction of the Procyonidæ. The cusps are lower and blunter than in the smaller White River dogs, the premolars are small, thick and closely crowded together and the upper sectorial ($p \overset{4}{}$) while still trenchant, has two internal cusps, the posterior one of which is not found in any other of the Canidæ and marks a step toward the assumption of the tuberculated pattern of the raccoons. The lower sectorial ($m\ \overline{1}$) has a very low cutting blade and a large heel; the other molars, both above and below, are low-crowned, wide and of subquadrate shape.

The skull is short and broad, with a narrower, less capacious brain-case than in *Procyon*, but with face as much shortened and orbits as far forward as in the latter. The lower jaw has a curved inferior border very much as in the modern genus. The limbs are more slender than in the Raccoon and the digits of the five-toed feet have canine rather than procyonine proportions.

The genus †*Parictis*, first described from the John Day and subsequently discovered in the White River also, is very incompletely known from lower-jaw fragments. So far as they go, the teeth of these fragments strongly suggest that †*Parictis*, rather than †*Pseudocynodictis*, is the actual ancestor of †*Phlaocyon*, for the premolars have the characteristically low and thick shape of the latter and the lower sectorial has a similarly low shearing blade. From present imperfect information, †*Parictis* would appear to be a migrant from Asia, being apparently related to the †*Cynodon* group of France. While †*Daphœnus* and †*Pseudocynodictis* seem to have been derived from Uinta ancestors, †*Prodaphœnus* and †*Procynodictis* respectively, nothing is known from the American Eocene which could have given rise to †*Parictis*. The two genera, †*Phlaocyon* and †*Parictis* strongly suggest that the Procyonidæ were descended from primitive dogs.

Family 3. Mustelidæ, Weasels, etc.

The weasel family is much the largest and most diversified of all the fissiped suborder and, in strong contrast to the limited numbers of the raccoon family, includes a great variety of small carnivores, such as weasels, stoats, sables, skunks, fishers, minks, otters, badgers, etc. Many of these are very small and none are large, the Wolverene (*Gulo*) and Sea Otter (*Latax*) being the largest. Most of the genera are ferocious little beasts of prey; otters and sea-otters subsist upon fish and a few, like badgers and skunks, are less bloodthirsty and are largely insectivorous, or even omnivorous. The subdivision of this large and heterogeneous assemblage into subfamilies and sections is a matter of debate, especially when the extinct genera are taken into account, and no general agreement has been reached. One authority admits three subfamilies, another six and a third fifteen, which shows how different are the opinions of specialists.

In the following table are listed the most important genera of North and South America.

MUSTELIDÆ

Mustela, Fishers, Rec., *Grison*, Grison, *Tayra*, Tayra, *Lyncodon*, S. A. Rec. *Martes*, Martens, Rec. to up. Mio. *Putorius*, Weasels, Minks, Rec. to Pleist. *Gulo*, Wolverene, Rec. to Pleist. †*Brachypsalis*, mid. Mio. †*Megalictis*, †*Paroligobunis*, low. Mio. †*Canimartes*, mid. Plio. †*Oligobunis*, mid. Mio. to up. Olig. †*Sthenictis*, low. Plio. †*Mionictis*, †*Plionictis*, mid. Mio. †*Bunælurus*, †*Mustelavus*, mid. Olig. *Taxidea*, Badgers, Rec. to Pleist. †*Leptarctus*, mid. Mio. *Mephitis*, Skunks, Rec. to Pleist. *Spilogale*, Spotted Skunk, do. *Conepatus*, S. A. Skunk, Rec. to Pleist., N. A. Rec. *Lutra*, Otters, Rec. to up. Mio., S. A. Rec. to Pleist. *Latax*, Sea Otter, Rec.

As is generally true of small mammals, with light and fragile bones, the fossils of this family are, for the most part, fragmentary and make it impossible to construct any adequate history of the group; very few entire skeletons have been found and even good skulls are rare.

The Mustelidæ are of Old World origin, but have spread until they are of universal distribution, Australia and Madagascar excepted; they are still mainly distributed in the Eastern Hemisphere. Though North and South America have many and varied representatives of the family, few peculiar types have been developed here. So unsatisfactory are most of the fossils, that any account of the family in North America can be little more than a stratigraphic catalogue of genera. Wave after wave of immigration came in from Asia, recruiting the fauna at each successive stage, but leaving little opportunity for new types to arise here. Even those genera which seem to be of native origin, might prove to be immigrants, if all their history were known.

Pleistocene mustelids in North America are very much the same as the Recent ones, and, no doubt, all the modern genera were represented in the fauna, but not all of them have been found as yet. The alternating severe and mild climates, which accompanied the Glacial and Interglacial stages of the Pleistocene, produced much shifting of distribution and, for example, in one cold period the Boreal Wolverene came down into Pennsylvania.

The latter part of the Pliocene epoch was not favourable to the preservation of small animals and therefore the mustelids are rare and fragmentary. The most numerous ones of the late Pliocene are otters and otter-like animals. In the middle Pliocene (Blanco) only one genus, †*Canimartes*, has been found, but in the lower Pliocene and throughout the Miocene the number of mustelids already known is large, a difference which is obviously due rather to more favourable conditions of fossilization than to larger numbers of these animals in the more ancient stages. The Pliocene and Miocene forms do not seem to be closely related to the modern American genera, all of which apparently migrated from the Old World. Even such characteristically American animals as skunks and the Grison and Tayra of South America, had ancestors in the Pliocene of the Eastern Hemisphere. All the known mustelids of the American Pliocene and Miocene were abortive side-branches of European or Asiatic stocks. In the Miocene genera, the tendency to broaden the inner half of the first upper molar ($m^{\underline{1}}$) which is so striking in the later genera, becomes more and more distinct and the characters of the cranial base become more and more different from those of the other families. In other words, a progressively divergent development, parallel to that which was taking place in the Old World at the same time, is clear.

The mustelids of the middle Miocene are much more diversified than those of the lower Pliocene, at least they appear to be so, but there is always the uncertainty as to how far conditions of preservation were responsible for the difference. In the middle and lower Miocene fossils of mustelids are particularly varied and frequent and the characters of the cranial basis distinguish them clearly from the Canidæ, Viverridæ and other families. The otters are represented by †*Brachypsalis* and †*Sthenictis*, the martens by †*Plionictis* and by a genus which, so far as it is known, is indistinguishable from the modern *Mustela*, while †*Mionictis* is an early skunk, though it cannot be considered as ancestral to any of the existing forms of that group.

A very remarkable animal is †*Leptarctus*, a relative of the badgers, which was long considered, from imperfect material, to be one of the raccoon family and which has so many likenesses to that family, as to raise the question whether the Procyonidæ are not an artificial assemblage, one part of which was derived from the primitive, early dogs through †*Phlaocyon* and the other from the Mustelidæ through †*Leptarctus*. For the present, the question must remain open, until more complete and more numerous fossils shall have been obtained that will make possible the determination of the genetic series.

In the lower Harrison and Gering (lower Miocene) the mustelids are much less numerously represented than in the middle Miocene; †*Paroligobunis* seems to be intermediate between the otter-like †*Brachypsalis*, of the middle Miocene, and †*Oligobunis*, a genus which extends its range in time from the lower Miocene down into the John Day. The fossils from the lower Miocene are much better preserved and among them is the only known skeleton, that in the museum of Amherst College. †*Oligobunis* is a very interesting animal, for it is so primitive and uncharacteristic, that it has been referred, at various times, to no less than three fissiped families. The skeleton referred to is that of a small species, †*O. gemmærosæ*, found in the lower Harrison. In this genus the dental formula is: $i \frac{3}{3}$, $c \frac{1}{1}$, $p \frac{4-3}{4}$, $m \frac{2}{2} \times 2 = 38$ or 40. It should be observed that no existing mustelid has more than one molar in each upper jaw. As before noted, there is in the Miocene Mustelidæ a progressive tendency to widen the inner half of the first upper molar ($m \frac{1}{}$), but in the primitive †*Oligobunis* no sign of this appears, the tooth retaining its original triangular form. The head is small and weasel-like, the body and tail long, the ordinary mustelid proportions, but the limbs are unlike those of other members of the family, in that the hind legs are much longer than the fore. In size, this species is about like the Fisher (*Martes pennanti*) of Maine.

It was a great surprise to find the largest of all known mustelids, Recent or fossil, in †*Megalictis* of the lower Miocene, which is as large as the Black Bear and may be described as a "primitive, gigantic wolverene." The upper sectorial ($p \frac{4}{}$) has a very large well-separated internal cusp, and the first upper molar ($m \frac{1}{}$) is wide transversely and has an internal shelf which is smaller than in the Recent, larger than in the Oligocene genera. On the whole, the teeth are intermediate in character between those of †*Oligobunis*, on the one hand, and those of the Wolverene and Honey Badger (*Mellivora*) of the Malay islands, on the other. The skull is short, broad and heavy, with very short face and elongate cranium, which is high over the orbits and low at the occiput. The auditory bulla is inflated and rounded, as in the dogs, but has the long, tubular entrance of the mustelids.

The lumbar vertebræ are relatively short and weak, but the caudals indicate a long and heavy tail. Limbs and feet are decidedly shorter than in the Wolverene, longer than in the badgers, and the claws which are thick, sharp-pointed and hooded at the base, are suggestive of fossorial habits. In many ways †*Megalictis* is, thus, intermediate between badgers and wolverenes, without being ancestral to either, for there is no indication that the line was continued after the lower Miocene. The long, heavy tail is a notable difference from both wolverenes and badgers.

In decided contrast to the Miocene stages, the American Oligocene is very poor in representatives of the Mustelidæ; the John Day has yielded but one genus, †*Oligobunis,* a Miocene species of which was described above, and two genera have been found in the White River, †*Bunælurus* in the Brulé and †*Mustelavus* in the Chadron. †*Bunælurus* was an immigrant from Asia, where it occurs in the Oligocene of Mongolia, and it differs from the French †*Palæogale* only in the retention of a minute second upper molar ($m\,\underline{2}$). It is so primitive, that it shows but few characteristics of the Mustelidæ and more of the small Oligocene dogs, such as †*Pseudocynodictis;* the auditory bullæ, especially, resemble those of the latter, being oval, inflated and without

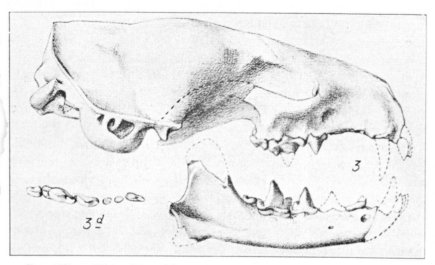

FIG. 367. — White River Musteline, *Bunælurus lagophagus.* *3,* skull from the right side, enlarged. *3d,* lower cheek-teeth. (Princeton Univ. Mus.; from Scott and Jepsen.)

tubular entrance, but the teeth are those of the primitive mustelids, in which the upper molars are triangular, without internal shelf. †*Bunælurus* was a very small animal and must have looked like a weasel with a long muzzle.

The most ancient known American mustelid is †*Mustelavus,* of the Chadron substage, which was also a manifest immigrant and differs from the French †*Plesictis* just as †*Bunælurus* does from †*Palæogale,* in the retention of a very small second upper molar. As its name indicates, †*Mustelavus* might well be ancestral to the family generally, only it was not in North America that the development took place, but in the great Euro-Asiatic land-mass, from which repeated migrations reached the Western Hemisphere.

The scanty mustelid fauna of Tertiary North America is in very strong contrast to conditions in Europe, where in the Oligocene, there was a multitude of mustelids, viverrids and small canids; of the last-named †*Cynodictis* and †*Cynodon* are the best known. These make it very probable that the mustelids arose as a branch of the canine stock, for in the Eocene the two families seem to merge into one.

Family 4. Ursidæ, Bears

The story of the bears in America is a very brief one (in the geological meaning of "brief") for it did not begin until the upper Pliocene. The bears have always been a northern family, rarely extending into the southern continents; at present, there is only one species of bear in northwestern Africa and another in the Andes of Ecuador and Peru; all the others are confined to North America, Asia and Europe. The American genera, North and South, are as follows:

URSIDÆ

Ursus, true bears, Rec. to Pleist. *Thalassarctus*, Polar Bear, Rec. *Tremarctus*, Spectacled Bear, Rec. S. A. †*Arctotherium*, Short-faced Bears, Pleist., N. and S. A., †*Plionarctus*, Plio. †*Indarctos*, Plio.

The dentition and skeleton of the bears are very characteristic and, in most respects, unlike those of any other carnivores. The incisors and canines are like those common among the Fissipedia, but the premolars are greatly reduced; the three anterior ones are very small, single-rooted and often shed early. The sectorials have lost their trenchant character and become tubercular, as are all the molars; the latter are nearly always longer antero-posteriorly than they are wide transversely, reversing the proportions seen in other fissipeds. The tuberculated teeth have considerable resemblance to those of pigs.

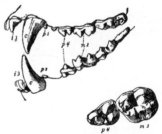

FIG. 368. — Dentition of Grizzly Bear, *Ursus horribilis*. *i 3*, external incisor. *c*, canine. *p 1*, first premolar. *p 4*, fourth premolar. *m 1*, first molar. Below is a view, on a larger scale, of the grinding surface of the fourth premolar and first molar, upper jaw.

Almost all bears live chiefly upon vegetable substances, and even the Polar Bear, which feeds upon fish and seals, will eat grass and berries in the brief Arctic summer; trenchant, shearing carnassials have thus become unnecessary.

The skull is not unlike that of existing Canidæ in shape, except for the concave forehead and that recurs in the †hyena-like dogs (†*Æluro-*

don), but the auditory bullæ are very different in being broad and flattened and not prominent and in having long tubular, bony entrances; the cranial foramina resemble those of the dogs. The body is very heavy and the tail is always short. The limbs are short and thick and have great muscular power; the humerus has lost the epi-

Fig. 369. — Restored head of the †Short-faced Bear, †*Arctotherium bonærense*. (From a skull in Nat. Mus., Buenos Aires.)

condylar foramen in all modern species save the Spectacled Bear (*Tremarctos ornatus*). The thigh-bone is relatively long, which brings the knee-joint so far down that it is free of the body and this, together with the completely plantigrade feet, gives to the bears a gait that seems entirely different from that of other Fissipedia, even of the plantigrade raccoons. The feet of the Polar Bear have hair-covered soles, but in all other existing members of the family the soles are naked. Fore- and hind-feet have five fully developed and functional digits, that have a spreading arrangement and are armed with long, decurved and sharp claws, which are not retractile; they are much longer in the fore-feet and are truly terrible weapons, especially in view of the great muscular power of the fore-legs.

Pleistocene American bears are of two types, (1) the true bears (*Ursus*) and (2) the short-faced bears (†*Arctotherium*). Perhaps a third type is indicated by the bones of a colossal bear found in Nebraska, and this astonishing beast was twice or thrice the size of the Alaskan Brown Bear, the hugest of existing Fissipedia. The known remains of this monster are, however, so scanty that nothing further can be said of them. The true bears are of Old World origin and migrated to this continent in Pleistocene time; at least no remains of them have been found in earlier formations. The small Black Bear (*Ursus americanus*) which is very close to the European *U. arctos*, and the Grizzly (*U. horribilis*) are both found in the tar of Rancho La Brea and in other Pleistocene deposits.

The †short-faced bears, or †arctotheres (†*Arctotherium*) were very large animals, rivalling the huge bears (*Ursus middendorfi*) of present-day Alaska. Their teeth are somewhat less specialized than those of *Ursus*, the sectorials retaining more of the trenchant shape, while the tuberculate molars are less elongate and more nearly square. The premolars are smaller and, in consequence of the shortening of the jaws, are much more crowded together. The inferior border of the mandible is strongly convex.

The †arctotheres were spread all over North America and have been reported from Alaska, California, Pennsylvania, Kentucky and Texas. In addition, they ranged through South America to Argentina; indeed, the genus was first described and named from Pampean skulls. The Spectacled Bear of the Andes (*Tremarctos*) seems to be a derivative of the same stock.

It is not unlikely that the †arctotheres originated in North America, though the fact that they have not been found in any part of the Old World is not conclusive evidence that they did not exist there. That absence, however, *as far as it goes*, favours the American origin of the group. More important is the recent (1926) discovery by Mr. Childs Frick of a primitive bear in the Pliocene of California, which he has named †*Plionarctos*, but the material is too scanty to prove connection with †*Arctotherium*. A Pliocene immigrant from Asia, †*Indarctos*, found in Oregon, is also a possible ancestor of the short-faced line.

Even in the Old World, the origin of the Ursidæ has not been satisfactorily determined.

Superfamily II. ÆLUROIDEA

This group of three families is united by the structure of the base of the cranium, though the †sabre-tooth cats are exceptional in some respects and the hyenas in others. The auditory bulla is in two chambers, which may be indistinguishably fused, or partially divided externally; these chambers are the tympanic and ento-tympanic respectively. Except in one genus (*Cryptoprocta*) the baculum is greatly reduced and irregular in shape. The claws are not retractile in the hyenas, partially so in many viverrines and completely so in the cats. As the hyenas and civets never had any representatives in the Western Hemisphere, they need not be further considered here, save incidentally for comparison.

Family 5. Felidæ, Cats

No other fissiped family is so isolated as the cats and the time and place of their origin are matters of speculation. At the present time, the family is cosmopolitan in distribution, except Australia and the polar regions, though lynxes extend very far north into the Boreal Zone.

It is customary to divide the Felidæ into two subfamilies, (a) the Felinæ, or true cats and (b) the †Machairodontinæ, or †sabre-tooth cats. Cope recognized a third group, which he called the "False †Sabre-tooths," without formally making a subfamily for them; that was done by Steinmann and Doederlein under the name †Nimravinæ, though the arrangement may be temporary.

(a) *Subfamily Felinæ.* — Tympanic bulla two-chambered and embraced behind by the paroccipital process as is "an acorn by its cup" and externally by the mastoid; condylar foramen included in *foramen lacerum posterius*, no alisphenoid canal: mastoid and glenoid processes of squamosal not forming pedicles; canines of the usual fissiped type and of nearly the same size in upper and lower jaws; lower sectorial ($m_{\overline{1}}$) without heel or internal cusp, two external blades in close contact, mandible with anterior face curving into external side without angulation, no flange from ventral border.

(b) *Subfamily †Machairodontinæ.* — Tympanic bulla imperfectly ossified, two chambers seldom distinguishable, paroccipital and mastoid processes not in contact with bullæ; condylar foramen separate, alisphenoid canal present. Glenoid and mastoid pedicles variable, usually very large and conspicuous; upper canines forming great, compressed and recurved laniary sabres, lower canines much reduced; lower sectorial generally with vestigial heel, sometimes with inner cusp; mandible with anterior and lateral faces separated by angulation, flange always indicated, but differing enormously in size in various genera. Skull longer than in Felinæ.

(c) *Subfamily* †*Nimravinæ.* — "False †Sabre-tooths." Cranial base, bullæ and foramina as in †machairodonts; no glenoid or mastoid pedicles; upper canines straight and shorter and less compressed than in the †sabre-tooths, more so than in true cats; lower sectorial with external blades well separated; mandibles with anterior and lateral faces separated by angulation; no indication of flange.

From the definitions, it is obvious that the †Nimravinæ are intermediate between the other subfamilies, sharing some characteristics with one, others with the other.

The principal American genera are listed in the subjoined table; it should be noted that the generic term *Felis* is used comprehensively.

FELIDÆ

a. FELINÆ, *Felis*, Rec. to Plio. N. A.; S. A. Rec. to Pleist.

b. †MACHAIRODONTINÆ, †*Smilodon*, Pleist. N. and S. A. †*Heterofelis* (†*Machairodus*) Plio. †*Dinictis*, up. and mid. Olig. †*Hoplophoneus*, do. †*Eusmilus*, mid. Olig.

c. †NIMRAVINÆ, †*Nimravus*, low. Mio. to mid. Olig. †*Dinælurus*, †*Archælurus*, up. Olig. †*Pseudælurus*, mid. Mio. †*Metailurus*, low. Plio. and up. Mio.

Subfamily a. Felinæ, True Cats. — Of the three groups into which the family is divided, this is the only one which survives and flourishes at the present time. In Recent times, North America has had but a small representation of this subfamily; the Puma (*Felis concolor*, also called Cougar and Mountain Lion) and two or three lynxes (*Lynx rufus* and *L. canadensis*) are the only characteristic forms, though two South American cats, the Jaguar (*F. onca*) and the Ocelot (*F. pardalis*) extend into the southern part of the Sonoran region.

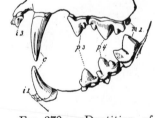

Fig. 370. — Dentition of Lynx, *L. rufus*, left side. *i 3*, external upper incisor. *i 1*, first lower incisor. *c*, canine. *p 3*, *p 4*, third and fourth premolars. *m 1*, first molar.

In the Pleistocene epoch the Recent cats, represented by both modern and extinct genera, were present in the fauna, but these modern animals were completely overshadowed by the †Sabre-tooth "Tigers" (†*Smilodon*) and by the gigantic true cats (*Felis* †*atrox*) which, for want of a better name, are called "lions." *F.* †*atrox* is larger by a quarter than the African Lion and equals the great †Cave Lion (*F.* †*spelæa*) of the European Pleistocene. The California †Lion was widely distributed over North America, from Alaska southward to

Florida and Texas, but, so far as is known, it did not enter South America. The species is very much less abundant in the tar-pits of

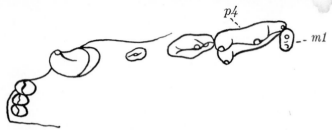

FIG. 371. — Upper teeth of Puma, *Felis concolor*, left side. *p 4*, fourth premolar. *m 1*, first molar.

Rancho La Brea than †*Smilodon*, which outnumbers it 30 to 1, but it cannot properly be inferred from this that the "†lion" was less com-

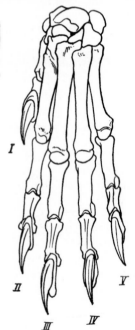

mon than the †sabre-tooth, for it had a better developed brain and was, no doubt, more intelligent in avoiding the treacherous pools. It can hardly be a mere coincidence that the two species which greatly preponderate in the asphalt, the †Dire Wolf (†*Ænocyon dirus*) and the †Sabre-tooth "Tiger" (†*Smilodon californicus*); both had brains which were inferior in type to those of their congeners.

Of the "†Lion," Merriam and Stock write: "In the more formidable male individuals of this species the massiveness of the head is a striking character and the biting strength of the jaws was probably tremendous.

"An open plain, or a rolling country, probably grass covered and supporting here and there a growth of trees and shrubs, presented an environment in which one might reasonably expect to find such carnivores as the great cat. Recognizing the variety and richness of the vertebrate life which prevailed here during that period, it appears entirely reasonable to assume a habitat for this type closely similar to that in which the lion is found to-day on the African veldt."

FIG. 372. — Left manus of Domestic Cat, *Felis domestica*. The horny claws are left in place, covering the ungual phalanges. (From Jayne.)

There can be no doubt that the California "†Lion," which was closely allied both to the great cats of the Old World and to the South

American Jaguar, was an immigrant from Asia, an inference which is supported, though not actually proved by the occurrence of *Felis †atrox* in the Pleistocene of Alaska. There had been previous

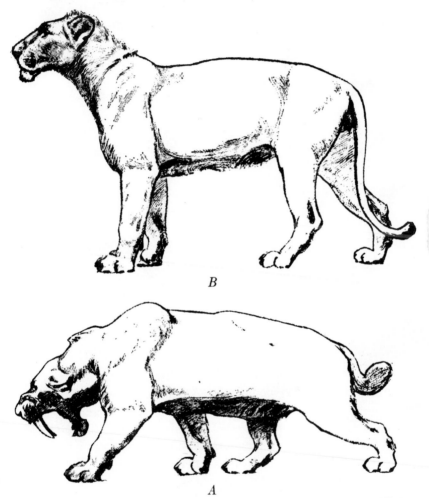

FIG. 373. — A, *†Smilodon californicus.* B, *Felis †atrox.* (Restored by C. R. Knight; from Merriam and Stock.)

arrivals of *Felis* in the Pliocene, which, when better known, may prove to be ancestors of the Puma (*F. concolor*). The lynxes also came in the Pleistocene.

The history of the Felinæ in America is thus a very short one and it was not very much longer in Europe, where *Felis* made its first known appearance in the middle Miocene of Sansan in France. There, also, it would seem to have been an immigrant, for nothing is known from earlier formations which can be considered as ancestral to it, all the Oligocene cats of Europe, as well as those of North America, being either †machairodonts, or †nimravines.

Subfamily b. †*Machairodontinæ,* †*Sabre-tooth Cats.* — The genus †*Smilodon* is the only well-defined one known from the American Pleistocene and it ranged all over the Americas, from California eastward to Pennsylvania and southward to Brazil and Argentina. Sev-

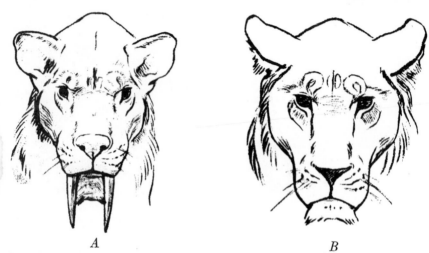

A   *B*

Fig. 374. — *A,* head of †*Smilodon californicus. B,* head of *Felis* †*atrox.* (Restored by C. R. Knight; from Merriam and Stock.)

eral complete skeletons have been obtained both from California and from the Pampean deposits of Argentina. Skulls and bones of †*Smilodon* are incredibly abundant in the asphalt and, next after the †Dire Wolf (†*Ænocyon dirus*) remains of the †Sabre-tooth far outnumber those of all other mammals combined.

Much the best-known North American species of †*Smilodon* is †*S. californicus,* the common species of Rancho La Brea, and this approximates the African Lion in size, though the limbs are shorter and the various proportions different. The most characteristic features of the genus are those of the skull and dentition.

The teeth are much reduced, but those which are retained are enlarged and elaborated. The dental formula is: $i \frac{3}{3-2}$, $c \frac{1}{1}$, $p \frac{2}{2-1}$, $m \frac{1}{1}$, the lower incisors and premolars being variable in number. The incisors are relatively small, but the upper canine is an immense, recurved and flattened, scimitar-like tusk, the edges of which are finely serrate; the blade is broad antero-posteriorly, thin and compressed transversely. Numbers of the skulls found in the tar-pits have had the sabres broken in life, as is shown by the way in which the fractured ends have been smoothed and rounded by subsequent wear.

The manner in which these great sabres were used, has been a subject of much discussion and, as will be subsequently shown,

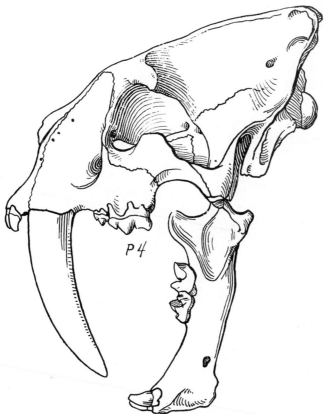

Fig. 375. — Skull of the Pleistocene †sabre-tooth "Tiger," †*Smilodon californicus. p 4*, fourth upper premolar, sectorial. (From Matthew.)

there are really two distinct problems involved here. Biting, in the ordinary sense of the word, was practically impossible, for entrance into the mouth was barred by the tusks and, it is generally agreed, the animal must have "struck" with his sabres as a snake "strikes" with his fangs. So far as the Pleistocene and Pliocene genera of the subfamily are concerned, it is not necessary to suppose that the lower jaw was so far dropped in an attack as to clear the points of the tusks, for, when the mouth was closed, the canines projected several inches below the lower jaw, enough to inflict frightful wounds, though, no doubt, open-mouthed blows were also struck. This conclusion, at first sight, seems incredible, yet it is the one at which all students of the problem have arrived, for not only is it the sole imaginable explanation of the extraordinary structure of †*Smilodon*, it is even more demanded by the Oligocene †sabre-tooths, such as †*Eusmilus* and †*Hoplophoneus*, in which the great protective flanges of the mandible made it impossible to use the sabres at all, until the mouth was so widely opened, that the points were freed. Thus, there is one problem for the Pliocene and Pleistocene genera and another for those of the Oligocene.

But this inference concerning the manner in which the sabre-tusks were used, does not depend entirely upon a consideration of the tusks and jaws alone; there are many modifications of the skull and cervical vertebræ which point to the same conclusion and are unintelligible on any other hypothesis. The glenoid cavity is brought down to a level far below that seen in the true cats, which adds greatly to the degree of depression which was possible for the mandible, and the angle of the lower jaw is everted, so as not to interfere with the post-glenoid process at the extreme point of depression. The united post-tympanic and mastoid processes form great, rugose pedicles, unlike anything seen in the true cats, which served for the attachment of the *sterno-cleido-mastoideus* muscles, and these evidently were larger and more powerful than in the Felinæ or †Nimravinæ. Contraction of these muscles brings the head down and it was chiefly they that delivered the stabbing blow.

The lower jaw bears out the same conclusion; as biting played a very subordinate part, it is not surprising to find that the mandible is weak and that the coronoid process is greatly reduced; this, in turn, implies that the temporal muscle, which is attached to the coronoid, was more or less atrophied and the masseter was the principal muscle of mastication.

"Sabre-teeth as weapons of offence and defence have been evolved on occasion in other mammals, but nowhere as in the culminating stage of the †smilodont cats do we find their use enhanced by the presence of so many coordinated structures. This remarkable combination of characters obviously permitted a unique dental mechanism to function with superb effectiveness. In the action of the several parts of the dentition as here surmised, the lower jaw seemingly played a less important rôle" (Merriam and Stock).

The stabbing hypothesis is strongly supported by the remarkable skull of †*Nimravus bumpensis* figured on page 617.

As in all the known members of the subfamily, the chin is flat, or slightly concave, and is demarcated from the buccal side of the jaw by a distinct angulation and, at this point, there is a small flange on the ventral side of each ramus; it is hardly more than vestigial and can have been of little use in protecting the sabres, which project far below it. Compared with the great flanges of the White River genera, †*Hoplophoneus* and †*Eusmilus*, those of †*Smilodon* seem absurdly inadequate.

The neck is heavy and the structure of the cervical vertebræ is such as to suggest that the great muscles which moved the head were uncommonly powerful, which fact is an additional support of the stabbing hypothesis. The back and loins are massive, relatively heavier than in the Tiger, but the tail is as short as in the Lynx. No other known cat, at all comparable in size, has so short a tail. The limbs are rather short proportionally and the anterior pair are much heavier than the posterior; when compared with the fore-legs of a Lion or a Tiger, those of the †Sabre-tooth are seen to be much more massive and give evidence of tremendous muscular power. The disproportion between fore- and hind-legs strongly suggests that in gait and habits †*Smilodon* must have been very different from the great cats of to-day and had a different manner of seizing and killing their prey. They probably were not swift runners, but made up in power what they lacked in speed. One may picture a huge †Sabretooth lying in wait near a water-hole, or in ambush by a forest trail and, when a victim has come within reach, striking it down in one immense leap, holding it on the ground with the great fore-paws and repeatedly stabbing it with the curved sabres. There are features of the hard palate, which, as Merriam and Stock suggest, intimate blood-drinking habits.

The humerus usually, but not always, lacks the epicondylar foramen, which almost all other cats retain.

Among the several thousand Carnivora which the Los Angeles Museum has reclaimed from the tar-pits of Rancho La Brea, by far the greatest numbers are of the †Dire Wolf and the †Sabre-tooth "Tiger." As already mentioned, this great preponderance was not improbably due to inferior intelligence in failing to avoid the deadly traps. There is much evidence among these bones that the †Dire Wolf and the "†Tiger" were savage fighters among themselves, for the bones show frequent tooth-marks which are so far healed, as to prove that they were made in the lifetime of the sufferer. (See Fig. 48, p. 60.) Many broken and reunited limb-bones are eloquent witnesses of infection and inflammation of the wounds, with deposits of bone, or exostoses. In addition, †*Smilodon* was frequently subject to the inflammatory disease, known in Man as *spondylitis deformans*, in which two or more lumbar vertebræ are co-ossified and bone is deposited in the muscles of the loins, which are thus rendered inflexible. Such a disease must have handicapped and crippled the victims of it, but they evidently lived for some time in that condition and, somehow or other, they obtained food.

†*Smilodon* has never been found in the Eastern Hemisphere, where, to all appearances, the †sabre-tooth line died out before the end of the Pliocene; this culminating genus of the subfamily seems to have been developed in North America from Pliocene ancestors which, themselves, were immigrants from Asia. The Pliocene forerunner of †*Smilodon*, if not its direct ancestor, is †*Heterofelis*, which, in all probability, should be referred to one of the Old World genera, but the nomenclature of those genera is in such a state of confusion that, for the present at least, it is better to keep a separate name. †*Heterofelis* differs merely in details from †*Smilodon;* for instance, in having a much higher occiput, with nearly parallel sides and rounded top. The flanges of the lower jaw are very small, no larger than in the Pleistocene genus. So far as the skull is concerned, †*Heterofelis* might very well be the direct ancestor of †*Smilodon*, but the limb- and foot-bones of the former render this unlikely. †*Heterofelis* had legs so much shorter and more slender than those of †*Smilodon* and fore- and hind-limbs were so equally developed, that the descent of the latter from the known species of †*Heterofelis*, †*H. catocopis*, does not seem probable. However, so little is known of the modes of evolutionary change, that no one can say such development is impossible. It is rather to be expected that a species with sturdier limbs will eventually be discovered and prove to be the ancestor sought for.

No member of the †machairodont subfamily has ever been found in the American Miocene and it looks very much as though that line had died out here at the end of the John Day stage and had been re-established by immigration in the Pliocene. At all events, it seems most improbable that †*Heterofelis* and †*Smilodon* could have been derived from any of the genera of the American Oligocene, with the possible exception of †*Dinictis*, but between the latter and the Pliocene genus there is such a long hiatus in time, that positive statements become inadmissible. The subfamily continued to thrive in Europe and Asia through the Miocene and Pliocene epochs. Once re-established in North America, it persisted longer in the Western than in the Eastern Hemisphere and in the Pleistocene it was one of the most conspicuous elements in the mammalian faunas of North and South America.

Before the Miocene hiatus, the North American Oligocene was rich in †sabre-tooth cats and at least two genera continued through

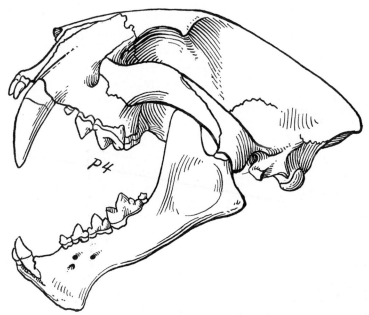

FIG. 376. — Skull of †*Dinictis squalidens*, White River. *p 4*, fourth upper premolar, sectorial. (From Matthew.)

the John Day and White River, possibly with ancestors in the Duchesne. These genera represent two very distinct tribes, one with a short-lived side-branch, which, as will be seen, presents some difficult geographical problems.

The first of the genera to be noted ended in the John Day in the relatively very large species †*Dinictis platycopis*, sometimes referred to a separate genus (†*Pogonodon*), which rivalled the modern Puma in size of skull, but the smaller White River species are far better known, as they are represented by several entire skeletons. The two skeletons especially made use of for the purposes of this study are †*D. felina* in the collection of the State School of Mines, Rapid City, South Dakota, and †*D. squalidens* in the Museum of Comparative Zoölogy at Harvard University. These skeletons, together with many additional skulls, give very full information concerning the most primitive of all known cats, which help to bridge the gap between the Æluroidea and other fissiped families. Because of the much more complete material, it will be convenient to deal first with the White River animals. No species of this genus has been found in the Chadron substage and it appears unheralded in the Brulé, no doubt by immigration. In †*Dinictis* the number of teeth, though much diminished, is greater than in any other known cat, with the exception of the John Day †*Archælurus;* the formula is: $i\frac{3}{3}$, $c\frac{1}{1}$, $p\frac{3}{3}$, $m\frac{1}{2} \times 2 = 34$. The upper canine is a thin, recurved sabre, elongate, yet shorter than in the other †sabre-tooth genera, and the lower canine is much smaller, but retains something of its original size and function and has not become incisiform. The upper sectorial is much like that of the dogs and had a rather large inner cusp and the cutting blade is without the antero-external accessory cusp which almost all other cats possess. The lower sectorial is decidedly more feline in form, but retains vestiges of a more primitive condition; there is a remnant of the heel and also of the internal cusp, but the latter is variable and is sometimes present on one side of the jaw and not on the other, a sign that it was on the point of disappearance. The single upper molar is like that of the dogs in pattern, but is greatly reduced in size and is not overlapped, or concealed in side-view by the sectorial. No other American †sabre-tooth has so primitive a dentition as this and, except for the canines and the lower sectorial, it might almost as well belong to a dog or a musteline.

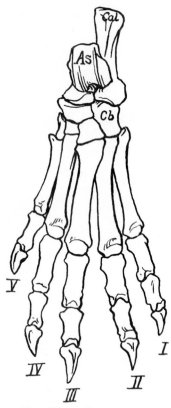

Fig. 377. — Left pes of †*Dinictis felina. Cal*, calcaneum. *As*, astragalus. *Cb*, cuboid. (Princeton Univ. Mus.)

The skull, while unmistakably cat-like, has a peculiar shape and displays many primitive features which other cats have lost and which are more cynoid than æluroid. In particular, the skull is more elongate, less bullet-like than in the modern genus *Felis*. When placed, with mouth closed and lower jaw horizontal, the upper profile of the face rises to the forehead, from which point that of the cranium descends to the occiput, the two lines meeting at the highest point in an obtuse angle. The very characteristic structure of the cranial basis has little that suggests relationship to the Felinæ. The auditory bullæ have not been found and either were not ossified, or were always detached and lost in fossilization, which does not seem very probable. The paroccipital process which, in the Felinæ, embraces

FIG. 378. — Primitive †sabre-tooth, †*Dinictis felina*, Oligocene, White River stage. (Restored from partial skeletons in Amer. Mus. Nat. Hist. and Princeton Univ. Mus.)

the hinder side of the bulla, is directed backward and could not have touched it. The highly characteristic mastoid pedicle, found only in the †machairodont subfamily, is variable in †*Dinictis*, one species showing little sign of it, while in the others, it is well developed.

In two significant respects the cranial foramina are different from those of the true cats: (1) an alisphenoid canal for the transmission of the internal carotid artery, is present, as in the dogs; (2) the condylar foramen is well separated from the *foramen lacerum posterius*, not enclosed in it; in all existing æluroids the condylar foramen is concealed in the posterior lacerated foramen. The flanges of the lower jaw are much smaller than in the other Oligocene genera, but more prominent than in those of the Pliocene and Pleistocene forms.

The body and tail are long, the limbs slender and relatively short and the feet are weak. Comparative measurements of †*Dinictis* and a modern cat, such as the Leopard (*Felis pardus*) bring out clearly the proportionally small size of the feet. The five digits are arranged in spreading fashion and the claws were imperfectly retractile; the ungual phalanges have very small bony hoods in the manus, and none in the pes, which were reflected over the base of the

FIG. 379. — White River †sabre-tooth "tiger," †*Hoplophoneus primœvus,* restored from a skeleton in Amer. Mus. Nat. Hist. †Oreodonts, †*Merycoidodon,* in the background.

horny claw. These hoods are well-nigh universal among the cats, in different degrees of development.

Altogether, †*Dinictis* is an exceedingly primitive cat and, though distinctly a †machairodont, it is not very far removed from the ancestor common to the three subfamilies of the †Felidæ. While it may possibly have descended from some Duchesne River type, it was much more probably a migrant from Asia, which arrived after the close of the Chadron.

The second series of the Oligocene †sabre-tooths is the John Day and White River †*Hoplophoneus,* which was likewise an immigrant from the Old World, coming in before †*Dinictis,* for two species of it occur in the Chadron substage. †*Hoplophoneus* is, in all respects, much more advanced and specialized than †*Dinictis* and is especially common in the White River beds, from which several beautifully preserved skeletons have been obtained and, thus, the entire dental and skeletal structure is known. †*Hoplophoneus* looks like a very much smaller †*Smilodon*, but there is only a general resemblance, for the White River genus is far more primitive and yet has certain premature specializations, which remove it from the possible ancestry of the Pleistocene †machairodonts. Several distinct species of the genus are found at different levels in the White River beds and these vary greatly in size and proportions; the largest equalled a short-legged Puma and the smallest was somewhat inferior to the "Bob Cat" (*Lynx rufus*).

The number of teeth is variable, for the foremost premolar in each jaw is minute and often absent. The dental formula is: $i \frac{3}{3}$, $c \frac{1}{1}$, $p \frac{3-2}{3-2}$, $m \frac{1}{1} \times 2 = 28$ or 32. The incisors are sharp-pointed and recurved; the upper canine is a long, broad, thin and curved sabre, with finely serrate edges, much longer and more curved than in †*Dinictis* and relatively thinner. The premolars are much as in the true cats and the upper sectorial is distinctly more feline than is that of †*Dinictis;* the anterio-external cusp, not present in the latter, is extremely small and the internal cusp is even smaller. In fact, this tooth is intermediate in character between †*Dinictis* and *Felis*. The lower sectorial ($m_{\overline{1}}$) is almost completely cat-like and the shearing blade consists of two thin, trenchant cusps, one behind the other in close approximation, their cutting edges meeting at right angles. Two vestiges, the heel and the inner cusp, remain as a connecting link between the highly specialized carnassial of the cats and the more generalized one of the dogs.

The skull of †*Hoplophoneus* is cat-like, but decidedly more elongate and less rounded than in *Felis*. Within the genus there are two groups of species, one with longer face, the other with shorter, a difference determined by the development of the sabre and the necessity of making room for it. The base of the cranium and its foramina are much the same as in †*Dinictis* and, therefore, with significant differences from the Felinæ. The auditory bulla appears to have been unossified, except for the tympanic, in most individuals, but sometimes the bulla is of extremely thin, papery bone and is widely removed from paroccipital and mastoid processes. The mastoid pedicle, though subject to much variation in size, is larger and more rugose and more conspicuous than in †*Dinictis*.

The lower jaw is remarkable for the small size of the coronoid process and the great development of the anterior flanges, which protect the sabre-tusks. These flanges project downward so far, that, when the mouth is closed, the points of the canines do not extend below them.   The animal could have made no use of the

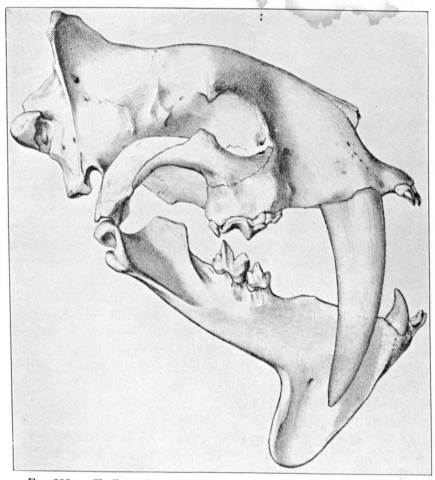

Fig. 380. — Skull, right side, of most advanced Oligocene †sabre-tooth, †*Eusmilus sicarius*, White River stage. (Princeton Univ. Mus.; from Scott and Jepsen.)

sabres, unless the jaws were so widely opened as to free the points for the downward stroke.

The neck of †*Hoplophoneus* is rather short, but the trunk is long; the massive lumbar vertebræ suggest that the loins were very powerful; the tail is unusually long, equalling that of the Leopard in relative length and surpassing it in thickness.   The limbs are short and the five-toed feet small; the limb-bones are much stouter than in †*Dinictis*, with far more prominent crests for muscular attachment.   Especially is this true of the largest species, †*Hoplophoneus occidentalis*, in which the bones are considerably heavier than in a full-grown Leopard. The ungual phalanges of the fore-feet have much more complete bony hoods than in †*Dinictis*, but not more than half as long as in *Felis*; in the hind-feet the hoods are hardly more than incipient.

A side-branch of the †*Hoplophoneus* stem is that of †*Eusmilus*, which last appeared in the upper part of the White River beds. In †*Eusmilus* the peculiarities of †*Hoplophoneus* are carried to their utmost extreme and, except in bodily stature, this Oligocene †sabre-tooth is more highly specialized than the great Pleistocene †*Smilodon* itself. The upper Brulé species, †*E. dakotensis*, is much the largest of the White River carnivores, equalling the Leopard in size. The lower Brulé, †*E. sicarius*, is considerably smaller, but is somewhat more completely known. In this genus the dentition is reduced to its lowest terms, as appears from the formula: $i\frac{3}{3-2}$, $c\frac{1}{1}$, $p\frac{2}{1}$, $m\frac{1}{1} \times 2 = 24$ or 26. Usually, there are but two lower incisors; the upper canines are relatively enormous, even more so than in †*Hoplophoneus*, while the lower canines are reduced to incisiform proportions. The third upper premolar and the single molar are so small that they can have been of little use and, to all intents and purposes, the sectorial ($p\frac{4}{}$) is the only cheek-tooth. The sectorial is a large, shearing blade of two principal cusps and a small, anterior, accessory one, while the internal cusp has almost disappeared. In the lower jaw there is a single three-cusped premolar and the sectorial molar is thoroughly cat-like, without heel or inner cusp.

The skull is that of †*Hoplophoneus* with its peculiarities exaggerated and having the relatively long face that certain species of that genus display. The great mastoid pedicle is even larger and the glenoid cavity is carried down by a projection of the zygomatic arch below the level of the teeth. These features, as above noted, are in proportion to the size of the sabres. The flanges of the lower jaw are immensely developed and are longer than in any other †machairodont.

In the lower White River (Chadron substage) occur two large species of †*Hoplophoneus*, †*H. mentalis* and †*H. oharrai*, either one of which might very well be the ancestor of †*Eusmilus*, and this offers a difficult problem, for the latter is a European genus and was first discovered and named in France. It may have originated in North America and spread into Asia and thence to Europe, or it may be a migrant to America and therefore, have nothing to do with the Chadron species of †*Hoplophoneus*, or it may have originated independently in the two continents. As no instance is known of such a dual origin of a mammalian genus, this third alternative is very much the least probable. If the French species, †*E. bidentatus* were more fully known, it might prove necessary to assign the American species to another genus.

Subfamily c. †*Nimravinæ. False* †*Sabre-tooths.* — This group is well characterized by the name which Cope gave it of the "False †Sabre-

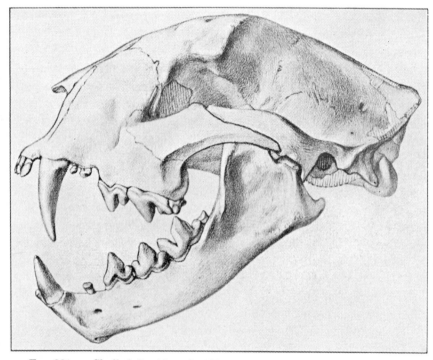

Fig. 381. — Skull, left side, of †*Nimravus bumpensis*, a false †sabre-tooth, upper White River stage. (Mus. State Sch. Mines, S. D.; from Scott and Jepsen.)

tooths," for they differ from both of the other subfamilies of the Felidæ and their affinities to those subfamilies are exceedingly difficult to understand, so complex are the cross-relationships of likenesses and differences, and the picture is obscured by the migrations back and forth between the Eastern and the Western Hemispheres. In North America the †nimravines extended back from the Pliocene to the middle Oligocene, while in Europe they first appeared in the lower Oligocene, perhaps even in the upper Eocene and in both continents they made an unheralded appearance, for no ancestry of them has been found.

It is difficult to frame a definition of the subfamily that will cover both the earlier and the later members of the group, for, in the course of their history, they underwent significant changes. The last of the genera is †*Metailurus*, late Pliocene to middle Miocene of China and the United States. This is a very cat-like animal and has generally been included in the Felinæ, or true cats, but it agrees better with the †Nimravinæ. The upper canines, though no longer than in *Felis*, are much thinner and more blade-like, and the lower

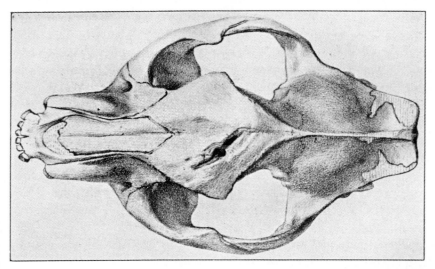

Fig. 382. — Top view of same skull of †*Nimravus bumpensis* as Fig. 381 showing partly healed wound, probably inflicted by sabre of †*Eusmilus*. (From Scott and Jepsen.)

jaw is feline in shape, the chin curving into the side without angulation or other definite boundary. On the other hand, the cranial basis is †nimravine, the auditory bullæ not touching the paroccipital or mastoid processes. The American species of †*Metailurus*, some of which have been incorrectly referred to the French †*Pseudælurus*, are manifestly immigrants from Asia.

No cats of any description have been found in the Harrison, upper or lower, and, though this absence may be deceptive, it is in the strongest possible contrast to the Oligocene, in which †machairodonts and false †sabre-tooths are relatively abundant. In the Gering occur the latest examples of †*Nimravus*, which made its first American appearance in the upper White River and is most common in the John Day. This genus has some characters in common with the †machairodonts and shares others with the true cats, while, in some respects, it differs from both. It first appeared in the lower Oligocene (or upper Eocene?) of France, so that it was an immigrant in North America and probably in Europe also, for nothing more ancient in that continent is known which could have given rise to it. It made an unheralded arrival there, just as it subsequently did here. The dental formula is: $i\,\frac{3}{3}, c\,\frac{1}{1}, p\,\frac{3-4}{2-3}, m\,\frac{1}{2} \times 2 = 32$ or 36. The upper canine is shorter and the lower longer than in any known †machairodont. The superior one is somewhat longer than in the Felinæ and, in cross-section, is intermediate between the latter and the †sabre-tooths, for it is straight and thicker than in the latter and thinner than in the former and has finely serrate edges. The upper sectorial ($p\,\underline{4}$) is very dog-like and resembles that of †Dinictis in having only a two-cusped exterior trenchant blade, without anterior basal cusp, but with small inner cusp. The single upper molar ($m\,\underline{1}$) differs from that of true cats and †machairodonts in being triangular, not a transverse ridge. The lower sectorial ($m\,\overline{1}$) is more primitive than in any of the Oligocene †sabre-tooths in retaining a well-formed trenchant heel, which is much more reduced in †Dinictis and †Hoplophoneus, and the two cusps of the trenchant blade are separated by a deep notch. On the other hand, the vestigial internal cusp, which persists in the two †machairodonts just mentioned, has altogether disappeared.

The functional premolars, both upper and lower, are notably large and high, much more so than in †Hoplophoneus.

†Nimravus is intermediate in the character of the skull between the †machairodonts and the true cats, agreeing with the latter in having no mastoid pedicle and no flanges on the lower jaw and with the former in the cranial foramina, in the shape and relations of the auditory bullæ and in the angles between the chin and the outer sides of the mandible.

The type-specimen of †Nimravus bumpensis, which belongs to the museum of the State School of Mines, Rapid City, South Dakota, is one of fascinating interest. In the left frontal region of the skull is a frightful wound, that was unquestionably inflicted in the lifetime of the victim, which must have survived the injury for a considerable time (Fig. 382). Deposition of new bone along the edges of the gash shows that progress in the healing of the wound had been made before the animal's death. There is no sign of infection, or inflammation and, no doubt, the wound was quite healed externally.

Contemporary with †Nimravus in the upper White River was the formidable †Eusmilus and, almost certainly, it was a stabbing blow from one of the sabres of that terrible beast that caused the

Fig. 383. — Combat between †*Nimravus*, "false †sabre-tooth," and †*Eusmilus*, a true †sabre-tooth, of White River times, over the carcass of †*Merycoidodon*. Other †oreodonts in background. See also Fig. 382.

wound, which is of the size proper to such a weapon. It is extraordinarily interesting to find this confirmation of the "stabbing hypothesis" concerning the manner in which the †machairodont sabres were used. If the wound was actually inflicted by †*Eusmilus*, and there is no other imaginable explanation of it, then the mouth of the latter must necessarily have been opened so far that the points of the great canines were cleared. The wound, it should be noted, penetrated the frontal sinus, and may have touched the left olfactory bulb, but did not reach the brain proper.

The White River species of †*Nimravus* is smaller than those of the John Day and differs in such a number of details, notably in having one more premolar in each jaw, as to be referable to a distinct species. Evidently, this species was an immigrant from the Old World, where the genus had existed since the lower Oligocene, at least.

Another John Day genus, †*Archælurus*, is so closely allied to †*Nimravus* that, by some authorities the two are merged into one, but this union obscures the fact that the former is in some respects the most primitive of all known cats. The upper canine is even shorter than in †*Nimravus* and has smooth, not serrate edges; there is an additional premolar in each jaw, giving the formula, $p \frac{4}{3}$, but not much importance can be attached to this fact, for $p \frac{1}{}$, $\frac{2}{}$ and $\frac{}{2}$ are so very small. The other premolars are, as in †*Nimravus*, large, high and effective teeth, decidedly different from those of the †machairodonts. The most important difference from †*Nimravus* and, indeed, from all other known Felidæ, is in the structure of the lower sectorial ($m \frac{}{1}$). In one respect, this tooth shows advanced specialization and that is the complete disappearance of the internal cusp, but, otherwise, the carnassial is exceedingly primitive. The anterior cusp of the trenchant blade is thin and sharp-edged, but is separated from the posterior cusp by a broad, deep notch, much broader than in †*Nimravus*, and that posterior cusp is not a cutting blade, but is high, conical and pointed; there is a small trenchant heel. This genus has not been found in the White River and must, to all appearances, have been an immigrant, for nothing is known in this country from which it could have been derived. On the other hand, it has not been found in the Old World, but such negative facts have no great weight.

Enough of the limb- and foot-bones of both of these John Day genera has been recovered to show that these animals must have had very different proportions from the true †machairodonts of the time; the limbs are long and slender and there are only four digits in the hind-foot, of which the median pair are elongate and the lateral pair shortened, producing a symmetry which is much more like that of the dogs than that of the cats and is strongly indicative of cursorial habits. The claws seem to have been only partially retractile. The proportions of body, limbs and feet are suggestively like those of the Cheeta, or Hunting Leopard of India (*Cynælurus jubatus*), the technical name of which means "the Spotted Dog-cat," in allusion to the dog-like limbs and feet.

A third John Day genus of this group is the remarkable †*Dinælurus*, which is the largest, most specialized and most feline of the three. The canines are thicker and more cat-like than in †*Nimravus*, the face greatly shortened and the zygomatic arches immensely expanded. These animals must have been extremely bullet-headed.

In the upper Oligocene and lowest Miocene, these cursorial cats quite displaced the leaping †machairodonts, such as †*Hoplophoneus* and †*Eusmilus*, at a time when, as noted above, there was such an abundance and variety of dogs. Dr. J. C. Merriam writes: "When the canines are not developed to the dagger-like form for stabbing, the premolar teeth serve a more definite purpose in the destruction of prey and would be less subject to reduction. The view suggested above finds support in that such evidence as we have indicates that during the deposition of the middle John Day beds this region [i.e. eastern Oregon] was in the main a country of open plains, offering advantages to running types of carnivores, and that during this period the †*Archælurus*-†*Nimravus* type of feline was by far the most common form."

ORIGIN OF THE FELIDÆ

This is a very obscure and baffling problem, for which no solution can, at present, be given, for the available evidence is not only incomplete, it also seems to be contradictory, but that unfortunate aspect of the question can only be seeming and is due to our ignorance of the laws of evolution. Two highly distinguished palæontologists, who died but a few years ago, Dr. Max Schlosser, of Munich, and Professor W. D. Matthew of the University of California, have propounded answers to this riddle of the Sphinx, which have nothing in common. Schlosser was so impressed by the isolated position of the cats, that he thought they must have arisen independently, and separately from all other fissipeds, from primitive †Creodonta and denied any relationship with the Viverridæ, a relationship which is accepted by almost all other naturalists. Matthew, who did not take the Viverridæ into account, held that the true cats (Felinæ) were derived from such primitive †sabre-tooths as †Dinictis through the false †sabre-tooths, †Nimravus and †Pseudælurus, to Felis of the Pliocene.

Even if it were germane to the purposes of this book to enter into a discussion of these views, space would be lacking for any adequate presentation of them. I can merely regret my inability to accept either of these opinions and to state the tentative conclusion at which I have arrived. It is probable, (1) that all the Fissipedia have a common origin and are therefore a "natural" group; (2) that the Felidæ and Viverridæ are closely related, the early viverrines giving rise to the cats. The Fossa, of Madagascar (Cryptoprocta ferox) is a persistent transitional form between the two families. This transitional creature is a confirmation of the inference, reached on other grounds, that the cats arose in Africa, whence they gradually spread to the northern continents, arriving in Europe considerably before reaching North America. This is a close parallel with the history of the elephants, which originated in Africa and extended to America by way of Europe and Asia. Almost from the beginning of their separate existence, the cats divided into three subfamilies, the †machairodonts, the false †sabre-tooths and the true cats. The two former groups reached Europe in the early Oligocene, or late Eocene; the †machairodonts arrived in North America in the early middle Oligocene, followed somewhat later by the †nimravines. In France, the true cats came in, unheralded, in the middle Miocene and in North America in the lower Pliocene.

The hypothesis here sketched is, by no means, free from difficulties, for the exposition of which there is no space; it can only be said that, in the writer's judgment, it best explains the facts of observation.

Superfamily III. †Miacoidea [1]

It has long been recognized that the †Creodonta, the primitive flesh-eaters of the Paleocene and Eocene, would fall naturally into two groups, one aberrant and wholly extinct, the other probably ancestral to most, if not all, of the Fissipedia. Dr. Matthew proposed to call these groups †Creodonta Inadaptiva and †Creodonta Adaptiva, respectively. Inasmuch as the system of genetic classification has been followed throughout this book, it is more logical and consistent to transfer the †Creodonta Adaptiva to the Fissipedia, in which it

[1] T. de Chardin's term is used, though the status of †Miacis is doubtful.

will form a third superfamily which de Chardin has called †Miacoidæ. The group cannot be included in any other family, because it is believed to be, directly or indirectly, ancestral to all the fissiped families.

The †miacoids agree with most other fissipeds and differ from the †creodonts in having a single pair of sectorial teeth, which are always the fourth upper premolar ($p\,\underline{4}$) and first lower molar ($m\,\overline{1}$), but, as carnassials, they are more primitive, less finished and effective than in the later families. The vertebræ of the lumbar and posterior dorsal regions are intermediate between †creodont and fissiped in the shape of the articulating processes, or zygapophyses, which, in the latter, are flat and, in the former semi-cylindrical and interlocking, convex and concave. In the †Creodonta the ungual phalanges have cleft tips, as in the Insectivora, a feature which is not found in the Fissipedia, but in the †Miacoidea, there is a slight, but recognizable vestige of the cleft, which has almost disappeared.

Finally, one very important characteristic should be mentioned. In all Fissipedia of the cynoid and æluroid groups, whether fossil or Recent, there is in the carpus a large, compound element, the *scapholunar*, which is made up of the co-ossified scaphoid, lunar and central. In the †Creodonta, with but one known exception, these carpals are separate, as in mammals generally. The Bridger, or middle Eocene, species of the †miacoids are, as in so many other respects, intermediate between the †creodonts and the typical fissipeds; the scaphoid and lunar are fused together, but the central remains free. In the lower Eocene and Paleocene members of this superfamily the carpus is not yet known, but it is logical to expect that, when discovered, the carpals will all prove to be separate.

So far as present knowledge extends, there is but one family in this group, though more extensive and complete material may necessitate the recognition of two or more families. The single one in use is generally called the †Miacidæ, but the law of priority, which requires that the family name shall be taken from the genus first described, or, in exceptional cases, from the one which is best known, makes it necessary to substitute the term †Uintacyonidæ, the definition of which is, for the present, the same as that of the superfamily.

Family 6. †Uintacyonidæ

Until more complete specimens shall have been obtained from the Uinta Eocene and, perhaps also, from the Duchesne River Oligo-

cene, it will not be practicable to determine when this family came
to an end, which it did, to all seeming, by merging in the Canidæ.
The Uinta genera, †*Prodaphœnus* and †*Procynodictis*, are so imperfectly known, that one cannot say whether they should be classed
with the Canidæ, or the †Uintacyonidæ; so far as they are known,
they might belong to either family. The beginnings of the †Uinta-
cyonidæ may be traced back to the Torrejon stage of the Paleocene,
but the time of their greatest abundance, diversity and relative
importance is the Bridger stage of the middle Eocene, in which some
seven or eight genera and many more species have been found and
the range in size is from a Coyote to a Weasel.

The family has not been identified in Europe; the most important
American genera are as follows:

†Uintacyonidæ

†*Uintacyon*, †*Miacis*, Mid. and low. Eoc. †*Viverravus*, †*Vulpavus*, †*Oödec-
tes*, †*Palæarctonyx*, mid. Eoc. †*Didymictis*, low. Eoc. to mid. Paleoc.

Much the best known of the Bridger genera and, indeed, of the
entire family is †*Vulpavus*, "Fox-ancestor," of which there are several
Bridger species; †*V. ovatus* and †*V. profectus* are the best known. In
this genus the full number of 44 teeth is preserved, but there is a decided tendency toward a reduction of the premolars, the first one in
each jaw being already minute, while the second lower, second and
third upper are very small. All the premolars, except the upper sectorial
($p \stackrel{4}{}$) are simple, of compressed-conical shape and sharp-pointed. The
sectorial ($p \stackrel{4}{}$) hardly deserves the name, for the posterior trenchant
blade is very small and the internal cusp is relatively large; no other
tooth in the jaw is at all like this. Of the three upper molars, the
first is much the largest and the third the smallest; the pattern is
tritubercular, with two external, conical cusps and a crescent-shaped
internal one.

The lower carnassial ($m \stackrel{}{\overline{1}}$) is of the primitive type known as
tuberculo-sectorial, in which the shearing blade is composed of a high
anterior triangle of three pointed cusps, and behind this a low, basin-
like heel; $m \stackrel{}{\overline{2}}$ has similar elements, but the anterior triangle is not
shearing and is no higher than the heel. The third lower molar is
implanted by two roots. The canines are relatively large and very
sharp-pointed and effective weapons, but the incisors, both above and
below, are conspicuously small and can have been of little use to their
possessor. The work of seizing and killing prey must have been done

almost entirely by the canines, for incisors and premolars were evidently inefficient.

The skull, in appearance and proportions, is very like that of the smaller and more primitive dogs, such as †*Pseudocynodictis*. The long cranium and short face are common to all the primitive flesh-eaters and are to be correlated with the notably small size of the teeth. The brain-case is rounded and capacious, which is in strong contrast with that of Bridger †creodonts of similar size, and the sagittal crest is low and weak. No auditory bulla has been found in connection with the skull and it seems not to have been ossified, though there was probably a tympanic ring of bone.

The bodily shape was much as in most †creodonts and many fissipeds, as well, such as the mustelines and viverrines, the neck about equalling the skull in length, trunk and tail very long, limbs and feet short. The articulations of the lumbar and posterior dorsal vertebræ are intermediate in character between †creodonts and most fissipeds, being somewhat more semi-cylindrical than in the latter, more nearly plane than in the former.

The humerus has very prominent ridges for the deltoid and supinator muscles and unusually large epicondyle and foramen. The radius has a discoidal head, almost like that of a monkey, indicating an equally free rotation of the fore-foot. The manus is intermediate in an interesting way, between †creodonts and typical fissipeds; as in the modern Carnivora generally, the scaphoid and lunar are co-ossified, but, as in the †creodonts, the central remains separate. There are five spreading digits, with complete pollex, and the ungual phalanges are thin and sharp-pointed and have only a vestige of the cleft. The femur has a remnant of the third trochanter, which is very high up on the shaft; the trochlea of the astragalus is almost flat, indicating a plantigrade gait. On the calcaneum there is no facet on which the fibula can rest, but, in one of the species (†*V. ovatus*) there is a lateral contact and a small articular surface on the external side of the calcaneum.

It does not seem possible that any of the later genera, so far as these are known, could have been derived from †*Vulpavus*, which was already more specialized in the reduction of the incisors and premolars than are most modern fissipeds, but †*Uintacyon* and †*Miacis* are very near to the common ancestry of all the Fissipedia. Not that these arose in North America, for the first generation of fissipeds, as it may be called, comprising the dogs and viverrines, was seemingly represented in North America only by the dogs, but both groups were common in the late Eocene of Europe. The mustelines migrated to America in successive waves, from the middle Oligocene to the Pleistocene, but the viverrines never came at all. Of the origin of the cats nothing is yet known, while the raccoons, bears and hyenas, which may be called the second generation, all made their first appearance at a much later time.

†*Uintacyon* and †*Miacis* are much alike and may be identical, but as the material referred to †*Miacis*, is more complete, it is here described. The teeth are present in the unreduced number of 44, though the last molar in each jaw ($m \frac{3}{3}$) is extremely small; the upper sectorial ($p \frac{4}{}$) has a small, unfinished sort of blade, with large internal cusp; in the lower sectorial ($m \frac{}{1}$) the anterior triangle is high and is composed of three, subequal, conical cusps, while the heel is low and basin-like. The upper molars have relatively high, sharp-pointed, conical cusps, somewhat as in the modern Grey Fox (*Urocyon*). The neural spines of the lumbar vertebræ are curiously rabbit-like, being short, slender and strongly inclined forward; the processes for the articulation of successive vertebræ are slightly concave and convex and thus more fissiped than †creodont in character.

The slender limbs are of unequal length, the hind legs being considerably longer than the fore. The humerus is nearly straight and has a very prominent deltoid ridge, as is also the internal epicondyle, which is perforated by the foramen for the median nerve. The trochlea is very low and has a strongly convex surface for the head of the radius. The radius is short and has a discoidal head, indicative of a very free rotation of the manus. The upper moiety of the slender shaft is rounded, but it broadens inferiorly. The ulna is likewise slender and has a short olecranon. The pelvis is very dog-like; the ilium is narrow and but slightly everted, the ischium is short, but the pubic symphysis is long. The femur is long and has an almost sessile head which is separated from the low great trochanter by a deep and narrow notch. The third trochanter is inconspicuous. The shaft is straight, slender and of cylindrical form. The tibia is nearly as long as the femur and even more slender; the articular surface for the astragalus is flat and has hardly any intercondylar tongue. The fibula is excluded from contact with the calcaneum and the ungual phalanges, in some species, at least, have no trace of a cleft at the tip.

A second and very distinct tribe of the †Uintacyonidæ is that exemplified by †*Didymictis*, which should perhaps be made into a different family, and must have been a side-branch of the same stock, primitive and yet, in some respects, prematurely specialized.

The genus is older than is any known species of †*Uintacyon*, or †*Miacis*, for it appears in the middle Paleocene (Torrejon stage) and did not pass beyond the lower Eocene, yet it was already so specialized that no later genus can be derived from it. It had lost the third molar in each jaw, above and below, giving a total of 40 teeth and the lower sectorial ($m_{\overline{1}}$) is different from that of any other carnivore. The anterior triangle is extraordinarily high and the trenchant blade is imperfectly developed; the outer cusp of the triangle is much higher than the two internal ones, which are of equal size; the basin-like heel is very low.

The skeleton, so far as it is known, agrees with that of †*Uintacyon* except in the structure of the hind-foot. The astragalus is perforated by a vascular canal, a very primitive feature, and the trochlea for the tibia has but a shallow groove. The calcaneum is short and stout and has a prominent, convex facet, upon which the fibula rests. It is unexampled, to find within the limits of the same family, genera which have the fibulo-calcaneal articulation and other genera in which the fibula is excluded from the calcaneum. (The *lateral* contact seen in †*Vulpavus* is not a real exception.) Such a difference is usually one of *ordinal* significance, as, for example, between artiodactyls and perissodactyls, and should, perhaps, separate †*Didymictis* from †*Uintacyon*, †*Vulpavus*, etc., in a different family. On the other hand, in all other respects the genera agree.

The metatarsus consists of five unreduced elements, which have a mesaxonic symmetry. The ungual phalanges are all long, and narrow, but not very thin, pointed, but not sharp; the distal ends are entire, but slight vestiges of the clefts may be seen.

SOUTH AMERICAN FISSIPEDIA

The history of the land Carnivora in South America is a comparatively brief one, for the Neotropical Region has no autochthonous carnivores in the sense of genera derived from a long series of native forms. Peculiar genera, there are, but these all descended from immigrants, for, before the Pliocene, South America had no Fissipedia of any kind, their place having been taken by predaceous marsupials. Recent Neotropical Fissipedia are enumerated in Chapter VII and there is no need to repeat the list here. Little can yet be done to trace the development of the genera which are now peculiar to the Neotropical Region since the migration of their ancestors from North America. Most of the modern genera with both existing and extinct species, have been found in the Pleistocene. For example, a gigantic

Raccoon (*Procyon* †*ursinus*) as large as a bear, has been found in the Brazilian caverns. The †sabre-tooth cats, †*Smilodon* and the †short-faced bears, †*Arctotherium*, were shared with North America. Most of the immigration of Fissipedia from the north must have taken place early in the Pliocene, yet very few fossils of these animals are known before the Pleistocene, a bear, a raccoon and a dog are the only ones yet reported and the supposed bear is very doubtful.

Evolution of the Fissipedia

The sketch of fissiped history given above is manifestly incomplete, even more so than the story of the ungulate orders told in the foregoing chapters, yet the broad outlines of an ordered development emerge from the confused mass of fragmentary detail. In each family may be noted the advance of specialization and adaptation to a narrower range of habits and, very generally also, to a gradual increase in size, though several families, such as the existing mustelines, viverrines and raccoons, are all small. Except the mustelines, all of the families attained the greatest size of individuals in the Pleistocene, when the †arctotheres, the †gigantic raccoons, the †dire wolves, the California "†Lion," the †Sabre-tooth "Tiger" (†*Smilodon*) and the †Cave Lion (*Felis* †*spelæa*), †Cave Hyena (*Hyæna* †*spelæa*) and †Cave Bear (*Ursus* †*spelæus*) of Europe were the giants of their respective tribes; the huge Brown Bear of Alaska (*Ursus middendorfi*) is the only living fissiped worthy to take rank in such an assemblage.

The Mustelidæ are exceptional in that their gigantic form (†*Megalictis*) was not Pleistocene, but lower Miocene.

Speaking generally, the teeth in most families gradually diminished in number and enlarged in size and were either complicated by the addition of new elements, as in the bears, raccoons and pandas, or simplified by the loss of elements, as in the cats and in certain viverrines and mustelines. The lower carnassial ($m_{\overline{1}}$) of the cats has had its cusps reduced from five to two, but the two remaining cusps are so shaped and enlarged, as to make a feline sectorial the most efficient of shearing blades. With the probable exception of the Long-eared Wolf (*Otocyon*), in none of the Fissipedia were teeth ever added to the primitive number of 44.

In the course of time the brain-case became more capacious and the brain increased in size and in the number and sinuosity of the convolutions of the cerebral cortex. This is true of all the families, but the increased size and complexity of the brain were carried farther in some groups than in others. The primæval fissiped skull had an elongate cranium of small capacity, and a short face; in most of the families the face was still further shortened, as in the mustelines and especially in the cats which, of all Carnivora, have the shortest and roundest heads. In other families, notably in the dogs, the face and jaws were elongated.

The primitive bodily form, as represented by the †Uintacyonidæ of the Eocene, is a long, slender trunk, short neck and very long tail, short legs and feet, and these proportions have been retained in most viverrines and mustelines and in certain of the raccoon family, but in others they have been greatly modified and the tail has usually undergone reduction in length, the extreme of which is seen in the hyenas, bears and lynxes. On the other hand, in most cats and viverrines and some raccoons, the tail remains very long.

In most families the legs have grown longer, the feet larger and more powerful. There has been little reduction of digits and no fissiped has less than four in each foot. In Recent dogs and cats there are five digits in the manus, though the pollex is a useless dew-claw, and four in the pes, as the hallux has been lost. The hyenas have four toes in front and behind, as has one genus of mustelines; all other existing fissipeds have five digits in each foot.

The dogs have developed into cursorial types; the hyenas also have limbs and feet of similar character. The cats are leapers, springing upon their prey; in them the claws have acquired the most perfect degree of retractility and are terrible weapons, as are, in a different way, the extremely long, fixed claws of the bears.

As the various families of fissipeds are traced back in time, the differences between them become less and less marked, and they were evidently converging toward a common ancestry, and that ancestry, so far as can be judged at present, is exemplified by the †Uintacyonidæ of the Eocene.

NOTE: The important paper on the genus †Cynarctus by Mr. Paul McGrew was, unfortunately, received too late for incorporation in this chapter. It adds materially to our knowledge of the Procyonidæ. The author's abstract is: "The genus Cynarctus, represented by three Miocene and one lower Pliocene species, which was formerly supposed to be intermediate between the dogs and the bears, is proved by new finds of C. acridens to be a relatively large dog-like raccoon, an aberrant branch of the Procyonidæ." (Journ. Paleont., Vol. II, No. 5, p. 449, July, 1937.)

CHAPTER XXII

HISTORY OF THE CARNIVORA

II. †CREODONTA

The †creodonts are a group of primitive flesh-eaters that have long been extinct, the recorded history of which ran, in North America, from the` Paleocene into the middle Oligocene and, in Europe, a few species persisted into the Miocene. A considerable number of genera and all of the recognized families are common to the Old World and the New and there was much intermigration back and forth between the continents.

The relationship between the †Creodonta and the other suborders of the Carnivora is a remote one and, with the †Uintacyonidæ removed, there would seem to be no compelling reason for including them all in the same order, but the established custom is here followed.

The †Creodonta form an exceedingly varied assemblage, in size, in structure and in inferred habits, though they are less diversified in these respects than the Fissipedia, which have a vastly longer history in time. So far as can be judged from teeth and skeleton, they had insectivorous, carnivorous and omnivorous members and all seem to have been terrestrial in habit. There is no obvious reason to think that any †creodont was aquatic, like otters, or fossorial, like badgers, or arboreal, like raccoons and kinkajous; cursorial and leaping types, there evidently were, more or less like dogs and cats, carrion-feeders like hyenas, and small, swift killers, like weasels, martens and civets. But these likenesses are in habits only and imply no relationship other than a common ancestry in early Paleocene or even in late Cretaceous times; assuredly, no fissiped was derived from any known †creodont, as that group is here limited by the removal of the †Uintacyonidæ, but in the period when that family contained the sole representatives of the fissipeds, the †creodonts took the place, more or less successfully, that the carnivores are filling in the modern world.

In size, the †Creodonta ranged from little creatures no larger than weasels, to the colossal †*Andrewsarchus* of the Eocene of Mongolia, which is, by far, the largest predaceous mammal ever dis-

covered. Beside this monster a Kadiak Bear would look like a puppy,
and there were other Mongolian †creodonts only less enormous.
Such is the variety in the suborder, that few statements can be made
of all the genera without qualification. Hardly a dozen genera are
known from skeletons and several more from skulls, but most of them
are represented only by jaws and teeth, though limb and foot-bones
give a conception of the structure of a considerable number.

As a rule, the dentition is complete and has the formula: $i\frac{3}{3}$, $c\frac{1}{1}$,
$p\frac{4}{4}$, $m\frac{3}{3} \times 2 = 44$, but the first premolar or the last molar may be
lost. The canines are always stout, sharp and well developed as
weapons and there are either no sectorial teeth, or else more than
one pair, a difference which separates the families into two groups:
(1) the †Hyænodontidæ and †Oxyænidæ have two or more pairs
of trenchant carnassial teeth; (2) the †Arctocyonidæ and †Oxyclæ-
nidæ have tuberculated, crushing teeth; (3) the †Mesonychidæ are
intermediate, having teeth which are trenchant in form, though not
in function, as is inferred from the mode of wear.

In the Fissipedia the first is the largest of the lower molars, but
in the †Creodonta it is usually the smallest. The premolars are simple,
compressed-conical teeth and the molars, notwithstanding their
great variety of form, may be derived from a common plan; the
upper molars are primitively tritubercular, with one internal and
two external cusps, and the lower ones are "tuberculo-sectorial,"
that is to say, are composed of an elevated anterior triangle of three
cusps, which form a shearing blade of varying degrees of efficiency,
and a low heel of two cusps.

The skull is almost always very large proportionally and the
cranium, though long, is of such small brain-capacity, that the
occipital and sagittal crests are very high and the latter is elongate
also. The comparison of a small †creodont, such as †Sinopa, of the
Bridger Eocene, and its contemporary primitive fissiped, †Vulpavus,
is interesting and instructive, as showing the great difference in the
development of the brain. The fissiped has a very much more capacious brain-case and correspondingly low sagittal and occipital
crests, while the small-brained †creodont has very prominent crests.
The length of the face and jaws varies much in the different families
and, in almost all the genera, the zygomatic arches are heavy and
curve out boldly from the sides of the head, forming very large
temporal openings. The tympanic bulla is not ossified, so far as is
known, except in one genus (†Mesonyx).

In all †creodonts of which the backbone has been found, there are 19 or 20 trunk-vertebræ; in the lumbar and posterior dorsal regions, the processes by which the successive vertebræ are articulated, are much more complicated than in the Fissipedia, being of semi-cylindrical shape; the anterior pair are concave and embrace the convex posterior pair, as in the Artiodactyla (Chap. XIII). The tail is very generally long and heavy, but a few species are known with tails of moderate length; this would seem to be very exceptional.

The limbs are usually short and thick; the femur, as in primitive mammals generally, almost always bears the third trochanter, and the humerus, as frequently, retains the epicondylar foramen; almost always the fore-paw could rotate freely. Except in the most specialized genera of one family, the †Mesonychidæ, the feet are five-toed and plantigrade, or semi-plantigrade; they are weak and of primitive construction. The three carpal bones, scaphoid, lunar and central, which are united in the fissipeds, remain separate; the only known exception is a French species of †Hyænodon. The astragalus almost always has a very shallow pulley for the tibia, or is quite flat. In many genera the fibula articulates with the calcaneum; the ungual phlanges are thick and blunt and, except in the †Arctocyonidæ, are cleft at the tip, as in the Insectivora. Cope, to whom is due the conception of the †Creodonta as a separate group of predaceous mammals, was, at first, inclined to rank them under the Insectivora and, broadly speaking, they may be regarded as intermediate between that order and the Carnivora.

Throughout the Paleocene and Eocene epochs the †Creodonta were numerous and varied, especially so in the middle Eocene of North America. Very notably reduced in the upper Eocene, they disappeared from North America after the middle Oligocene, apparently because of the competition of the much more intelligent and better equipped Fissipedia.

Family 1. †Hyænodontidæ

The †hyænodonts were the last surviving †creodont family both in North America and in Europe, coming to an end here in the middle Oligocene, but in Europe continuing into the lower Miocene. In some respects the members of this family were the most advanced and specialized of all †creodonts, as the †Mesonychidæ were in others. As the †Mesonychids may be considered the †creodont analogue of the dogs, the †oxyænids of the cats and the †arctocyonids of the bears, so the †hyænodonts, as their name suggests, might be said to represent the hyenas, while the smaller and more ancient genera of the family probably filled the rôle of existing mustelines. Following is the list of the more important American genera:

†HYÆNODONTIDÆ

†*Hyænodon*, mid. and low. Olig. †*Hemipsalodon*, mid. Olig. †*Pterodon*, low. Olig. †*Tritemnodon*, mid. Eoc. †*Sinopa*, mid. and low. Eoc.

The White River representative of the family is †*Hyænodon*, the various species of which are among the commoner fossils of the stage. The history of the genus begins in the Eocene of Europe, whence it

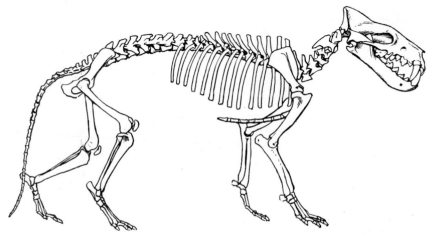

FIG. 384. — Skeleton of †*Hyænodon*. (Amer. Mus. Nat. Hist.)

spread to America, appearing first in the lower Oligocene of the Duchesne River and the Sespé of California; in the latter it is associated with †*Pterodon*, another European genus. In the Cypress Hills region of Saskatchewan, Canada, where beds of the Chadron substage occur, has been found a very large †hyænodont, which Cope named †*Hemipsalodon*, and which is, by far, the largest of American †creodonts. In the Chadron and lower Brulé of the United States are five (perhaps only four) species of †*Hyænodon*, the skulls of which range in size from a small Coyote to a large Grizzly Bear. It is surprising that these comparatively lowly †creodonts should have been able to hold their own so long against their superior fissiped rivals, but they succumbed at last to the inevitable.

In this genus the teeth are somewhat reduced in number, the incisors being sometimes $\frac{2}{2}$ and the molars constantly $\frac{2}{3}$. The upper incisors, especially $i^{\underline{3}}$, are rather large and of simple conical shape;

the lower incisors are much smaller and are crowded closely together by the thick roots of the canines. The latter, both above and below, are conspicuously long and sharp. There are three pairs of carnassial teeth on each side, of which the second upper and third lower molars ($m\,\underline{2}$ and $m\,\overline{3}$) form the principal pair; the accessory pairs are the first upper and second lower molars ($m\,\underline{1}$ and $m\,\overline{2}$) and the fourth

Fig. 385. — †*Hyænodon horridus*, a White River †creodont, restored from skeleton shown in Fig. 384. †*Leptomeryx evansi* in the background.

upper premolar and first lower molar ($p\,\underline{4}$ and $m\,\overline{1}$), the latter the smallest of the three pairs. In most skulls the first lower molar ($m\,\overline{1}$) seems almost atrophied, but this is due to its very early eruption and long-continued wear. The upper molars have lost the inner cusps and the outer, shearing portion consists of two more or less completely fused conical cusps and a posterior trenchant ridge. The third lower molar ($m\,\overline{3}$) is very like the carnassial of the cats and is made up of two large, thin and trenchant cusps, which form a very efficient shearing blade. The other lower molars are similar except that they are smaller and retain a vestige of the heel. The premolars are high, sharp-pointed and of compressed-conical shape, but they lack the massiveness of hyena premolars.

The skull, as in almost all †creodonts, is very large in proportion

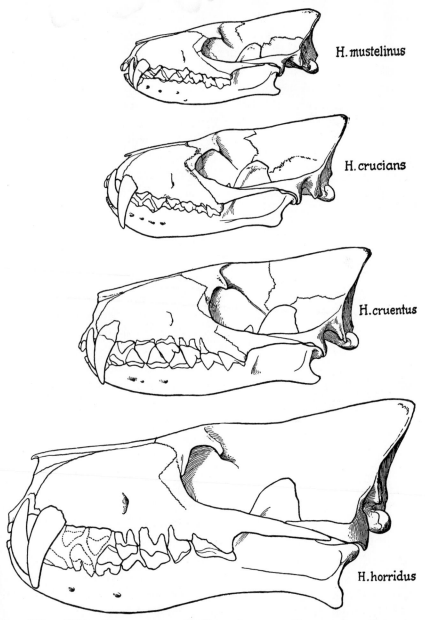

Fig. 386. — White River species of †*Hyænodon*, on uniform scale. (Princeton Univ. Mus.)

to the size of the whole skeleton. The face and jaws are very long, longer than in any other known †creodont family and these elongate jaws give the skull something of a wolf-like appearance. The brain-case is more capacious and the cerebral hemispheres had a more convoluted cortex than in other †creodonts, yet nevertheless, the occiput is very high and narrow and the sagittal and occipital crests are very prominent, indicating extremely powerful temporal muscles. The zygomatic arches are surprisingly weak and frail; they do not curve out boldly from the sides of the skull, as is the rule in carnivores, but pursue a straight course. A very exceptional feature is the insertion of the last upper molar ($m\,\underline{2}$) in the maxillary portion of the zygomatic arch, thus bringing the tooth outside of, instead of beneath, the eye-ball.

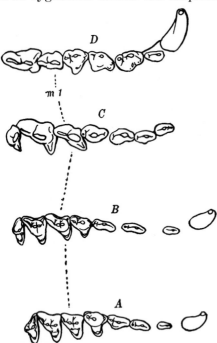

FIG. 387. — Development of upper teeth in †Hyænodontidæ. *A*, †*Sinopa*. *B*, †*Tritemodon*. *C*, †*Pterodon*. *D*, †*Hyænodon*.

The lower jaw is very long and slender; the two halves are indistinguishably co-ossified in an uncommonly long symphysis; the coronoid process is well developed and affords a strong point of insertion for the great temporal muscle. A puzzling circumstance is the depth and size of the pit for the masseter, which is the other principal muscle of biting and mastication. This muscle arises along the zygomatic arch and is inserted in the pit on the outside of the lower jaw; it is difficult to understand how that slender arch could have withstood the pull of a powerful muscle.

The neck is rather short, not equalling the skull in length; the trunk is elongate and the loins are very heavy and must have had great muscular power in the living animal. The length of the tail varies in the different species; in †*H. horridus*, for example, it is relatively somewhat longer than in a wolf, but in the small †*H. mustelinus* it is much longer and more slender.

In the †creodonts generally, the limbs are short, but in †*Hyænodon* they are proportionally longer, though the spreading arrangement of the five digits in each foot makes it unlikely that these creatures were particularly swift runners. Many primitive features which are found in almost all †creodonts are retained in †*Hyænodon,* such as the epicondylar foramen of the humerus, the third trochanter of the femur, and the articulation of the fibula and calcaneum. Except in certain European species, the bones of the carpus are all separate; the five-toed feet have blunt ungual phalanges, which are cleft at the tip.

In the restoration (Fig. 385) the animal is given much the appearance of the hyenas, and possibly errs in making the resemblance so close; the complete skeleton, however, shows that the drawing cannot have gone very far astray.

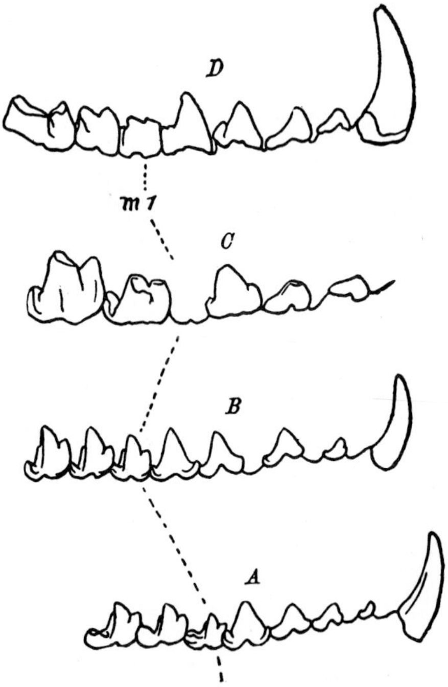

The Canadian genus †*Hemipsalodon* is too incompletely known for description; the newly discovered skull in the Canadian Museum at Ottawa, will, no doubt make plain the position of the genus. In most respects †*Pterodon* is very like †*Hyænodon,* but is distinctly less specialized and, though it cannot be regarded as directly ancestral

FIG. 388. — Development of lower teeth in †Hyænodontidæ. Letters as in Fig. 387.

to the latter, it serves to connect it with the more ancient and primitive genera of the family. In †*Pterodon* the upper molars have large internal cusps and the third upper one ($m \underline{3}$) had not been lost, the two external cusps of the molars are connate, but not completely fused together, and the posterior trenchant ridge is not so well developed as in †*Hyænodon,* nor is the fourth upper premolar ($p \underline{4}$) so nearly a carnassial. The lower molars are shearing blades, but retain the heel. So far as they are known, skull and skeleton are like those of †*Hyænodon.*

The two most specialized genera of the family, †*Hyænodon* and †*Pterodon,* were evidently descended from a group of small †creodonts, which, in the lower and middle Eocene, were spread all over the northern hemisphere and which were more numerous and varied in North America, but that circumstance, very probably, is due to the accidents of preservation. It is not yet possible to arrange the successive genera in the order of descent, but it is clear that †*Hyænodon* and †*Pterodon* originated in the Old World and entered North America early in the Oligocene epoch. The genera †*Sinopa* and †*Tritemnodon*,

Fig. 389. — †*Tritemnodon agilis*, a primitive †hyænodont, Bridger stage. (Restored from a skeleton in Amer. Mus. Nat. Hist.)

of the American Eocene, must be very similar to the actual ancestors of the Oligocene genera.

†*Tritemnodon* is of the middle Eocene and †*Sinopa* of the middle and lower; they are much smaller than their Oligocene successors and ranged in size from a weasel to a small fox. The teeth are unreduced in number and there are three pairs of sectorials. The first and second upper molars ($m \underline{1}$ and $\underline{2}$) are not far from the primitive tritubercular form, but the two external cusps are very close together and a small, posterior trenchant ridge has been added; the third upper molar ($m \underline{3}$) was progressively reduced in size. The three lower molars are carnassials of an imperfect sort and the first ($m \overline{1}$) is the smallest of the series; the shearing blade is formed by the two outer

cusps of the anterior, primitive triangle, and there is a low, basin-like heel. It is perfectly evident that this form of dentition is the starting point, whence came the †pterodont-†hyænodont type.

The skull in †*Sinopa* and †*Tritemnodon*, has prominent sagittal and occipital crests, and the cranium, despite the very small brain-case, is especially elongate, though the jaws are also relatively long, in anticipation of the proportions found in †*Hyænodon*. The short and delicate limbs are of very primitive character, yet the radius had already lost its power of rotation; the feet have five spreading digits, which were armed with sharp claws, an unusual feature among the †Creodonta. Sharp claws notwithstanding, the ungual phalanges are cleft at the tip.

No Paleocene ancestors of this family have yet been found, but it seems probable that it arose from a stock common to itself and the †Uintacyonidæ, three pairs of sectorials developing in one group and one pair in the other.

Family 2. †*Oxyænidæ*

As the †Mesonychidæ are the †creodont analogue of the dogs, the †*Oxyænidæ* are the cat-like group and more than one palæontologist has been misled into the belief that they were the actual ancestors of the Felidæ. In the †oxyænids there are two pairs of sectorial teeth, of which the larger pair are the first upper $(m \overset{1}{})$ and second lower molar $(m \overset{}{_2})$ and the smaller pair consists of the fourth upper pre-molar $(p \overset{4}{})$ and first lower molar $(m \overset{}{_1})$ as in the fissipeds. Within the family are three distinct series, or tribes, which have not been named, though they should, perhaps, be regarded as subfamilies, all of which are known only in the Eocene of Europe, Asia and North America and are much more numerous and diversified in the last-named continent. The principal genera are as follows:

†Oxyænidæ

†*Oxyænodon*, †*Apatælurus*, up. Eoc. †*Patriofelis*, †*Machairoides*, †*Limnocyon*, mid. Eoc. †*Oxyæna*, †*Palæonictis*, low. Eoc. (†*Sarkastodon*, Eoc. Mongolia.)

The last surviving members of the family, so far made known, are †*Oxyænodon* and †*Apatælurus*, of the Uinta, or upper Eocene. The former is the smallest of the family with the exception of one very imperfect Bridger fossil, which, though suggestive, is yet too incomplete for description. As its name implies, the Uinta genus resembles

†*Oxyæna*, of the lower Eocene, in its dentition and has the same dental formula, but the premolars are simplified and reduced in size and the lower jaw is shallower and thicker. There, for the present at least, the line comes to an end, and there is nothing known in the Oligocene which could have been derived from it. †*Apatælurus* is an astonishing imitation of the †sabre-tooth cats, with flanged lower jaw and mandibular condyle below the level of the teeth. †*A. kayi* is from the mid-

Fig. 390. — †*Patriofelis ferox*, middle Eocene, Bridger stage. (Restored from a skeleton in Amer. Mus. Nat. Hist.)

dle Uinta beds and is, perhaps, more properly referable to the †Hyænodontidæ.

Very much more complete information is available regarding the Bridger genus †*Patriofelis*, of which entire skeletons have been recovered. The teeth are considerably reduced in number and have lost at least 12 from the original number of 44; the formula is: $i\frac{?}{2}$, $c\frac{1}{1}$, $p\frac{3}{3}$, $m\frac{1}{2}$. The single upper molar is a large carnassial and is formed very much as in the †hyænodonts; the two external cusps are connate, not indistinguishably fused together, and there is a long, trenchant ridge behind them, while the inner cusp has been almost completely lost. The second lower molar is a nearly perfect copy of the cat sectorial, but, it should be noted, it is not the same tooth in the series, for a cat's lower sectorial is the first molar ($m_{\overline{1}}$) and in †*Patriofelis* it is the second ($m_{\overline{2}}$). In the latter genus $m_{\overline{2}}$ has a cutting blade of two sharp-edged shearing cusps; there is no trace of the internal cusp and only a vestige of the heel.

The skull is very large and massive, almost equalling that of the Lion, but the rest of the skeleton is disproportionately smaller; the cranium is elongate and the face is short, with broad, abruptly truncate muzzle. The brain-case is unbelievably small, and has a very long and prominent sagittal crest; the zygomatic arches are very stout and curve so far out from the sides of the head, that, notwithstanding the absurdly small brain-case, the head was very wide. The creature must have been ineffably stupid. The lower jaw is very deep and heavy and the chin is abruptly rounded and almost vertical. The unusual massiveness of the zygomatic arches, the great development of the crests and ridges for muscular attachment, and the short, heavy lower jaw, all indicate such power in the biting and shearing apparatus, as occurs in no other known †creodont.

The neck is of medium length and the body is relatively shorter than in most other †creodont genera. The lumbar vertebræ are very heavy and the loins must have been extremely powerful in the living animal. In this region the articulations between successive vertebræ are even more complex than in other †creodonts and in only a few artiodactyls do they attain such a degree of elaborateness. Even for a †creodont, the tail is long and uncommonly heavy. The ribs are long and thick and the thorax deep and capacious.

The limbs, especially the anterior pair, are short and very stout; the humerus has an immensely developed deltoid crest which extends down two-thirds of the length of the bone and there is a very prominent ridge for the supinator muscle. The fore-arm bones are heavy, especially the ulna, and the radius had but a limited power of rotation. The feet are short and broad, each with five complete, spreading toes, ending in thick, blunt claws, the ungual phalanges deeply cleft at the end.

†*Patriofelis* must have been much the most formidable of Bridger Carnivora and, except †*Harpagolestes* (one of the †Mesonychidæ) the largest of them. From the modern point of view, its appearance must have been decidedly curious, with its disproportionately large and leonine head, thick body and long, heavy tail. As is true of many other †creodonts, the combination of characters in teeth and skeleton makes it very difficult to imagine the living animal's mode of life. The teeth indicate habits as exclusively predaceous as those of the cats, but the short feet and legs seem incompatible with swift running. The humerus and fore-foot might indicate fossorial habits, but,

assuredly, so large a creature could not have been a burrower. An arboreal life appears to be out of the question with such feet, which, together with the otter-like proportions, appear to favour an aquatic manner of life. On the other hand, these proportions are common to most of the more ancient Carnivora and it is hardly probable that they were all amphibious. Whatever the principal diet of †*Patriofelis*,

Fig. 391. — †*Oxyæna lupina*, Gray Bull stage. (Restored from a skeleton in Amer. Mus. Nat. Hist.)

it must have been very abrasive, for, in old animals, the teeth are worn to stumps.

The fragmentary remains of the family which have, so far, been found in the Wind River beds, seem to belong to the genera of the Bridger rather than to those of the Gray Bull, but in the latter a very distinct genus, †*Oxyæna*, the type of the family, takes the place of †*Patriofelis* and is just what might have been expected as the immediately ancestral form, being less specialized and of smaller size. Tooth reduction had not proceeded so far, as is shown in the formula: $i\frac{3}{3}$, $c\frac{1}{1}$, $p\frac{4}{4}$, $m\frac{2}{2} \times 2 = 40$; the sectorial teeth are the same, the major pair being the first upper ($m\frac{1}{}$) and second lower ($m\frac{}{2}$) molars, and the minor pair the fourth upper premolar ($p\frac{4}{}$) and first lower molar ($m\frac{}{1}$), but these teeth were a less efficient shearing apparatus and both upper carnassials have large internal cusps, which have been almost completely suppressed in †*Patriofelis*. The second upper molar (m ²), which has been lost in the latter, though retained in the Uinta †*Oxyænodon*, is a transverse ridge, like the first and only upper molar (m ¹) in the cats. This transverse tooth engages the heel of the second lower molar (m ₂) which in †*Patriofelis* has no heel. In †*Oxyæna*, this second lower molar, though the principal sectorial, is much less completely trenchant than in the Bridger genus and retains an internal cusp as well as a large heel.

The skull is like that of †*Patriofelis*, but smaller and less massive; the face is not so much shortened, nor are the zygomatic arches so heavy or so widely expanded; the lower jaw is lighter and has a more sloping chin. The body is relatively longer and more slender and the tail is even longer and not nearly so thick. The articulations of the lumbar and posterior dorsal vertebræ are of the usual †creodont type and much less complicated than in the Bridger genus. Except for their somewhat greater relative length and slenderness, the limbs and feet of †*Oxyæna* differ but little from those of †*Patriofelis*.

In appearance, †*Oxyæna* must have been a smaller, lighter and less powerful version of its Bridger descendants and, no doubt, its manner of life was much the same, but, in teeth and skeleton there are many minor differences which emphasize the more primitive structure of the more ancient and ancestral genus.

The origin of this line, which cannot yet be traced into the Paleocene, is still unknown, though persistent and belated ancestral forms survived into the Bridger, where they are represented by the genus †*Limnocyon*, described below, as belonging to a third tribe, the early members of which were, presumably, ancestral to the other two.

A second tribe, which is represented only by †*Palæonictis*, of the lower Eocene, was manifestly of immigrant origin, for the genus was first discovered and named in France and it cannot have been derived from progenitors in the American Paleocene. So long as only the dentition and incomplete skulls were known, there was room for doubt as to the family relations of these animals, which were sometimes referred to the †Oxyænidæ and sometimes made the type of a distinct family. The finding of a complete skeleton by the late Professor W. J. Sinclair, of Princeton, makes it plain that inclusion in the present family is the better course.

In †*Palaeonictis* the dental formula is the same as in †*Oxyæna*, but the principal pair of sectorials is, as in the Fissipedia, the fourth upper premolar ($p \underline{4}$) and the first lower molar ($m \overline{1}$), and the secondary pair comprises the first upper ($m \underline{1}$) and second lower molar ($m \overline{2}$), but this accessory pair are, as it were, very unfinished, for the first upper molar ($m \underline{1}$) is hardly trenchant at all; its two external cusps are long, sharp-pointed cones and the posterior cutting ridge is no more than a tubercle.

While the teeth are, thus, very distinctive, the skeleton closely resembles that of †*Oxyæna* and leaves no doubt that the two genera should be included in the same family. The skull is large, short-faced and somewhat cat-like; the body and tail are very long, and the limbs are short; the five-toed feet would seem to have been plantigrade in gait. †*Palæonictis* left no successors and nothing is known of its immediate ancestry.

As mentioned above, there is a third tribe within the family, unknown except in the middle Eocene. The genus †*Limnocyon* is clearly a persistent survivor of the more ancient and primitive progenitors of the family. The species of this genus are all small. The number and kind of teeth are the same as in †*Oxyæna*, but the external cusps of the first upper molar ($m \underline{1}$) are separate, not connate, and the posterior cutting ridge is very low. The second upper molar ($m \underline{2}$) has all the elements of the primitive tritubercular tooth. The two lower molars are likewise very primitive and have a high anterior triangle of three cusps, and a low heel behind. This type of dentition approximates that of the more ancient and smaller †hyæenodonts and shows how the two families may have had a common origin and, indeed, they probably had such an ancestry. The skull of †*Limnocyon* has a much longer face and longer, more slender jaws than have †*Patriofelis*, †*Oxyæna* or †*Palæonictis*, which is still another resemblance to the †hyæenodonts.

An interesting genus of this tribe is the very incompletely known †*Machairoides*, also of the Bridger; the flanges on the lower jaw of this animal indicate that it had scimitar-like upper tusks, as in the †sabre-tooth cats, with which †*Machairoides* can have had no relations. This is, perhaps, the ancestor of †*Apatælurus*, of the Uinta. An enormous creature, (†*Sarkastodon*) representative of this family, is found in the Eocene of Mongolia. Though not comparable in size to the colossal †*Andrewsarchus*, a †mesonychid from the same region, it is far larger than any existing carnivore. This remarkable genus is distinguished, among other things, by the reduction of the incisor teeth to one on each side of each jaw, making a total of four, which are all that remain of the original twelve. The canines are very massive, though rather short, and are as thick as those of the Grizzly Bear; all the teeth are very heavy.

Family 3. †Mesonychidæ

In some respects this family was the most highly specialized of all the †creodonts, for they were the only ones in which cursorial limbs and feet were attained. These genera are chiefly North American and, in time, they extended from the middle Paleocene to the upper Eocene. The principal genera are as follows:

†MESONYCHIDÆ

†Harpagolestes, up. and mid. Eoc. †Mesonyx, †Dromocyon, mid. Eoc. †Pachyæna, low. Eoc. †Dissacus, †Triisodon, Paleoc.

In this family the teeth show a curious mingling of primitiveness with an advanced degree of specialization, yet none of them, properly speaking, could be called sectorial; the lower teeth have the shearing form, but not the shearing function. The incisors are small, the canines large, heavy and bear-like and the premolars of simple, compressed-conical shape. The upper molars are very primitive, as they retain the tritubercular pattern, with one internal and two external cusps, but the lower molars have lost the internal cusp and the heel and, with two blade-like lobes, one behind the other, have taken on the semblance of sectorials, though the blades are thick and heavy. The mode of wear, however, shows that they had no shearing action, but occluded directly against the upper teeth and were abraded down from the tips and edges, until, in old animals, they became mere shapeless stumps.

The last American genus of the family and much the largest is †Harpagolestes, of the Uinta and upper Bridger stages; the disproportionately large skull exceeded that of the Grizzly Bear in size, and the upper profile had considerable resemblance to that of a bear in the steep descent at the forehead. The dentition is reduced by the loss of the first premolar ($p\ \underline{1}$) and last molar ($m\ \underline{3}$) of the upper jaw. Little of the skeleton has been recovered, but the humerus affords a significant piece of information, viz., that it had a long and prominent deltoid crest and retained the epicondylar foramen.

In the middle Bridger occur two genera, †Dromocyon and †Mesonyx; of which the latter has given its name to the family. The two are very closely alike in size and structure and, in appearance, they must have resembled small, large-headed wolves, with skull as long as that of a Black Bear (Ursus americanus). Though the cranium is elongate, the brain-cavity is very small and the large nasal chamber is extended back over the eyes. In consequence of the small size of the brain-case and the need of sufficient surface of attachment for the powerful temporal muscles, there is an enormously high sagittal crest and correspondingly high, narrow occiput. The tympanic bullæ are ossified and have long tubular entrances, a feature which has been found in no other †creodont skull. The face and jaws are elon-

Fig. 392. — A mesonychid †creodont, †*Dromocyon velox*, Bridger stage. (Restored from a skeleton in Yale Univ. Mus.)

gate, giving the head a wolf-like appearance. Neck and body are of moderate length, but the tail is extremely long, slender and whip-like.

Limbs and feet are more specialized than those of any other †creodonts and the adaptations are for swift running. The humerus is very smooth, with low and inconspicuous ridges for muscular attachment, and looks more like that of an ungulate than of a carnivore. These two genera are the only known †creodonts in which the humerus has lost the epicondylar foramen and this shows that †*Harpagolestes* must have had some other lower Bridger ancestor, as yet undiscovered, for it is a very general law of development that "structures once lost are not regained." The radius has a wide head, so interlocking with the humerus as to preclude rotation of the fore-paw. The femur retains the primitive feature of the third trochanter.

The feet, both manus and pes, are four-toed and greatly resemble those of modern dogs; they are, indeed, much more modernized than the feet of the Oligocene Canidæ, such as †*Daphœnus* (p. 583) or †*Pseudocynodictis* (p. 584). In each foot the metapodials are closely appressed and parallel, not spreading, but arranged in two symmetrical pairs, the third and fourth digits forming the median and longer pair, while the second and fifth are the shorter, lateral pair. The astragalus, or ankle bone, has a decidedly artiodactyl appearance, with its deeply grooved trochlea for the tibia and pulley-like lower end, which rests upon the navicular and cuboid. The ungual phalanges are so short and broad, as to be almost more hoof-like than claw-like, a fact which is expressed in the generic name †*Mesonyx*, which may be translated as "intermediate claw"; as in nearly all †creodonts, they are cleft at the tip. The feet, especially the posterior ones, make it plain that the gait was as completely digitigrade as in a wolf and these two genera are the only known †creodonts of which this is assuredly true, though it probably applies to †*Hyænodon* and †*Pterodon* also.

The genera †*Mesonyx* and †*Dromocyon* and, perhaps, another Bridger genus, not yet known, form an aberrant side-branch of the family, the relations of which are still to be elucidated, for they were not the direct ancestors of the Uinta forms, nor can they be derived from the lower Eocene †*Pachyæna*, some of the species of which are very large and gave rise to the great †*Harpagolestes* and probably also to the colossal Mongolian representatives of the family. †*Pachyæna* is, in all respects, less specialized than †*Mesonyx* and has the full number of teeth, which are so heavy as to suggest habits of carrion-feeding. The humerus retains the epicondylar foramen which †*Mesonyx* and †*Dromocyon* had lost, and the feet, both fore and hind, are five-toed.

Much less specialized than any of the preceding genera is †*Dissacus*, of the Torrejon stage of the Paleocene, which was probably the direct ancestor of both lower and middle Eocene genera; the upper molars are substantially as in the latter and the lower molars resemble those of the later genera in form, though retaining the inner cusp of the primitive triangle. The feet have five well-developed digits, with a spreading arrangement, and the gait was evidently plantigrade; the ungual phalanges are longer, more pointed and much less hoof-like than those of †*Mesonyx*.

In the Puerco, the oldest Paleocene stage, occurs the genus †*Triisodon*, which may have been the direct ancestor of †*Dissacus* and, at all events, represents very nearly what that ancestor must have been. The teeth are much more primitive than those of †*Dissacus;* the tritubercular upper molars are broader and the two external cusps are more separated, while, in the lower molars, all of the five original cusps are present; of these, the anterior triangle has three of nearly equal size (which is expressed in the name of the genus), and the heel has two, internal and external. The skull has a very narrow brain-case and a long, thick sagittal crest.

The most interesting feature in the history of this family is the highly probable derivation of the cursorial, digitigrade, four-toed and almost hoofed mid-Eocene genera, from the plantigrade, five-toed and sharp-clawed †*Dissacus* of the Paleocene and from some more ancient genus like †*Triisodon.*

Mention should be made of the remarkable Mongolian genus †*Andrewsarchus,* from the Eocene of the Gobi Desert. This colossal creature, with a skull a yard or more in length is, by far, the largest of known carnivores and is, as yet, the only member of the family found outside of North America. It must, however, have had a series of Asiatic ancestors derived from American immigrants.

Families 4, 5. †Arctocyonidæ and †Oxyclænidæ

The members of these families have no sectorial teeth even in form, such as are the lower molars of the †Mesonychidæ. To the first-named family has been given the infelicitous name of †Arctocyonidæ, "†bear-dogs," from †*Arctocyon,* of the French Paleocene, though these animals were not in any way related to either bears or dogs. The name was given on account of the tubercular molar teeth, which led Dr. Matthew to the belief, subsequently abandoned, that the ancestors of the bears were to be found in this group. The family was a very ancient one and confined to the lower Eocene and Paleocene of North America and Europe. The molar teeth are very low-crowned and quadritubercular in pattern, with numerous small tubercles in addition to the four principal cusps, an arrangement which is pig-like rather than bear-like and indicates omnivorous habits.

The lower Eocene genus of this family is †*Anacodon,* known only from jaws and teeth, in which the premolars are reduced both in number and in size. The lower jaw, wonderful to relate! has flanges at the anterior end, like those of the †sabre-tooth cats, for the protection of the upper canines, which, presumably, were long and sabre-like. With such molars, †*Anacodon* can hardly have had predaceous habits, and laniary tusks could only have been used as defensive weapons, as they are in the hornless and small-antlered deer of to-day. In the Paleocene genus †*Clænodon* (Torrejon stage), which is much more completely known, the premolars, though small, are unreduced in number. The skull resembles that of †*Mesonyx* in the relative lengths of cranium and face, in the very small size of the brain-chamber and in the great prominence of the sagittal and occipital crests. These resemblances are merely primitive characteristics and do not imply any close relationship between the families. The feet of †*Clænodon* are five-toed and plantigrade and the ungual phalanges are long, thin and sharp-pointed, without clefts; no other †creodont family has uncleft unguals.

The †OXYCLÆNIDÆ are very imperfectly known and may not have been †creodonts at all. They were small animals and confined to the Paleocene. The cusps of the teeth are conical and sharp-pointed; the upper molars are triangular and tritubercular, with one internal and two external cusps, which are well separated; the lower molars have a high anterior triangle and a low heel. This is the type of dentition from which those of all the varied †creodont and fissiped families were probably derived, but it does not follow that the †*Oxyclænidæ* were the actual ancestors, for teeth of that description are common to the early members of most other orders of mammals.

The two principal genera of this family are †*Oxyclænus* and, somewhat doubtfully, †*Deltatherium*. The former, from which the family name is taken, has furnished the foregoing description of the family, but the latter is different and may be described as a premature specialization which led to nothing, while †*Oxyclænus* is a very possible ancestor of several †creodont groups. In †*Deltatherium* the dental formula is: $i\frac{3}{?}, c\frac{1}{1}, p\frac{3}{3}, m\frac{3}{3} \times 2 = ?\,40$; the foremost upper premolar ($p\,\underline{2}$) is very small and simple, the other two ($p\,\underline{3}$ and $\underline{4}$) have internal cusps; the upper molars are simply tritubercular. The lower molars are tuberculo-sectorial, with anterior triangle and very large heel.

This genus may, perhaps, be referable to the Insectivora and its special interest lies in its likeness to the insectivorous †*Deltatheridium*, of the Mongolian Cretaceous (p. 95, Fig. 64), the name of which was devised to mark the resemblance.

The †Creodonta, as here limited by the transference of the †Uintacyonidæ to the Fissipedia, represent a side-branch of the carnivorous stock, which is altogether extinct and came to an end in the Oligocene of this country and the Miocene of France.

CHAPTER XXIII

HISTORY OF THE EDENTATA

Though parts of the history of the Edentata are very fully recorded, especially in South America, the origin and relationships of the order have long been veiled in a mystery from which they are slowly emerging, as the light of new discoveries is thrown upon their early story. Even the limits of the order are more or less uncertain and two Old World groups, the Pangolins, or Scaly Anteaters (*Manis*) and the Aard Vark (*Orycteropus*) are included by some authorities, not by others. For the present, these Asiatic and African genera may be omitted and only the American families taken into consideration.

So strange are the edentates and so widely different from other placental mammals, that it has several times been proposed to make them a distinct superorder, or even a subclass. American edentates, or Xenarthra, are, at the present time, almost confined to the Neotropical region, an armadillo which extends into Texas, being the sole exception, but in the Pliocene and Pleistocene xenarthrous edentates were common all over most of North America as far north as the existing international boundary, but their numbers and variety were far below those of South America, where, from the Miocene through the Pleistocene they were the dominant group of mammals especially the †Gravigrada, or †Ground-sloths. At present, the groups of the Edentata now living are very different from one another and seem to have little in common; the three surviving superfamilies, tree-sloths, ant-bears and armadillos, are natural, well distinguished and circumscribed groups, but when their structure is examined, the unity of the suborder is clearly brought out. The classification given in the table below is almost universally accepted; such differences of usage as there are, affect chiefly the rank and name to be employed for some of the groups.

SUPERORDER EDENTATA

ORDER **XENARTHRA**
  SERIES A. PILOSA, Hairy Edentates.
    SUBORDER I, **Tardigrada,** Tree-sloths.
      FAMILY 1, BRADYPODIDÆ

650

SUBORDER II, **Vermilingua,** Anteaters.
    FAMILY 2, MYRMECOPHAGIDÆ
SUBORDER III, †**Gravigrada,** †Ground-sloths.
    FAMILY 3, †MEGALONYCHIDÆ
    FAMILY 4, †MEGATHERIIDÆ
    FAMILY 5, †MYLODONTIDÆ
SERIES B. LORICATA, Armoured Edentates.
SUBORDER IV, **Dasypoda,** Armadillos.
    FAMILY 6, DASYPODIDÆ
    FAMILY 7, †PELTEPHILIDÆ, †Horned **Armadillos.**
SUBORDER V, †**Glyptodontia**
    FAMILY 8, †GLYPTODONTIDÆ
ORDER †**PALÆANODONTA**
    FAMILY 9, †PALÆANODONTIDÆ
    FAMILY 10, †METACHEIROMYIDÆ

ORDER **XENARTHRA**

The name Edentata, or toothless, applies strictly only to the ant-eaters of South America and the Old World, but all of the existing and most of the extinct edentates, which are not toothless, have simple cylindrical, or columnar teeth, without roots or enamel. In nearly all the genera the teeth are all alike and are not divisible into regions, except that in the tree-sloths and in most of the †ground-sloths the first tooth in each jaw is set off by a diastema and is more or less caniniform and tusk-like. Most of the living genera have no incisors. Though enamel early disappeared, an Eocene armadillo, †*Utaëtus,* being the latest known genus to display vestiges of it, there are, in several groups, two kinds of dentine, of different degrees of hardness, and, in some of the †ground-sloths, there is a sheathing of cement. In most of the suborders the teeth are few in number, $\frac{5}{4}$, $\frac{8}{8}$ or $\frac{8}{9}$, but in the Giant Armadillo, *Priodontes,* there may be as many as 100 small, simple teeth $\frac{25}{25}$.

Few edentates have milk-teeth other than embryonic vestiges, but certain armadillos show primitive conditions of great interest.

The skull of the edentates differs much in the various groups in accordance with the diet and the manner of feeding. The tree-sloths have short, rounded heads and in the †ground-sloths the skull is remarkably small in proportion to the size of the skeleton. For example, the contrast between †*Megatherium* and an elephant in the relative size of the skull is very striking. In shape, the skull of the †Gravigrada varies from short and deep to narrow and elongate. In the †glyptodonts the skull is short and extremely deep vertically, while the armadillos have long, shallow skulls, with tapering muzzle, the length and slenderness of which differ much in the various genera. The extreme of elongation and slenderness is reached in the ant-eaters and, more particularly in the Great Ant-bear (*Myrmecophaga jubata*), which has a grotesquely elongate, narrow and almost cylindrical head and skull.

The backbone displays some of the most extraordinary peculiarities of the suborder. The articulations between vertebræ in the lumbar and posterior dorsal regions are far more complicated than in any other mammals, whence comes the name, Xenarthra ("Strange-joints") for the order. In the hinder part of the dorsal region, there appears an additional pair of articular processes, and these increase in number posteriorly, until, in the middle of the loins, there are no less than four accessory pairs (making ten in all). Such an elaborately complex mode of articulation is altogether unique among mammals. In the tree-sloths the accessory articulations are in a rudimentary condition and it is difficult to decide whether they were never fully developed, or whether they have degenerated.

The cervical vertebræ have peculiarities in several of the suborders. In the armadillos and †glyptodonts most of these vertebræ are fused into a single mass, but the atlas always remains separate, permitting movement of the head. In the †glyptodonts, which are encased in a carapace as fixed and solid as that of a tortoise, the trunk-vertebræ are united into two segments, one including all the dorsals, the other made up of the lumbars and sacrum. In all of the Xenarthra the sacrum consists of an unusually large number of vertebræ and is attached to the hip-bones at two points instead of only one, as in other mammals.

The tail differs greatly in the suborders; the tree-sloths, or Tardigrada are almost tailless; in the armadillos, or Dasypoda, the tail is of moderate length and in the †glyptodonts it is relatively longer and, in some genera very much so. In most of them, the tail is sheathed in dense bone and, very probably was used as a weapon in much the same way as an alligator uses his tail. In the larger †ground-sloths, or †Gravigrada, the tail is of extraordinary massiveness and, almost certainly, was employed as a third hind-leg upon which the body was supported, when raised into the browsing position. The kangaroos make a similar use of the tail, but in them the fore-legs are greatly reduced and only the hind-legs used in a leaping gait. Most assuredly, the cumbrous, slow-moving †ground-sloths were not leapers.

Equally exceptional is the structure of the sternum and sternal ribs; the latter are fully ossified, not cartilaginous as in other mammals, and articulate with the vertebral ribs and the sternum by means of true synovial joints. At the lower end these sternal ribs have separate heads and, on the segments of the mesosternum, there are articular facets to receive them. The most elaborate joints are in the anteaters and †ground-sloths.

In the limbs and feet of the Xenarthra there is great variety, in accordance with the manner of their employment. The shoulder-blade has an uncommonly long acromion and a very large coracoid, which long remains separate from the scapula. Collar-bones (clavicles) are usually present, though often in a reduced condition. In the tree-sloths, †ground-sloths and †glyptodonts, the hip-bones (pelvis) have expanded ilia, but in the other suborders the ilia are narrow. The humerus generally has very prominent deltoid and supinator crests and epicondylar foramen. The fore-arm bones are always separate and, generally speaking, there is much freedom of rotation of the fore-foot, but tibia and fibula are frequently united. The tree-sloths, which are strictly arboreal and well-nigh helpless on the ground, are exceptional among mammals, in that, as in bats, the body habitually hangs *suspended* from the legs and is not carried upon them. The stresses are thus, in the engineer's phrase, *tensional*, instead of the normal compressive ones. The feet are curved hooks, which fit over the branches of trees and thus carry the weight of the body without muscular effort. The leg-bones are very long and slender, the claws long, curved and sharp, and the metapodials of each foot, two or three in number, are short and fused together.

The anteaters (Vermilingua) have a very curious gait; the five-toed hind-feet are plantigrade, but the fore-feet have the claws and sole turned inward, so that the knuckles are in contact with the ground, supporting the weight upon a pad over the three external digits. The third toe is immensely developed and has a great, curved claw, which not only serves to tear open the hard earth of the Termite (White-ant) nests, but also is a weapon that even the great cats respect.

In the recorded history of the †ground-sloths, or †Gravigrada, the foot-structure underwent great changes; in the Pleistocene genera the manus rests upon the knuckles and the pes upon the external border and turning the claws and soles of the feet inward. Both fore- and hind-feet are armed with immense claws, the number of which differs in the various genera. If the Pangolins, or Scaly Anteaters

(*Manis*) of Asia and Africa are properly included in the Edentata, then the peculiar method of walking on the knuckles of the fore-feet is an exclusively edentate character, though the Loricate families do not display it.

The armadillos (Dasypoda) are mostly burrowers; in the fore-foot the number and size of the digits and claws differ according to the genus, but the hind-foot usually has nails rather than claws. In gait, the armadillos are mostly plantigrade.

The huge †Glyptodontia have short, broad feet, shod with hoofs, but in some of the genera the hoofs of the fore-feet were more claw-like.

The primary division of the Xenarthra into the Pilosa and Loricata is made in accordance with the external covering; the Pilosa, or hairy edentates, are clothed with a thick coat of coarse hair, and there are neither horny scales nor bony scutes except in one family of the †ground-sloths, the †Mylodontidæ, in which the deeper layers of the skin are filled with bony scutes, not visible externally. The armoured edentates, or Loricata, have a dermal armour of bony scutes covered with scales of horn. The armadillos have a greater or less number (3 to 13) of movable bands of scutes and scales, which permit flexibility of the body, but in the extinct †glyptodonts the thick scutes of bone form a massive, fixed carapace, in which no movement was possible. In the armadillos and, no doubt, in the †glyptodonts also, the ventral surface and the inner sides of the legs are covered with hair, which also grows more or less scantily through the carapace. Head and tail are likewise protected by armour.

Of great significance is the body-temperature of the Edentata, which has but recently been ascertained. The edentates agree with the monotremes, the egg-laying, primitive mammals, and the marsupials, in having a body temperature which is very low and as in cold-blooded animals, is much influenced by the temperature of the surrounding air and may range through 15° or 20°, a fluctuation which would be speedily fatal to any of the higher mammals, save when in a state of hibernation. In other words, the edentates are but imperfectly warm-blooded and this demarcates them sharply from other placental mammals

SERIES A. PILOSA

SUBORDER III. †Gravigrada. †GROUND-SLOTHS

The other suborders of the hairy edentates, the anteaters and the tree-sloths, are not known before the Pleistocene; they are tropical and forest-dwelling animals and their development must have taken place in the warm, forested regions far to the north of the fossiliferous parts of Patagonia. The history of the †ground-sloths, on the other hand, is better known than that of any other edentate group; from the middle Miocene to the end of the Pleistocene, they were the dominant mammals of the Neotropical Region. In the Pliocene, they began to spread into North America and the Antilles and, in the Pleistocene they were conspicuous elements in the fauna of this continent, with all of the three families represented, but in generic and specific variety and in individual abundance, they were never comparable to the South American members of the suborder.

In the †Gravigrada are united characteristics of the tree-sloths and the anteaters together with features peculiar to themselves and it is evident that the three suborders were derived from a common ancestry, the discovery of which can hardly be expected until fossiliferous Oligocene and Eocene deposits shall have been found much farther north than any which are now known.

Family 3. †Megalonychidæ

†*Megalonyx*, Pleist. N. A. †*Nothrotherium*, Pleist. N. and S. A. †*Megalocnus*, †*Mesocnus*, †*Microcnus*, etc., Pleist. Cuba. †*Acratocnus*, Pleist. Puerto Rico. †*Pronothrotherium*, Plio. Catamarca. †*Hyperleptus*, †*Eucholœops*, †*Schismotherium*, †*Pelecyodon*, †*Megalonychotherium*, etc., Santa Cruz. †*Hapalops*, Santa Cruz and Deseado. †*Orophodon*, Deseado.

There is a wonderful contrast between the Pampean and the Santa Cruz faunas in regard to the dominant family of †Gravigrada; in the Pampean, it was the †Mylodontidæ, with one genus each of the other two families, while, as before stated, the †Megalonychidæ greatly preponderated in the Santa Cruz. In the North American Pleistocene all three families were represented and, judging from such fossils as have already been collected and classified, the †Megalonychidæ were in the lead as regards diversity, abundance and geographical range.

Within the family there are three distinct tribes, two of which seem to have been derived from a common Miocene ancestor. As the first of these may be taken the one culminating in †*Nothrotherium*, which was common to the Pleistocene of both South and North America and in the latter continent persisted into the Recent, as is indicated by a remarkable skeleton, found in an extinct volcanic crater, 100 feet below the surface, in Dona Ana County, New Mexico, and now in the Yale Museum, in which the tendons, ligaments, horny claws and parts of the skin still adhere to the bones. This is an interesting parallel to the case of the †*Neomylodon* skin fragments, which were recovered from a cave in Patagonia (p. 671). In the Los Angeles Museum is an almost complete skeleton from Rancho La Brea. This genus comprises the smallest species of Pleistocene †ground-sloths, the common North American species, †*N. shastense*, not exceeding a tapir in size; the immature Yale skeleton is rather less than five feet long from the tip of the snout to the root of the tail.

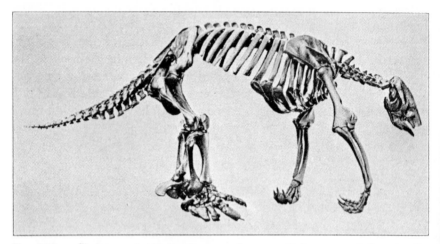

Fɪɢ. 393. — Skeleton of †*Nothrotherium shastense*, Pleistocene of Rancho La Brea, Cal. (Los Angeles Mus.)

In several respects, †*Nothrotherium* is more primitive and departs less from its Miocene ancestors than do the large †ground-sloths of the Pleistocene, but, in certain other features, it is even more specialized. In correlation with its smaller size, this skeleton is less massive than in the other genera and the fore-leg is very slender, almost "spidery" in appearance.

In †*Nothrotherium* the anterior, tusk-like teeth, so conspicuous in †*Megalonyx*, have been suppressed, making the dental formula $\frac{4}{3} \times 2 = 14$, and the grinding teeth are like those of the latter, except that they are more trapezoidal and less triangular in shape. The skull has great resemblance to that of the Santa Cruz genus †*Hapalops* on a much larger scale; even the rod-like, Y-shaped premaxillæ are similar, and thus very different from the small, triangular plates of †*Megalonyx*. The pterygoids are curiously inflated. A difference from †*Megalonyx* is the lack of a sagittal crest, which is replaced by a narrow sagittal area, as in †*Megatherium*, but longer than in that genus. A conspicuous difference from †*Megalonyx* is in the form of the lower jaw, which has a prolonged predentary spout, while in the last-named genus this spout is reduced to a vestige. In †*Hapalops*, of the Santa Cruz, the mandible is very like that of †*Nothrotherium*. The neck is elongate, but the trunk is relatively short, having only 17 vertebræ, and the tail is of moderate length and very heavy, the anterior caudal vertebræ are provided with chevron bones, as in the other †Gravigrada. The limb-bones resemble those of †*Megalonyx*, but are far lighter, especially those of the fore-leg. The fore-foot has five digits, all of them with claws, which are much larger than the ungual phalanges. The pollex (digit I) is short and light and can have been of little functional use; the second and third metacarpals (mc. II and III) are short and very much the heaviest of the series, the fourth (mc. IV) is more than twice as long and not so heavy and the fifth (mc. V) is almost as long, but so slender as to be practically vestigial. The phalanges of the three median digits (II–IV) are large and stout, while those of the laterals (I,V) are very much smaller.

The hind-foot has four digits, the first having been reduced to a small nodule. The astragalus is much more modified in the sense of †*Megatherium* and †*Mylodon* than is that of †*Megalonyx* and the calcaneum has no such exaggerated proportions as in the latter. The third metatarsal (mt. III) is much the shortest and heaviest of the series, being twice as broad as it is long, the second (mt. II) is much longer and the fourth (mt. IV) still longer, though both are short in comparison with the metacarpals; the fifth (mt. V) is a triangular plate very like that of †*Megalonyx;* claws are present in the three median digits (II–IV) and that of digit III is much the largest of the three; digit V has two nodules attached, which are the vestiges of the first and second phalanges.

"The digits are inclosed in a common integument near the base of the second claw, but involving a portion of the third and fourth claws" (Lull).

The hair is smooth, straight, rather coarse and of a pale yellow colour, as is also true of the Patagonian †*Neomylodon*, which belongs to a different family, the †Mylodontidæ, and the agreement would seem to indicate that this colouring was general throughout the Pleistocene †Gravigrada.

Gait. — The Yale skeleton is particularly instructive in giving positive information regarding the gait of these strange creatures. In walking, the fore-foot rested upon the knuckles of the three median digits, in quite the same way as in the Great Ant-bear (*Myrmeco-*

phaga) and the Pangolins (*Manis*) of the Old World. In the hind-foot, the external, or fibular, border supported the weight, the sole and claws being so turned inward that the sole is perpendicular to the ground. Judging from the unmodified form of the astragalus, †*Megalonyx* may have been able to walk with a plantigrade gait as well as with a "pedolateral" one, to use Stock's term.

Diet. — Found in association with the Yale skeleton is a "food-ball," or coprolite, which gives very welcome information concerning

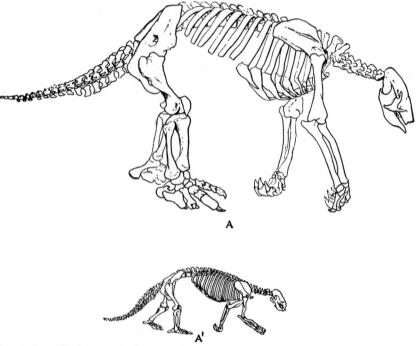

Fig. 394. — Skeletons of †Gravigrada, drawn to same scale. A, †*Nothrotherium*, Pleistocene. A', †*Hapalops*, Santa Cruz. (From Stock.)

the feeding habits of †*Nothrotherium*. The material which remains after mastication and digestion is a mass of coarsely chopped twigs and roots of a desert scrub-vegetation and the proportion of large roots confirms the inference that the great claws were used in digging as well as for weapons of defence. This particular individual of †*N. shastense* was living in an arid region, where the vegetation was quite the same as it is to-day. Representatives of the same species which dwelt in California must have fed upon very different plants.

†*Nothrotherium* was almost certainly descended from †*Hapalops*, of the Santa Cruz and has, on the whole, departed less from its Mio-

cene ancestors than have the other Pleistocene genera. The most fundamental changes are the shortening of the body by reduction in the number of vertebræ, †*Hapalops* having 22 dorso-lumbar vertebræ and †*Nothrotherium* only 17, and in the articulations of the feet. Another, but less important change is the loss of the first and caniniform tooth in both jaws, making the formula $\frac{4}{3} \times 2 = 14$. (Fig. 408, p. 689.)

As previously pointed out, the †Megalonychidæ greatly preponderate in the Santa Cruz fauna over the other two families of †Gravigrada and, while there are many genera and species, they are all very much alike; all of them are small animals and some are very small, and they are much less specialized than the lumbering monsters of the Pleistocene. In all of the genera the dental formula is $\frac{5}{4}$; the first tooth in each jaw is isolated as a caniniform tusk and, usually, the tusks are slender and cylindrical, but in †*Eucholœops* they are much larger and more formidable.

In these small Miocene †megalonychids there are at least two types of premaxillary bones and two of the predentary spout of the mandible and these are exemplified in the Pleistocene by †*Nothrotherium* and †*Megalonyx*. There may have been several other forms of premaxillæ in the Santa Cruz, for these bones are nearly always missing from the fossil skulls of that formation. One type of premaxilla is to be seen in †*Hapalops* and is Y-shaped with long, cylindrical, rod-like anterior portion and a forked base which articulates with the maxillary. The second type is that of †*Hyperleptus*, in which the bones are small triangular plates, which fill up a notch in the front end of the hard palate. †*Hapalops* agrees with †*Nothrotherium* in the form of the premaxillaries and of the mandibular spout, which is long, decurved, with nearly parallel sides and rounded tip. In †*Eucholœops*, the premaxillaries of which are not known, the spout is short, triangular and pointed; the vestige of a spout which †*Megalonyx* has (p. 662) was probably derived from the †*Eucholœops* type of jaw.

The skeleton is known in only a few of the Santa Cruz genera of the †Megalonychidæ, but more or less extensive parts of others show that there was great uniformity of structure throughout; in all, the trunk is long, with 22 or more dorso-lumbar vertebræ, and the limbs are short; the feet are five-toed and all digits are clawed; the astragalus is symmetrical and the gait seems to have been plantigrade, or pedolateral at will.

In the Pliocene of Catamarca occurs a genus, †*Pronothrotherium*, which is intermediate between †*Nothrotherium* and †*Hapalops*, but is somewhat closer to the latter. A beautifully complete skeleton of this genus is in the Field Museum, Chicago, but the description of it has not yet been published. It has the long trunk with numerous vertebræ of †*Hapalops* and the same type of premaxillary bones and mandibular spout. In size, the animal surpasses the Santa Cruz genus, but is much inferior to †*Nothrotherium*.

This series cannot, as yet, be traced farther back than the Miocene. The second tribe within the family is that which terminated in the Pleistocene †*Megalonyx*. As yet, this genus is known only from North America and, though several times reported from South America, these reports have not been verified. Assuredly, however, the genus is of Neotropical origin and, in all probability, it arose far to the north of the Tertiary fossiliferous areas and spread into North America in the Pliocene.

†*Megalonyx*, or "Great Claw," is of peculiar interest, for it was named by President Thomas Jefferson. Two papers on this animal, read before the American Philosophical Society in 1797, were the beginning of vertebrate palæontology in America. One of these papers was by Mr. Jefferson, the other by Dr. Caspar Wistar, Professor of Anatomy in the University of Pennsylvania. Dr. Wistar made use of Cuvier's description of the Madrid skeleton of †*Megatherium* to interpret the scattered remains of †*Megalonyx*. In proposing the generic term Mr. Jefferson did not suggest any name for the species and this omission was not corrected until 1822, when the French naturalist, Desmarest, gave it the very appropriate term of †*M. jeffersoni*. Nearly a dozen species have been proposed, but all save the first are of very doubtful validity. These animals have been most frequently found in the forested regions of the East, Middle West and Pacific Coast, ranging from southern California to eastern Pennsylvania.

The only assembled skeleton of †*Megalonyx* is that in the museum of the Ohio State University at Columbus. The genus is very much smaller and less massive than †*Megatherium;* the linear dimensions, as compared with the latter are in about the ratio of 11 to 18; the Columbus skeleton measures 11 feet 4 inches in length, including the tail. †*Megalonyx* is less extremely specialized than either †*Megatherium*, or †*Mylodon*, but, nevertheless, has a decided likeness to both of them; it is in the comparison of details that important differences present themselves.

In †*Megalonyx* the usual dental formula of $\frac{5}{4}$ recurs, but in strong contrast to †*Megatherium* the first tooth in each jaw is separated from those behind it by a considerable space and in form it is a tusk. Though growing permanently through life, these tusks project but little above and below the jaws and must have been kept worn down by use in feeding. Had their principal function been defensive, they would have been used only occasionally and would, consequently, have grown to considerable length. The grinding teeth are more or less triangular prisms; in the upper jaw, they are broad internally,

Fig. 395. — Skeleton of †*Megalonyx jeffersoni*, restored. In background cast of the London skeleton of †*Megatherium americanum*. In both skeletons the sternum is incorrectly restored and in that of †*Megalonyx* the fifth digit of the right fore-foot is inaccurate. (Mus. Ohio State Univ.)

narrow externally and in the lower jaw these proportions are reversed, except in the last tooth, or they may be quadrate, perhaps a specific difference. The masticating surface is hollow, with raised periphery formed by the harder dentine; the cement covering is bevelled by wear.

The skull has a remarkably short face and very elongate cranium; the upper profile is nearly horizontal and is made up of two very gentle convexities. Unlike the other genera of the North American Pleistocene, there is a distinct and rugose, but not prominent sagittal crest, which for a greater or less part of its length, is cleft by an irregular fissure, apparently a gaping parietal suture. The cranium is not elevated above the face and the occipital condyles are level with the teeth. The orbital depression is exceedingly shallow and the eye-socket is widely open behind (in contrast to †*Megatherium*) for there is hardly any post-orbital process of the frontal and that of the jugal is a mere angulation.

As in †*Megatherium*, the jugal is fixed in the zygomatic arch by co-ossification and the bone is shaped much more as in the genus last named than as in †*Mylodon*. In the †Gravigrada generally, the jugal has a highly characteristic, three-branched shape. In †*Megalonyx* the horizontal portion gives off two vertical branches, a dorsal one behind the eye and a ventral one, which is very long and descends to the ventral border of the mandible. This suborbital process is much narrower than in †*Megatherium*, but thin and plate-like as in that genus. A notable difference from the latter is in the shape of the premaxillæ, which are co-ossified with the hard palate and do not extend in front of the tusks; they are very small and of triangular shape.

Each of the four genera of the North American Pleistocene †ground-sloths has its own peculiar form of lower jaw, which differs from that of all the others. As usual in the group, the two halves of the jaw are, in †*Megalonyx*, united into one mandible; the symphysis is narrow and on its upper edge is a small, triangular projection between the tusks, which continues down the chin as a thin keel. This is evidently a remnant of the small, triangular spout which occurs in many Santa Cruz genera, such as †*Eucholæops*. In the anterior, tooth-bearing part of the jaw, it is vertically deep and its lower border is convex, but becomes concave in the posterior part; the angular process is of a regularly broad sickle-shape, and the condyle is set on a long neck with strong backward inclination, which makes a deep notch between condyle and angle.

The vertebræ are smaller and lighter than those of †*Megatherium*, but otherwise like them and the tail is almost as massive proportionally. The limbs also lack the great massiveness of †*Megatherium*, but they are very heavy and in shape are decidedly more like those of the latter than those of †*Mylodon*, but the feet are more peculiar and unlike those of the other genera named.

The fore-foot, or manus, is not completely known, for some of the phalanges have not been recovered. There are five functional digits, all of which, except perhaps V, were provided with claws. In †*Megatherium* the four functional metacarpals are closely pressed together and, for one-half or more of their length, articulate with each other, but in †*Megalonyx* the metacarpals are divergent and only between mc. III and IV is there an extensive contact. The first metacarpal (mc. I) is very short; mc. II and III, though short and very heavy, are more than twice as long as mc. I. The fourth and fifth (mc. IV and V) are much longer and more slender than mc. II and III and of entirely different shape. Four of the toes, I–IV, are clawed, the fifth (mc. V) probably was not; the phalanges of the first row are very short, but those of the second row are so elongate that they make the digits relatively long. The ungual phalanx of digit I, is much the smallest of the series, those of digits II–IV are very large, a feature from which Mr. Jefferson took the name for the genus; the bony hood is much shorter than in †*Megatherium* and fails along the upper median line. The articulations indicate that the claws had a considerable degree of retractility, produced in quite a different manner from that of the cats.

The pelvis has the same great expansion to support the viscera as the other large †Gravigrada, and the hind limb-bones are much heavier than those of the fore-leg, though far less massive than in †*Megatherium*, from which and from †*Mylodon* the present genus differs in having a third trochanter on the femur, but agrees with them in that the shaft is very much flattened, as in massive mammals generally. Tibia and fibula are also very heavy and are separate, not co-ossified at the ends; the fibula differs from that seen in the two genera last named, in which it is straight, while in †*Megalonyx*, its strongly concave inner border makes the interosseous space very wide, more so than in the other genera named.

The hind-foot is not so well preserved as the fore-foot and the first digit is not known. The astragalus is very much less modified than in any other of the North American Pleistocene †ground-sloths and closely resembles the form seen in almost all of the Santa Cruz genera of the suborder. The calcaneum, on the other hand, is the strangest bone of a very strange skeleton and, as Owen long ago remarked, it looks more like the pelvis of a moderate-sized animal than it does like a heel-bone; it resembles in shape the calcaneum of the Santa Cruz †megalonychids in enormously exaggerated size and differs altogether from those of †*Megatherium* and †*Mylodon*. It is difficult to imagine what such a leg and foot can have looked like in life. Though the first metatarsal (mt. I) has not been found, its presence is indicated by facets upon the adjoining bones and it may be assumed that in †*Megalonyx* the hind-foot had five toes, all of which, except the fifth, had claws. The second and third metatarsals (mt. II and III) are very short and heavy; mt. IV is much the longest of the series and mt. V is of very peculiar form, having a triangular, plate-like shape, the outer border of which rested on the ground in walking; the fifth digit has no phalanges. In the other digits the first phalanx is very short and heavy, the second much more elongate, though not so long as in the fore-foot.

Ten or a dozen species of †*Megalonyx* have been described, but the fragmentary material upon which most of them were founded makes it impossible to determine the extent of individual variation and there may have been only one Pleistocene species, with local

FIG. 396. — Side view of skull of †*Megalocnus*, Pleistocene of Cuba. (Amer. Mus. Nat. Hist.)

races, such as the †*M. jeffersoni californicus* described by Professor Stock. To bring together all the material which makes it possible

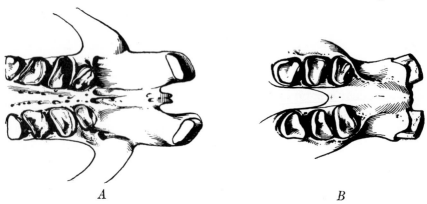

A   B

FIG. 397. — †*Megalocnus*, same specimen as Fig. 396. *A*, view of palate from below. *B*, lower jaw, from above.

to give an account of all parts of the skeleton, it has required the labours of many collectors for more than a century and extending over the whole country from Louisiana to Pennsylvania, Ohio, Indiana, Tennessee, Kansas, California and Washington.

The †Megalonychidæ were represented in the North American Pliocene, but so scanty and incomplete are the fossils that generic determinations are impracticable. †*Megalonyx* itself has been reported from the middle Pliocene (Blanco stage) but upon insufficient grounds. Between the North American Pleistocene and the Santa Cruz Miocene there is a long hiatus in time, during which nothing is known of this tribe, though, as above stated, the †*Nothrotherium* series is represented in the Pliocene of Catamarca. Among the Santa Cruz genera of the family, it is not yet possible to point out the presumable ancestor of †*Megalonyx*, because of incomplete materials. Such ancestor must have had premaxillæ in the form of small, triangular plates, united with the maxillaries, such as are found in †*Hyperleptus;* the caniniform tusks probably had the shape seen in †*Megalonychotherium*, though a derivation from the †*Eucholœops* type is not unlikely. The mandibular spout must have been like that of †*Eucholœops*, short, triangular, pointed at the end and constricted at the base. It would be premature to assert that any or all of these genera were ancestral to †*Megalonyx*. The Deseado genus †*Orophodon* is too incompletely known for description.

The third tribe of the family is that which came to an end in the Pleistocene Antillean genera, †*Megalocnus*, †*Mesocnus*, †*Microcnus*, etc., of Cuba, and †*Acratocnus*, of Puerto Rico. These are all of small or moderate size, not exceeding that of †*Nothrotherium* and, except for some modifications of the teeth, they are but little advanced over the Santa Cruz genera. The anterior teeth above and below have the shape and, no doubt, had the functions, of rodent incisors. In the Pliocene, when the Greater Antilles were united with each other and with Central America, these animals entered Cuba and, when cut off from the main land, they remained as isolated colonies.

Family 4. †Megatheriidæ

The history of the †megatheres is not so well known as that of the †megalonychids and as only two or three genera, †*Megatherium*, †*Planops* and †*Prepotherium* (if the two latter are properly separated), need be considered, no formal table of genera is required. The typical genus, †*Megatherium*, was common to both North and South America in the Pleistocene, but, in this country, it had a more southerly range than the other genera of the suborder, occurring chiefly in Georgia and Florida, though it has been found as far north as New Jersey; so far as is yet known, it did not extend over the Great Plains or to the Pacific Coast. This was the first of the †ground-sloths to be named; a skeleton found near Buenos Aires and sent to Madrid, was described by Cuvier in 1797 and another skeleton from the same region was the subject of a very complete monograph by Sir Richard Owen (1851–

1860). No skeleton of this genus has yet been found in North America, but the fossils obtained are quite sufficient to establish its presence here in the Pleistocene, though it is rare.

The genus †*Megatherium* includes the largest and most massive members of the suborder; †*M. americanum*, though having shorter legs, is larger than a modern elephant and the limbs, especially the

FIG. 398. — *Megatherium americanum*, Pampean of Argentina, the largest of known †ground-sloths. (Restored from a skeleton in La Plata Mus.)

hinder pair, are of extraordinary bulk; some of the skeletons are 20 feet long, including the tail.

The teeth number $\frac{5}{4} \times 2 = 18$, and are all alike, in uninterrupted sequence in each jaw and differ only in size; they are quadrate, rootless prisms which grew throughout life, attaining a length of six or eight inches, and are thickly covered with cement, especially on the anterior and posterior faces. Unlike the teeth of most †Gravigrada, those of †*Megatherium* have transverse crests and look very much like the lower molars of a tapir, but the shape is entirely due to abrasion and the arrangement of the vertical layers of hard and soft dentine and cement; the edges of the harder dentine plates form the crests and the valleys between are worn in the softer dentine, while the anterior and posterior slopes are formed by the abraded cement.

The low and narrow skull is small in proportion to the huge body; the cranium has a narrow sagittal area, but no crest. The orbit is nearly, or quite encircled in bone and the descending process of the jugal beneath the eye-socket is very long and conspicuous and the jugal itself is firmly fixed in the zygomatic arch by sutures with the squamosal and maxillary; in the more ancient genera this bone is but loosely attached in the arch and is generally missing from the fossil skulls. The nasal bones are short, the long, narrow and toothless premaxillaries project far in front of them. The lower jaw has a long, spout-like symphysis, which is deeply channelled on the upper side and rounded, not pointed, in front. This spout presumably lodged a long, flexible tongue, which the animal used in gathering the leaves that formed most of the diet. Below the teeth the lower jaw becomes very deep vertically, affording space for the very long grinders, and the lower border of the jaw in the dentigerous region describes a strongly convex curve. The combination of this convexity with the concave lower border of the spout is highly characteristic of the family and goes back to the Santa Cruz Miocene.

The neck is rather short and has but seven vertebræ, a difference from the tree-sloths; the body is very long and its vertebræ have the complex articulations common to all the Xenarthra, and all the neural spines, back to the tail, incline posteriorly. The three lumbars are separate from each other and from the sacrum. The tail is extremely massive, and large chevron bones are attached to the anterior vertebræ. The length and curvature of the ribs show that the body was enormously heavy.

The immense shoulder-blade has a very long acromion, which curves forward and inward, uniting with the coracoid to form a bony loop. The enormous pelvis has the ilia very widely expanded, to carry the huge mass of viscera in the semi-erect position, which, there is every reason to believe, was the usual posture in feeding, when the body-weight was supported on a tripod made of the hind-legs and the tail.

The limbs are of nearly equal length, but the fore-legs are somewhat longer and very much less massive than the hind, which are extraordinarily heavy and must have been enormously powerful in life. The humerus is long and has a comparatively slender upper portion, while the lower end is made extremely broad by the great supinator ridge and internal epicondyle, which has no foramen. The radius evidently had the power of free rotation. The femur is relatively short and is flattened antero-posteriorly, but is extremely broad and massive and has lost the third trochanter. The tibia and fibula are likewise short and immensely heavy; they are so extensively co-ossified at both ends that only a small interosseous space remains; in some young individuals the two bones are separate.

The very peculiar feet are connected with the limbs in such a manner that the animal must have walked upon the knuckles and the outside edge, probably in much the same fashion as the Ant-bear uses his fore-feet. The manus has four functional digits and the vestige of a pollex; the fifth digit, on which the weight rested in walking, has two small phalanges and no claw, the other digits, the second, third and fourth, have long, sharp claws, with an extensive bony hood reflected over the base, as in the modern cats.

The ankle-bone (astragalus) has a peculiar shape, which must have made it impossible for the animal to rest the sole of the foot on the ground; the heel-bone (calcaneum) is club-like and enormously heavy and formed part of the support of the body-weight, when placed on the ground. The hind-foot has three functional digits, for the first and second are reduced to vestiges; digit III has an enormous claw and a short, very heavy metatarsal and, in this digit the first and second phalanges are co-ossified. Digits IV and V, which form the weight-carrying outer border of the foot, have no claws.

Those who have studied the structure of †*Megatherium* are in very general agreement as to its appearance and habits. Evidently, it could not have moved with any speed and must have walked with an awkward, lumbering gait; it must have fed chiefly upon leaves and soft twigs and, very probably, it stood, when browsing, in a more or less erect attitude, supported upon the hind-legs and tail, and using the clawed fore-feet to draw branches down within reach of the extensible tongue. What can have been the use of the single huge claw of the hind-foot, it is difficult to say, unless it was a defensive weapon. Possibly, it was employed to uproot small trees, as the African Elephant uses his tusks.

No bony scutes have been found in association with any member of this family.

†Megatheres occur in the various Pliocene and Miocene formations as far back as the Santa Cruz, but the material is still so incomplete that little can be done with it. In the Santa Cruz stage itself †Gravigrada are among the commonest of fossils and occur in such bewildering variety and abundance, that the discrimination of species is well-nigh impossible, though the genera may be readily distin-

guished. It is of great interest to observe that in the Santa Cruz fauna the three families have almost converged back into a common term; they are still distinguishable, but, were it not for subsequent developments, it may be doubted whether any one would think it worth while to separate them. Of the three, the †Megalonychidæ greatly preponderate, while the other two groups are relatively rare.

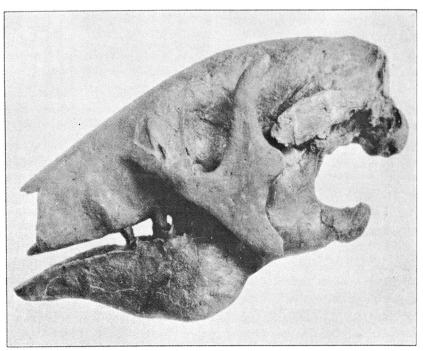

FIG. 399. — †*Planops longirostratus*, Santa Cruz. (Skull modelled from specimens in Field Mus. Nat. Hist. and Princeton Univ. Mus.)

The Santa Cruz beds have yielded two supposedly different genera, †*Planops* and †*Prepotherium*, which are very much alike and may be identical; if so, the name †*Planops* has priority and will be here used to cover both forms. The species of this genus (or these genera) are by far the largest of the Santa Cruz †ground-sloths, rivalling a Wild Boar in height and far exceeding it in massiveness; many structural features require the reference of these species to the †Megatheriidæ, though they are very much less specialized and of far smaller size than their Pliocene and Pleistocene successors. The difference, indeed, is so great that it seems questionable whether there was sufficient time for such extensive changes to be effected. There is little about the teeth of †*Planops* to suggest relationship with †*Megatherium;* the formula is the same, $\frac{5}{4}$, but the first tooth, above and below, is separated from the others by a considerable diastema, is smaller than the others and of a different shape, being cylindrical and caniniform; the grinding teeth are transversely oval and have no crests, but a raised periphery around a depression due to wear. No cement appears on any of the teeth. The isolated, canine-like teeth are common to all of the Santa Cruz †ground-sloths, but in the various genera, they differ much in size and shape.

The skull is long and narrow, with smoothly rounded cranium, which has no sagittal crest; the jugal is loosely attached and differs in shape from that of †*Megatherium,* the suborbital process being much shorter. The lower jaw differs markedly from that of all other known Santa Cruz genera, but has a striking likeness to that of †*Megatherium,* though the characteristics are less extremely developed. The lower border of the dentigerous region is strongly convex, but not so much so as in the Pampean genus, and the anterior spout is not prolonged so far. The Santa Cruz genera of the †Megalonychidæ all have a symphyseal spout, but it is shorter and of a different shape from that of †*Planops.*

The peculiar characteristics of the femur and the knee-joint are those of †*Megatherium* in an incipient stage and are what might be expected in an ancestor of the latter. Tibia and fibula are separate. The feet are very much less specialized than those of the Pleistocene genera, among which †*Megatherium* displays the most advanced degree of adaptation to peculiar modes of life. There are five toes in both fore- and hind-feet, all of which have claws and none of which are co-ossified. In the hind-foot the astragalus has already begun to assume the extraordinary shape, which, in †*Megatherium* forces the sole of the hind-foot to face inward and the outer edge to rest upon the ground. In †*Planops,* on the contrary, there would seem to have been much greater freedom of motion in the ankle-joint, so that the animal could walk either upon the sole or upon the outer edge of the foot.

Until the upper Miocene and Pliocene genera of this family shall have been recovered in a state so far complete as to make clear the essentials of structure, it would not be justifiable to assert that †*Planops,* or †*Prepotherium* is the actual ancestor of †*Megatherium,* for the relation may have been collateral rather than direct, yet these Santa Cruz genera enable us to form a reasonable and probable conception of what those ancestors must have been.

Family 5. †Mylodontidæ

This group includes smaller and lighter animals than the †megatheres, though larger and stouter than †Megalonyx. In the Pleistocene and Pliocene of South America this was the predominant family, the †megalonychids having lost the preponderance which was so markedly theirs in the Santa Cruz. The best-known and most important genera of the family are as follows:

†MYLODONTIDÆ

?†Neomylodon, Rec. S. A. †Mylodon, Pleist., N. and S. A. †Paramylodon, Pleist., N. A. †Lestodon, †Scelidotherium, †Scelidodon, †Glossotherium, †Grypotherium, etc., Pleist., S. A. †Pseudolestodon, Pleist. and Plio., S. A. †Nematherium, †Analcitherium, Santa Cruz. †Octodontotherium, Deseado.

The type-genus of the family, †Mylodon, is common to the Pleistocene of both North and South America and very complete skeletons have been obtained in both continents. †M. robustus, from Argentina, was described in an exhaustive monograph by Sir Richard Owen in 1842, and equally perfect skeletons of †M. harlani have been found in the tar of Rancho La Brea and of †Paramylodon garmani in the loess of northern Nebraska. A nearly allied genus of the same family, †Neomylodon (if actually separable from †Grypotherium) survived in Patagonia until the Recent epoch; there is every reason to believe that the animal of which remains were found in a cave on Last Hope Inlet, was put to death by human agency. These remains, a skull, large pieces of the hide, covered with hair, and a quantity of dried dung, are in the Museum of La Plata, Argentina, and can hardly be more than a few centuries old. The skin is filled with pebble-like dermal ossicles, which, when the innermost layer of the dermis is removed, look like a cobblestone pavement. The ossicles are not visible externally, as they are *within* the hide. The hair is coarse and straight and of a yellowish colour somewhat lighter than that of †Nothrotherium. Similar ossicles had previously been found in association with skeletons of †Mylodon and had been correctly interpreted.

The skeletons of †Mylodon are smaller by $\frac{1}{3}$ or $\frac{1}{4}$ in linear dimensions than those of †Megatherium, but, in structure, the two are so much alike that their manner of living must have been substantially the same. The teeth number $\frac{5}{4} \times 2 = 18$; the anterior one, in each jaw, is separated from the others and is more or less tusk-like and caniniform; these teeth are especially enlarged in †Lestodon; the

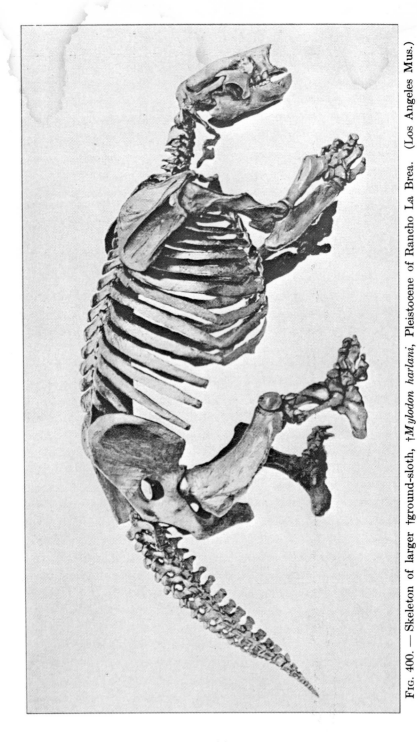

Fig. 400. — Skeleton of larger †ground-sloth, †*Mylodon harlani*, Pleistocene of Rancho La Brea. (Los Angeles Mus.)

other teeth are worn off evenly and have nearly horizontal grinding surfaces, but a broad, vertical groove on the inner, or lingual side, gives them a subtriangular, lobate shape. Such lobation is confined to the present family and goes back to the earliest known members of it.

The skull is short and broad, with flat top and neither sagittal area or crest; an extensive system of small chambers is interposed

FIG. 401. — †Ground-sloth, †*Mylodon robustus*, Pampean of Argentina. (Restored from Sir R. Owen's figure of the skeleton.)

between the inner and outer tables of the cranial bones. The orbit is widely open behind and the jugal, which is but loosely attached in the zygomatic arch, is shaped much more as in †*Nothrotherium* and †*Hapalops* than as in †*Megatherium*. The premaxillaries are small, triangular plates and the muzzle is broad, abruptly truncated and with very large nasal opening. The lower jaw is altogether different from that of †*Megatherium* and more like the mandible of †*Megalonyx*, having a straight lower border and a short, very wide and shovel-shaped symphysis and square chin; there is no anterior spout. The heads of the living †*Mylodon* and †*Megatherium* must have been very unlike.

Except for its smaller size and less massive proportions, the skeleton of †*Mylodon* resembles that of †*Megatherium* and has a similarly long trunk of 19 vertebræ. The three lumbar vertebræ are co-ossified with the sacrum. The fore-leg is relatively shorter and stouter than in †*Megatherium;* the humerus has no epicondylar foramen, the femur no third trochanter and the bones of the lower leg are not co-ossified. The fore-foot has five digits, of which the three inner ones (I, II, III) are clawed, while the others (IV, V) have

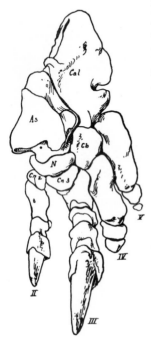

no claws; the claw of digit III is especially large. The pes is less extremely modified than in †*Megatherium*, though the animal had a similar gait, walking on the outer edge of the foot, with the sole perpendicular and facing inward; the first digit has been suppressed, the second and third have claws, but not the fourth and fifth upon which the weight rested.

One other genus of the family, †*Paramylodon*, has been found in the North American Pleistocene; it is distinguished by the absence of the first upper tooth, making the formula $\frac{4}{4}$, and by the elongate skull and inflated muzzle, but in South America there was a much larger number of genera and a host of species and individuals, the †mylodonts being by far the preponderating family of †ground-sloths, completely reversing the proportions which prevailed in Santa

FIG. 402. — Left pes of †*Mylodon*, Pampean. *Cal*, calcaneum. *As*, astragalus. *N*, navicular. *Cn 2, Cn 3*, middle and external cuneiforms. *Cb*, cuboid. (From Owen.)

Cruz times. The various Pampean genera of the family differ from one another chiefly in size and in the characters of teeth and skull. In †*Lestodon*, for example, the first tooth in each jaw is a large, sharp-pointed tusk, the muzzle is much broader than in †*Mylodon* and the whole animal larger. In †*Glossotherium*, †*Grypotherium* and †*Neomylodon*, if they are properly regarded as separate genera, the skull is elongate and there is an arched bony bridge connecting the nasals and premaxillaries and dividing the nasal opening into two parts.

The smallest Pleistocene member of the family is †*Scelidotherium*, which has a very different-looking skull from that of †*Mylodon* and †*Lestodon;* it is long and narrow and has a slender, tapering, bluntly pointed muzzle with elongate premaxillaries, instead of the broad, abruptly truncated muzzle of the other genera. The lower jaw differs correspondingly in having a very long predentary spout. As with the †megatheres, it is necessary to go back to the Santa Cruz to find well-defined ancestors of the Pampean genera. The family was represented in the Pliocene and upper Miocene, but the known fossils are too incomplete to afford much information as to the development of the group. In the Santa Cruz the best-known genera of the family are †*Analcitherium* and †*Nematherium.* These are very small, no larger than the Red Fox, and have long, narrow skulls with typically †mylodont teeth. No dermal ossicles have been found in association with these genera, but in the absence of skeletons, the lack is not significant.

In the Deseado formation this family appears to be represented by †*Octodontotherium,* the known remains of which are very fragmentary, but they suffice to show that these were much larger animals than the Santa Cruz genera, though far inferior in size to the Pampean giants.

SERIES B. LORICATA. ARMOURED EDENTATES

SUBORDER IV. **Dasypoda.** ARMADILLOS

The armadillos are a conspicuous element in the Neotropical fauna of to-day and they are also the most ancient of the Xenarthra, going back to the Casa Mayor. They are, at present, distributed from Patagonia to Texas, though they are much more numerous and varied in the tropical and subtropical regions than in temperate climates; in very cold areas they are entirely lacking. All existing and most fossil genera belong to the family Dasypodidæ, of which the most important genera are listed below.

Family 6. Dasypodidæ

Tolypeutes, Apar. *Zaëdyus,* Pygmy Armadillo. *Scleropleura, Praopus, Chlamyphorus,* Pichiciago, Rec. S. A. *Dasypus,* 6-, 7- and 8-Banded Armadillos. *Cabassous,* 11-Banded Armadillo. *Priodontes,* Giant Armadillo. *Tatu,* Peba, 9-Banded Armadillo, Pleist. and Rec. S. A., Rec. Texas. †*Eutatus,* †*Chlamydotherium,* Pleist. and Plio. S. A. †*Holmesina,* Pleist. N. A. †*Stegotherium,* Santa Cruz. †*Proeutatus,* †*Prodasypus,* †*Prozaëdius,* Santa Cruz and Deseado. †*Proeuphractus,* †*Meteutatus,* †*Sadypus,* †*Amblytatus,* Deseado. †*Utaëtus,* Casa Mayor.

Recent armadillos are small; the largest one now living, the Giant Armadillo (*Priodontes gigas*), may exceed three feet in length, exclusive of the tail, and the smallest is the little Pichiciago, or "Fairy Armadillo" (*Chlamyphorus truncatus*), which is hardly more than five inches long. Much larger animals of this family occurred in the Pleistocene of North America and in the Pleistocene and Pliocene of South America.

In most armadillos, *Praopus* and *Chlamyphorus* excepted, the hair is scanty and coarse and there is (except in *Scleropleura* and *Chlamyphorus*) a very complete armour of bony scutes, covered with plates of horn. A head-shield covers the top of the skull, the body is protected by the carapace and the tail is enclosed in a sheath which is made up of more or less regular rings; the outer sides of the limbs are covered by irregular scutes and scales, leaving only the ventral side of the body, neck and head and the inner sides of the limbs unprotected. Among the different genera, there is great variety as to the size, arrangement and ornamentation of the scutes and scales. In most Recent armadillos the carapace is in three segments, the anterior and posterior *bucklers*, in which the bony scutes are immovably fixed together by their edges and, between the bucklers, a zone made up of movable, overlapping bands in variable number. The bands, numbering from 3 to 13, provide for the flexibility of the body. One genus, *Tolypeutes*, has the power of rolling itself into a ball, the head-shield exactly fitting in the anterior notch of the carapace and the folded-in tail-sheath filling the posterior notch. In this fashion, the animal is made secure against attack and does not dig itself in, as other kinds of armadillos do and with a rapidity that is astonishing.

The Pichiciago (*Chlamyphorus*), which is almost as completely subterranean in habits as are the moles, has a carapace so different from that of other armadillos, that the genus is placed in a separate subfamily. The carapace proper is without bucklers, but is composed of some 20 transverse bands of very thin scutes and delicate plates of horn. The rump is covered by an oval shield of bone, which is solid, not made up of separate scutes, and firmly co-ossified with the pelvis by means of five bony processes. This rump-shield is covered with horny plates and is notched below for the passage of the short tail. The hair is white and silky and very different from the coarse bristles of other genera. In *Scleropleura* the carapace is confined to the sides and is missing along the middle of the back, while in *Praopus* the whole carapace is covered with a thick growth of hair.

In existing armadillos the teeth are simple, cylindrical, without roots and continuing to grow through the lifetime of the animal; in certain extinct genera (e.g: †*Holmesina*, †*Proeutatus*) there is more or less distinct lobation, produced by vertical grooves. None of the Recent genera has enamel on the teeth, but in †*Utaëtus*, of the Casa Mayor, there are remains of enamel and, as Spurgin has shown, the enamel organ appears in the embryonic milk-teeth of *Dasypus*, which never cut the gum. As the teeth are nearly all alike, they cannot be separated into regions, though in some genera (e.g. *Dasypus*) there is a single tooth in each premaxilla, which must be regarded as an incisor. As in the other suborders of the Xenarthra, therefore, the dental formulas give only the total number of teeth, which varies in the different genera, but is more commonly $\frac{8}{8}$, or $\frac{9}{8}$, though in the Giant Armadillo (*Priodontes gigas*) there may be $\frac{25}{25}$, or 100 in all.

So far as present information extends, nearly all existing armadillos have but a single dentition, save for embryonic vestiges, but in *Tatu* each of the nine permanent teeth except the last, has a two-rooted predecessor and these milk-teeth remain in use until the animal is nearly full-grown. Presumably, all of the genera have embryonic teeth of the first series, which are not erupted, but only a few have been examined; in *Dasypus*, which has but one permanent incisor on each side, there are five embryonic incisors in each premaxillary.

The skull is low and flattened and, in most of the genera, has a long, slender and tapering muzzle, but in the mole-like *Chlamyphorus*, the head is short and pointed. The lower jaw is usually weak and its two halves are permanently separate. The neck is short and so covered by the carapace that little movement would be possible, even were not several of the cervical vertebræ co-ossified into a single mass. The body is elongate and the tail varies much in length and thickness in the different genera. In the lumbar and posterior dorsal regions there are not only the extraordinarily complex articulations between vertebræ which are characteristic of the Xenarthra, but, in addition, each vertebra has a pair of high processes (metapophyses) which extend upward to support the carapace. The sternal ribs are fully ossified and their heads articulate with the sternum by means of synovial joints, but as these ribs are without tubercles, there are no such double articulations as occur in the ant-bears and †ground-sloths.

The limbs are short in comparison with the length of the body, yet the armadillos are swift runners for their size, although the fore-feet are more or less extensively modified in adaptation to the digging habits which they all have. Only one genus (*Chlamyphorus*), however, is a true burrower.

The shoulder-blade has a very long acromion, which does not form a bony loop with the coracoid; the clavicles are complete and relatively heavy. The anterior element of the hip-bone is narrow and trihedral, very different from the broad plate of the †Gravigrada. The humerus has the prominent deltoid and supinator ridges common to the fossorial mammals. Ulna and radius are separate, but there is no power of rotation of the fore-foot; tibia and fibula are co-ossified at both ends.

There is no great variety of structure in the hind-foot, it is plantigrade and five-toed, each digit provided with a claw, which is usually sharp-pointed; but may be an almost hoof-like nail. On the other hand, the manus, which is used in digging, displays very different degrees of specialization in the various genera. In *Tatu*, which in many ways is very primitive, there is little difference between fore- and hind-foot, except that there are five digits with claws, in the pes, of which the three median ones (II, III, IV) are long and the laterals short; in the manus there are four functional digits and a vestige of the fifth. Much more specialized is the manus of the Giant Armadillo (*Priodontes gigas*) in which the third digit is greatly enlarged and carries an immense claw, while the other digits are reduced. The fore-foot of the Apar (*Tolypeutes*) is like that of *Priodontes*, but even more extremely modified. The claw of the third digit is very long and this animal has an extremely peculiar gait, only the tips of the long claws touching the ground as it swiftly runs.

The armadillos feed chiefly upon insects and worms, and they sometimes capture and devour lizards and small rodents, but they are omnivorous and will eat carrion and even roots.

The edentates which spread into North America in the Pliocene and Pleistocene were mostly †ground-sloths, accompanied by a few †glyptodonts; ant-bears and tree-sloths have not been reported at all. Armadillos arrived in very limited number and variety and, so far as is yet known, they did not extend beyond the southeastern states; none, for example, have been found in the Great Plains, or in California. In the Pleistocene of Florida occurs a very large genus, †*Holmesina*, the fragmentary remains of which were, when first found, supposed to be those of a †glyptodont, because of the lobate teeth, which are considerably extended in the antero-posterior dimension and are divided by vertical grooves; both in shape and structure these teeth have a decided resemblance to those of the †glyptodonts. More complete material showed that the animal was not a †glyptodont, but an armadillo related to the genus †*Chlamydotherium*, of the South American Pleistocene and Pliocene.

In Pleistocene South America the picture was very different, for there armadillos were abundantly common and very diversified, being represented by numerous genera and species. No doubt, all of the Recent genera were then in existence, for nearly all of them have been found in the Pampean loess of Argentina, or in the Brazilian caverns and, in addition, there were several forms which are now extinct and of these some were very large. One genus, †*Eutatus* has a carapace without bucklers and consisting of 33 transverse, overlapping and movable bands. The species of †*Chlamydotherium* are the largest of known armadillos, †*C. giganteum* equalling a rhinoceros in bulk, though having shorter legs. In this genus the carapace is of the usual type, with anterior and posterior bucklers, with a number of movable bands between. The teeth, like those of the nearly allied North American †*Holmesina*, have a distinct resemblance to those of †glyptodonts, in their antero-posterior extension, their division into lobes by vertical grooves and in the arrangement of harder and softer dentine.

Considerably smaller species of †*Chlamydotherium* occur in the Pliocene of Catamarca in a fine state of preservation, but, otherwise, the known armadillos of the Pliocene and upper Miocene are so fragmentary, that they afford little information concerning the development of the suborder. In the Santa Cruz stage, on the contrary, the armadillos are abundant and often beautifully preserved, both skeleton and carapace. As a whole, the Santa Cruz assemblage of armadillos is radically different from that of either the Pleistocene or the Recent and includes but few ancestors of those later genera. As in so many other cases, we must assume that the ancestors sought for were then living in the warmer regions of the north. Most of the Santa Cruz armadillos belong to aberrant side-branches which are more or less peculiarly specialized; none the less, these genera have a real value in determining the modes of evolutionary change in the Dasypoda.

These middle Miocene armadillos had the complete armour of head-shield, carapace and tail-sheath of bony scutes; no doubt, the horny scales were also present, but, of course, no vestige of these is preserved in the fossils. None of the genera has an anterior buckler, and some have no posterior buckler either. In these instances the carapace is made up of transverse movable bands. In most of the genera the teeth have the same simply cylindrical shape that occurs in the modern genera and they are arranged in the same way, but in †*Proeutatus*, which was much the largest of Santa Cruz armadillos and was a collateral ancestor of the Pliocene and Pleistocene †*Eutatus*, the last five teeth in each jaw are trihedral in shape and are sheathed in a harder dentine, while most of the tooth consists of a softer dentine, an arrangement which kept the masticating surfaces rough. Probably the animal fed, for the most part, on plants and the food was of such a nature as to keep the teeth worn down despite continuous growth.

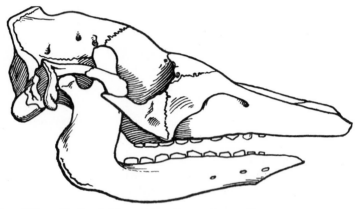

Fig. 403. — Skull of †*Proeutatus*, Santa Cruz. (Princeton Univ. Mus.)

Dentition of a second type is displayed by †*Stegotherium*, in which the teeth are so minute, though retaining the original cylindrical shape, that they can have had no functional significance. It is very likely that this animal fed upon white ants, as do the Recent ant-bears.

A third pattern of teeth is the cylindrical, peg-like form which is found in much the greater number of known armadillos from all geological horizons. In the Santa Cruz fauna this type of dentition is exemplified by †*Prozaëdius*, a very probable ancestor of the modern *Zaëdyus*, and is like that of *Dasypus* and most other modern armadillos.

Among the Santa Cruz members of the family may be noted three types of skull, each of which coincides with one of the kinds of dentition mentioned above. (1) In †*Proeutatus*, which is either directly, or collaterally ancestral to †*Eutatus*, the cranium is higher and less flattened than that of *Dasypus*, with the occipital condyles raised above the level of the teeth, and there is a very long, cylindrical muzzle, or rostrum, with nearly parallel sides; the lower jaw is exceptionally stout. (2) In †*Stegotherium* the cranium is relatively high and narrow, but the occipital condyles are below the level of the upper teeth. The face is drawn out into a very long, slender and tapering muzzle and the lower jaw is extraordinarily thin and weak, with ascending ramus low and ill-defined, and greatly reduced condyle and coronoid process. No other known armadillo has a skull like this, or such weak and fragile jaws, but there is a distinct likeness to that of the Ant-bear, due, perhaps, to similar food-habits.

FIG. 404. — †*Stegotherium tesselatum*, Santa Cruz. See also Fig. 324, p. 514. (Princeton Univ. Mus.)

(3) The skull of *Prozaëdius* is very like that of *Dasypus* and most other Recent members of the family.

Aside from carapace and skull, the skeleton of the Santa Cruz Dasypodidæ is very uniform through the various genera and differs relatively little from that of the modern armadillos. The vertebræ of the neck are already fused together and those of the lumbar and posterior dorsal regions have the extreme specialization seen in the Recent genera. The limb-bones do not differ in any significant way from those of the latter; the feet resemble those of *Dasypus* and no such specialization as occurs in *Cabassous*, *Priodontes* or *Tolypeutes*, has been found in any Santa Cruz genus.

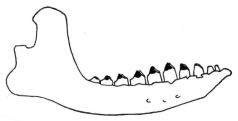

FIG. 405. — Primitive armadillo, †*Utaë-tus*, with enamel-tipped teeth, Casa Mayor. (From Simpson.)

Armadillos are abundantly represented in the beds of the Deseado formation and among them are several of the Santa Cruz genera. The family goes through the Musters and the Casa Mayor stages and, in the latter represents the only one of the xenarthrous suborders yet discovered. The armadillos are thus the most ancient and primitive of the Xenarthra and they are not far removed from the common ancestry of all the suborders. As previously mentioned, †*Utaëtus*, one of the Casa Mayor armadillos, has a remnant of enamel on the teeth. Presumably, when first erupted, those teeth were completely sheathed in enamel, but, as the teeth continued to grow through life and the enamel was not renewed, it was eventually worn away.

The armadillos are, thus, of very great antiquity and are not only the most ancient of the xenarthrous suborders, but they are not far removed from the ancestors common to all these suborders. It may be assumed that the actual ancestors were not armoured, but this is a moot point.

Family 7. †Peltephilidæ

As yet, only a single genus of this family, †*Peltephilus*, has been discovered, but that genus is so peculiar, that it cannot be included with other armadillos in the same family. Known only from the Santa Cruz and Deseado formations, it apparently came from nothing and led to nothing. These are the marks of a straggler from some other region, which can only have been the warmer lands that lay to the north of Patagonia. With all its peculiarities, †*Peltephilus* is an unmistakable armadillo and is unquestionably referable to the suborder Dasypoda, which implies that it is an aberrant branch of the armadillo stem.

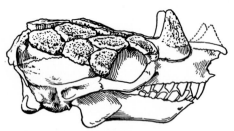

FIG. 406. — †Horned armadillo, †*Peltephilus*, Santa Cruz. (Ameghino Collection.)

The most conspicuous characteristic of †*Peltephilus* is the head-shield, which is entirely unlike that of any other known armadillo; it consists of 19 or 21 large and heavy scutes, which are very rugose and are ornamented by smooth channels around the periphery. The scutes are arranged in a definite pattern; in the median line, from the occipital crest to the anterior rim of the orbit, are three large, symmetrical, unpaired and polygonal plates. On each side of the median series are seven plates of different sizes and shapes, but all polygonal, except the post-orbital plate, which curves downward, almost reaching the zygomatic arch and enclosing the orbit behind. Placed on the nasal and maxillary bones are two high sharp-pointed, incurved and recurved horn-cores, with quadrate bases, which are scutes of the head-shield, not outgrowths of the skull. Ameghino believed that there was an anterior pair of horn-like scutes, but this has not been confirmed.

From the point of view of evolutionary philosophy, it is of particular interest to note that the horned rodent, †*Ceratogaulus*, of the North American Miocene (Fig. 147, p. 193) has horns of the same character, dermal ossifications which rest upon the skull, but are separate from it.

No complete carapace of †*Peltephilus* has been found, but a great many separate scutes are in the collections and these differ much from the scutes of any other armadillos. There was a buckler, probably the posterior one, the plates of which appear not to have been suturally united, but merely to have been in juxtaposition. The scutes of the movable bands are unusually broad in proportion to their antero-posterior length and are very thin; the part of each scute overlapped by the preceding band is remarkably narrow. In the exposed portion of the scute are three conspicuous pits which, no doubt, lodged tufts of hair.

The dentition is as peculiar and unlike that of other armadillos as is the head-shield; the dental formula is $\frac{7}{7}$ and, in both jaws, the teeth are in continuous series, without gaps, and forming so well-defined an arch that there appear to be several incisors, but, actually, there is only one on each side, above and below. With closed jaws, the upper front teeth pass outside of the lower ones and are bevelled by wear on the posterior side. All the teeth have a sheathing of hard and polished dentine that looks almost like enamel.

In striking contrast to all the other Santa Cruz armadillos, †*Peltephilus* has a broad and heavy skull, with short, wide rostrum, which gives a certain resemblance to the skulls of the †ground-sloths and entirely different from the long, slender muzzles of the contemporary Dasypodidæ. The tympanic differs from that of the latter in forming an inflated and ossified bulla, which is firmly fixed in place and has a tubular, bony entrance. The lower jaw is altogether different from that of other armadillos; the two halves are co-ossified at the symphysis and the short, curved jaw has considerable resemblance to the mandible of a tortoise.

The vertebræ, for the most part, differ little from those of other armadillos, but the tail is unusually long and stout.

Limbs and feet, while typically armadillo-like, differ in many characteristic details. On the humerus the bicipital groove is converted into a foramen by a bony bridge which connects the tuberosities. In the fore-foot the first digit is more reduced than in other Santa Cruz armadillos and the claws are short and pointed. The hind-foot, as in *Tatu*, is functionally three-toed, the lateral digits (I and V) being so reduced that they can have been of little use. The three median digits (II, III, IV) are of nearly equal length and are slender and elongate and have hoof-like ungual phalanges.

SUBORDER V. †Glyptodontia. †GLYPTODONTS

In the Pliocene and Pleistocene these huge armoured creatures ranged from the southern United States to Patagonia. That they were nearly related to the armadillos is clear, but they were so greatly modified and specialized as to demand recognition as a distinct suborder. The most important genera are as follows:

Family 8. †Glyptodontidæ

†*Glyptodon*, Plio. and Pleist., N. and S. A. †*Dœdicurus*, Pleist., S. A. †*Panochthus*, do. †*Sclerocalyptus*, Plio. and Pleist., S. A. †*Glyptotherium*, mid. Plio., N. A. †*Propalæohoplophorus*, Deseado and Santa Cruz. †*Cochlops*, Santa Cruz. †*Eucinepeltus*, do. †*Asterostemma*, do.

Aside from their enormous size, the most striking feature of the †Glyptodontia is the extraordinary development of their defensive armour, which is far more complete and massive than in the armadillos. The top of the head is protected by a thick head-shield, or *casque*, composed of several co-ossified plates; the body and much of the limbs are enclosed in the immense carapace of elongate-oval, domed shape, which covers the neck and trunk and on the sides almost reaches to the ground. This tortoise-like carapace is composed of very thick, polygonal plates of bone (no doubt covered externally with horny scales in the living animal) immovably fixed together by their rough edges, and ornamented with an elaborate pattern of sculpture, which varies according to the genus. With one or two exceptions, the plates of the carapace are not arranged in transverse rows, but form a mosaic without discernible banding. In the exceptions noted, the sides of the carapace are made up of bands, and near the margins are two or three overlapping transverse bands which permitted a minimal degree of flexibility. The tail-sheath is remarkable and differs much in appearance and make-up in the various genera. In †*Glyptodon* the tail is comparatively short and the tail-sheath is composed of a series of overlapping rings, each ring consisting of two rows of plates; those of the second row are ornamented, on the top and sides of the tail, with very prominent, conical projections, capped, in the living animal, no doubt, with still longer and sharper spines of horn, so that the tail must have bristled with spikes. A more usual type of tail-sheath is exemplified by †*Sclerocalyptus*, in which there are several overlapping rings at the root of the tail, but for much the greater part of its length the plates of the sheath are fused together into a long, transversely oval tube, tapering very gently to the free end, where it is bluntly rounded.

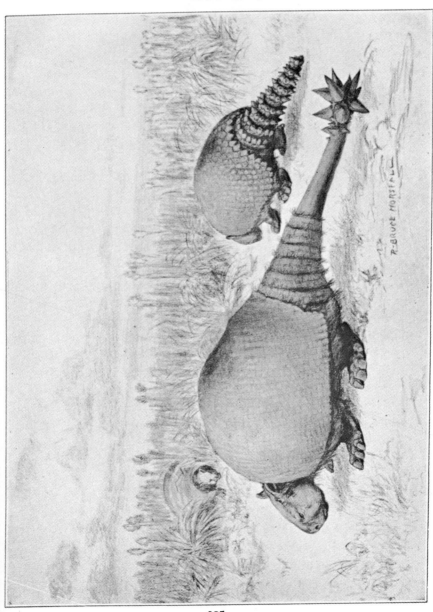

Fig. 407. — Pampean †glyptodonts, †Dædicurus clavicaudatus and †Glyptodon clavipes. (Restored from skeletons in La Plata Mus. and Mus. of Buenos Aires.)

A modification of this type is the very long tail-sheath of †*Panochthus*, in which there are seven overlapping rings at the root, followed by a long, massive tube, the sides of which were set with three or more large and heavy, horn-like spines. In †*Dœdicurus* is reached the maximum specialization of this type; the very long tube has its free end greatly expanded and thickened into a huge, club-shaped mass, on the top and sides of which must have been fixed long and sharp horns.

The teeth, which in all the known genera number $\frac{8}{8}$, are all very much alike; each is divided by two broad and deep vertical grooves on each side into three pillars, connected by narrow necks. Harder dentine in the centre and on the periphery of the tooth, with a softer intermediate layer, kept the grinding surface rough through differential wear. Teeth of this character are indicative of a vegetable diet and these great creatures were, no doubt, as harmless and inoffensive as possible.

The skull is remarkably short, broad and high, the facial region being especially abbreviated; the cranium, though forming the greater part of the skull, is yet small in comparison with the size of the animal; it has a distinct, though not prominent, sagittal crest. The occipital surface is inclined forward and has a very elevated position, the condyles being near the top of the head and raised very far above the level of the teeth. The orbits are relatively small, more or less completely encircled with bone and as near to the top of the head as they could be brought; this is to make room for the extremely high teeth, which require a great depth of jaw; the elevation of the whole cranium leaves unlimited space for the jaws beneath it. The zygomatic arches are strong and curve out widely from the sides of the skull; beneath each eye is given off a very long descending process which projects downward, outside of the lower jaw. In most of the species the upper profile of the skull is nearly straight, but in †*Panochthus* it descends very steeply from the forehead to the nose. The forehead is dome-like and the nasals are extremely short. Sinuses are extensively developed, especially in the frontals, and in †*Sclerocalyptus* the bones around the nostrils are grotesquely inflated. The two halves of the lower jaw are fused together, and the symphysis is prolonged into a short, wide spout, which projects considerably in advance of the upper jaw, showing that the soft parts of the muzzle must have had a corresponding extension. The horizontal portion of the lower jaw, carrying the teeth, is short and very deep; the posterior, ascending portion has a forward inclination and is very high.

The skeleton of the Pleistocene †glyptodonts is unique among mammals, though evidently a modification of the armadillo type. This extreme modification was conditioned by the enormous weight of the carapace, which the skeleton had to support. The neck is very short, made up of short vertebræ, which are extensively co-ossified; the atlas is always free, but the axis is fused with a varying number of the succeeding vertebræ; usually, the axis and the third to the sixth form one mass, while the seventh is fused with the dorsals. The joint between the sixth and seventh vertebræ was such as to permit at least a partial downward bending of the head beneath the carapace, closing its anterior opening with the head-shield. The seventh neck vertebra and all the dorsals, except the last one, are co-ossified into a heavy, curved rod, the "dorsal tube"; the conjoined neural arches form a tunnel for the spinal cord and the spines make a continuous ridge. As the hind-legs are very much longer than the fore, the back is strongly arched upward from the neck to the hips. The last dorsal, the lumbars and the sacrum are all fused together to form the "lumbo-sacral tube," of which the co-ossified neural spines make a very prominent ridge, the principal support of the carapace in the median line; the anterior half of the trunk skeleton, comprising the short, deep thorax, is free from the carapace, which in that region must have rested upon the muscles of the back and shoulders. The number of neck and trunk vertebræ combined varies in the different genera from 26 to 28, but fusion had reduced the number of separate parts to four, or at most five. Such greatly diminished flexibility of the back was rather an advantage. The tail differs much in length in the various genera, but is always massive; the anterior vertebræ, usually seven in number, are free, the others are fused into a heavy, tapering rod; but for nearly its whole length the processes of the vertebræ are very prominent, each vertebra touching the tail-sheath at five points and thus giving it very effective support. In †Glyptodon the tail-vertebræ are all free.

In most of the genera the scapula is very broad and has the very long acromion common to all the edentates; there are no clavicles. The hip-bones are very peculiar; the anterior element (ilium) stands almost vertically, at right angles to the backbone, and forms a broad plate, facing forward, the top of which is roughened and thickened to support the carapace. The posterior element (ischium) is also much expanded, but faces outward, and its hinder end, curved upward and thickened, is another point of strong support for the carapace. The two elements together form an inverted arch, the crown of which rests on the heads of the thigh-bones.

Though less massive than those of the hind-leg, the bones of the fore-limb are yet very heavy. The humerus is short and has reduced deltoid and supinator ridges and no epicondylar foramen; the short fore-arm bones are separate and heavy, the ulna especially so. The femur is much the longest of the limb-bones and is extremely strong, especially in its great breadth, the antero-posterior flattening, common to nearly all very heavy mammals, being well marked. A very unusual feature is the position of the third trochanter near the lower end of the shaft. The tibia and fibula are much shorter than the femur, extremely heavy and co-ossified at both ends. The very short and broad feet retain five digits; in the manus the claws are sometimes comparatively long and sharp, sometimes blunt and hoof-like; those of the hind-foot are always broad hoofs.

Among all the many strange and grotesque mammals which the study of fossils has brought to light, none can have been more remarkable than the Pleistocene †glyptodonts; slow-moving hillocks they must have seemed, the larger species 12 to 14 feet long and 5 feet or more in height. Those that had claws on the fore-feet probably used them to dig for roots and tubers, but all were plant-feeders. When attacked by the †sabre-tooth tigers (†*Smilodon*) or the great bears (†*Arctotherium*) they needed only to squat down, bringing the edges of the carapace to the ground, and draw in the head, to be protected, while a sweep of the spiny or club-like and horned tail would have been fatal to anything in its path.

As in the case of so many other groups, little has yet been learned regarding the history of the †glyptodonts during the interval between the later Pliocene and the Santa Cruz; the intermediate formations have yielded many †glyptodonts, but not in such preservation as to be of any service in this connection. We find, as might be expected, many and very great differences between the Pampean and the Santa Cruz representatives of the suborder, the latter being in all respects less modified and less widely removed from the armadillos.

(1) The most obvious and striking distinction is in size, the Santa Cruz forms being all small and some of them very small.

(2) In all cases the carapace is made up of transverse bands, which permitted a slight degree of flexibility, and near the anterior end, at the margins of the shell, are two or three overlapping bands. The plates are thin and were but rarely co-ossified; the ornamentation is made by shallow grooves, except in †*Cochlops*, which has certain scutes in the pelvic region marked by conical, rugose spines.

(3) The tail-sheath, which is of very uniform character, consists

FIG. 408. — Santa Cruz †ground-sloth, †*Hapalops longiceps*, and †glyptodont, †*Propalæohoplophorus australis*. (Restored by Knight from skeletons in Princeton Univ. Mus. and La Plata Mus.)

of two quite distinct portions; the anterior region of five or more freely movable, overlapping rings, each of two rows of plates, and in the posterior region the rings are closely fitted together, less distinctly marked and not movable. This posterior portion is sometimes thick and ends abruptly, sometimes slender and tapering and in one genus (†*Asterostemma*) it is very armadillo-like. In none of the genera were there any spines or horns on the tail, nor are the separate plates ever fused together to form a tube.

(4) There is considerable variety in the head-shield, which is usually made up of many separate plates, but in one genus (†*Eucinepeltus*) they are co-ossified into a single heavy casque.

(5) The teeth have a less extreme height and the four anterior ones of each jaw are much simpler than in the Pampean forms. An interesting survival is the retention of two minute incisors in each premaxillary bone, in one genus (†*Propalæhoplophorus*), but these were of no functional value and were early lost.

(6) The skull is much longer, narrower and lower and has a relatively longer facial portion; the occiput is higher and more erect, and the condyles have no such elevation above the level of the teeth; the orbit is widely open behind and the descending process given off from the zygomatic arch beneath the eye has no such exaggerated length; the bones are not conspicuously inflated by sinuses. The lower jaw is shallower, the symphysis and anterior spout shorter and the ascending portion far lower.

(7) The backbone has a greater number of separate parts; the atlas, as always, is free, the axis is fused with two or three of the following vertebræ; the sixth is free and the seventh fused with the first and second dorsals to form one piece, which is succeeded by two or three separate vertebræ: the other dorsals, except the last one, are united in the dorsal tube, and the lumbo-sacral tube is already complete. Thus, instead of four or five, there are eight or nine distinct parts. None of the tail-vertebræ are fused together.

(8) There is the same disparity in the length of the fore- and hind-limbs, but the bones are far more slender and armadillo-like; this is especially true of the radius and humerus, the latter having well-developed deltoid and supinator ridges and epicondylar foramen; the ulna is more massive and glyptodont-like. The femur is very much more slender and rounded and the third trochanter is placed higher up the shaft; tibia and fibula are co-ossified at both ends and resemble those of the Pampean genera, except for their much greater slenderness.

(9) The feet are much as in the latter, but relatively narrower, and the manus has longer claws.

In short, the Santa Cruz †glyptodonts depart much less widely from the armadillos than do the Pliocene and Pleistocene genera, and, to a certain extent, they bridged over the gap between the two suborders. Such backward convergence in time is very strong evidence for the community of origin of the two groups.

The †glyptodonts of the more ancient formations, so far as they are known, teach us little concerning the stages of modification in these extraordinary animals, because of their fragmentary condition. The oldest formation in which representatives of the suborder have been detected is the Musters stage, which may be Oligocene or upper Eocene. On the face of the records, therefore, the †glyptodonts had no such antiquity as the armadillos.

Order †PALÆANODONTA

This group of ancient and long-extinct edentates of North America extended in time from the middle Oligocene back to the upper Paleocene and, while they would seem to have died out without leaving any descendants, they enable us to form a conception of what the early ancestors of the Xenarthra must have been. They differ from the latter order principally in having a normal type of articulations between the vertebræ of the lumbar and posterior dorsal regions. The dentition is much specialized.

Family 9. †Metacheiromyidæ

Only three genera of this family have as yet been identified and one of these is of doubtful reference. The list is as follows:

?†*Epoicotherium*, mid. Olig. †*Metacheiromys*, mid. Eoc. †*Palæanodon*, low. Eoc. and up. Paleoc.

The White River genus, †*Epoicotherium*, represented by a single skull in the Carnegie Museum, is the only known North American edentate between the lower Pliocene and the middle Oligocene. It is a very small animal, originally referred to the Monotremata and then to the Insectivora, but it is much more probably the latest surviving member of the †Palæanodonta, terminating an aberrant offshoot from the main stem, which ended in the Bridger. The teeth are not known, except the minute last one, but the sockets show them to have been peg-like; presumably they were rootless, growing from permanent pulps, and without enamel covering. The skull is short and wedge-shaped.

broad behind, slender and tapering in front; very armadillo-like is the flask-shaped auditory bulla, with its inflated tympanic and tubular entrance. As in the Bridger †*Metacheiromys*, but not in the South American armadillos, the mastoid is large and strongly inflated.

The Bridger genus †*Metacheiromys* is, fortunately, very well known from the skeletons of two species in the American Museum. As a whole, these skeletons have very much the appearance of armadillos and the genus was originally referred to the Dasypoda, but it does not even belong to the Xenarthra. On the other hand, if the armadillos, as there is much reason to believe, are the most ancient and primitive of the Xenarthra, then their resemblance to the †Palæanodonta might have been expected.

The lumbar and posterior dorsal vertebræ make it exceedingly probable that some sort of a carapace was present, either leathery, or, as seems more likely, made up of horny scales, but without bony scutes. In any formation in which fossil armadillos are found, it is the experience of every collector that scutes outnumber jaws a hundred fold and it is well-nigh certain that such skeletons as those of the Bridger genus would have been accompanied by scutes, had the living animal possessed them. The only scutes ever found in the beds of the North American Eocene are those of lizards and crocodiles and it is as certain as negative evidence can make it, that the †Palæanodonta had no scutes.

The dentition of †*Metacheiromys* is greatly reduced and the only teeth of any functional importance are the canines, which are relatively large, sharp-pointed, partially covered with enamel and rooted, not growing from persistent pulps. In the upper jaw there is a single very small cheek-tooth and, in the lower jaw, two such cheek-teeth and one minute incisor. The formula therefore reads: $i \frac{0}{1}, c \frac{1}{1}, p \frac{1}{2}$. All of these tiny, vestigial teeth are known only from their empty sockets, but, obviously, they were useless. In place of teeth, there would seem to have been horny plates, attached to the jaws and analogous to those of the modern Duck-billed Mole (*Ornithorhynchus*) of Australia. These plates must have been used for grinding vegetable substances, while the stout, sharp and recurved canines can only have served as weapons.

The skull is long and low, with inconspicuous sagittal and occipital crests and shallow post-orbital constriction. The flask-shaped tympanic bulla is very armadillo-like and, together with the inflated mastoid, is much as in †*Epoicotherium*, and the muzzle is very short, as in †*Peltephilus*. The almost toothless lower jaw is shallow, but thick

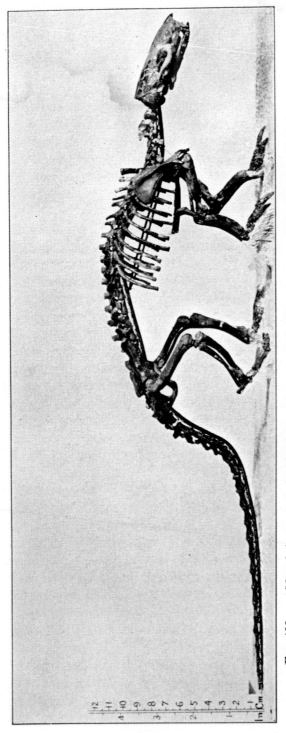

Fig. 409. — †*Metacheiromys tatusia*, North American armadillo-like edentate, middle Eocene, Bridger stage. (Amer. Mus. Nat. Hist.)

transversely and on the inner side are two longitudinal grooves, which often appear in Xenarthra, but seldom in other mammals. Despite its almost edentulous character, the mandible is not unlike that of *Tatu*.

The general appearance of the skeleton is strikingly armadillo-like and, in particular, resembles that of *Tatu;* the neck is short, about half the length of the skull, and its vertebræ are all separate. Body and tail are elongate; the vertebral formula is: C. 7, D. 11, L. 6, S. 4, Cd. ± 25. The posterior dorsals and the lumbars have each a pair of very high processes (metapophyses), which were apparently, but not necessarily, for the support of a carapace. The various processes of these vertebræ, while not having the accessory articulations of the Xenarthra, are yet so very like those of the armadillos as to afford an excellent starting point for the development of those articulations and clearly represent an ancestral type.

The sacrum, which consists of four vertebræ, differs from that of the Xenarthra in supporting the pelvis only in one line, not in two.

The tail is long and stout and must have had about 25 vertebræ, more or less; the anterior vertebræ have chevron-bones and all of them are rather more primitive than in any of the Xenarthra.

Of the eleven pairs of ribs, the first pair are very much like those of modern armadillos, but the others are thicker and less plate-like, as they also are in the strange Santa Cruz armadillo †*Peltephilus* (p. 682). No trace of a sternal rib has been found and no synovial facets for them occur on the sternum; almost certainly, therefore, these ribs cannot have been ossified.

The scapula is remarkably like that of the armadillos, especially in the long, bifurcated acromion, which curved downward and inward around the upper end of the humerus just as in the typical Xenarthra. The clavicles are complete and must have been functional, though they are slender. The pelvis is of a primitive type, from which that of the modern armadillos might well have been derived.

The limbs are short and stout, though relatively less heavy than in Recent armadillos. The humerus is obviously that of a fossorial animal and very armadillo-like, but the deltoid and supinator crests and internal epicondyle, with its foramen, are all more extremely developed than in the armadillos and look like those of miniature primitive †ground-sloths. Ulna and radius are stout and free from each other; the olecranon is of extraordinary length. The femur is armadillo-like save for a few details, and the tibia and fibula are separate.

In the fore-foot five digits are indicated by articular surfaces, but only the three middle ones, II, III and IV, have been found. These are short and heavy and are armed with strong, sharp-pointed claws; the phalanges are short and thick, of the double-pulley type and strikingly armadillo-like. The hind-foot, or pes, is also five-toed, but longer and narrower than the manus, and the very small ungual phalanges must have supported nails rather than claws. The notable difference between fore- and hind-feet is another indication of burrowing habits.

Not nearly so well known as †*Metacheiromys* is the lower Eocene and Paleocene genus †*Palæanodon*, that, so far as can be judged from extant material, seems to have been the direct ancestor of the Bridger genus, which it greatly resembles; at all events, the actual ancestor cannot have been very different. The teeth of †*Palæanodon* are not known, but from the empty sockets it may be seen that there were at least five cheek-teeth in each jaw and that these were simple, cylindrical and, presumably, covered with enamel. They are much larger than in †*Metacheiromys*, though the presence of the horny plates is already indicated. The auditory bullæ which are completely ossified and flask-like in the Bridger genus, are but partially ossified in †*Palæanodon* and the mastoids are less inflated.

The brain-case in the latter is of a low and primitive type; though the post-orbital constriction is very shallow, the hemispheres are broader behind than in front. The olfactory bulbs and the cerebellum are exposed, not overlapped by the hemispheres, and all three parts of the brain are on the same level. The hemispheres are smooth and unconvoluted, and the cerebellum is a narrow transverse band. In proportions and character this brain is very edentate-like and is intermediate between the brains of the simpler insectivores and that of the armadillo, *Dasypus*, and it corroborates the inferences drawn from the skeleton of these North American Eocene genera. The vertebræ are less specialized than those of †*Metacheiromys;* the limb-bones are more slender and the feet are more elongate, less armadillo-like.

The known North American Eocene genera of the †Palæanodonta cannot have been the actual ancestors of the Xenarthra, for they were already too far specialized, more particularly in the greatly reduced dentition, but they formed a short-lived side-branch of the ancestral stock from which the Xenarthra were derived. From present knowledge, it seems probable that the ancestors of the †Condylarthra, †Notoungulata and Xenarthra spread from North to South America in the Paleocene, when there is strong evidence of a land-connection between the two continents. It seems strange that the †Creodonta, or primeval carnivores, did not take part in this migration, but the large predaceous marsupials, already present in South America, may have kept them out. Another paradox is that there seems to have been no counter-migration from south to north, but the records of that early day are so scanty that much remains unexplained.

Whether the †Palæanodonta arose in Asia and entered North America with the middle Paleocene immigration, or whether they were indigenous here, cannot yet be positively determined. The Old World scaly anteaters, of the order Pholidota, seem to have been derived from ancestors that were nearly allied to the †Palæanodonta, but nothing is known to indicate that they were ever in America and it seems more probable, therefore, that these common ancestors were Asiatic. All of the Edentata, both of the Old World and the New, would seem to have descended, in common with the other groups of placental mammals, from Cretaceous Insectivora, such as have been found in Mongolia.

Pliocene predaceous animal, is a veritable marsupial †sabre-tooth, as its name indicates, and mimics, so to speak, the †sabre-tooth cats in the most extraordinary way. At the same time, there are many strange characteristics which are peculiar to this paradoxical beast. While there is an extraordinary likeness to the †sabre-tooth cats, there is no identity and the differences from the †machairodonts are, of course, more fundamental and significant.

The dental formula of †*Thylacosmilus* is: $i\ \frac{0}{0}$, $c\ \frac{1}{1}$, $p + m\ \frac{6}{6} \times 2 = 28$. The incisors, above and below, have been completely eliminated;

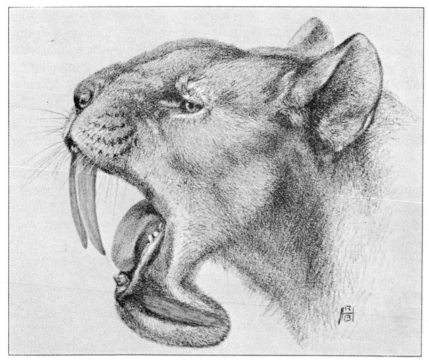

Fig. 412. — Head of †*Thylacosmilus atrox*. (Restored from skull in Fig. 411.)

the upper canine is an immense, recurved and sharp-pointed tusk, resembling, yet not altogether like the sabres of the larger †machairodonts. The tusk grew from a permanent pulp and is of compressed-trihedral shape, a conspicuous angulation running down the outer side of the tooth. The enamel is exceedingly thin and is usually restricted to the external side; the posterior edge is minutely, almost microscopically, serrate. The lower canine is incomparably smaller than the upper and is a short, stout, peg-like tooth, standing isolated at the anterior angle of the jaw.

The cheek-teeth are typically marsupial in character; the first tooth in the upper jaw is one-rooted and simple, the second two-rooted, the others have large inner cusps and three roots; the two external cusps are trenchant, but the last tooth is reduced to a vestige. In the lower jaw the first two teeth are small and simply conical; then follow four sectorial teeth, which increase in size posteriorly.

The extraordinary skull is unlike that of any other known animal; the cranium, which is made up of massive bones, is remarkably short, while the face and jaws are relatively elongate. The sagittal crest is very short and of no great height, but thick and heavy, as is also the occipital crest. The brain-case and temporal fossæ are surprisingly short, the jaws comparatively long; the cerebral chamber is disproportionately small, suggesting such a lack of intelligence as to account for the early extinction of this branch of the family. The occiput is low and wide, and the heavy lambdoidal crest describes a regular curve of somewhat more than half a circle, ending below upon the mastoid processes, which take the place of the paroccipitals. The condyles protrude prominently behind the occipital surface and are raised high above the level of the teeth.

Both cranial and facial bones are much encroached upon and crowded together by the inordinate extension of the convex sheaths of the canine sabres. The very small orbit is placed low on the side of the face and is completely encircled in bone by the extension of the frontal post-orbital process to a contact with the jugal, a feature unique among marsupials. The zygomatic arch is very short and heavy and the jugal is deeply emarginated to receive the zygomatic process of the squamosal. According to Riggs, the jugal is highly exceptional in that it forms the entire lower border of the orbit and, with the lachrymal, excludes the maxillary from forming any part of the orbital boundary. The inferior branch of the jugal extends to the glenoid cavity, which is carried upon a massive, downward projecting pedicle, very much as in the larger Oligocene †machairodonts, †*Hoplophoneus* and †*Eusmilus*. The post-tympanic process of the squamosal, to which the mastoid process is closely applied, also forms a massive pedicle, like that seen in the †sabre-tooth cats. On the basisphenoid are two very prominent tubercles for attachment of the *longi capitis* muscles; in no other known skull are these tubercles so greatly developed. As in most marsupials, the alisphenoids enter into the formation of the auditory bullæ. The lachrymal has but a small preorbital extension upon the face, but is produced in a very unusual manner, as a long, triangular plate, upward and backward, between the frontal and the canine sheath of the maxillary, ending behind in a point.

The largest, as well as the most exceptional elements of this unique skull are the maxillaries, which form nearly the whole of the face. Their most conspicuous feature is made by the great, prominent, convex sheaths of the canine sabres, which meet in sutural contact on the upper surface of the skull, wedged in between the frontals and reducing these bones to very small proportions. They also cover over the posterior half, or more, of the nasals, but diverge forward, exposing the anterior moiety of those bones. Posteriorly, the sheaths extend far behind the orbits and almost reach the parietals. The facial part of each maxillary is very large, long antero-posteriorly and deep vertically and this depth is all the more striking because the cheek-teeth have such very low crowns. The infraorbital foramen should rather be called the preorbital, for it is on a line with the middle of the orbit and unusually far in advance of it; it is further peculiar in being a canal with a broad, bony bridge over it. The palatine processes of the maxillaries are broad behind, narrowing forward to a minimum width between the canines. The hard palate is entire and without the vacuities which almost all existing marsupials display.

The premaxillaries are small, edentulous bones, which extend but little in front of the canines; the palatine processes are perforated by small incisive foramina. The ascending ramus is narrow and thin, but extends to a contact with the nasal.

The nasals are long, broad and transversely convex in front, narrowing posteriorly, as the maxillaries extend over them; the hinder parts of the nasals, where they are concealed from sight by the maxillary sheaths, are seen, in cross-section, to be thin, vertical plates, but how they terminate behind, is not made visible in any of the specimens.

The lower jaw is very much like that of the larger Oligocene †machairodonts, though in extreme and exaggerated form. The two halves of the jaw remain separate; the horizontal ramus is relatively much longer than in the †sabre-tooth cats, is nearly straight and moderately thick. The anterior flange, for the protection of the sabre-tusk, is relatively enormous and much larger than in any of the †sabre-tooths, even †Eusmilus, and is more recurved, with more prominent anterior border; the symphysis has a correspondingly deep vertical extension. The hinder part of the jaw is weak and resembles the same part in the Oligocene †machairodonts; the coronoid process is very low and narrow and the condyle is placed below the level of the teeth. The masseteric fossa is small, but deep and well defined and the angle is much reduced, but what remains of it is inflected.

The problem concerning the manner in which †*Thylacosmilus* could have used its great canines is the same as for the †machairodonts and, no doubt, the solution found for them (p. 605) will apply equally well to the †sabre-tooth marsupial. There is every reason to infer that the lower jaw was very freely movable and could be depressed so far as to disengage the points of the tusks and, with such wide-open mouth, the only way in which the sabres could have been effectively used was by striking a downward, stabbing blow with the whole head. The surfaces and projections for muscular attachment all bear out this conclusion. The temporal and masseter muscles, which are the principal ones employed in ordinary biting and masticating, were evidently reduced, while the muscles that move the whole head, especially in a downward stroke, were as evidently developed to an unusual extent. The area for the insertion of the sterno-mastoid and tubercles for the *longi capitis* muscles are far larger than in other marsupials. The latter muscles are powerful depressors of the head and arise along the sides of the cervical vertebræ, which are disproportionately heavy.

Of the vertebræ, there are known all the cervicals and a few from each of the other regions. The cervicals, as mentioned above, are disproportionately heavy and indicate that the neck was exceptionally powerful. The atlas resembles that of the †machairodonts in shape and differs from that of *Thylacynus* in not having a separate intercentrum, the inferior arch being fused with the neural arch. The axis is like that of the Santa Cruz carnivorous marsupials, such as †*Borhyæna*. The succeeding cervical vertebræ have heavy spines and processes for muscular attachment and the 7th vertebra, as is usual in marsupials, but not in placentals, has the transverse processes perforated by the canals for the vertebral arteries. The body-vertebræ, those of the dorsal, lumbar and sacral regions, resemble the corresponding ones of †*Borhyæna*, and the tail was evidently long and heavy.

The limbs and feet are short and sturdy and, in general, resemble those of the larger Santa Cruz genera of the family such as †*Borhyæna* and †*Prothylacynus*. The humerus is short and stout, with large and prominent deltoid and supinator ridges; the radius has a discoidal head and it is evident that the fore-feet could be rotated with considerable freedom. The femur has an unusually straight shaft, with no third trochanter. The tibia is about three-fourths as long as the femur and the fibula is very heavy. The manus has five short digits, and in the pes the hallux is vestigial and without phalanges.

As yet, this astonishing †sabre-tooth marsupial stands entirely isolated; it is undoubtedly related to the Santa Cruz genera, but they cannot have been directly ancestral to it. The lower Pliocene and upper Miocene deposits of the more northerly parts of Argentina have yielded only such fragmentary remains of marsupials, that the absence of any recognizable forerunners of †*Thylacosmilus* is without significance and the resemblance to the †sabre-tooth cats, surprising as it is, is not due to relationship, but to convergent development. The extraordinary †*Arminiheringia* of the Casa Mayor (*q.v.*), the giant of its day, may prove to be the ancestor sought for, but the intermediate links of the chain must be found, before any positive statement can be justified.

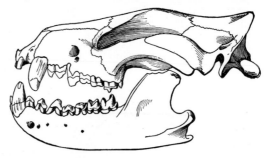

FIG. 413. — Skull of †*Borhyæna*, Santa Cruz. (From Sinclair.)

The next formation, more ancient than the Catamarca, in which well-preserved marsupials have been found is the Santa Cruz, the beds of which were laid down at a time when marsupials were the only beasts of prey in South America, filling the rôles now taken by the Fissipedia. Four well-defined genera have been named, two equalling a Coyote in size, †*Prothylacynus* and †*Borhyæna*, and two fox-like and marten-like, †*Cladosictis* and †*Amphiproviverra*. Though differing much in size and in various details of structure, the four genera are very much alike. They all have relatively large heads, long necks and bodies and long, heavy tails; in all, the facial part of the skull is proportionately short and the orbits are farther forward than in the Recent members of the family. The brain-case is much less capacious and the post-orbital constriction deeper than in the latter. The lachrymal is large and articulates with the nasal and the foramen is within the orbit; there are no palatal vacuities. The molar teeth are of the same type as in *Thylacynus*, differing in a few details such as the greater reduction of the last upper molar.

In †*Borhyæna* and †*Amphiproviverra* the atlas has a separate intercentrum, while in the other two genera, the inferior arch is complete and fused with the neural arch.

FIG. 414. — Santa Cruz predaceous marsupial, †*Prothylacynus patagonicus*, and †typothere, †*Interatherium robustum*. (Restored by C. Knight from skeletons in Princeton Univ. Mus.)

The limbs are short in proportion to the size of the body, especially the bones of the fore-leg. The skeleton of †*Prothylacynus* is about equal in size to that of the Tasmanian Wolf and very like it in structure. When living, the Santa Cruz animal must have resembled the existing one, except perhaps, in colouration. As shown in the restoration, the stripes are longitudinal instead of transverse, as this is the most primitive pattern among mammals and it seems likely that so ancient a genus might well have retained it.

In †*Prothylacynus* the dental formula is: $i\frac{4}{3}, c\frac{1}{1}, p + m\frac{7}{7} \times 2 = 46$. Face and jaws are elongate and, differing from almost all other marsupials, the

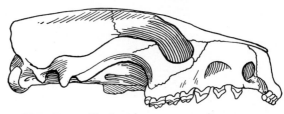

Fig. 415. — Skull of small predaceous marsupial, †*Amphiproviverra manzaniana*, showing the punctured wound from a bite. (Princeton Univ. Mus.)

alisphenoids do not form auditory bullæ. The humerus retains the epicondylar foramen. The patella is ossified, which is exceptional among existing marsupials. The hind-foot has a large vestige of the hallux, which probably was not visible externally.

The genus †*Borhyæna* about equalled †*Prothylacynus* in stature, but was much heavier and more powerful, as well as more specialized. The dental formula is: $i\frac{3}{3}, c\frac{1}{1}, p + m\frac{7}{7} \times 2 = 44$, and is very exceptional among the Polyprotodonta in having upper and lower incisors of the same number. The jaws are long and the brain-case very small, with high sagittal and occipital crests. The zygomatic arches are stout and have great spread, giving a rounded, almost cat-like appearance to the head, as is shown in the restoration (see p. 555). As in †*Prothylacynus*, there are no alisphenoid bullæ; but, differing from that genus, the humerus has lost the epicondylar foramen.

It does not seem probable that these predaceous marsupials were able to cope with the larger contemporary hoofed animals, such as †*Astrapotherium*, but the smaller ungulates, perhaps even †*Nesodon*, no doubt fell victims to these savage destroyers.

Associated with the large predatory marsupials were several much smaller ones, ranging in size from a fox to a weasel, which must have preyed upon the numerous rodents and †typotheres of Santa Cruz times, as well as upon lizards and birds. One of these smaller genera, †*Amphiproviverra*, had an opposable hallux, indicative of arboreal habits and thus confirmatory of Dollo's hypothesis, that

FIG. 416. — Small predaceous marsupial, †*Cladosictis lustratus*, and rabbit-like ††typothere, †*Pachyrukhos moyani*, Santa Cruz stage. (Restored by C. Knight from skeletons in Princeton Univ. Mus. and Amer. Mus. Nat. His.)

existing marsupials, with the possible exception of *Cænolestes* and *Notoryctes*, passed through an arboreal stage of development, in which, of course, many of them still remain. In this genus and in the similarly small †*Cladosictis* the alisphenoids form inflated auditory bullæ, as in nearly all other marsupials. In the restoration of the genus last named (Fig. 416) the animal is given a spotted coat like that of the Australian "Native Cats" (*Dasyurus*). This is perhaps questionable, for spots are especially characteristic of forest-dwellers and the Patagonia of Santa Cruz times would seem to have been treeless.

A skull of †*Amphiproviverra* in the Princeton collection (Fig. 415) is of particular interest as giving eloquent testimony as to the habits of these bloodthirsty little creatures; the right upper canine was completely bitten out in a fight with a rival, which took place a considerable time before the victim's death, for the socket of the lost tooth is completely filled up with a secondary deposit of bone and the edge of the circular wound punctured in the maxillary also shows a deposit of new bone.

In the Colhué-huapi, two of the Santa Cruz genera have been found, †*Borhyæna*, which is represented by a smaller species, and †*Cladosictis* by a larger one. A third genus, †*Proborhyæna*, occurs at this level; it has a short face, massive canine fangs, and reduced premolars and anterior molars. This is a very different animal from the long-jawed genera of the Santa Cruz.

The characteristic genus of this family in the Deseado stage is the immense †*Pharsophorus*, one of the two largest known predaceous marsupials, with skull equal to that of a large bear in size, but, otherwise, not very different from †*Borhyæna*. This is another instance, like †*Asmodeus* and †*Parastrapotherium*, of the Deseado genus greatly exceeding in size its nearest ally of the succeeding Santa Cruz. This is an altogether exceptional relation between earlier and later geological stages; almost always the mammals of a genetic series grow larger with the progress of time until a climax is reached. A similar relation was noted (p. 189) between the Pleistocene and the Recent, the former having many more large animals.

The members of the family which have been found in the Casa Mayor beds are of two strongly contrasted types: (1) there are the small, very primitive animals, such as †*Procladosictis* and †*Pseudo-cladosictis*, which, as their names imply, bear some resemblance to the Santa Cruz genus †*Cladosictis*, but with less specialized dentition, the molars being more opossum-like. (2) There is, astonishing to relate, the relatively gigantic †*Arminiheringia*, which is as large as the great †*Pharsophorus* of the Deseado and seems completely out of place in the Casa Mayor fauna. Ordinarily, there is some proportion in size between a predaceous mammal and the Herbivora upon which it preys, but the Casa Mayor fauna is made up of small mammals and the disproportion is inexplicable. Not only is †*Arminiheringia* remarkable for its great size, but also for its relatively advanced degree of specialization. The incisors are very small and

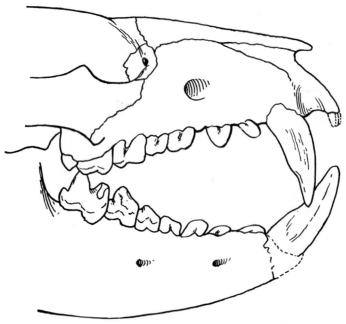

FIG. 417. — Facial part of skull of †*Arminiheringia*, Casa Mayor. (From Simpson.)

number $\frac{3}{2}$; in the lower jaw these teeth are so crowded together that the external one is behind the median one. The premolars are well spaced and the molars are so modified by the elimination of cusps, that they have become almost completely trenchant. Face and jaws are very elongate.

As previously intimated †*Arminiheringia* is a very possible ancestor of the marsupial †sabre-tooth †*Thylacosmilus*, though the hiatus between them is so great that the relation is conjectural.

The most ancient known South American genus of the family is †*Patene* of the Casa Mayor and Rio Chico, an animal of medium to small size, with very primitive teeth; the genus is very incompletely known.

SUBORDER Diprotodonta

It is, at present, customary to admit a third suborder of the marsupials, the Paucituberculata, or Cænolestoidea, but the classification followed by Dr. W. H. Osgood, of the Field Museum, Chicago, is here adopted, Dr. Osgood having had more favourable opportunities of studying the group than any other zoölogist. He writes: "The view that *Caenolestes* is a primitive diprotodont is not proved, but is strongly supported by its resemblance to the peramelids which of all polyprotodonts are the ones most suggestive of the incipient stages leading from one large group to the other. It is probably not too much to say that if the caenolestids had been discovered in Australia, they would have been accepted without question as ancestral diprotodonts."

Family 4. Epanorthidæ

Various names, such as Cænolestidæ and Palæothentidæ, have been used for this family, but, according to Palmer, Epanorthidæ has the priority. Nearly 30 genera have been assigned to the family, a number which will assuredly be drastically reduced, when better material shall have been obtained. A selection of the more significant and better-known genera is listed below. The group is one of great antiquity and has never been found outside of South America.

EPANORTHIDÆ

Cænolestes, Orolestes, Rhyncholestes, Rec. †*Zygolestes*, Entrerian. †*Epanorthus*, †*Abderites*, †*Acdestis*, †*Garzonia*, †*Halmarhiphus*, †*Cladoclinus*, †*Callomenus*, Santa Cruz. †*Palæepanorthus*, Deseado. †*Progarzonia*, Casa Mayor.

The group of Recent genera, of which *Cænolestes* is the best known, together with their ancestors of the Santa Cruz, form a subfamily, or tribe, which goes back to the Casa Mayor formation, in which the allied, but more specialized family of the †Polydolopidæ was predominant. Between the lower Pliocene of the Entrerian and the Recent no representative of the Epanorthidæ has been found, the middle and upper Pliocene and all the Pleistocene having as yet proved barren of them. This is a striking instance of "the imperfection of the geological record," so often insisted upon, for the group is still in existence and must have continued to exist throughout the time in which there is no discoverable trace of it. It cannot be believed that the family became extinct and was afterwards resurrected, for there is no known region whence it could have re-entered South America

The three Recent genera are closely similar and differ only in a few details of minor importance and in their geographical range: *Cænolestes* occurs in the Andes of Colombia and Ecuador, *Orolestes* in those of Peru and *Rhyncholestes* in the Island of Chiloé, southern Chile. For the purposes of this book, only *Cænolestes* need be considered and only the species *C. obscurus*, which is the subject of Osgood's monograph.

Cænolestes obscurus (Fig. 140, p. 175) is a little animal, about equalling the House-rat in size; it has a long, pointed head, more

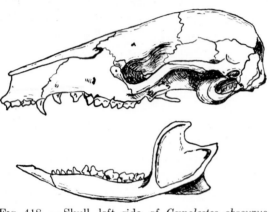

shrew-like than rat-like in appearance, with the slender, flexible snout which so many marsupials and insectivores possess; the eyes are very small, the ears small and rounded. The elongate body is covered with a remarkably uniform coat of dull brown, but little

FIG. 418. — Skull, left side, of *Cænolestes obscurus.* (After Osgood, modified from Miss Dederer.)

lighter on the underparts. The pouch is wanting in the adult, but there is reason to believe that a vestige of it is present in the young. The long, tapering tail, which is not prehensile, is "thickly set with short, stiff hairs which nearly or quite conceal the underlying scaly annulations" (Osgood). The limbs are short, the feet five-toed and plantigrade.

The dentition is intermediate in character between that of the Polyprotodonta and that of the Diprotodonta and has the formula: $i \frac{4}{3-4}$, $c \frac{1}{1}$, $p + m \frac{7}{7} \times 2 = 46\text{--}48$. The upper incisors are small, the second one slightly larger than the others. The lower incisors are normally three in number, but may be four, and sometimes differ in number on the two sides of the jaw; the first of the series is very much larger than the others and is long, pointed and directed almost straight forward, its *side* biting against the upper incisors. The upper canine is a sharp-pointed, recurved little fang, larger than any of the incisors except the first lower and distinctly larger in the male.

Behind the enlarged lower incisor there follow four, or sometimes, five minute, conical, one-rooted teeth, which are interpreted as two (or three) incisors, the canine and first premolar. The molariform teeth are tuberculo-sectorial, with the anterior triangle rising but little above the level of the heel. In the upper jaw the premolars are small, conical, compressed and two-rooted; the third one is not trenchant, or enlarged. The first of the molar-like teeth is quadri-tubercular, not trenchant; the second is like it, the third is tritubercular and the fourth greatly reduced. These teeth resemble those of some of the Australian phalangers. Though the teeth would seem to indicate a vegetable diet, it has been ascertained that *Cænolestes* is insectivorous in habit.

The skeleton, as a whole, resembles in general appearance and proportions that of such an insectivore as *Nesogale*. The skull is most like that of the Australian Peramelidæ; face and jaws are elongate and the muzzle is slender and tapering. Though the brain is of a very low and primitive type, the brain-case is full and rounded and is without crests or ridges.

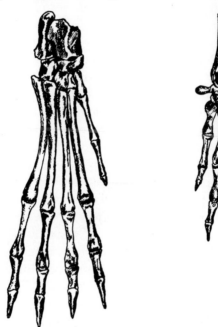

FIG. 419. — Right fore- and hind-feet of *Cænolestes obscurus*, enlarged. (From Osgood.)

In detail, the skull has all the typical marsupial features; for example, the tympanic is an incomplete ring and the inflated auditory bulla is formed by the alisphenoid, and the bony palate has two pairs of large vacuities in it. Peculiar is the very large exposure on the side of the cranium of the mastoid portion of the periotic and also the narrow vacuity on the face between the nasal, frontal and maxillary bones. Vacuities at this point are found in hoofed animals, especially the Artiodactyla, not in other marsupials.

Systematists attach much importance to the chain of three tiny bones, or ossicles, which transmit vibrations from the ear-drum to the internal ear. One of these little bones, the *stapes*, in *Cænolestes*, as in lizards, is cylindrical and rod-like, not forked, or perforated. This is an exceedingly primitive feature, which is shared by the Peramelidæ, but not by the opossums. "So far as the auditory ossicles are concerned, therefore, *Caenolestes* resembles Australian rather than American forms" (Osgood).

The vertebral column has the formula: C. 7, D. 13, L. 6, S. 2, Cd. 25+. The cervical vertebræ are more like those of the Australian *Perameles* than they are like those of the American opossums. As in that genus, the axis carries a pair of vestigial ribs, and the canals for the vertebral arteries of the 7th vertebra are in process of elimination. The dorsal vertebræ have very low spines and short processes for muscular attachments; a notable difference from the Didelphiidæ is that, in the latter, the spines all incline backward, whereas, in *Cænolestes* the spine of the 10th dorsal is erect and, behind that point, the spines incline forward. On the lumbars all the processes are short and inconspicuous. The marsupial bones are remarkable for the great breadth of the bases, which are attached to the pelvis.

The limbs are short, especially the anterior pair, though the humerus is the longest and stoutest of the limb-bones; it has a very prominent deltoid ridge and internal epicondyle, which is perforated by the foramen. The femur is shorter and very straight and has a very prominent second and vestigial third trochanter. The patella is small, but completely ossified, which is rarely the case among marsupials, as this bone is present only in three other Recent genera. In their inferior half the two bones of the lower leg are closely appressed, though not co-ossified, while the upper half of the tibia is strongly arched forward, making a wide interosseous space, and does not extend over the head of the fibula. The fibula is straight and its upper end is almost as wide as that of the tibia, and nearly reaches the femur; the large fabella rests upon the upper end of the fibula instead of upon the femoral condyle.

The feet are five-toed, the manus shorter, but much broader than the pes. In the carpus the lunar is reduced to exceedingly small size by the widening of the scaphoid. The three median digits, II, III, IV, are of nearly equal length and have sharp claws, the laterals, I and V, are much shorter and have flat nails. The long and narrow hind-foot has four elongate toes, II–V, which have much larger and sharper claws than those of the manus. The first digit, or hallux, which bears a nail, is hardly more than a vestige and can be of little functional importance. At the same time, it is slightly divergent from the others and may perhaps be the remnant of an opposable toe; if so, this genus would not be an exception to the arboreal descent of marsupials.

Save one little known genus, †*Zygolestes* of the lower Pliocene, no representative of this family has been found between the Recent and the Santa Cruz. In the latter formation the family reached its acme, so far as the geological record may be trusted, in diversity and in numbers, both individual and generic. Three distinctly differentiated subfamilies, or tribes, may be distinguished in the Santa Cruz fauna. The first of these, or Cænolestinæ, comprises the genera which are more or less directly ancestral to the Recent forms, such as †*Halmarhiphus* and †*Garzonia*. These agree with *Cænolestes* and its modern relatives in having no trenchant or shearing teeth. †*Garzonia* has more teeth in the lower jaw than has any other known diprotodont. Six single-rooted, minute teeth follow the enlarged incisor and two small, but functional, conical premolars come next, making the remarkable number of nine antemolars, which is, perhaps, not constant. Another difference from *Cænolestes* is the reduction of the last molar, which is very small and has but a single root.

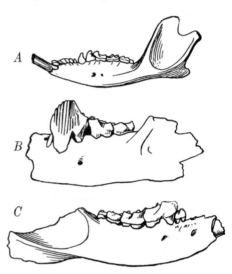

Fig. 420. — Lower jaws of Santa Cruz cænolestids, enlarged. *A*, †*Garzonia patagonica*. *B*, †*Abderites crassignathus*. *C*, †*Callomenus ligatus*. (After Sinclair, in Reports Princeton University Expeditions to Patagonia, Vol. IV.)

The bones of the fore-limb are remarkably short and slender, not exceeding the lower jaw in length. The humerus is strongly curved antero-posteriorly and its lower end is made relatively broad by the supinator ridge and internal epicondyle, which is perforated by the foramen. The radius is extremely slender and its oval head indicates some freedom of rotation of the fore-foot. It would seem that this foot was used like a hand.

As yet, †*Halmarhiphus* is known only from the lower jaw, which, so far as it goes, would seem to indicate that this genus was directly ancestral to *Cænolestes*, or, at all events, was very near to the real ancestor. The formula of the lower teeth may be written: $i\frac{}{4}$, $c\frac{}{1}$, $p\frac{}{3}$, $m\frac{}{4}$, "if definite homologies are assigned to the vestigial antemolars" (Sinclair). Five minute, closely crowded teeth follow the enlarged incisor, then two functional, compressed-conical premolars. The molariform teeth resemble those of *Cænolestes*, but with more distinct cusps; the last molariform tooth is smaller than the others, but is double-rooted and not nearly so reduced as in †*Garzonia*.

The second subfamily is that of the †Epanorthinæ, in which the last upper premolar and the first lower molar are sectorials, with smooth trenchant blades. In †*Callomenus* the lower sectorial has a large, basin-like heel, as large and high as the anterior cutting blade. The last molar is very small and one-rooted. There are only six antemolars, three less than in †*Garzonia*. The skull differs much from that of *Cænolestes* in the smaller brain-case and prominent sagittal crest and in the relatively smaller palatine vacuities.

The third subfamily, the †Abderitinæ, is much the most advanced and specialized of them all; the sectorial blade of the first molariform tooth is relatively much larger than in †*Callomenus* and rises high above the level of the tooth-row and its outer side has five or six ridges, which form serrations on the cutting edge; the internal cusp has been eliminated and the heel is much smaller and lower than the blade, a notable difference from the preceding subfamily. Attention should be called to the fact that it was not the most advanced and specialized of the subfamilies, the †Abderitinæ, that outlived the others, surviving to the present day, but the least specialized, of which so many instances have been noted in the preceding chapters. It is, as Dr. Simpson has said: "almost the general rule in the evolution of the vertebrates that *the more specialized phyla tend to become extinct before the less specialized ones of the same group.*" This principle is even more strikingly illustrated by the next succeeding family, the †Polydolopidæ.

That the †Epanorthidæ were represented in the Casa Mayor fauna is very probable, but the only fossils yet found, those of †*Progarzonia*, are so very imperfect, that little can be predicated of the genus.

Family 5.   †*Polydolopidæ*

This family has generally been referred to the order Multituberculata of the subclass †Allotheria (see p. 83), but, as Dr. Simpson has shown, they are referable to an aberrant family of marsupials, nearly allied to the †Epanorthidæ, which he thus defines: "Characterized by the presence of an enlarged procumbent incisor; reduction of the premolars; presence of a much enlarged laterally compressed, trenchant lower cheek tooth ($M_{\overline{1}}$); elevation and compression of the anterior part of the succeeding tooth (M $\frac{.}{2}$), broad, low, basined $m\,\overline{3}-\overline{4}$, with multicuspidate rims; two trenchant upper cheek teeth (P $\frac{3}{.}$ and M $\frac{1}{.}$) and multicuspidate M $\frac{3}{.}-\frac{4}{.}$."

The family is entirely confined to the lowest known Eocene of Patagonia, the Casa Mayor and Rio Chico, and many genera have been named, of which the most distinctive and best preserved are as follows:

†POLYDOLOPIDÆ

†*Polydolops*, Casa Mayor and Rio Chico. †*Orthodolops*, †*Archæodolops*, †*Pliodolops*, †*Eudolops*, †*Propolymastodon*, etc., Casa Mayor. †*Seumadia*, Rio Chico.

These various genera, which differ but little from one another, are more specialized than the Epanorthidæ in the development of *two* pairs of sectorial teeth and in the reduction of the premolars. In †*Propolymastodon*, for example, the canines and all the premolars (according to the usual notation) have been eliminated, leaving only four grinding teeth in each jaw; the first one of these is small, but trenchant and has finely serrate edges. The other genera of the family show different degrees of enlargement of this tooth, which is always trenchant. In †*Archæodolops* the edge is entire and in †*Polydolops* it is coarsely notched; the other cheek-teeth are tuberculate. The upper jaw has two trenchant teeth, $p\,\frac{3}{.}$ and $m\,\frac{1}{.}$, of which the anterior one is much the larger, and both have serrate edges.

RELATIONS OF THE AUSTRALIAN AND SOUTH AMERICAN MARSUPIALS

The problem concerning the origin and mutual relationships of the Australian and South American marsupials has been much debated and can be but briefly touched upon here. It must be admitted that the conclusion reached has often been shaped in the interests of a geographical theory, regarding the former existence of land-connections between South America, Antarctica and Australia. Most writers on this topic have overlooked the fact that an upper Eocene, or lower Miocene junction of Antarctica with Australia and South America is well-nigh certain, as is shown by the distribution of the shoal-water Mollusca and other invertebrates of the marine Patagonian formation. As von Zittel and Ortmann long ago pointed out, these animals could not have crossed the deep sea, but required a continuous coast-line for their spread, though chains of islands may have been partial interruptions of the continuity. Patagonia, Tierra del Fuego, probably the South Shetland Islands, within the Antarctic

Circle, Australia and New Zealand have such a community of genera and even species, as to require the connection postulated. At all events, the land-bridges between the three continents offered but a difficult route of migration for land animals and only a few kinds could take advantage of it, though the lack of Tertiary mammals in Australia forbids positive statements on this head.

In the upper Cretaceous and Paleocene the more primitive didelphids were spread all over the world, with the possible exception of Africa and Australia, as to which we have no information. It is a significant fact that no other family of marsupials has ever been found in any part of the northern hemisphere (†*Myrmecoboides* is not a marsupial, but an insectivore) and therefore the attempt to explain the resemblances of South American and Australian genera by separate migrations from the north into the two continents has no basis in observed fact. The only hypothesis that covers all the data is that these animals originated in the southern hemisphere by descent from the cosmopolitan didelphids. It is, on the whole, more probable that the place of origin was Australia rather than South America, but until the Tertiary mammals of the former shall have been brought to light, it will not be possible to decide this question. To maintain that the Australian genera, on the one hand, and the South American genera, on the other, were independently derived from didelphid ancestors, involves such a degree of convergence as has never been admitted for any other group and for which there is no warrant.

CHAPTER XXV [1]

THE EVOLUTIONARY PROCESS

In Chapter XI were pointed out the postulates, or working hypotheses, in accordance with which the various genetic sequences, set forth in the preceding chapters, were constructed, but, it must be recognized, there are wide differences of opinion among palæontologists as to the validity of some of these presuppositions, or if their general applicability is admitted, exceptional departures from them are insisted upon. It is probable that none of the "laws of development" is without exceptions; all that can be claimed for them, at present, is that they seem to represent the usual course of evolution and that some of them are much more securely founded than others.

While Palæontology must be the principal source of information concerning the genetic series of the various mammalian families, all the other biological sciences contribute indispensable data toward the solution of the problems involved. Comparative anatomy is the foundation upon which the whole palæontological superstructure must be reared. Embryology, the development of the individual from the fertilized egg, often records stages which have vanished from the adult and, used in connection with palæontology, gives most valuable aid in the solution of evolutionary problems.

Fifty years ago embryology was the supreme court of appeal in all questions of evolution and relationship. To a certain extent, varying much in different groups, individual development does give a greatly abbreviated, somewhat distorted version of the group-history in time. This is the "recapitulation theory" which Hæckel called the "Fundamental Biogenetic Law." By many modern naturalists the recapitulation theory has been abandoned and embryology is now undervalued as much as it was formerly overestimated. As a matter of simple fact, the data of embryology are often most suggestive.

To take but a narrow field, that of dentition, embryology has given a satisfactory solution of problems which no other method of investigation could reach. Marsupials, for example, differ from most

[1] The substance of this chapter was delivered as a public lecture at Cambridge, Mass., on Sept. 9, 1936, in connection with the Tercentenary Celebration of Harvard University.

placentals, in the very limited replacement of teeth which they display. In some genera there is no change at all, but in most a single tooth in each jaw, the third premolar, has a predecessor. Many attempts were made to explain this exceptional condition, but all were inconclusive, until embryological examination showed that two complete sets of tooth-germs, with their enamel organs, are formed in the fœtal jaws and that all the functional teeth, usually with the exception of the third premolar, belong to the first, or milk-series, while the second set has been almost completely eliminated.

In the modern Edentata most of those Xenarthra which are not toothless, have but a single series of simple, peg-like, rootless teeth, which are completely devoid of enamel, and are not replaced, forming only a single series. In some of the armadillos (e.g. *Tatu*) there is a change of teeth, six or seven of the anterior teeth have milk-predecessors and, in the embryo, are the germs of six teeth in advance of those which are erupted, making 15 in each side of upper and lower jaws, 60 in all. Very similar facts have been learned concerning the Rodentia. As far back in time as this order can be traced (low. Eocene) its members have but a single pair of chisel-like incisors above and below, no canines and not more than two premolars in each jaw and thus palæontology supplies no information as to the origin of this type of dentition. Embryological examination, however, shows that the ancestors of the rodents had a complete dentition and that the teeth now missing have been suppressed.

Though not strictly embryological, observations on the milk-dentition frequently show that the first set of teeth is more conservative than the second and retains ancestral features which the permanent teeth have lost. Striking instances of this have been observed in the horses and the South American †typotheres. In the middle Miocene horse †*Merychippus*, the permanent grinding teeth, molars and premolars alike, are of the high-crowned, rootless, cement-covered type, such as occur in all the subsequent genera of this tribe, from the upper Miocene to the Recent. The milk-premolars, on the other hand, are low crowned, rooted and free of cement, as are the permanent grinders in all the preceding genera from the lower Miocene to the lower Eocene. The same is true of †*Interatherium*, of the †Typotheria, in which the milk-premolars are low crowned and rooted, while all the permanent grinders are high crowned and rootless.

The new science of Genetics promises to throw much light upon the modes of evolutionary change and has already furnished some information of importance. Especially has it been made clear that new features must arise in the germinal substance (*germ plasm*), not in the adult, in order to be transmitted to the offspring. More or less unconsciously, palæontologists have been in the habit of making genetic series as though the transformation were of one adult into another, as in the series of horses, camels, etc., figured in the preceding chapters. They could not be figured in any other way, yet it must not be forgotten that every individual begins as a microscopic ovum. It is the germ plasm that has continuity; it is, in Galton's simile, the chain-necklace, from each link of which a pendant represents the individual. Though new species of animals have been experimentally produced, fulfilling Huxley's criteria, no one contends that natural species arise in any such fashion. Genetics deals with individuals, palæontology chiefly with genera, and the two categories are incommensurable.

Taking a comprehensive view of the whole field of mammalian evolution, a number of salient facts present themselves. (1) The extinction of groups, from species to subclass, played a highly important part in winnowing out those forms which through change of conditions, were no longer adapted to their environment. Because the geological record is not continuous, but is interrupted by many gaps, longer and shorter, these extinctions seem to have been sudden and, perhaps, they sometimes were so, but as a rule, they were gradual. A genus, or family, or order, widely spread over one or more continents, first began to diminish in the number of individuals and then to die out, now here, now there, persisting much longer in some regions than in others. The extinctions may be partial, as in so many existing families that formerly had a far wider range than they do at present, such as elephants, rhinoceroses, tapirs, horses, camels, etc. More frequently, so far as families and genera are concerned, the decrease in individuals continued until extinction became total.

In the late Pleistocene and early Recent, there was the most radical and widespread extirpation of mammals of which there is any record. Over more than three-fifths of the land-surface of the earth and in all the continents save tropical Asia, central and southern Africa, all the largest and strangest animals, the elephants, †mastodonts, †ground-sloths, †glyptodonts, †"sabre-tooth tigers" the huge †"American lions" and the †giant beavers, disappeared, impoverishing the whole Western Hemisphere, Europe, temperate Asia and Australia.

While the post-Pleistocene extinctions were the most radically destructive in the history of mammals, they differed only in degree from many that went before. If a series of successive faunas are compared, it becomes evident that during, or at the end of each geological stage, nearly or quite all of the larger and more specialized mammals died out. "The survival of the unspecialized" almost deserves to be called a general law, though it is not without exceptions. We often have occasion to speak of "prematurely specialized" genera, but that phrase merely signifies that such genera were more specialized than their contemporaries and died out before them. There are many known instances of this sort, but the contrast in the history of the cement-covered grinding teeth among the hoofed mammals of North and South America is one of the most instructive. In the former, the sporadic appearance of such teeth began in the Oligocene, but they did not become common before the middle and upper Miocene and continued increasing in the number of families involved throughout the Tertiary. In South America, on the contrary, they were numerous in the Oligocene and early Miocene and then disappeared almost completely. It seems as though the experiment were highly successful in the northern continent, but were almost a failure in the southern.

One can readily understand that, the more exactly adapted to its environment any animal is, the more fatal will be any important change of conditions. Climatic changes were, presumably, the most important, but there were many other factors which would seem to have been very efficient, such as the impact of new infectious diseases, new deadly insects and the like. The largest mammals of the lower Eocene were the †coryphodonts, but they died out, both in Europe and North America, at the end of the Wasatch, though in Mongolia they lingered into the Miocene. The giants of the middle Eocene were the †Dinocerata, or †uintatheres, the ancestors of which in the Paleocene and older Eocene, had been small. Great size did not save them from extinction and they disappeared after the upper Eocene, in which they had already become rare.

The history of the perissodactyl family of the †brontotheres is very similar. First appearing in the Wind River stage as small animals, they gradually increased in size throughout the Eocene, attaining the stature and proportions of modern tapirs in the Bridger and becoming still larger in the Uinta-Duchesne. In the Chadron substage of the White River the family culminated in a variety of forms so fluctuating and bewildering, that no two observers agree as to the number of genera and species that should be recognized. In size these lower Oligocene species far surpassed those of the Eocene, rivalling small elephants. After the Chadron the family was swept away with what seems like startling suddenness, but which was, no doubt, more gradual than it would appear to have been.

Taking the palæontological records at their face value, which seldom can be unreservedly done, each of the successive faunas largely dies out at the end of the stage and the following one develops, partly by the radiating, or divergent evolution of a comparatively few types, supplemented by some survivals from the preceding stage and by a larger or smaller number of immigrants from some other region. These migrants may have been derived from another continent, or from another part of the same continent. Though South America was long completely isolated, there is every evidence of intramigrations within the continent, apparently from the north.

In Mongolia there appeared in the Oligocene a number of gigantic members of families, of which the American representatives were of moderate size; †*Andrewsarchus* and †*Sarkastodon* were colossal †creodonts; †*Baluchitherium*, an overwhelming rhinoceros, first found in Baluchistan, was the largest land mammal of which anything is known. The life-sized mural relief in the American Museum is 17 feet high at the shoulder and seems to be altogether incredible, yet there is no escape from the proportions of the bones. These overpowering monsters all had a short career, geologically speaking, and but a limited geographical range.

Instances that go to substantiate the truth of the rule, that extremes of size or specialization lead to early extinction, might be almost indefinitely multiplied, but that would be useless. It was noted above that the rule of the "survival of the less specialized" has its exceptions, which are exemplified in the more advanced existing groups; save in size, the elephants, horses, camels, deer, antelopes, etc., were more highly specialized, at each stage of their career than most of their contemporaries, yet they are few in comparison with the many extinct groups, which were the most advanced of their time. These surviving groups had some particular advantage of adaptability that enabled them to maintain themselves, though it is seldom possible to point out just what that advantage was.

The modes of mammalian evolution are to be deduced from a study of the longer and more complete genetic series and it is significant that they all seem to develop in much the same general way, with modifications according to light or heavy weight, slender or massive form. Specialization in a hoofed animal is a very different thing from what it is in a carnivore and, among the beasts of prey, the great cats are very different from bears or wolves, yet with different beginnings and still more different endings, there is much similarity in the steps of modification. Taking the best-known history, that of the horse family, from the lower Eocene †*Hyracotherium* to the modern *Equus*, it is clear: (1) that there is a continuous increment in size, each genus of the series being larger than its predecessor, smaller than its successor. †*Hyracotherium* is no larger than a fox, *Equus* †*giganteus*, of the Pleistocene, exceeds the largest domestic breeds in height and weight. (2) Neck, limbs and feet grew relatively, as well as actually, longer. (3) Limb- and foot-bones were reduced in number and some in size, while others were enlarged. Ulna and fibula became hardly more than vestiges, while radius and tibia greatly increased in size, so as to carry the entire weight. (4) The toes, which were originally four in the front foot, three in the hind, were first reduced by one digit in the manus, then the median digit (III) was enlarged, as the laterals (II and IV) dwindled to dew-claws and then, losing the phalanges, were shortened into splint-bones, while the median hoof took on the characteristic equine shape, adapted to support the whole body-weight. (5) The premolar teeth, at first all smaller and of simpler pattern than the molars, one by one, assumed the molar pattern, until the posterior three had become molariform, a rare thing in mammals. (6) All the grinding teeth, except the first, originally low-crowned, with roots and with cement on the roots only, gradually became very high-crowned, rootless and with the whole crown thickly covered with cement. (7) The skull was remodelled, to make room for these very high teeth.

In such a series as this, one is immediately struck by the direct, unwavering course of its development; there is no slipping back from vantage-ground once gained and no zigzagging in direction. True, as will be seen, side-branches may be given off from the principal line and diverge more and more from it, but such branching does not affect the course of the main stem. Among the horses, there is one group, exemplified by †*Hypohippus*, to which the simile of branch and stem does not very well apply, and that is the series of †"browsing horses," or †"forest horses," which were simply conservative and persisted into the lower Pliocene, with hardly any change other than increase of size. It is a group that was left behind, rather than branched off, but the peculiar South American horses (†*Hippidion*, etc.) formed a real branch.

As compared with most long-persisting mammalian families, there was very little branching of the Equidæ, yet, when the inquiry is carried farther back than the known beginnings of this family, divergent branching is seen to be significant. Probably in the late Paleocene of the Old World, the first Perissodactyla divided into two stems, one of which immediately ramified into three families, the horses, the †brontotheres and the †palæotheres. The last group has not been found outside of Europe, but its relationships with the horses are plain; both †palæotheres and †brontotheres were comparatively short-lived, in the geological sense, and the former were an example of premature specialization.

Divergent evolution is thus seen to be the more usual and normal method of development, by which a few genera at each stage ramify into a much larger number in the succeeding stage.

It is instructive to examine the history of the †Brontotheriidæ, which is in such strong contrast to that of the horses and yet illustrates a modification of similar principles. The family, long ago extinct, ran a very much shorter course than the horses, from the lower Eocene to the lower Oligocene inclusive and was restricted to North America and Asia, one species penetrating into southeastern Europe. The most ancient known †brontotheres (lower Wind River) are not very unlike the contemporary horses, to which they have sometimes been mistakenly referred, but they are of somewhat larger size and sturdier build. As in almost all Eocene perissodactyls, the †brontotheres had four digits in the front foot, three in the hind, and premolars which were smaller and of simpler pattern than the molars. In the middle Eocene, the †brontotheres had become the dominant family, many genera and species arising by divergence from the few of the lower Eocene. The larger ones of these about equalled an American Tapir in size and resembled it in proportions. In some of the species of the upper Bridger an incipient pair of horn-like protuberances appeared far back on the nasal bones. In the upper Eocene the number of genera was reduced, but those that remained were much larger and had more prominent "horns."

The culmination of the family came in the Chadron substage of the White River in an extraordinary outburst of variability, which affected chiefly the skull, length and shape of the "horns," and the number of genera and species which should be recognized offers an unsolved problem. In size, the larger species were elephantine and had more massive proportions than the heaviest of existing African rhinoceroses. Development of the †brontotheres followed an almost opposite direction from that taken by the horses. The process of reduction, whether in the number or the size of elements, was arrested at the point where increase in relative bulk and weight began; ulna and fibula even grew heavier and the femur lost the third trochanter, assumed a flattened shape and like the other long bones, had the marrow-cavities filled with spongy bone. The number of digits remained the same as it had been in the lower Eocene, but the feet evidently took on the columnar shape and the hoofs were reduced to nails. The huge skull came to have much resemblance to that of the large-horned rhinoceroses and elephants, in the great number of cells and sinuses in the roof and sides of the cranium. The premolars had begun to take on the molar pattern, but the process was arrested by extinction before it was complete.

Despite the great contrast between the rather small, slender and cursorial horses and the huge, massive, elephantine †brontotheres, there are marked similarities in the mode of development; in both there is the increase in the size of each successive genus, the direct evolution, as if toward a selected goal, with more or less of ramification, the transformation of the premolars, incomplete in the †brontotheres, because of the ending of the family, and the reduction in size of the canine teeth. Horses and †brontotheres afford an excellent instance of *divergent evolution* combined with a likeness in the mode.

By *parallel evolution*, or *parallelism*, is meant that allied forms, having a common origin, may independently follow similar lines of development and arrive at similar results. The parallelism may affect single structures, or may involve the entire organism; it is often conspicuously displayed in the tribes of a family and, somewhat less exactly, in related orders. Development of this sort was expressly accepted by Darwin, who thought that species nearly allied and having a similar physiological constitution might be expected to show similar variations, but he seems to have attributed no great importance to this process.

So far as single structures and organs are concerned, the list of *demonstrable* parallelisms might be indefinitely extended, demonstrable because the development may be followed step by step in the different genetic series. For example, the primitive and usual shape of the odontoid process of the axis is a conical peg, of circular cross-section, but in nearly all long-necked mammals, the odontoid is spout-shaped and embraces the spinal cord on three sides, protecting it from compression, when the neck is bent. The spout-shaped odontoid occurs in the true ruminants (Pecora), camels (Tylopoda), in horses and, in somewhat less perfect form, tapirs. In Eocene horses and camels the process is of the usual peg-like form, but in the Oligocene members of both families it is transitional, flat on top and convex below, taking on the spout-shape in the Miocene. The history of the change in ruminants and tapirs has not been brought to light, but it must have gone on independently of the camels and horses.

There are many instances of independent acquisition of similar characters of the teeth, but these are more conveniently dealt with under convergent evolution, for it is not always possible to decide whether a given example is to be regarded as convergence or parallelism.

Parallelism may extend much farther than single structures and involve the entire organism. A striking case of parallel tribes within the family is that of the true cats and the †sabre-tooths. Whatever view be held concerning the relationships of these two subfamilies, no one questions that they are related and that they have been separate since the Oligocene. Aside from the modifications made necessary by the hypertrophy of the great canine tusks, the two groups pursued a remarkably parallel course from the Oligocene to the Pleistocene.

Within the order Proboscidea, Osborn discriminated more than twenty-five subfamilies and tribes which all developed along parallel lines. The conception of parallelism was first clearly formulated by Cope, who was led to it by the conditions which he found among the Miocene and Pliocene camels of North America.

Parallel development may be more comprehensive than in the preceding instances; though the earliest history of neither artiodactyls nor perissodactyls is known, there is reason to believe that all the hoofed animals, at least of the northern hemisphere, are related and had a common origin. Whether this is true or not, they all fall naturally into parallel series, two of which have already been discussed, as exemplifying the light, cursorial and the heavy, slow-moving types, the horses and the †brontotheres. Parallel with the horses and with each other are several lines of the light, swift-running deer, antelopes, tragulines, camels and llamas, and these followed lines of development similar to those of the horses, which they rival in speed, becoming long-legged and long-footed and in reducing the number or size of certain bones, enlarging those of others. The ulna and fibula almost disappear, while the radius and tibia are correspondingly enlarged and the feet are greatly elongated through the lengthening of the metapodials. In all these respects the horses are closely paralleled, but the starting point was different and in a manner that conditioned the entire course of evolution. As far back in time as the artiodactyls can be traced, they had *paraxonic* feet, the plane of symmetry passing between the third and fourth digits, which always form a symmetrical pair. Thus, the limit of digital reduction in an artiodactyl is two and no member of the order with less than two toes has ever been found, or is likely to be. The true ruminants and the camel tribe, to some extent, overcame functionally the difference from the horses through the formation of cannon-bones by the coalescence of the third and fourth metapodials of each foot, though the phalanges of the two digits remained separate, whence the seemingly "cloven hoof."

There is another body of hoofed mammals, an entirely heterogeneous and artificial assemblage of distantly related groups, which yet followed parallel lines of development. These are the massive, short-footed, often short-legged and slow-moving creatures, one family of which, the †brontotheres, has already been considered. The point here raised is the similarity in the mode of development of all these groups, four orders and six families, a similarity which is largely conditioned by the mechanical necessities involved in making provision for great bulk and weight and immense muscular power. In this assemblage of large and heavy mammals, there are, in addition to the †brontotheres, two perissodactyl families, the rhinoceroses and tapirs, one artiodactyl family, the hippopotamuses, and two orders, the Proboscidea and the extinct †Amblypoda. In the †brontotheres and the rhinoceroses there is considerable resemblance in the form of the skull, a resemblance which is, itself, an expression of parallel development, for in both families there is great difference in skull-form between the earlier and later genera. In each of the other four families the shape of the head is characteristically different, but the body and especially the limbs and feet are very much alike and the more nearly alike in size and weight the animals are, the greater are the structural resemblances. The †Amblypoda, and especially the suborder †Dinocerata, are so like elephants that they have been mistakenly referred to the Proboscidea, but the resemblance is due to parallel, or convergent, development, not to a common inheritance. All these very heavy animals agree in having short necks, long bodies, longer or shorter limbs and relatively short feet. The reduction of ulna and fibula and in the number of digits ceased, when marked increase of weight began. At this point, the †brontotheres had reached the "tapiroid" stage and so even the latest and largest of them had four toes in the front foot, three in the hind, while the rhinoceroses had already acquired tridactyl feet. In the hippopotamuses the digits are four in number and in the elephants and †uintatheres there are five. The tapirs, which have been aptly called "living fossils," have advanced but little beyond the middle Eocene grade of development and still have functional, weight-carrying hoofs, but in the other groups, presumably including the fossils, the columnar foot, supported on an elastic pad, with hoofs reduced to peripheral nails, is common to them all. The history of these families (fairly well known except in the hippopotamuses) shows that this type of foot has been separately acquired in all four *orders*.

Omitting the tapirs, which, so to speak, were "left at the post," the five other families have long, strongly arched ribs, indicative of an immense mass of viscera, to support which the hip-bones are greatly expanded and everted. The length of the hind leg is due to the elongation of the femur and in the three families of very large animals, elephants, †uintatheres and †brontotheres, this bone is very similar in all. It has lost the third trochanter and the shaft is no longer cylindrical, but flattened by antero-posterior compression and in all the long bones the marrow cavities are filled up with spongy bone.

While *convergence* is clearly distinguishable in principle from parallelism, it is not always practicable to make the distinction, because of lack of information regarding the history of the groups concerned. Convergence implies that two more or less similar groups are more alike than their ancestors were, and is thus the opposite of divergence. Independent acquisition of single, or a few correlated structures is exceedingly common and a very long list of such convergences might be cited, were it worth while to do so. In the form of the teeth there are countless such likenesses, of which it will suffice to enumerate a few typical instances without attempting to discriminate between parallel and convergent development. The ruminant pattern of molar teeth, with the crown composed of two pairs of crescents, has been developed four or five different times from as many differing ancestors. The type of molars which has two simple transverse crests and is found in the lower teeth of the tapirs, appears in both jaws of a genus of Old World true swine, †*Listriodon*, in one of the American peccaries, †*Platygonus*, in the Proboscidea, †*Dinotherium*, in certain rodents and in the Kangaroos. The remarkable and enigmatical order of the †Pyrotheria, found in the Eocene and Oligocene of South America, has grinding teeth of this kind, and, on the strength of them, the order has been variously referred to the elephants and the marsupials!

The true elephants, as distinguished from the †mastodonts, have grinding teeth of enormous size and great complexity; the masticating s\rface is made up of alternating, vertical plates of dentine, enamel and cement and the recorded history of the family demonstrates that these teeth arose from the much simpler grinders of the †mastodonts. The African Wart-hog (*Phacochœrus*) has very similar teeth, as has also the Capybara, or Water-hog (*Hydrochœrus*), largest of existing rodents, though in this case the imitation is not so close. The extinct †Giant Beaver (†*Castoroides*) is, as the whole skeleton shows, unmistakably one of the beaver family, yet it has molar teeth so like those of the Capybara, that it has been classed (and by excellent authority) with that South American family.

A remarkable instance of wholesale convergence in dentition is afforded by the high-crowned or prismatic, rootless and cement-covered molars, which are to be seen in the grazing members of so many herbivorous families. The genealogy of these families is known sufficiently to show that, in almost all of them, this type of tooth was independently developed. As previously pointed out, grass contains so much silica that it is highly abrasive and wears down teeth rapidly, but in the high-crowned teeth the abrasion is compensated for by continued growth throughout life or to old age, when the formation of roots put a stop to growth. As Kowalevsky long ago suggested, it was the spread of grassy plains in the early Miocene which brought about, directly or indirectly, the development of the prismatic grinding teeth in so many different groups of herbivores, for no insectivorous or carnivorous mammal ever showed the slightest tendency to the formation of such teeth. There were a few sporadic instances of the appearance of prismatic teeth in the Oligocene of Europe and North America and, on a much wider scale in South America. In Europe the perissodactyl family of the †palæotheres terminated in the hypsodont †*Paloplotherium;* in North America the camel †*Poëbrotherium* and the tiny †*Hypisodus* of the †Leptomerycidæ, of the White River, and the rabbits had teeth of this kind. In Patagonia the Oligocene and lower Miocene had many genera of †notoungulates, especially ††toxodonts and ††typotheres, which had prismatic teeth, most of them with molars thickly covered with cement. In one family of ††toxodonts, the †Notohippidæ, the molars are so deceptively horse-like, that Ameghino referred these genera to the Equidæ. With the exception of †*Poëbrotherium*, which seems to have been a truly ancestral camel, and the rabbits, all these genera in the three continents were examples of premature specialization and were eliminated.

In the middle and upper Miocene arose most of the grazing types which are still thriving, or, at least, survived until swept away in the great post-Pleistocene extinctions. Conspicuous among the grazers are the horses, oxen, some antelopes, camels, certain †oreodonts, a great many families of rodents. At a later date, not yet definitely ascertained, some of the rhinoceroses acquired teeth of this description; the Broad Lipped African Rhinoceros has incompletely hypsodont teeth, while in the enormous †*Elasmotherium*, of the Old World Pleistocene, the molars are as completely prismatic as those of a horse. Indeed, the molars of this huge creature are deceptively like those of a colossal horse, with winding, crenulated enamel ridges. The extremely large and complex elephant molars were late in attaining their full development, which came in the Pliocene.

The foregoing examples of convergent development are those in which only a single set of organs, such as the teeth, are involved. More extensive convergence is illustrated by the marsupial †*Thylacosmilus* (see p. 706), of the Argentinian Pliocene, which imitates the †sabre-tooth cats in the most astonishing way. Not only are the upper canines converted into immense, recurved, laniary tusks, almost exactly like the sabres of †*Eusmilus*, but the protective bony flanges of the lower jaw are even larger, though of similar shape. The modifications of the skull which enabled the mouth to be so widely opened that the sabre-points were cleared and the great mastoid and post-glenoid pedicles, with the attachments for greatly enlarged mastoid muscles, are just as in the †machairodonts and indicate a similar stabbing manner of using the canines. Along with these similarities are several equally striking differences, which are not characteristically marsupial features, but extreme and unique specializations. Thus, the great sheaths of the upper canines almost crowd out the frontals and meet in the middle line, covering over the hinder part of the nasals and the *longi colli* muscles would seem to have been enlarged, adding much to the power of the stabbing stroke.

The upper Eocene †creodont, †*Apatælurus*, one of the †Oxyænidæ, has independently acquired the †sabre-tooth mechanism, including the flanged mandible.

A fourth instance of enlarged upper canine tusks with protective flanges of similar shape on the lower jaw is afforded by the Eocene †*Uintatherium*, which is not remotely related, save as all mammals are interallied, either to cats or marsupials. The grotesque skull of †*Uintatherium*, with its three pairs of horn-like protuberances is sur-

prisingly imitated by that of the bizarre White River artiodactyl
†*Protoceras*, which, in appearance, is that of †*Uintatherium* in miniature. Here again, there is no relationship between the groups involved.

Most extreme of all, is the much debated case of the †pro-
terotheres, a family of the South American order of the †Litopterna,
the genera of which resemble the three-toed and one-toed horses of
the North American Tertiary in marvellous fashion. †*Thoatherium*,
of the Santa Cruz, is the most completely monodactyl mammal
known, surpassing even the modern horses in the complete reduction
of the splint-bones. The similarities are not confined to single parts,
or organs, but extend through the entire skeleton; every bone and
almost every tooth share in these likenesses and many palæontologists
long refused to admit that such striking and general resemblances
could possibly be the result of convergence and therefore included
the †Litopterna in the Perissodactyla. This view has, however, been
generally abandoned, and the alternative of convergence accepted.

The reality of parallel and convergent development has long been
admitted by palæontologists, but most zoölogists denied it in the
interests of the theory of Natural Selection, with which these processes do not seem to be compatible. Nowadays, the pendulum has
swung in the opposite direction and convergence is in danger of being
overworked, as it is appealed to on all sides to explain away likenesses that do not suit somebody's book. It is, therefore, important
to ascertain, if possible, what the limits of convergence are. One
such limit may be tentatively drawn and that is that this mode of
development never produces identity. In the case of the †pro-
terotheres, though all parts of the skeleton show resemblance to the
horses, yet no competent anatomist would mistake one for the other,
and in the fundamental essentials, there are profound differences.
The †proterotheres are not only not horses, they are not even perissodactyls and the other family of the †Litopterna, the †Macrau-
chenidæ, while obviously nearly related to the †proterotheres, have
no resemblance to horses whatever and are more like llamas, for
which they were originally mistaken. This is another instance of
convergence, for the members of this family, like the camels and
llamas and *like no other mammals*, have the canal for the vertebral
artery piercing the neural arch in the cervical vertebræ. It is manifestly impossible that this maze of resemblances, pointing in so many
different directions, should be due to relationship; only convergence
will explain the facts. Yet, there is no reason to believe that convergence can ever produce identity. If the same species of mammal

ever arose independently in disconnected areas, it must have been the rarest of events.

These general principles, of divergence, parallelism and convergence may be accepted as established to a high degree of probability, but there are many other problems, only less important, that must be considered in a general view of evolution. A very old question, that Darwin himself discussed, is whether development normally takes place through continuous variation, or whether it may not occur through a succession of sudden changes, *per saltum*. In domestication, such a sudden and considerable change is called a "sport" and many varieties of animals and plants have arisen in this manner, but it does not follow that they could so arise in nature. That brings up the distinction between *variation* and *mutation*, first formulated in its modern sense by the Austrian palæontologist W. von Waagen, who studied the succession of limestones in the Salt Range of northwestern India, and found a remarkably complete series of †Ammonites, each bed having a different species, with numerous fluctuating varieties. von Waagen wrote: "One must, therefore, distinguish strictly between varieties in space and those in time. To describe the former, the long-used name 'variety' will suffice, for the latter, on the other hand, I would propose, for the sake of brevity, a new term 'mutation.' A species, as such, with reference to its connection with earlier or later forms, may be conceived and regarded as a mutation. But also in regard to the value of these two concepts, just established [variety and mutation] an entirely different value is displayed on closer consideration. While the former appears extremely vacillating, of small systematic value, the latter, even though in minute characteristics, is extremely constant and always to be recognized with certainty." [1] The same conception was adopted and elaborated by Neumayr: "Still other characteristics appear, which mark mutations as something different from varieties, especially that, as a rule, there is a definite direction of mutation in each series, the same characteristic changing in the same sense through a considerable succession of strata." [2]

The conception of mutation was adopted by the famous Dutch botanist, the late Hugo de Vries, one of the re-discoverers of Mendel's laws of heredity, and the geneticists have developed it much further. According to this modern view, a mutation may be large or small in

[1] W. von Waagen, Die Formenreihe des Ammonites subradiatus, *Benecke's Geognost.-Paläontolog. Beitr.*, Bd. I, p. 185.

[2] M. Neumayr, *Die Stämme des Thierreiches*, Bd. I, p. 60.

amount, but is constant and heritable and therefore must arise in the germ-substance. Natural mutations are characterized, as Neumayr observed, by continuing in the same sense "through a considerable thickness of strata," the cumulative effects resulting in important changes. This direct and unswerving development has impressed almost all palæontologists who have studied genetic series. Orthogenesis, a term devised to express this directness, was suggested by Eimer from his studies of butterflies and Osborn used *rectigradation* in the same sense for genetic series of fossils. Orthogenesis, admitting its reality, is not incompatible with branching, or dichotomous division, but does preclude the notion of a zig-zag, or frequently changing direction of development.

On the other hand, orthogenesis is not to be conceived of as something rigid and unchangeable and permitting no fluctuation in small details. Though, as will be subsequently seen, structures once lost are seldom, if ever, regained, it would seem that structures once gained, may sometimes be lost afterwards. For example, the White River peccary, †*Perchœrus*, has a slight external swelling of the upper jaw, which looks like an enlarged antrum; in the succeeding John Day genus, †*Thinohyus*, the swelling is very conspicuous, but in the peccaries of the Miocene to Recent times, no such swelling is visible. It is, of course, possible that †*Perchœrus* and †*Thinohyus* were aberrant forms, off the direct line, and that the real ancestors remain to be discovered, but this alternative seems less likely.

Indeed, the direction of change long followed may be departed from, the deviation being due to the introduction of a new factor. In the earliest deer the males were hornless, but they developed effective weapons of defence by the enlargement of the upper canine teeth into long and sharp, sabre-like tusks. When antlers appeared, the work of defence was transferred to them, and the tusks began to dwindle, being eventually suppressed in those deer which had large and complex antlers, though persisting to the present time in the hornless Musk-deer and Chinese Water-deer (*Hydropotes inermis*) and in the small-antlered muntjaks, which can defend themselves with their sharp tusks.

If Dr. Matthew's interesting theory as to the origin of the true felines from primitive †sabre-tooth cats (see p. 622) should be confirmed, it would furnish a very striking example of fluctuating development. The acceptance of the theory involves the admission of the following changes: (1) The upper canine was enlarged and changed into a thin, recurved, scimitar-like tusk; (2) the lower canine was much reduced, becoming little larger than the incisors; (3) the lower jaw developed a flange on each side from its inferior border, against which the inner side of the upper canine rested, when the mouth was closed, and the chin was nearly flat, meeting the outer surface of the jaw at a right angle. After these peculiarities had been fully established, the stock divided into two series; in one, the †machairodonts, the specialization continued along the same lines, assuming more and more exaggerated forms, while in the true cats it was reversed. The upper canine grew shorter and thicker, the lower canine was very greatly enlarged, the lower jaw lost its flange, and its external and anterior surfaces no longer met at a right angle, but curved gradually into each other. As previously stated, such a reversal strikes me as improbable and not to be accepted without very much more complete evidence than we now have, but it is perfectly possible that such evidence may be forthcoming.

Making the fullest allowance for all such cases of fluctuation, it remains true that in the great majority of the phyla whose history may be followed in some detail, development has been remarkably direct and unswerving. Plasticity of organization and capacity for differentiation of structure in widely different directions would seem to be limited in the mammals, especially among the more advanced groups.

The genealogy of the North American equines has long been regarded as the clearest and best established genetic series known among mammals, and yet, if minutiæ are taken into account, the upper Miocene and Pliocene parts of the story are full of difficulties. "It appears that the Lower Pliocene Equidæ represent six nearly related groups, of about equal value. . . . All are derivable from different species of *Merychippus*, transitional species being found in the Upper Miocene. Each is progressive toward *Equus* in some features, persistently primitive in some, aberrantly specialized in others, but it is not probable that *Equus* is directly derived from any one of them." [1] Either nature follows in such matters the legal principle of *de minimis non curat lex*, or the direct ancestors of modern horses are still to seek.

A general rule of evolutionary change is that modification is accomplished through a reduction in the number of parts together with an enlargement and elaboration of the parts which are retained. From their reptilian ancestors, the early Mesozoic mammals derived large numbers of body and tail vertebræ, ribs, skull-bones, teeth

[1] Matthew and Stirton, 1930, pp. 355–356.

and elements of the shoulder-girdle, and the placental mammals have lost many of these various parts, hardly ever adding any new element. "Development is by reduction in the number of parts," may be formulated as a law that has very few exceptions. For example, Eocene placentals very generally have the dental formula: $i \frac{3}{3}$, $c \frac{1}{1}$, $p \frac{4}{4}$, $m \frac{3}{3} \times 2 = 44$. This number is greatly exceeded in certain armadillos and such toothed whales as the dolphins and porpoises, but, in these instances the teeth are all alike and are greatly simplified into conical or cylindrical pegs. The only example known of an ordinary placental mammal that exceeds in number of the teeth the primitive formula above given is the Large-eared Wolf of South Africa (*Otocyon megalotis*) in which the formula is: $i \frac{3}{3}$, $c \frac{1}{1}$, $p \frac{4}{4}$, $m \frac{3-4}{4} \times 2 = 46$ or 48. Huxley was so much impressed by this highly exceptional number of teeth, that he regarded it as a survival of marsupial conditions. Few existing mammals retain the primitive number of 44 teeth, the great majority having lost more or fewer of that number. Thus the ruminants have lost all the upper incisors and usually the upper canines and one premolar above and below, giving a total of 32; rodents have lost all the incisors but one, the canines, most or all of the premolars and, in some instances one of the molars; the formulas range from $i \frac{1}{1}$, $c \frac{0}{0}$, $p \frac{2}{2}$, $m \frac{3}{3}$ to $p \frac{0}{0}$, $m \frac{2}{2}$; the anteaters of various orders have lost all their teeth. In the elephants the grinding teeth have become so large, that there is room for only two on each side, above and below, or eight in all, at any one time. As the grinders are worn down, they are pushed out by new teeth coming in from behind. This method of tooth replacement is peculiar to the Proboscidea and unique among mammals.

The loss of elements is not restricted to the teeth, but affects all parts of the skeleton. In nearly all Paleocene and Eocene mammals the trunk and tail are long, much longer than in their successors and even in Recent times many of the more primitive mammals retain very long bodies or tails. The opossums have from 26 to 29 caudal vertebræ; the klipdasses, or Hyracoidea, have very long bodies, *Procavia* having 30 trunk-vertebræ and *Dendrohyrax* 28. No existing perissodactyl has more than 23 dorso-lumbar vertebræ, but †*Hyrachyus*, of the Bridger Eocene has 25. The early ungulates and carnivores are conspicuously long-tailed.

The same rule of reduction in the number of parts applies to the limbs and feet also. In almost all Eocene genera and in most of the more primitive Recent mammals, there are five toes on each foot, never more and rarely less. Ulna and fibula are relatively as stout and well developed as the radius and tibia respectively and such proportions occur in most Recent families, but there are several groups, notably the swift-running hoofed animals, in which as previously explained, the number of digits was steadily reduced, to one in the horses and two in the ruminants; in the latter the long bones of the feet, or metapodials, unite to form cannon-bones. Concomitantly, ulna and fibula are reduced almost to the vanishing point, only more or less of the two ends persisting.

While the number of parts is thus steadily reduced, those which are retained are enlarged and elaborated. In the more advanced and specialized of the artiodactyls and perissodactyls, for instance, the radius and tibia are increased in size, to carry the whole body-weight and the joints are more elaborately interlocked, so as to prevent dislocation. In the horses the entire weight is supported on the single toe (3rd of the original five) of each foot, but that single digit is greatly modified, effectively to do the work once done by five toes. Not only is the functional metapodial much enlarged, but its articulations with carpus, or tarsus, are rearranged, to give a better distribution of the weight and make stronger joints. The keel at the lower end of the metapodial is brought around the entire circumference of the joint and fits into a groove on the upper end of the first phalanx, preventing lateral dislocation of the toe. The ungual phalanx and enclosing, box-like hoof are like those of no other mammal and are admirably adapted to swift, sure-footed running. Even †*Thoatherium*, which is more completely monodactyl than any horse, has a different kind of ungual and obviously had a hoof of different shape, being thinner and flatter. The feet of the true ruminants (Pecora) exhibit an essentially similar kind of specialization, reducing the number of parts, enlarging and elaborating those that are retained.

The specialization of teeth may be accomplished in either of two ways: (1) by the suppression of some of the cusps, with enlargement and transformation of those that remain, and (2) by the addition of many new elements, coupled with great enlargement of the whole tooth. An excellent illustration of the first mode is furnished by the lower sectorial (first molar) of a cat. In its earliest form this tooth consisted of an anterior shearing triangle of three cusps, two external and one internal, followed by a low basin-like heel of two cusps, inner and outer. The heel and the antero-internal cusp gradually dwindle until they disappear and only two cusps, the antero-external ones, remain. These are much extended antero-posteriorly, but made thinner transversely and have very sharp edges, forming a highly efficient shearing blade. It is of interest to note that the last lower molar of †*Hyænodon* is a very exact imitation of a cat's sectorial. By no possibility can one of these teeth have been derived from the other, nor could both have come from a common ancestry. Aside from all other objections, the two teeth are not even homologous, one being the first, the other the third molar.

Of the second method of tooth-specialization, formation of additional cusps and enlargement of the whole, there are many instances, which exemplify all degrees of enlargement and complication, from the true swine and the bears, which have molars of many cusps, but low-crowned and rooted, to the extreme complexity of the elephant molars and the elaborate repetition of plates in the Capybara. Enlargement of some teeth is generally carried out at the expense of others, as, in the bears, the large, tuberculated molars are compensated by dwindling premolars.

Teeth are the only organs in which the addition and multiplication of parts among land mammals can be demonstrated. So far as is at present known, no vertebra, skull-bones, or elements of the limbs or feet has ever been added to the skeleton of terrestrial mammals, and though many additional joints are developed in the flippers of whales, it is evidently a highly exceptional procedure. This is somewhat surprising in view of the frequency of polydactylism in families of six-toed cats and six-fingered men.

It appears to be a law of evolution that parts or structures once lost can never be regained. The late Dr. L. Dollo, of Brussels expressed this idea somewhat differently by saying that the evolutionary process is irreversible, but, in this form, the principle probably has exceptions, as was shown in the case of the peccaries above cited, the Oligocene genera had swollen antra, which subsequent genera lost. However, Dr. Dollo would hardly have considered such trivial instances as real exceptions. In certain domestic and experimental breeds, animals have redeveloped digits which had been lost in the wild ancestors of those breeds, but whether the lost digits could ever have been reacquired under natural conditions, it is impossible to say. Palæontology is not well fitted to solve this problem, because of our inability to distinguish, among the fossils, between cases of belated retention and those of reacquisition. Be that as it may, the redevelopment of a lost part must be highly exceptional, if, indeed, it ever took place.

The early extinction of the huge and massive †Dinocerata late in the Eocene and of the †Brontotheriidæ early in the Oligocene has been repeatedly mentioned and both of these entirely unrelated groups agree in the extraordinary variability which they displayed before dying out, a variability so great and so inconstant, that the subdivision and classification of these two families are a well-nigh impossible task. It is as though the great creatures foresaw their approaching doom and strove in every way to escape it. Of course, nothing of the kind took place, but that is the impression one receives. A third group that had an almost similar history is that of the Proboscidea; all over the world, in every continent except Australia, Pliocene and Pleistocene elephants and †mastodonts became extraordinarily diversified and ramified into many genera, when the post-Pleistocene extinctions wiped them out, cutting down the number of genera to two and reducing the almost cosmopolitan range to tropical Asia and Africa. In the case of the †brontotheres and †dinocerates, no doubt, one factor in their early extinction was the preposterously small size of their brains; they must have been ineffably stupid.

Indeed, an examination of successive faunas, that followed one another in time throws some light upon the dark mystery of extinction. Fifty years ago, Professor Marsh remarked that in each of the earlier Tertiary stages, there were certain mammals with relatively well-developed brains and others in which the brains were conspicuously underdeveloped; the latter all died out early. Not that some small-brained animals, such as the Insectivora and Rodentia, have not survived to Recent times, but these are all of small size; among those of larger stature, the victory has usually been to the better brains. Apparently, a higher type of brain did not always suffice to overcome handicaps of another kind. The primitive flesh-eater †*Hyænodon* continued into the White River and long held its own against the dogs and †sabre-tooth cats of that time, seemingly because it had a relatively larger and better convoluted brain, but, eventually, the more specialized limbs and feet carried off the victory.

An apparently trivial drawback may be the deciding factor that leads to extinction. As Kowalevsky was the first to point out, two methods of digital reduction have been followed by the Artiodactyla, which he called respectively the inadaptive and the adaptive. In the former the reduced and vestigial metapodials, as well as the functional ones, retained their original carpal and tarsal connections, while in the adaptive method, the persistent, functional metapodials broadened so as to take over the carpal and tarsal articulations formerly held by the reduced or vanished digits. It cannot be a coincidence that not a single artiodactyl with inadaptively reduced feet has survived to the present time. The difference between the two methods does not seem to be important, even though the adaptive method produces stronger joints. Horses have adaptively reduced feet, but in the monodactyl and tridactyl feet of the †proterotheres the feet are inadaptive.

There is no discoverable relation between variability and the number of mutants that arise from any stem; variations may be many and mutants few, or vice versa. The brachiopod shell, *Rhynchonella*, is a surviving genus of great antiquity, that dates far back into the Palæozoic era. Throughout its history it has been very variable, yet has given rise to few new forms.

While most mammalian families and orders have progressed in the course of their history, it has been in very unequal degrees and the geological dates of origin of the various groups have been very different. No doubt, the Monotremata are the most ancient of all orders, as they are by far the most primitive, but materials are lacking for positive statements on this head. Marsupials are next in point of antiquity and of all existing mammalian families, much the most ancient is that of the Didelphiidæ, or opossums, which is at least as old as the middle of the upper Cretaceous, from which time these most conservative of mammals have undergone substantially no change at all. The modern genus, *Didelphis* itself, dates from the middle Pliocene of South America (Catamarca) and its differences from the preceding genera of the family are slight. The most ancient of the Monodelphia are the Insectivora, which may be traced into the late upper Cretaceous and owe their continued existence to their small size and concealed mode of life. The date of origin of many other mammalian groups may be approximately fixed, but it is needless to enumerate them, as they all testify to the differences in geological date of their origin, as appears so distinctly in the families of the Carnivora Fissipedia (Chap. XXI). Very few families were as unchangeable as the opossums and yet survived; nearly all underwent a greater or less amount of change, but in none of them has degeneration, save in single organs, been observed. Burrowers have, in varying degrees, lost the use of their eyes, but true degeneracy arises from parasitism and there are no parasitic mammals. Arrested development, such as is displayed by the opossums, is rare among mammals, of actual deterioration, no instance is known.

The great debates concerning evolutionary philosophy have centred around the problem of *species;* the title of Darwin's great work is: *The Origin of Species,* and it was the same problem with which his famous predecessor, Lamarck, concerned himself. Before Darwin's day, species were regarded as essentially immutable entities, which had been specially created and which it was the function of the naturalist to identify and describe. When Darwin converted the world to a belief in evolution, one consequence was an overhasty abandonment of the species-concept in favour of the belief that species were purely subjective, nature dealing only with individuals. This was going too far; a great series of blood-tests shows that species are chemical entities, each with its own peculiar type of blood. The modern representatives of the Equidæ are species of the genus *Equus,* horses, asses, zebras and quaggas, each of which is chemically different from the others. There are also chemical differences between individuals, as indicated by the four types of human blood, which must be carefully discriminated and kept apart in the operation of transfusion, but these differences are more of the nature of fluctuating variations.

As to how species, as distinct from variants and hereditable mutants, are actually produced in nature, we are still very much in the dark and it will be necessary to learn what chemical differences, if any, distinguish subspecies, varieties, geographical races, etc., before this difficulty can be cleared up. As separate from evolution in general, the species problem remains very much what it was when Darwin attacked it.

While the theory of evolution is accepted by naturalists with substantial unanimity, there is great divergence of opinion among them concerning the efficient causes of the marvellous transformations which the fossils reveal. Darwin's theory of Natural Selection does offer an explanation, though he himself was far from attributing to that agency the exclusive importance which his modern followers ("Neodarwinians") ascribe to it. He also attached much significance to the direct action of the environment and to the effects of use and disuse and, toward the end of his life, he was inclined to the belief that he had underestimated these factors and overestimated Natural Selection. According to the modern version of Darwin's theory, random variations supply the material from which Natural Selection picks out the favourable ones, just as does the breeder of animals or plants in establishing a new variety. Natural Selection, in Darwin's view, was the exact analogue of the breeder's artificial selection.

This is not the place to present the arguments, *pro* and *con,* over this famous theory, which is still upheld by many high authorities, further than to say that, in the writer's opinion the observed facts of parallelism and convergence are fatal to it. The chances that random variations should bring about the astonishing likeness between the marsupial †*Thylacosmilus*, the carnivore †*Eusmilus* and the ungulate †*Uintatherium*, or the conversion of hoofs into claws in three unrelated groups, are mathematically *nil*. Few palæontologists have felt that the direct, unswerving, step by step development of the †ammonites studied by von Waagen and Neumayr, or of the many mammalian series, which have been described in the preceding chapters, were satisfactorily accounted for by Natural Selection. In giving up this theory, it must be admitted, there is nothing to put in its place. Darwin's theory does offer an explanation of the evolutionary process and this no other theory does, but the question remains: is it an adequate explanation?

Almost all zoölogists now accept Weissmann's dictum that characters acquired in the lifetime of the individual cannot be transmitted to the offspring. Adoption of this view excludes any appeal to the effects of use and disuse and therewith abandons hope of explaining the dwindling and disappearance of parts. Darwin believed that the blindness common to all classes of cave animals was brought about by the cumulative and hereditary effects of darkness, but, if there are no hereditary effects, the explanation fails and no satisfactory substitute has been suggested.

In the first edition of this book, the final chapter ended as follows:

"It is only too clear that the principles as to the modes of mammalian development which can be deduced from the history of the various groups must, for the most part, be stated in a cautious and tentative manner, so as not to give an undue appearance of certainty to preliminary conclusions, which should be held as subject to revision with the advance of knowledge. Much has, however, been already learned, and there is every reason to hope that Experimental Zoölogy and Palæontology, by combining their resources, will eventually shed full light upon a subject of such exceptional difficulty."

This remains true to-day; it is, however, significant that it has not been necessary to abandon any of the tentative conclusions concerning the modes and factors of mammalian evolution which were formulated so many years ago, and this gives increased confidence in the validity of those conclusions.

INDEX

N. B. — The most important references in bold-faced type; technical names of genera and species and Latin words italicized. Extinct groups indicated by a dagger (†); an asterisk (*) before a page-number denotes a figure and an R. following, a restoration. The index is, thus, designed to replace glossary and list of illustrations. Names of persons are in small capitals. N.A. = North America; S.A. = South America.